D0280699

The Guide to Selecting Plays for Performance

94th Edition

Samuel French Ltd
52 Fitzroy Street London W1T 5JR
www.samuelfrench-london.co.uk

DISCLAIMER

The publication of an advertisement in *The Guide* must not be taken as a recommendation by Samuel French Ltd.

ISBN – 978 0 573 09145 2

Contents

Contents – continued

Welcome

Welcome to the 94th edition of *The Guide to Selecting Plays* – the first and only play selection catalogue you will ever need. Titles can also be viewed, and ordered, online at:

www.samuelfrench-london.co.uk

We have over 2000 titles to choose from and if you take a moment to view the New Additions to the Guide on the following pages you will see the broad range of new acquisitions from which to choose your next play. You will find full length plays by Tim Firth (*Calendar Girls*), Alan Ayckbourn (*My Wonderful Day*, *If I Were You*), Paul Carpenter and Ian Gower (*Hi-di-Hi*), Peter Nichols (*Lingua Franca*), Terence Rattigan (*Love In Idleness*, *Who Is Sylvia?*), John Godber (*Christmas Crackers*, *Our House*, *Sold*), Nicholas de Jongh (*Plague Over England*), Patrick Barlow from Buchan and Hitchcock (*The 39 Steps*) and Charlotte Jones (*Martha, Josie and the Chinese Elvis*) to name but a few.

We are also very pleased to include in the Guide a new section (in pink) dedicated to plays published by **Oberon Books** which Samuel French Ltd is licensing for amateur performance on Oberon's behalf. Please apply to our Amateur Rights Department in the usual way for these titles.

This Guide will have the usual twice-yearly Supplements mailed out in paper format to our Mailing List. In addition, the Supplements will be found on our website for downloading and if you sign up to our e-mailing list you will receive regular Newsletters detailing all the news and latest releases.

Samuel French Ltd

www.samuelfrench-london.co.uk

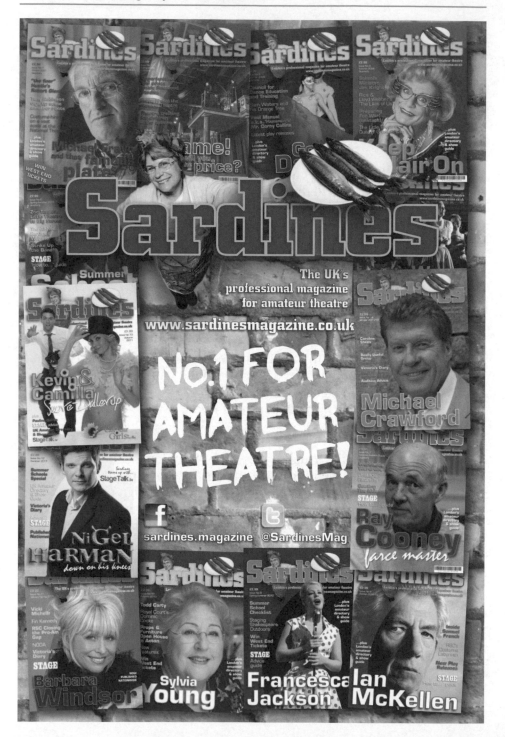

Introduction

Sections of *The Guide*

The plays are divided into four main sections: Section A, full length plays; Section B, one act plays (both sections include mixed cast, all-female and all-male cast titles); Section C, plays for children and young people; Section D, pantomimes and seasonal plays.

All plays new to this edition of the Guide are denoted by a bullet mark ♦ next to the title and the authors' indexes join the classified indexes at the beginning of Sections A and B (these are printed on yellow paper for Section A, blue for Section B).

In Section C the plays are listed alphabetically in one section with marginal marks to indicate the approximate playing time of the individual titles and suggestions as to whether they are for performance by children, young people or adults to children. In addition to the classified index at the beginning of this section there is an authors' index. For details of the marginal markings please see page 434.

Cast Descriptions

The cast breakdown for each play gives the male/female ratio and the playing range of ages only, together with a note of any ethnic roles involved. Contemporary casting often has actors playing roles outside their actual age range and the details in our Guide reflect this.

Thus

M5 (18, 20s-50s)

indicates there are five male roles – aged eighteen and ranging in age from the twenties to the fifties.

Similarly

F5 (18, 20s (1 Asian), 40, 50)

indicates five women's roles – one aged eighteen, and the other four roles being for two in their twenties (one of whom is an Asian) one aged forty and one aged fifty.

Updating *The Guide*

To keep your copy of *The Guide* up to date please see page xxiii for details of our mailing list and website.

Licences to Perform French's Plays

Licences to perform are issued by:

SAMUEL FRENCH Ltd, 52 Fitzroy Street, Fitzrovia, London W1T 5JR
Telephone: 020 7387 9373   *Fax:* 020 7387 2161   *Email:* theatre@samuelfrench-london.co.uk
and their authorized UK and Overseas Agents as follows:

NOTTINGHAM
Theatre Royal and Royal Concert Hall, Theatre Square, Nottingham NG1 5ND
Telephone: 0115 989 5500 *Fax:* 0115 947 4218 *Email:* enquiry@royalcentre-nottingham.co.uk

REPUBLIC OF IRELAND AND NORTHERN IRELAND
Drama League of Ireland, The Mill Theatre, Dundrum Town Centre, Dundrum, Dublin 16
Telephone: (00) 353 1296 9343 *Email:* dli@eircom.net

AUSTRALIA
Origin Theatrical, Level 1, 213 Clarence Street, Sydney, NSW 2000.
Telephone: 00 612 8514 5204. *Email:* enquiries@originmusic.com.au

EAST AFRICA
Phoenix Players Ltd, P.O. Box 52383, 00200, Nairobi, Kenya *Email:* phoenix@swiftkenya.com

INDIA
JAGRITI, Ramagondanahalli, Varthur Road, Whitefield, Bangalore 560 066
Email: samfren@jagrititheatre.com

MALTA
Dingli Co. International Ltd, 18/2 South Street, Valetta VLT 11 *Email:* prs@maltanet.net

NEW ZEALAND
Play Bureau (NZ) Ltd, P.O. Box 420, New Plymouth *Email:* play.bureau.nz@xtra.co.nz

SOUTH AFRICA (AND NAMIBIA, SWAZILAND, BOTSWANA, LESOTHO)
D.A.L.R.O. (Pty) Ltd, P.O. Box 31627 Braamfontein 2017, Johannesburg *Email:*dalro@dalro.co.za

USA AND CANADA
SAMUEL FRENCH INC *Email:* info@samuelfrench.com
SAMUEL FRENCH Inc. 45 West 25th Street, New York, NY 10010, USA
Telephone: 212 206-8990 *Fax:* 212 206-1429
SAMUEL FRENCH Inc. 7623 Sunset Boulevard, Hollywood, CA 90046, USA
Telephone: 323 876-0570 *Fax:* 323 876-6822

The fees quoted in this catalogue were correct at the time of going to press. They relate to performances within the United Kingdom only and may be subject to revision during the period in which this Guide remains current. If you are in any doubt as to the correct current fee, please apply to Samuel French London, or to one of our authorized agents, for a quotation.

The current prices of play copies can be found in our price list, published separately.

Please read the Notice on page xix concerning restrictions on Amateur Rights.

SAMUEL FRENCH THEATRE BOOKS LISTS

Free lists are available of theatre books stocked in our bookshop

- Acting

- Audition material

- Circus, magic, comedy, clowns, pantomime and puppetry

- Costume and make-up

- Criticism

- Drama in education and drama training

- Mime, movement and dance

- Musical interest

- Production, stage management, directing and marketing

- Shakespeare

- Speech training

- Stagecraft, design and lighting

- Theatre biography

- Theatre

- Theatre history

- Writing, television and radio

Please enquire

Important Notice

Public Performances

Protection against unlawful performances of plays is afforded to dramatic authors by means of copyright. Under the Copyright Law no public performance or reading of a protected play may be given, either in its entirety or in the form of excerpts, without the prior consent of the owner of the copyright. The majority of plays in this Guide are copyright, and as agents for the copyright owners we issue licenses for performances on payment of a fee. The fees quoted in this Guide are subject to contract and subject to variation at the sole discretion of Samuel French Ltd. Fees for performances given in premises seating 400 or more persons will be subject to negotiation.

Private and Domestic Performances

The precise stage at which a reading or other representation of a play ceases to be a public performance and becomes a private and domestic one will depend entirely upon circumstances. Performances that take place in one's own home – and under certain conditions in hospitals and institutions – can be domestic; but it is not safe to assume that they are invariably so. It is always advisable to furnish us with the full facts of each individual case, and to apply for a free licence before any performance or reading takes place.

Charity Performances

Because it is intended to give a performance in aid of charity the owner of the copyright will not consent to reduce, or waive claim to, the usual fee. The writing of plays is a means of livelihood, and every performance reduces the potential audience – and therefore the earning capacity of the play. The cause of charity does not excuse infringement of the author's rights.

Performances Overseas

The plays listed in this Guide are generally available for performances by amateurs in the British Isles. There may be restrictions on the performance of certain plays overseas. Amateurs intending production overseas must, in their own interest, make application to us before starting rehearsals or booking a theatre or hall.

Prior Consent

It is important that the consent of the copyright owner should be obtained before any performance of a play is given. Willingness to pay the fee and obtain the licence after the event would not render those organizing, and those taking part in, the play any less liable for infringement of the copyright.

Restrictions

From time to time it may be necessary for us to withdraw or restrict the Amateur Rights of Performance of certain plays. In their own interests, therefore, societies should always apply for written permission before committing themselves to a production.

Copyright Information

Copyright Protection in Written Works

The titles in this catalogue are fully protected under the Copyright Laws of the British Commonwealth of Nations, the United States of America and all countries of the Berne and Universal Copyright Conventions.

All rights, including Stage, Motion Picture, Radio, Television, Public Reading, and Translations into Foreign Languages, are strictly reserved.

No part of these works may lawfully be reproduced in ANY form or by any means – photocopying, typescript, recording (including video-recording), manuscript, electronic, mechanical, or otherwise – or be transmitted or stored in a retrieval system, without prior permission.

Changes in UK Copyright Laws

Copyright now subsists in the work of a writer until the end of the seventieth year following his or her death, rather than the end of the fiftieth year as hitherto and works which were considered to be out of copyright have been brought back into protection and become liable for royalty payment when performed if the author has been dead for less than seventy years. Thus, a number of writers whose work was in the public domain are affected.

It is not safe to assume that a work is out of copyright. Therefore, be sure to check very carefully the availability of rights and royalty requirements. We are always prepared to help you in this respect.

Video-recordings

The copyright laws governing video-recording are extremely complex and it should not be assumed that any play may be video-recorded *for whatever purpose* without first obtaining the permission of the appropriate agents. The fact that a play is included in the Samuel French Ltd catalogue does not indicate that video rights are available or that Samuel French Ltd controls such rights. Our Performing Rights Department will be happy to give advice on this point.

New additions to this Guide

Listed below are all the titles that are new to this edition of the Guide. In the main sections of the Guide these titles are identified with a bullet mark beside the title.

SECTION A. FULL LENGTH PLAYS

An Absolute Turkey. Georges Feydeau, adapted by Nicki Frei and Peter Hall
Alice. Laura Wade
And Evermore Shall Be So. Norman Robbins
After September. Jimmie Chinn
Amidst the Gladiolas. Vito Gentile
Café Brosse. Jean McConnell
Calendar Girls. Tim Firth
Caucasian Chalk Circle. Bertolt Brecht, translated by Alistair Beaton
The Cherry Orchard. Anton Chekhov. New version by Mike Poulton
Cheshire Cats. Gail Young
Christmas Crackers. John Godber
The City. Martin Crimp
Crown Prince. John Godber
Dick Barton Episode II : The Curse of the Pharoah's Tomb. Phil Willmott
Dick Barton Episode III: The Tango of Terror. Phil Willmott
Duets. Peter Quilter
Eigengrau. Penelope Skinner
Edward Gant's Amazing Feats of Loneliness. Anthony Neilson
The English Game. Richard Bean
Enlightenment. Shelagh Stephenson
Enron. Lucy Prebble
Entertaining Angels. Richard Everett
The Good Person of Szechwan. Bertolt Brecht, Translated by Tony Kushner.
Her Naked Skin. Rebecca Lenkiewicz
Hi-di-Hi. Paul Carpenter and Ian Gower, adapted from the TV series by Jimmy Perry and David Croft
I Am Of Ireland: An entertainment of W.B. Yeats. Edward Callan
If I Were You. Alan Ayckbourn
Less Than Kind. Terence Rattigan
Lingua Franca. Peter Nichols
Lizzy, Darcy and Jane. Joanna Norland
Love in Idleness. Terence Rattigan
Lysistrata – the Sex Strike. Germaine Greer and Phil Willmott
Making Money. Adapted by Stephen Briggs from Terry Pratchett's novel
Martha, Josie and the Chinese Elvis. Charlotte Jones
Mickey Salberg's Crystal Ballroom Dance Band. Ade Morris
Mother Courage and Her Children. Bertolt Brecht, translated by Eric Bentley
Mrs Affleck. Samuel Adamson from Ibsen's *Little Eyolf*
My Romantic History. D.C. Jackson
My Wonderful Day. AlanAyckbourn
On the Rocks. Amy Rosenthal
Our House. John Godber
Painting by Numbers. Simon Mawdsley
Passion Play. Peter Nichols
Plague Over England. Nicholas de Jongh
Posh. Laura Wade
Prepare to Meet Thy Tomb. Norman Robbins
Punk Rock. Simon Stephens
Purgatorio. Ariel Dorfman

New additions to this Guide

SECTION A. FULL LENGTH PLAYS (continued)

Rock 'n' Roll.Tom Stoppard
Searching for Docotor Branovic. David Tristram
Shady Business. Robin Hawden
Sold. John Godber
Spygame. Bettine Manktelow
The 39 Steps. Patrick Barlow from John Buchan's novel and Alfred Hitchcock's film.
  Original concept by Simon Corble and Nobby Dimon
The Threefold Cord. Scott Marshall
Tusk Tusk. Polly Stenham
Untimely Frost. Colin and Mary Crowther
Vertical Hour. David Hare
Who Is Sylvia? Terence Rattigan
Wife After Death. Eric Chappell
Wuthering Heights. April de Angelis from Emily Bronte
Yellow Moon. David Greig

New additions to this Guide

SECTION B. ONE ACT PLAYS

Blind Date. Peter Quilter (from *Duets*)
The Bride-to-Be. Peter Quilter (from *Duets*)
Calling. Colin and Mary Crowther
Carrot. David Tristram
Carry Me Kate. Rachel Musgrove
Come and Go. Samuel Beckett
Drunk Enough to Say I Love You. Caryl Churchill
Fatal Loins. Perry Pontac (from *Codpieces*)
Flash, Bam, Alakazam. Sue Wilding
Hamlet Part II. Perry Pontac (from *Codpieces*)
Happy Birthday to Me. Simon Williams
The Holiday. Peter Quilter (from *Duets*)
Just the Two of Us. Ros Moruzzi
Oubliette. David Foxton
Party. Tom Basden
Peas. David Tristram
Pineapple. Robert Messik
Prince Lear. Perry Pontac (from *Codpieces*)
Secretarial Skills. Peter Quilter (from *Duets*)
The Sociable Plover. Tim Whitnall

New additions to this Guide

SECTION C. PLAYS FOR CHILDREN, YOUTH GROUPS AND STUDENTS

The Adventures of Jason and the Argonauts. Phil Willmott
Blackout. Davey Anderson
Emperor's New Clothes, or, Five Beans For Jack. David Foxton
A Handbag. Anthony Horowitz
Playing With My Heart. Shaun Prendergast
Punk Rock. Simon Stephens
The Secret Garden (Spring Version). Marsha Norman. Music by Lucy Simon
Tracy Beaker Gets Real. Mary Morris, based on the book by Jacqueline Wilson.
   Music by Grant Olding

SECTION D. PANTOMIMES

Little Bo-Peep. Paul Reakes
Tom Thumb. Paul Reakes

SECTION E. MUSICAL PLAYS

Happy Days. Garry Marshall and Paul Williams
Thrill Me. The Leopold and Loeb Story. Stephen Dolginoff

Last Minute Acquisitions

FULL LENGTH PLAYS

False Pretences. Eric Chappell. M5 F2 Fee Code M
Life and Beth. Alan Ayckbourn. M4 F4 Fee Code M
The Priory. Michael Wynne. M4 F3. Fee Code M
Really Old, Like Fortyfive. Tamsin Oglesby. M4 F6. Fee Code M
Practice to Deceive. Norman Robbins. M3 F5 2 m or f. Fee Code L
This Is How It Goes. Neil Labute. M2 F1. Fee Code M

ONE ACT PLAYS

As We Forgive Those. Andrew Smith. F3. Fee Code D
Autobahn. Collection of one-act plays by Neil Labute:
> Funny
> Bench Seat
> All Apologies
> Merge
> Road Trip
> Autobahn

Mixed casts of M and F. Individual plays on Fee Code B. If all six performed together the fee will be Code M.
Prince of Denmark. Michael Lesslie. M9 F1 (plus ensemble). Fee Code F
Silent Night. Colin and Mary Crowther. M3 F2. Fee Code D

PLAYS FOR CHILDREN AND YOUNG PEOPLE

George's Marvellous Medicine. Adapted by David Wood from the book by Roald Dahl. M2 or 3 F 2 or 3. Fee Code M

PANTOMIME

Old King Cole. Paul Reakes. 12 Characters, chorus. New for 2012!

Full details are available on our website and will be published in the first Supplement to The Guide

---

RESTRICTIONS

From time to time it may be necessary for us to withdraw or restrict the Amateur Rights of Performance of certain plays. In their own interests, therefore, societies should always apply for written permission before committing themselves to a production.

LET US SET THE SCENE ...

The year 1830. King William succeeded George IV and his niece, the future Queen Victoria, was a girl of eleven. Charles Dickens was a shorthand writer in Doctors' Commons and theatre history had been made by *Black Ey'd Susan* which ran for a 150 performances at the Surrey Theatre. In this year too the forerunner to the firm which was to become Samuel French Ltd was founded.

Actor Thomas Hailes Lacy, aged twenty, set up as a publisher of plays in Acting Editions, just off The Strand, London, acquiring the printing plates of earlier publishers such as Webster, Oxberry and Cumberland. The works of John Cumberland were the most extensive, and Lacy became proprietor of Cumberland's British Theatre (printed from acting copies as performed at the Theatres Royal, London) and Cumberland's Minor Theatre. Lacy also published his own editions and by 1873 Lacy's Acting Editions of Plays ran to 99 volumes and contained 1,485 pieces.

Thomas Hailes Lacy

In 1854, in New York, Samuel French, whose family had travelled to America with later waves of Pilgrims, had started a similar play publishing venture by acquiring "The Standard and Minor Drama". Five years later he came to London on a visit and about this time the two of them were doing business together, each acting as the other's agent across the Atlantic.

The first title to be published under the Samuel French imprint was *A Midsummer Night's Dream with Cast of Characters, Stage Business, Costumes, Relative Positions etc. etc*. French traded across the Atlantic with Lacy for some years and in 1872 he acquired Lacy's business

Samuel French
in 1851

which became "Samuel French, late Lacy's". The New York side was left in the care of his son, Thomas, and the financial foundations of the American business were firmly set with an extended tour of *Little Lord Fauntleroy*!

Samuel French died in 1898 and it is doubtful if there was then a single famous English playwright of the past 60 or 70 years that had not been represented by his firm. The British side of the business passed through the Hogg family, first as French's managers and then as owners. In 1975 the two firms merged again and a descendant of the first American Board is still President and Chairman of the companies.

Performance rights were granted to playwrights by an amendment to the 1846 Copyright Act and the London end of the business developed the idea of controlling the performing rights and the collection of royalties on them. In 1936 French's fought the case known as Jennings v Stephens that clarified the legal distinction between public performances and those that were private and domestic, thereby establishing a code of practice which has helped to safeguard authors' rights ever since.

Samuel French Ltd at
89 The Strand, London in 1899

Lacy laid a sound foundation, French brought from America his useful commercialism and the Hoggs added the confidence that springs from a high degree of integrity. But no company can thrive only on its leading actors and French's has been fortunate in having a supporting cast whose commitment and involvement has been second to none.

In the 21st century French's continues to seek out, publish and license for performance the best of British plays, with a firm eye on titles suitable for performance by non-professional societies, schools, youth theatres and musical societies, whilst keeping alive a 2000-title backlist and many hundreds of earlier plays, from 1830, in archive format. The publishing side is complemented by a theatre bookshop full of technical information, backed by an organization big enough to promote its authors but small enough to help any aspiring actor or theatre group choose the right play for performance.

Adapted from *Truly Yours*, published in 1980 to celebrate 150 years of Samuel French.

Samuel French Ltd at 26 Southampton Street in Covent Garden, London (from 1900 to 1983)

Keeping Up to Date

You can keep your *Guide* up to date either by joining our mailing list or visiting our website which is constantly updated to give details of all new and future releases as they become available.

Mailing List

In Spring and Autumn we publish a supplement to *The Guide* which details all new and future releases and which is available free to all those on our mailing list. To obtain your copy please contact:

> Customer Services Department
> Samuel French Ltd
> 52 Fitzroy Street
> London W1T 5JR
>
> Telephone: 020 7387 9373
> Fax: 020 7387 2161
> e-mail: theatre@samuelfrench-london.co.uk

Web Site

If you have access to the world wide web (local libraries often have internet facilities) you may like to visit our site:

http://www.samuelfrench-london.co.uk

and obtain the supplement to *The Guide* online (available on our **New Releases** page).

In addition, we aim to provide regular updates on new French's publications, new releases available for amateur performance, details of theatre books on a wide range of topics available from our bookshop, and much more. The site includes:

♦ **New Releases**. Plays released for amateur performance with a link to the individual page giving full details of the title – casting, synopsis, fee code, set, etc.
♦ **Future Releases**. Plays released for amateur performance from the date given. Each title is linked to give full details of the play.
♦ **New Titles**. Newly published French's acting editions. (Please note that these titles, although available on sale, may not be available for amateur performance.)

LOGO PACKS
from Samuel French Inc

We have logo packs for 150 American titles. For a small fee you can use the show's logo on your programmes and posters. The titles include:

Be My Baby (Ken Ludwig)
Happy Days (Garry Marshall and Paul Williams)
The Musical of Musicals The Musical (Eric Rockwell and Joanne Bogart)
The Normal Heart (Larry Kramer)

For further details contact:
Editorial Department   Samuel French Ltd   52 Fitzroy Street   London W1T 5JR
email: editorial@samuelfrench-london.co.uk

How to Order Your Books

Retail Mail Order

RETAIL MAIL ORDER

Unless you already have an Account with us, pre-payment is required for ALL orders, either

a) by cheque or postal order made out to Samuel French Ltd OR

b) by credit/debit card when the number, expiry date, start date, issuing bank and issue number (if applicable) of the registered card MUST be quoted.

Please send your order to:

Customer Services Department
Samuel French Ltd
52 Fitzroy Street
London W1T 5JR

Or you may telephone your order on 020 7255 4300 or fax on 020 7387 2161 and quote your credit/debit card number.

Credit/debit card orders may also be left on our telephone answering service outside office hours. Please leave a daytime telephone number should we need to contact you during office hours (Monday to Friday 9.30 a.m. to 5.30 p.m.).

Please ensure when ordering by credit/debit card that your card number is correctly quoted, together with the date of expiry, start date, issuing bank and issue number (if applicable) and the address of the registered card owner.

ONLINE ORDERING

Please check our website www.samuelfrench-london.co.uk to check the status of online ordering.

Trade Customers

TRADE CUSTOMERS

Please enquire for trade terms and conditions.

The current prices of the plays in this Guide, together with postage rates for inland and overseas customers, can be found in our Price List, issued separately.

Orders for books may also be addressed to our authorized agents whose names and addresses appear on page ix of this Guide.

SECTION A
Full Length Plays

CONTENTS

A

Classified Index

Titles arranged according to number of characters

ONE PERSON PLAYS

M1
Anorak of Fire
Brief Lives
Bullet
I Am of Ireland
One Fine Day
Some Voices

F1
My Brilliant Divorce
Rose
Shirley Valentine
Spoonface Steinberg

TWO CHARACTERS

COMEDIES

M1 F1
April in Paris
Comedy of Terrors!
Different Way Home
Elsie and Norm's 'Macbeth'
Owl and the Pussycat
Same Time, Next Year
Second Time Around
Secret Lives of Henry and Alice
They're Playing Our Song
Two (*min. cast*)

M2
Mystery of Irma Vep
Number

PLAYS

M1 F1
Bash (*min. cast*)
Blackbird
Blue Room (*min. cast*)
Conjugal Rites
Decadence
Educating Rita
Happy Jack

Intimate Exchanges
Laughing Wild
Purgatorio
Secret Love Life of Ophelia
Separation
September in the Rain
Two of Us
Unexpected Man
What the Night Is For

M2
Staircase

F2
Breath of Life
Vita and Virginia

SERIOUS PLAYS

M1 F1
Duet for One
Gin Game
Mercy Seat
When the Wind Blows

M2
Not About Heroes

DRAMAS

M1 F1
Collector
Deceptions
Double Double
Killing Time
Mysterious Mr Love
Petition

M2
Sleuth

THREE CHARACTERS

COMEDIES

M1 F2
Decorator
Old Times
Teechers (*min. cast*)

M2 F1
Double Vision
Inspector Drake and the Black Widow
Kingfisher
Ruffian on the Stair
Speed-the-Plow

PLAYS

M1 F2
After Miss Julie
City
Country
Fall of the House of Usher (adapt.)
Just the Three of Us
Moment of Weakness
My Romantic History (*min. cast*)
Painting Churches
Stevie
Women on the Verge of HRT

M2 F1
Best of Friends
Betrayal
I Dreamt I Dwelt ...
Love and Understanding
Men of the World
Micky Salberg ... Band
Mixed Doubles
My Zinc Bed
Sorry, I Love You ...
Star-Spangled Girl
To Meet Oscar Wilde
Weekend Breaks

M3
American Buffalo
Art
Blue/Orange
Caretaker
Heroes
Life in the Theatre

F3
Love in the Title

SERIOUS PLAYS

Fewer Emergencies

M1 F2
Frozen
Summit Conference

M2 F1
Copenhagen
Death and the Maiden (Dorfman)
Fall of the House of Usher (*adapt.*)
Kingdom of Earth
Massage

F3
Low Level Panic

DRAMAS

M2 F1
Business of Murder
Dangerous Obsession
Faith Healer
Inside Job
Mindgame
Promise
Skylight

M3
Orphans
Someone Who'll Watch Over Me

F3
Agnes of God
Mrs Klein
Skirmishes
Snake in the Grass

FOUR CHARACTERS

FARCE

M2 F2
Alarms and Excursions (*min. cast*)

COMEDIES

Travels With My Aunt (*variable, min. cast*)

M1 F3
Last of the Red Hot Lovers

5

M2 F2
About Alice
Bolt from the Blue
Born in the Gardens
Butterflies Are Free
California Suite
Father's Day
Forget-Me-Knot
Funny About Love
Groping for Words
Lunatic View
Me and Mamie O'Rourke
Nobody's Perfect
On Approval
One for the Road
Opposite Sex
Relatively Speaking
Two of a Kind
You Say Tomatoes

M3 F1
Entertaining Mr Sloane
Hysteria
Knack
My Fat Friend
Rising Damp
Skull in Connemara

M4
Neville's Island

F4
Killing of Sister George

PLAYS

M1 F3
Colder Than Here
Threefold Cord
When I Was a Girl, I Used to Scream and
   Shout ...

M2 F2
Accommodations
Bash
Benefactors
Closer
Cocktail Hour
Cooking with Elvis
Come As You Are
Double Death
Eigengrau
Equally Divided
Fat Pig
Going Dutch

Good Grief
In Two Minds
Kiss Me Like You Mean It
Life X 3
Lucky Sods (*min. cast*)
Madame Melville
On the Rocks
Other Hands
Perfect Pitch
Playing the Wife
Proof
Pyrenees
Quartet
Road to the Sea
Shades
Shape of Things
Sugar Syndrome
Things We Do For Love
Women Laughing

M3 F1
Golden Pathway Annual
Landscape With Weapon
Lonesome West
Moonlight and Magnolias
Passionate Woman
Searching for Dr Branovic
Straits
39 Steps

M4
Gagarin Way
No Man's Land
Painting by Numbers
Wild Turkey

F4
If We Are Women
One Last Card Trick

SERIOUS PLAYS

M1 F3
Extremities
Far Away

M2 F2
Brimstone and Treacle
Exorcism
Glass Menagerie
Me and My Friend
Real Estate
Retreat From Moscow
Who's Afraid of Virginia Woolf?

M3 F1
After Darwin (*min. cast*)
Edward Gant ... Loneliness
Hollow Crown
In Praise of Love
Insignificance
Tom and Clem

DRAMAS

M1 F3
Blood Money
Dead Guilty
Deadly Embrace

M2 F2
Anastasia File
Audience With Murder
Beauty Queen of Leenane
Dead of Night
Devil at Midnight
Greek
Hard Times (*min. cast*)
I'll Be Back Before Midnight!
Late Edwina Black
Murder Game
Murderer
Nightmare: The Fright of Your Life
Recipe for Murder
Veronica's Room

M3 F1
Darkness Falls
Death is Catching
It's Ralph
Kiss of Death
Murder By Misadventure
Stage Struck

F4
Bold Girls
My Mother Said I Never Should
My Sister In This House

FIVE CHARACTERS

FARCE

M3 F2
Can't Pay? Won't Pay!

COMEDIES

M1 F4
Cemetery Club
Farndale Avenue/*Chase Me Up*
Farndale Avenue/*A Christmas Carol*
Farndale Avenue/*Murder Mystery*
They Came From Mars ...

M2 F3
Abigail's Party
Baby with the Bathwater (*min. cast*)
Falling Off a Log
Good Doctor
Happy Birthday
Henceforward ...
Imaginary Lines
Lettice and Lovage
Life Goes On
Look Who's Talking!
Nobody's Fool
Office Suite
Perfect Party
Private Lives
Second Time Around
Something's Burning
Touch and Go
We Found Love ... Aboard the SS Farndale
    Avenue

M3 F2
Bedside Manners
Birthday Suite
Cat in the Bag
Confusions
Dead Funny
Ding Dong
Don't Lose the Place!
Gasping (*min. cast*)
Greetings!
Inspector Drake and the Perfekt Crime
Other People's Money
Plaza Suite
Second from Last in the Sack Race (*min. cast*)
sex, drugs & rick 'n' noel
Silly Cow
Theft
Time and Time Again
Titfield Thunderbolt
Why Not Stay for Breakfast?

M4 F1
Corpse!
Entertaining Angels

A

F5
Curtain Up!
Kiss on the Bottom (*min. cast*)

PLAYS

M1 F4
Leaves
My Own Show

M2 F3
Actor's Nightmare (*see* Sister Mary
   Ignatius ...)
Anna's Room
Biting the Bullet
Blind Fiddler
Blood, Sweat and Tears
Going Straight
Just Between Ourselves
Like a Virgin
Loose Ends
Pizzazz
Sense and Sensibility
Some Girls
Something To Remember You By
Sugar Daddies
There Came a Gypsy Riding
Wedding Story
When the Reaper Calls

M3 F2
Audacity
Can You Hear Me at the Back?
Christmas Crackers (*min. cast*)
Double Death
God Only Knows
Going Dutch
Hitchcock Blonde
I Dreamt I Dwelt ...
If I Were You
Invisible River
Jeffrey Bernard Is Unwell
Lent
Metamorphosis (*min. cast*)
Mr Wonderful
Natural Causes
Peggy for You
Smelling a Rat
Unleashed
Vertical Hour
Yellow Moon

M4 F1
East

M5
Waiting for Godot

F5
Effect of Gamma Rays on Man-in-the-Moon
   Marigolds
New Anatomies (*min. cast*)
Playhouse Creatures

SERIOUS PLAYS

M1 F4
Stages

M2 F3
Kennedy's Children
Mail Order Bride

M3 F2
Another Time
Clocks and Whistles
Five Finger Exercise
Ghosts
Home
Kvetch
Letter of Resignation
Look Back in Anger
Old Masters

M4 F1
Killing Game
Next Time I'll Sing to You
Portraits (*min. cast*)

M5
Rents (*min. cast*)

DRAMAS

M1 F4
Summer End

M2 F3
Being of Sound Mind
Caravan
Gaslight
March on Russia

M3 F2
Bad Blood
Checkmate
Choice

A

Day in the Death of Joe Egg
Dead-Lock
Deathtrap
In for the Kill
In the Bar of a Tokyo Hotel
Portrait of Fear
Strictly Murder
Suspects
Taste of Honey
That Good Night

M4 F1
Accounts
Darkness Falls
Dial 'M' for Murder
Undertaking

SIX CHARACTERS

FARCES

M3 F3
Don't Dress for Dinner
Murder Room

M4 F2
Taking Steps

M5 F1
Accidental Death of an Anarchist

COMEDIES

M1 F5
Haunted Through Lounge ... Farndale Castle

M2 F4
All's Fair
Aspern Papers
Haywire
Look, No Hans!
No Dinner For Sinners
Over My Dead Body
Perfect Wedding
Prisoner of Second Avenue
Romantic Comedy
Visiting Hour (*min. cast*)
When the Cat's Away
Wife After Death

M3 F3
Absent Friends
Absurd Person Singular

Anyone For Breakfast?
Café Brosse
Cleo, Camping, Emmanuelle and Dick
Communicating Doors
Don't Dress for Dinner
First Things First
Fly In The Ointment
Foot in the Door
Ghost Writer
Gingerbread Lady
Good and Faithful Servant
How the Other Half Loves
Humble Boy
In at the Deep End
It Could Be Any One of Us
London Suite
Love in a Mist
My Friend Miss Flint
Norman Conquests
Pullin' the Wool
Safari Party
Salt of the Earth (*min. cast*)
Situation Comedy
Ski Whizz
Toe in the Water
Two and Two Make Sex
Up and Running
Why Me?

M4 F2
Barefoot in the Park
Beyond Therapy
False Servant
Funny Business
Heatstroke
Mixed Feelings
Pratt of the *Argus* (*min. cast*)
Searching for Dr Branovic
Slight Hangover
Torch Song Trilogy
Unoriginal Sin
What the Butler Saw
Wife Begins at Forty

M5 F1
Alone It Stands
End of the Food Chain
It Can Damage Your Health
Kafka's Dick
Loot
Rough Crossing

F6
Bazaar and Rummage

PLAYS

M1 F5
Cheshire Cats
Come Back for Light Refreshments After
   the Service

M2 F4
Ancient Lights
Crimes of the Heart
Day After the Fair
Glorious!
In Flame
It Started with a Kiss
Life After George
Lost Garden
Lovers
Mammals
Martha, Josie and Chinese Elvis
Memory of Water
My Heart's a Suitcase
My Wonderful Day
Passion Play
Pictures of Clay
Positive Hour
So Long Life
Sold
That Face
Untimely Frost
You Should See Us Now

M3 F3
Action Replay
Adam Bede
Amy's View
Anniversary
Conversations After a Burial
Dining Room (*min. cast*)
Grace Note
Gym and Tonic
Hard Feelings
Honeymoon Suite
Mahler's Conversion
My Brilliant Divorce
Play With Repeats
Private Fears in Public Places
Rise and Fall of Little Voice
Roots and Wings
Sister Mary Ignatius Explains It All for You

M4 F2
Broadway Bound
Chasing the Moment
Crown Prince
Elizabeth: Almost By Chance a Woman
Elton John's Glasses
Haunted

Mappa Mundi (*plus dancers*)
Maths Tutor
Not Quite Jerusalem
Some Sunny Day
Spokesong
Valued Friends

M5 F1
Acapulco
Building Blocks
Common Pursuit
End of the Affair

SERIOUS PLAYS

Fen (*varied cast*)

M2 F4
Aurelia
Delicate Balance
Messiah
Remembrance
Secret Rapture

M3 F3
Bloody Poetry
Enlightenment
Icecream
Kennedy's Children
Month of Sundays (Larbey)
Nabokov's Gloves
Old Country
Sweet Panic

M4 F2
Birthday Party
I Have Been Here Before
Light Shining In Buckinghamshire
Taking Sides
Traps

M5 F1
After Darwin
Homecoming
Single Spies

DRAMAS

M2 F4
Let It Be Me
Proscenophobia
Power of the Dog (Dryden)
Turn of the Screw

M3 F3
Anagram of Murder
Anybody for Murder?
Britannicus
Dead Man's Hand
Dining Room (*min. cast*)
Edge of Darkness
Exit the King
Fatal Attraction
Making Waves
Party to Murder
Sad Hotel
September Tide

M4 F2
Interpreters
Lenz
Madhouse in Goa
Making History
Paddywack
Silhouette (*min. cast*)
Without Trace

M6
Birdy
Choice
Dealers
Our Boys

F6
Steel Magnolias

SEVEN CHARACTERS

FARCES

M2 F5
Blithe Spirit

M3 F4
Big Bad Mouse
Kindly Keep It Covered

M4 F3
Pull the Other One

M5 F2
Who's Under Where?

COMEDIES

M1 F6
Caramba's Revenge

M3 F4
Children's Day
Come Blow Your Horn
Every Other Evening
Family Planning
Fish Out of Water (*revised*)
Improbable Fiction
Key for Two
Not With a Bang
Spygame
Up for Grabs
Way Upstream
Will You Still Love Me in the Morning?

M4 F3
And a Nightingale Sang
Bedfull of Foreigners
Breathing Corpses
Caught in the Net
Drowning On Dry Land
Good Morning, Bill
Holiday Snap
Lost In Yonkers
Lying Kind
Night on the Tiles
Party Piece
Passion Killers (*min. cast*)
Philanthropist
Ring Sisters
Rise and Fall of Little Voice
Rise in the Market
Straight and Narrow
Two and Two Together
US and Them
Who Dies Wins
Will You Still Love Me in the Morning?

M5 F2
God's Favorite
I'm Not Rappaport
Shady Business
Sunshine Boys
Up and Coming

M6 F1
Up 'n' Under

F7
Kiss on the Bottom

A

PLAYS

Vanity Fair (*min. cast*)

M1 F6
Compact Failure
Steaming

M2 F5
Laying the Ghost
White Cliffs

M3 F4
Brighton Beach Memoirs
84 Charing Cross Road
FlatSpin
GamePlan
Lingua Franca
Night Season
Piano Forte
Prescription for Murder
RolePlay
Sense and Sensibility
Take Away the Lady

M4 F3
All Things Considered
Alphabetical Order
Brideshead Revisited
Butley
Calico
Cloud Nine
Crown Prince
Dinner
Dresser
Family Dance
Geometry of Love (*min. cast*)
Getting On
Invisible River
Life Is a Dream
Lost In Yonkers
Never Land
Our Song
Real Thing
Sneeze (*min. cast*)
Sylvia's Wedding
Time of My Life
Tusk Tusk
York Realist

M5 F2
Abducting Diana
Blue Murder
Blue Remembered Hills

Borders of Paradise
Breaking the Silence
Fiddlers Three
Otherwise Engaged
Quartermaine's Terms
Samson Riddle

M6 F1
Artist Descending a Staircase

SERIOUS PLAYS

M3 F4
Children of a Lesser God

M4 F3
Architect
Getting Attention
Holy Terror (*min. cast*)
Inspector Calls
Moonlight
Road (*min. cast*)
Talking Cure

M5 F2
Animal Farm (adapt. Bond)
Lion in Winter
Single Spies

M7
Glengarry Glen Ross

F7
Top Girls (*min. cast*)

DRAMAS

M2 F5
Positive Hour

M3 F4
Dangerous Corner
Death Walked In
Deliver Us From Evil
Doll's House
Experiment with an Air Pump
Hedda Gabler
Maiden Stone
Miss Roach's War (*min. cast*)
New England
Nightmare
Restoration of Arnold Middleton

Tess of the D'Urbervilles (*min. cast*)
They Call It Murder
Turn of the Screw

M4 F3
Les Misérables
Red in the Morning
Scarlet Letter
Shock!
Silas Marner (*min. cast*)

M5 F2
Man and Boy
My Cousin Rachel
Pillowman
Strangers on a Train
Talented Mr Ripley

M6 F1
Hothouse
Never the Sinner

EIGHT CHARACTERS

Gasping (*variable cast*)

FARCE

M4 F4
Amorous Ambassador

M6 F2
Can't Pay? Won't Pay!

COMEDIES

M2 F6
Odd Couple (*female version*)

M3 F5
Billy Liar
Breath of Spring
Curtain Call
Kindly Leave the Stage
Murder In Play
So What Do We Do About Henry?

M4 F4
Bedroom Farce
Beyond a Joke

Caught on the Hop
Duets
Holiday Snap
Increased Difficulty of Concentration
Lady Audley's Secret
Late Mrs Early
Lend Me a Tenor
Over the Moon (Moon Over Buffalo)
Period of Adjustment
Spring and Port Wine
Wildest Dreams
Woman in Mind

M5 F3
Enter a Free Man
False Admissions
Serious Money (*min. cast*)
Travesties

M6 F2
Balmoral
Funny Money
Odd Couple
Run for Your Wife

PLAYS

M1 F7
Day of Reckoning

M2 F6
Warwickshire Testimony

M3 F5
Curtain Up on Murder
Curtains
84 Charing Cross Road
Five Wives of Maurice Pinder
Happy Families
Lovers
Same Old Moon (*min. cast*)
Winter Guest

M4 F4
Arsonists
Bed
Blinded by the Sun
Family Circles
Garden Party
Joking Apart
Life
Lightning Play
Lucky Sods
Semi-Detached

Sisters Rosensweig
Summer

M5 F3
Body Language
Disposing of the Body
Editing Process
Grace of Mary Traverse
Hock and Soda Water (*min. cast*)
Rehearsal
Tom and Viv
Two Thousand Years

M6 F2
Bad Company
Howard Katz (*min. cast*)
King Cromwell

M7 F1
Bacchae
Hapgood
Lieutenant of Inishmore
Night and Day

SERIOUS PLAYS

M2 F6
Gut Girls (*min. cast*)

M3 F5
Find Me
Pack of Lies

M4 F4
Doll's House
Fighting Chance
Map of the Heart
Now You Know
Rutherford and Son

M5 F3
Deep Blue Sea
Elephant Man
Hidden Laughter

M6 F2
Progress

DRAMAS

M3 F5
At the Sign of "The Crippled Harlequin"
Dancing at Lughnasa
Little Photographer
Miss Roach's War

M4 F4
Frankenstein
House Guest
Love from a Stranger
Murder in Company
New England
Suddenly at Home

M5 F3
Dark River
Disappeared
Entertainer
Far from the Madding Crowd (*min. cast*)
Fatal Encounter
Silhouette
Small Hours

M6 F2
Gentle Hook
Rope
Wait Until Dark

M7 F1
Russian in the Woods

M8
Long and the Short and the Tall
Thyestes

NINE CHARACTERS

Blue Heart (*variable cast*)
Inspector Drake and the Time Machine
   (*variable cast*)

FARCES

M3 F6
Darling Mr London

M4 F5
I'll Get My Man
Panic Stations
Pardon Me, Prime Minister
Rumours (British Version)

M5 F4
Come On, Jeeves
Keeping Down with the Joneses

M6 F3
See How They Run
When Did You Last See Your Trousers?

COMEDIES

M3 F6
Bums on Seats (*min. cast*)
Departures
Flying Feathers
Murder Weekend

M4 F5
Cut and Run
East Lynne
Hay Fever
Local Affairs
Out of Sight ... Out of Murder
Passion Killers
Popcorn
Sailor, Beware!
Three Birds Alighting on a Field
Weekend

M5 F4
Cracked Pot
Importance of Being Earnest (3 act version)
Milk Train Doesn't Stop Here Any More
Season's Greetings
Star Quality

M6 F3
Corpsing
Erpingham Camp
Misanthrope (trans. Crimp)
Real Story of Puss in Boots (*min. cast*)
Servant to Two Masters
Shut Your Eyes and Think of England
Tom, Dick and Harry

M7 F2
Biloxi Blues
Picasso at the Lapin Agile
Trumpets and Raspberries
Up 'n' Under II

PLAYS

M1 F8
Come Back to the 5 & Dime, Jimmy Dean

M2 F7
Visitors

M3 F6
Happy Families
Kerry Dance
Love in Idleness

M4 F5
Albert Make Us Laugh
Cripple of Inishmaan
Dearly Beloved
Less Than Kind
Word from Our Sponsor

M5 F4
Breezeblock Park
Cider With Rosie
Cracks
Dolly West's Kitchen
Mrs Affleck
Outside Edge
Punk Rock

M6 F3
Hock and Soda Water

M7 F2
Shadowlands

M8 F1
Donkeys' Years

F9
Passing-Out Parade

SERIOUS PLAYS

Vinegar Tom (*variable cast*)

M4 F5
Give Me Your Answer, Do!
They Came to a City
Wings

M5 F4
Amongst Barbarians
Buried Alive
Distance From Here
Roots
Equus

M6 F3
Aristocrats
When the Barbarians Came

M7 F2
West

DRAMAS

M3 F6
Les Liaisons Dangereuses

M4 F5
Gift of the Gorgon (*plus extras*)
Jekyll and Hyde
Night Must Fall
Someone Waiting

M5 F4
Far from the Madding Crowd
Living Quarters
Night Watch
Steward of Christendom
Touch of Danger
Uncle Vanya (*adapt. Mamet*)

M6 F3
Murder with Love
Sweet Revenge
Temptation

M7 F2
Breaking the Code
Count Dracula
Fortune's Fool (*plus extras*)
Perfect Murder
Scent of Flowers

M8 F1
Oedipus (*plus chorus*)

M9
Boys in the Band
Observe the Sons of Ulster Marching Towards
   the Somme
Seagulls Over Sorrento

TEN CHARACTERS

FARCES

M4 F6
Continental Quilt
Gypsy's Revenge

M5 F5
Gypsy's Revenge

M6 F4
Cash on Delivery
Charley's Aunt
No Sex, Please – We're British!
Noises Off
Tons of Money

M8 F2
Dirty Linen and Newfoundland

COMEDIES

M1 F9
Stepping Out

M2 F8
Baby with the Bathwater

M3 F7
Farndale Avenue/*Macbeth*
Ladies Who Lunch
Play On!

M4 F6
I'll Leave It to You
Prepare to Meet Thy Tomb
Tiptoe Through the Tombstones
Tomb with a View
Wedding of the Year
What Are Little Girls Made Of?

M5 F5
Comfort and Joy (*min.cast*)
Comic Potential
Lord Arthur Savile's Crime
Relative Values
Sisterhood
Two Into One

M6 F4
House of Frankenstein!
Man of the Moment

A

Out of Order
Zack

M7 F3
Fools
French Without Tears
My Three Angels
Whodunnit

PLAYS

M2 F8
Cranford

M4 F6
Female Transport
Loves of Cass McGuire
Soft September Air
Sitting Pretty
Time and the Conways
Trivial Pursuits

M5 F5
Alfie
Blue Room
Dream Play (*min. cast*)
Gym and Tonic
Our House
La Ronde
Shell Seekers

M6 F4
Fred and Madge
Jack the Lad
On the Shore of the Wide World
Play On!
Ten Times Table
Uncle Vanya (*adapt. Friel*)
Uncle Vanya (*adapt. Poulton*)

M7 F3
Alice
BoyBand
Don Juan in Soho

M8 F2
Parasol

M10
Another Country

SERIOUS PLAYS

M5 F5
Accrington Pals
Diary of Anne Frank
Eccentricities of a Nightingale
Sword Against the Sea

M6 F4
Brassed Off (*plus extras*)
Edmond
Killers
Treatment

M7 F3
Fallout
Holy Terror
Redevelopment

M10
Democracy
Rent

F10
Whale Music

DRAMAS

M3 F7
Restless Evil

M4 F6
Black Widow
House of Mirth
Jane Eyre (*adapt. Vance*)
Murder Has Been Arranged

M5 F5
And Evermore Shall Be So
Forsyte Saga
Hound of the Baskervilles
Vieux Carré

M6 F4
Deadly Nightcap
Three Judgements in One
Verdict
Wuthering Heights

M7 F3
Cat on a Hot Tin Roof
Translations
Unexpected Guest

M8 F2
Trial

ELEVEN CHARACTERS

FARCES

M5 F6
Rookery Nook

COMEDIES

M3 F8
Play It Again, Sam

M4 F7
Sing On!

M5 F6
Make Way for Lucia
Present Laughter

M6 F5
Graduate
House of Dracula
Stags and Hens

M7 F4
All in Good Time
Are You Being Served?
Falling Short
Importance of Being Earnest (4 act)
Inspector Drake's Last Case
Laughter in the Dark
Lunatic View
Mr Whatnot
Real Story of Puss in Boots

M8 F3
Pope and the Witch
Servant of Two Masters

PLAYS

M4 F7
Little Women

M5 F6
After October
Salt of the Earth

M6 F5
Cruel and Tender
Filumena
Habeas Corpus
Rock 'N' Roll (*min. cast*)
Who Is Sylvia?

M7 F4
Katherine Howard
Seagull (Crimp)

M8 F3
Home Place
Mary Stuart

M9 F2
Forget Herostratus!
Henry IV

M10 F1
End of the Affair
Privates on Parade

M11
Comedians

SERIOUS PLAYS

M3 F8
Separate Tables

M7 F4
Winslow Boy

M8 F3
Credible Witness
Hiawatha
Racing Demon

DRAMAS

Mad Forest (*variable cast*)

M10 F1
Savages
To The Green Fields Beyond

M3 F8
Bonaventure

M4 F7
Jane Eyre (*adapt. Vance*)

M5 F6
Murder at Rutherford House

M6 F5
Forsyte Saga
Woman in White

M7 F4
August
Flare Path
Our Country's Good
Total Eclipse

M8 F3
Holmes and the Ripper
Lady's Not For Burning
Léocadia
Passage to India (*min. cast*)
Rebecca
Spider's Web
Sweeney Todd
Warrior

M10 F1
Crucifer of Blood
Normal Heart (*min. cast*)

M11
Bent

F11
House of Bernarda Alba

TWELVE CHARACTERS

FARCES

COMEDIES

M6 F6
Comfort and Joy

M7 F5
Flint Street Nativity
Hobson's Choice
House of Dracula
Inspector Drake's Last Case
It's Later Than You Think
It Runs In The Family

M8 F4
Aren't We All?
Imaginary Invalid
Inspecting Carol

Sisterly Feelings
Tartuffe (Malleson)

M10 F2
Inside Trading (*min. cast*)

PLAYS

M4 F8
Last Tango in Whitby
Sold

M5 F7
Lizzy, Darcy and Jane

M6 F6
Shell Seekers

M7 F5
Canterbury Tales
Month in the Country (Friel)
Pale Horse
Seagull

M8 F4
Alice
Arcadia

M9 F3
Yard of Sun

F12
Passing-Out Parade

SERIOUS PLAYS

M5 F7
This Happy Breed

M6 F6
Streetcar Named Desire

M7 F5
Made in Bangkok

M9 F3
Largo Desolato

DRAMAS

M4 F8
Jane Eyre (*adapt. Hall*)

M5 F7
Cards on the Table
Murder Is Announced

M6 F6
Hollow

M7 F5
Cat on a Hot Tin Roof
Ivanov

M8 F4
Antigone (Anouilh)
Ghost Train

M9 F3
After the Rain
And Then There Were None
Les Misérables

M10 F2
Prisoner of Zenda

M11 F1
Crucifer of Blood

THIRTEEN CHARACTERS AND OVER

FARCES

Absolute Turkey
Alarms and Excursions
Amphibious Spangulatos
Cat Among the Pigeons (Feydeau)
Flea in Her Ear
Happiest Days of Your Life
Hotel Paradiso
Keep an Eye on Amélie
Little Hotel on the Side
Matchmaker
On the Razzle
One Way Pendulum
Winner Takes All

COMEDIES

'Allo 'Allo
Are You Being Served?
Black Snow
Bone-Chiller
Bums on Seats
Busy Day

Carpe Jugulum
Celebration
Chorus of Disapproval
Calendar Girls
Dad's Army
Darling Buds of May
Dick Barton – Special Agent
Dick Barton II
Dick Barton III
Dogg's Hamlet, Cahoot's Macbeth
Don't Drink the Water
Drunkard
Enjoy
Forty Years On
Fur Coat and No Knickers
Graduate
Government Inspector
Hi-de-Hi
I Have Five Daughters
Inside Trading
It Was a Dark and Stormy Night
Joseph Andrews
Laughter in the Dark
Leave It To Psmith
Miser
Mr Quigley's Revenge
Murder of Maria Marten
Nil By Mouth
Northanger Abbey
Nude With Violin
On Monday Next
Once a Catholic
Once in a Lifetime
One O'Clock from the House
Peer Gynt
Prodigious Snob
Revengers' Comedies
Robin Hood (Blamire)
Robin Hood (Wood)
Rosencrantz and Guildenstern Are Dead
Royal Pardon
Rumpelstiltzkin
Scapino!
Sea
Seagull
Second from Last in the Sack Race
The Secret Diary of Adrian Mole
    Aged 13¾
Serious Money
Servant of Two Masters
Small Family Business
Suicide
Sweeney Todd
Sweeney Todd, the Barber
Sweeney Todd, the Demon Barber of Fleet
    Street

A

Tartuffe (Hampton)
Titfield Thunderbolt
Tom Jones
Travels With My Aunt
Trelawny of the 'Wells'
When We Are Married
Wild Honey

PLAYS

Adam Bede
Adventures of Huckleberry Finn
After Liverpool
Albert Make Us Laugh
Alfie
Alice
Anne of Green Gables
Ash Girl
Back to the Land
Bottom's Dream
Brideshead Revisited
Camino Real
Candleford
Canterbury Tales
Child's Christmas in Wales
Chinchilla
Christmas Carol
Christmas Crackers
Cider With Rosie
Close the Coalhouse Door
Coast of Utopia
Cold Comfort Farm
Come As You Are
Corn is Green
Dahling You Were Marvellous
Daisy Pulls It Off
Dream Play
Dreaming
English Game
Enron
Games
Geometry of Love
Golden Pathway Annual
Government Inspector
Grand Magic
Her Naked Skin
History Boys
Home Before Dark
House & Garden
Howard Katz
I Remember Mama
Indian Ink
Invention of Love
Invisible Man

Jack the Ripper
Jumpers
Lady in the Van
Lark Rise
Laughing Matter
Little Women (*adapt. Reeves*)
Lords and Ladies
Lysistrata – Sex Strike
Make and Break
Making Money
Mansfield Park
Mary Stuart
Maskerade
Men Should Weep
Mummy's Tomb
Murder on the Nile
My Romantic History
Napoli Milionaria
National Health
Philadelphia, Here I Come!
Pied Piper
Pinocchio
Plague Over England
Posh
Pratt of the *Argus*
Ring Round the Moon
Rock 'N' Roll
Salvage
Same Old Moon
Samson Riddle
Sand Castles
Saturday, Sunday, Monday
Scarlet Pimpernel
Scottish Play
Semi-Monde
Shadowlands
Shipwreck
Sing Yer Heart Out for the Lads
Tales from Hollywood
Tales of King Arthur
Thieves' Carnival
Three Musketeers
Treasure Island
Two Planks and a Passion
Undiscovered Country
Under Milk Wood
Vanity Fair
Voyage
Waiting in the Wings
When Five Years Pass
Women
Wonderful World of Dissocia
Wind in the Willows

SERIOUS PLAYS

Absolute Hell
Animal Farm (*adapt. Hall*)
At Break of Day
Battle of Angels
Becket
Break of Day
Cause Célèbre
Cherry Orchard
Christmas Carol
Destiny
Elephant Man
Edmond
Equus
Fen
Few Good Men
Francis
Freedom of the City
Gentle Island
Ghetto
Heart of a Dog
Icecream
Lark
Light Shining in Buckinghamshire
Madness of George III
Man for All Seasons
Messiah (*Berkoff*)
Miracle Worker
Murmuring Judges
Night of the Iguana
One Flew Over the Cuckoo's Nest
Our Town
Physicists
Prime of Miss Jean Brodie
Roses of Eyam
Royal Hunt of the Sun
Skin of Our Teeth
Son of Man
Surgeon of Honour
Taking Care of Baby
Temptation
Three Sisters
Twelve Angry Men
Vinegar Tom
Vivat! Vivat Regina!
Whose Life Is It Anyway?
Widows

DRAMAS

After Easter
Amadeus
Anastasia
Antigone (Brecht)
Appointment With Death

Baal
Baby Doll
Bad Dream
Beyond Reasonable Doubt
Black Coffee
Blood Wedding
Camille
Cards on the Table
Caucasian Chalk Circle
Clothes for a Summer Hotel
Coriolanus (Brecht)
Curtmantle
Dark Is Light Enough
David Copperfield
Days of the Commune
Devils
Dining Room
Don Juan
Doña Rosita the Spinster
Dreaming
Drums in the Night
Entertaining Strangers
Fathers and Sons
Fears and Miseries of the Third Reich
Fifteen Streets
Firstborn
Front Page
Gift of the Gorgon
Good Hope
Good Person of Sichuan
Good Person of Szechwan (Good Woman of Setzuan)
Great Expectations
Holmes and the Ripper
Ion
In the Jungle of the Cities (In the Cities' Jungle)
Jane Eyre
Journey's End
Juno and the Paycock
Life of Galileo
Local Authority
Love of the Nightingale
Mad Forest
Man Is Man (Man Equals Man)
Month in the Country
Mother
Mother Courage and Her Children
Mr Puntilla and his Man Matti
Not About Nightingales
Oliver Twist
Orpheus Descending
Our Country's Good
Passage to India
Perfect Murder
Picture of Dorian Gray
Plough and the Stars
Prisoner of Zenda

Ramayana
Resistible Rise of Arturo Ui
Ritual in Blood
Rose Tattoo
Round Heads and Pointed Heads (Money
    Calls to Money)
Roundheads and Peakheads (Rich and Rich)
Royal Baccarat Scandal
Sarcophagus
Schweyk in the Second World War
Silas Marner
Sink the Belgrano!
Slapstick Tragedy
St Joan of the Stockyards
Strange Case of Dr Jekyll and Mr Hyde
Summer and Smoke
Sweet Bird of Youth
Tale of Two Cities
Tess of the d'Urbervilles
Tower
Trumpets and Drums
Turandot
Tutor
Visions of Simone Machard
Visit
Webster
Wild Duck
Witness for the Prosecution
Wolf at the Door
Woyzeck
Wuthering Heights
Yerma

Titles arranged according to period and/or type of play

THE CLASSICS

Britannicus
Cyrano de Bergerac
False Admissions (Les Fausses Confidences)
False Servant
Imaginary Invalid (Malade Imaginaire)
Importance of Being Earnest
Lysistrata – Sex Strike
Misanthrope
Miser
Prodigious Snob (Bourgeois Gentilhomme)
Ramayana
Rivals
School for Wives (L'École des Femmes)
She Stoops to Conquer
Sisterhood (Les Femmes Savantes)
Successful Strategies (L'Heureux Stratagème)
Tartuffe

COSTUME PLAYS

(Dates are given in round figures as an approximate guide)

Ancient Greek
Bacchae
Ion
Love of the Nightingale
Lysistrata – Sex Strike
Thyestes

Ancient Roman
Britannicus

Biblical
Firstborn
Son of Man

Arthurian
Tales of King Arthur

Gothic 1100-1450
Becket
Canterbury Tales
Curtmantle
Francis
Lady's Not For Burning
Lark
Lion in Winter
Ritual in Blood
Robin Hood (Blamire)
Robin Hood (Wood)

Tower
Two Planks and a Passion

Renaissance 1450-1500
Dreaming

Tudor 1500-1550
Katherine Howard
Man for All Seasons
Royal Hunt of the Sun

Elizabethan 1550-1620
Bottom's Dream
Devils
Life Is a Dream
Making History
Mary Stuart
Pictures of Clay
Rosencrantz and Guildenstern Are Dead
Spring 1600
Surgeon of Honour
Three Judgements in One
Vinegar Tom
Vivat! Vivat Regina!
Webster

Civil War
Light Shining in Buckinghamshire

Restoration 1660-1700
Brief Lives
London Cuckolds
Lorna Doone
Messiah
Mother Courage and Her Children
Playhouse Creatures
Roses of Eyam
Three Musketeers

Louis XIV 1660 onwards
Imaginary Invalid
Inconstant Couple
Miser
Prodigious Snob
Scarlet Letter (USA)
Servant of Two Masters
Tartuffe

Georgian 1714-1750
False Admissions
Joseph Andrews
Tom Jones
Warrior

Late Georgian 1750-1800
Amadeus
Grace of Mary Traverse
Lenz
Les Liaisons Dangereuses
Lizzy, Darcy and Jane
Madness of George III
Our Country's Good
Rivals
Tale of Two Cities (Francis)
Trumpets and Drums
Warrior

Directoire and 1st Empire 1790-1810
Busy Day
Northanger Abbey
Scarlet Pimpernel
Vanity Fair

Regency 1810-1820
Bloody Poetry
Cracked Pot
Frankenstein
Geometry of Love
Les Misérables
Maiden Stone
Mansfield Park
Sense and Sensibility

Romantic 1820-1840
Cranford
David Copperfield
Great Expectations
Murder of Maria Marten
Peer Gynt
Silas Marner (to 1860)

Early Victorian 1840-1865 (Crinoline)
Adam Bede
Camille
Christmas Carol
Coast of Utopia
Dark Is Light Enough
Doña Rosita the Spinster
Drunkard
East Lynne
Entertaining Strangers
Fathers and Sons
Hard Times
Jane Eyre
Lady Audley's Secret
Little Women
Month in the Country
My Cousin Rachel
On the Razzle
Salvage
Shipwreck

Sweeney Todd
Sweeney Todd the Barber
Sweeney Todd, the Demon Barber of Fleet
    Street
Tale of Two Cities (Fitzgibbon)
Translations
Treasure Island
Trelawny of the 'Wells'
Virtue Triumphant
Voyage
Woman in White
Wuthering Heights

Late Victorian 1865-1900 (Bustle)
Adventures of Huckleberry Finn
Aspern Papers
August
Candleford
Charley's Aunt
Cherry Orchard
Corn Is Green
Count Dracula
Crucifer of Blood
Day After the Fair
Days of the Commune
Doll's House
Edward Gant … Loneliness
Elephant Man
Far from the Madding Crowd
Female Transport
Fools
Forsyte Saga (to 1920)
Fortune's Fool
Gaslight
Ghost
Good Hope
Government Inspector
Hedda Gabler
Hobson's Choice
Holmes and the Ripper
Home Place
Hound of the Baskervilles
Importance of Being Earnest
Invention of Love (to 1936)
Ivanov
Jack the Ripper
Lark Rise
Lord Arthur Savile's Crime
Mahler's Conversion
Matchmaker
Miracle Worker
New Anatomies
Odd Women
Oliver Twist
Parasol
Picture of Dorian Gray
Pillars of the Community

Playing the Wife
Royal Baccarat Scandal
Seagull
Strange Case of Dr Jekyll and Mr Hyde
Tess of the d'Urbervilles
Total Eclipse
Turn of the Screw
Uncle Vanya
Undiscovered Country
Wild Duck
Wild Honey
Wind of Heaven
Wolf at the Door

Edwardian 1900-1910
Absolute Turkey
Admirable Crichton
Anne of Green Gables
Black Widow
Cat Among the Pigeons (Feydeau)
Dream Play
Edge of Darkness
Fifteen Streets
Flea in Her Ear
Fosdyke Saga
Gigi
Gut Girls
Hotel Paradiso
House of Mirth
I Remember Mama
Keep An Eye On Amélie
Little Hotel on the Side
Little Photographer
My Three Angels
Passage to India
Picasso at the Lapin Agile
Prisoner of Zenda
La Ronde
Seagull
Summer and Smoke
Talking Cure
To Meet Oscar Wilde
Watcher in the Shadow
When We are Married
Winner Takes All
Winslow Boy

1910s
Accrington Pals
Breaking the Silence
Eccentricities of a Nightingale
Fifteen Streets
Her Naked Skin
In the Jungle of the Cities
Inspector Calls
Journey's End
Mother

Mysterious Mr Love
Not About Heroes
Observe the Sons of Ulster ...
On the Rocks
Plough and the Stars
Rutherford and Son
To the Green Fields Beyond
Travesties

1920s
Aren't We All?
Black Snow
Blood Wedding
Breaking the Silence
Brideshead Revisited
Calico
Cider With Rosie
Come On, Jeeves
Daisy Pulls It Off
Front Page
Ghost Train
Hay Fever
I'll Leave It To You
Juno and the Paycock
Never the Sinner
On Approval
Once in a Lifetime
Rookery Nook
Sacred Flame
Semi-Monde
Shadow of a Gunman
Suicide
This Happy Breed (1919-1937)
Three Sisters Two
Time and the Conways (1919-1937)
Tom and Viv
Tons of Money
Vita and Virginia (1922-1941)
Zack

1930s
After You with the Milk
Anastasia
Another Country
Balmoral
Bent
Birdy (and 1946)
Brighton Beach Memoirs
Cause Célèbre
Cold Comfort Farm
Corpse!
Cripple of Inishmaan
Cuckoo
Dancing at Lughnasa
Dark River
Fears and Miseries of the Third Reich
Hysteria

Lend Me a Tenor
Men Should Weep
Moonlight and Magnolias
Mrs Klein
My Sister In This House
Night Must Fall
Not About Nightingales
Old Masters
Once in a Lifetime
Prime of Miss Jean Brodie
Private Lives
Rough Crossing
Round Heads and Pointed Heads
Roundheads and Peakheads
Second from Last in the Sack Race (to 1950s)
Steward of Christendom
Strictly Murder
Tales from Hollywood (to 1950s)
39 Steps
Tutor
Vieux Carré
Whodunnit

1940s
Absolute Hell
After Miss Julie
After October
All's Fair
'Allo 'Allo
And a Nightingale Sang
Back to the Land
Biloxi Blues
Blue Remembered Hills
Breaking the Code
Brideshead Revisited
Broadway Bound
Caucasian Chalk Circle
Copenhagen
Dad's Army
Dame of Sark
Diary of Anne Frank
Dick Barton – Special Agent
Dick Barton II
Dick Barton III
Dolly West's Kitchen
Dresser
End of the Affair
Filumena
Flare Path
Ghetto
Glass Menagerie
Golden Pathway Annual (to late 1960s)
Happiest Days of Your Life
Home Before Dark (to 1964)
Long and the Short and the Tall
Lost In Yonkers
Men Should Weep

Miss Roach's War
Morning Star
Napoli Millionara
Next Time I'll Sing to You
Night of the Iguana
Orpheus Descending
Passing-Out Parade
Privates on Parade
Promise
Rebecca
Russian in the Woods
Schweyk in the Second World War
See How They Run
Some Sunny Day
Summit Conference
Taking Sides
To the Green Fields Beyond
Tom and Clem
Trespass
White Cliffs

1950s
Albert Make Us Laugh
Baby Doll
Billy Liar
Bonaventure
Cat Among the Pigeons (Greenwood)
Come Back to the 5 & Dime (to 1970s)
Darling Buds of May
Deep Blue Sea
Five Finger Exercise
Heroes
Hi-de-Hi
Insignificance
Lent
Lingua Franca
Marvellous Party
Mrs Affleck
Micky Salberg … Band
Once a Catholic
Pack of Lies
Plague Over England
Portraits
Pratt of the *Argus*
Roots
September Tide
Single Spies (to 1960s)
Shadowlands
Someone Waiting
Star Quality
Stevie
Strangers on a Train
Talented Mr Ripley
Taste of Honey
Titfield Thunderbolt
Twelve Angry Men

1960s

Alfie
Blue Murder
Cleo, Camping, Emmanuelle and Dick
Kerry Dance
Kingdom of Earth
Knack
Letter of Resignation
Madame Melville
Peggy for You (to 1980s)
Quartermaine's Terms
Rising Damp
Sad Hotel
Savages
Spring and Port Wine
Visitors
What I Did in the Holidays
York Realist

1970s

Alone It Stands
Aristocrats
Blind Fiddler
Cracks
Freedom of the City
Rents
Why Not Stay for Breakfast?

1980s

Dealing With Clair
History Boys

1990s

Enron
Let It Be Me
Lieutenant of Inishmore
Sitting Pretty

Modern and Period

After Darwin
Amy's View
Anastasia File
Another Time
Arcadia
Artist Descending a Staircase
Buried Alive
Child's Christmas in Wales
Chinchilla
Cloud Nine
84 Charing Cross Road
Experiment with an Air Pump
Feed
Gift of the Gorgon
Happy Families
In Flame

Indian Ink
Kafka's Dick
Lessons and Lovers
Life
Little Like Drowning
Love Forty
Moving (Leonard)
Rehearsal
Salt of the Earth
Same Old Moon
Shell Seekers
Spokesong
Veronica's Room
Warwickshire Testimony
When I was a Girl, I Used to Scream and Shout

HISTORICAL PLAYS

Ancient Greece
Ion

Ancient Rome
Britannicus

12th Century
Becket
Curtmantle
Lion in Winter

13th Century
Francis

15th Century
Dreaming
Lark

16th Century
Katherine Howard
Luther
Man for All Seasons
Mary Stuart

Tudor
Royal Hunt of the Sun

Elizabethan
Devils
Making History
Vivat! Vivat Regina!

Stuart and Protectorate
King Cromwell
Light Shining in Buckinghamshire
Roses of Eyam

Late Georgian
Laughing Matter
Madness of George III

Victorian
Miracle Worker

Edwardian
Talking Cure
Winslow Boy

1920s
Calico

1930s
Old Masters

1940s
Copenhagen
Diary of Anne Frank
Glorious!
Passing-Out Parade
Taking Sides
Tom and Clem

1960s
Democracy
Letter of Resignation

1970s
It Started with a Kiss

Modern Costume
Hollow Crown

DRAMATIZED NOVELS AND STORIES

Adam Bede
Adventures of Huckleberry Finn
Alan Turing: The Enigma (*see* Breaking
    the Code)
Animal Farm
Anne of Green Gables
Aurelia
Birdy
Brassed Off
Brideshead Revisited
Canterbury Tales
Cards on the Table
Carpe Jugulum
Christmas Carol
Cider With Rosie
Cold Comfort Farm
Cranford
Collector

Dame Aux Camélias (*see* Camille)
David Copperfield
Devils
Diary of Anne Frank
Dr Jekyll and Mr Hyde (*see* Strange Case of
    Dr Jekyll and Mr Hyde)
Dracula (*see* Count Dracula)
East Lynne
84 Charing Cross Road
End of the Affair
Fall of the House of Usher
Far from the Madding Crowd
Fathers and Sons
Fifteen Streets
Frankenstein
Forsyte Saga
Graduate
Good Grief
Great Expectations
Hard Times
Hiawatha
I Dreamt I Dwelt ...
Jack the Ripper, the Final Solution (*see*
    Holmes and the Ripper)
Jane Eyre
Joseph Andrews
Lark Rise to Candleford (*see* Candleford
    and Lark Rise)
Lenz
Little Women
Lord Arthur Savile's Crime
Lords and Ladies
Lost In Yonkers
Lucia novels by E. F. Benson (*see* Make Way
    for Lucia)
Making Money
Mansfield Park
Maskerade
Metamorphosis
Monkey's Paw
My Cousin Rachel
Northanger Abbey
Now You Know
Oliver Twist
On the Western Circuit (*see* Day After the
    Fair)
One Flew Over the Cuckoo's Nest
Our Song
Passage to India
Perfect Murder
Picture of Dorian Gray
Pied Piper
Pinocchio
Playmaker (*see* Our Country's Good)
Popcorn
Pride and Prejudice
Prime of Miss Jean Brodie

A

Prisoner of Zenda
Rebecca
Royal Baccarat Scandal
Scarlet Letter
Scarlet Pimpernel
Second From Last in the Sack Race
Sense and Sensibility
Shell Seekers
Sign of Four (*see* Crucifer of Blood)
Silas Marner
Slaves of Solitude (*see* Miss Roach's War)
Sneeze
Strangers on a Train
Tale of Two Cities
Talented Mr Ripley
Tess of the d'Urbervilles
39 Steps
Three Years (*see* Parasol)
Tom Jones
Travels With My Aunt
Trial
Turn of the Screw
Vanity Fair
Washington Square (*see* Heiress)
Wind in the Willows
Woman in White
Wuthering Heights

DRAMATIZED TELEVISION SERIES

'Allo 'Allo
Are You Being Served
Dad's Army
Fawlty Towers
Fiddler's Three
George and Mildred (*TV series, see* When the Cat's Away)
Home to Roost (*see* Father's Day)
Only When I Laugh (*TV series, see* It Can Damage Your Health)
Outside Edge
Rising Damp

SOCIAL PLAYS
(Plays with a Social Interest)

Absolute Hell
After Darwin
After Miss Julie
All Things Bright and Beautiful
All Things Considered
Animal Farm
Arsonists
Back to the Land
Bad Company

Bazaar and Rummage
Benefactors
Blackbird
Brassed Off
Breezeblock Park
Buried Alive
Credible Witness
Children of a Lesser God
Choice
Curtains
Day in the Death of Joe Egg
Duet for One
Elephant Man
Enjoy
Equus
Exorcism
Fallout
Far Away
Fighting Chance
Find Me
Gasping
Getting Attention
Groping for Words
Gut Girls
Hard Feelings
Her Naked Skin
Home
Inspector Calls
Invisible River
Killers
Lady in the Van
Life After George
Look Back in Anger
Low Level Panic
Mad Forest
Made in Bangkok
Massage
Me and My Friend
Mercy Seat
Miracle Worker
Month of Sundays (Larbey)
Murmuring Judges
Nabokov's Gloves
National Health
Normal Heart
Not Quite Jerusalem
Not With a Bang
Now You Know
Number
Odd Women
One Fine Day
One Flew Over the Cuckoo's Nest
Other People's Money
Physicists
Plague Over England
Progress
Racing Demon

Real Estate
Rents
Road
Sarcophagus
Savages
Serious Money
Sing Yer Heart Out for the Lads
Skin of Our Teeth
Sold
Strangeness of Others
Sugar Syndrome
Sweet Panic
Taking Care of Baby
Taste of Honey
That Face
That Good Night
They Came to a City
Thickness of Skin
Tom and Clem
Undertaking
Valued Friends
Whose Life Is It Anyway?
Why Me?
Widows
Winslow Boy

PLAYS WITH COURTROOM SCENES

Beyond Reasonable Doubt
Cause Célèbre
Cracked Pot
Few Good Men
Magistrate
Murmuring Judges
Never the Sinner
One Way Pendulum
Perfect Murder
Royal Baccarat Scandal
Twelve Angry Men
Witness for the Prosecution

PLAYS SET IN CONVENTS

Agnes of God
Bonaventure
Devils
Once a Catholic

MILITARY PLAYS
(Plays with a Military Interest)

Accrington Pals
'Allo 'Allo

Back to the Land
Biloxi Blues
Birdy
Dad's Army
Few Good Men
Flare Path
Journey's End
Killing Game
Long and the Short and the Tall
Not About Heroes
Observe the Sons of Ulster ...
Our Boys
Our Country's Good
Passing-Out Parade
Privates on Parade
Russian in the Woods
Sink the Belgrano!
To the Green Fields Beyond
Translations

NAVAL PLAYS
(Plays with a Naval Interest)

Good Hope
Making Waves
Rough Crossing
Sailor Beware!
Sink the Belgrano!
Winslow Boy

PLAYS WITH A SCHOLASTIC
SETTING

All Things Considered
Another Country
Butley
Daisy Pulls It Off
Donkeys' Years
Educating Rita
Forty Years On
Groping for Words
Happiest Days of Your Life
History Boys
Lent
Lingua Franca
Prime of Miss Jean Brodie
Punk Rock
Quartermaine's Terms
sex, drugs & rick 'n' noel
Shadowlands
Teechers
Translations

PLAYS SET IN HOSPITALS

Clothes for a Summer Hotel
Cut and Run
It Can Damage Your Health
It Runs in the Family
Kiss on the Bottom
National Health
Nil by Mouth
One Flew Over the Cuckoo's Nest
Our Boys
Roots and Wings
Sarcophagus
Visiting Hour
What the Butler Saw
Wings
Whose Life Is It Anyway?

PLAYS SET IN SHOPS

American Buffalo
Come Back to the 5 & Dime, Jimmy Dean
84 Charing Cross Road
Hobson's Choice
Imaginary Lines
Laughing Wild
Orpheus Descending
Staircase
Spokesong
What Are Little Girls Made Of?

PLAYS WITH A THEATRICAL INTEREST

Actor's Nightmare (see Sister Mary Ignatius ...)
Amy's View
Bad Dream
Bums on Seats
Chorus of Disapproval
Corpsing
Curtain Call
Curtain Up on Murder
Dresser
Entertainer
Inspecting Carol
Invisible Man
Kerry Dance
Killing of Sister George
Laughing Matter
Laying the Ghost
Life in the Theatre
Maiden Stone
Marvellous Party

Murder Has Been Arranged
Murder in Company
Murder In Play
Noises Off
On Monday Next
Our Country's Good
Over the Moon (Moon Over Buffalo)
Peggy for You
Play On!
Playing the Wife
Pocket Dream
Proscenophobia
Real Thing
Rehearsal
Scottish Play
Spring, 1600
Stage Struck
Star Quality
Trivial Pursuits
Webster
York Realist

PLAYS WITH A NATIONAL OR REGIONAL SETTING OR INTEREST

AMERICAN

Accommodations
Adventures of Huckleberry Finn
American Buffalo
Amorous Ambassador
Baby Doll
Barefoot in the Park
Bash
Battle of Angels
Beyond Therapy
Biloxi Blues
Birdy
Bone-Chiller
Brighton Beach Memoirs
Broadway Bound
Butterflies Are Free
California Suite
Cat on a Hot Tin Roof
Cemetery Club
Clothes for a Summer Hotel
Cocktail Hour
Come Back to the 5 & Dime, Jimmy Dean
Come Blow Your Horn
Cracks
Crimes of the Heart
Deathtrap
Delicate Balance
Dining Room

A

Disappeared
Distance from Here
Don't Drink the Water
Eccentricities of a Nightingale
Edmond
Extremities
Effect of Gamma Rays ...
Fatal Attraction
Few Good Men
Front Page
Gin Game
Gingerbread Lady
Glass Menagerie
Glengarry Glen Ross
God's Favorite
Graduate
Greetings!
Hiawatha
House of Mirth
I Remember Mama
If We Are Women
I'm Not Rappaport
In the Bar of a Tokyo Hotel
Insignificance
Inspecting Carol
Invisible Man
It Was a Dark and Stormy Night
Kingdom of Earth
Last of the Red Hot Lovers
Laughing Wild
Lend Me a Tenor
Lost In Yonkers
Matchmaker
Me and Mamie O'Rourke
Mercy Seat
Miracle Worker
Murder Room
Never the Sinner
New England
Night of the Iguana
Night Watch
Normal Heart
Not About Nightingales
Odd Couple
Odd Couple (female)
Once in a Lifetime
One Flew Over the Cuckoo's Nest
Orphans
Orpheus Descending
Other People's Money
Our Town
Out of Sight ... Out of Murder
Owl and the Pussycat
Painting Churches
Party to Murder
Perfect Party
Period of Adjustment

Play It Again, Sam
Play On!
Plaza Suite
Popcorn
Prisoner of 2nd Avenue
Proof
Resistable Rise of Arturo Ui
Romantic Comedy
Rose
Rose Tattoo
Sad Hotel
Scarlet Letter
Shape of Things
Sing On!
Skin of Our Teeth
Same Time, Next Year
Sisters Rosensweig
Slapstick Tragedy
Small Craft Warnings
Speed-the-Plow
Steel Magnolias
Strangers on a Train
Streetcar Named Desire
Summer and Smoke
Sunshine Boys
Sweet Bird of Youth
Talented Mr Ripley
Tales from Hollywood
They're Playing Our Song
Torch Song Trilogy
Treatment
US and Them
Veronica's Room
Vieux Carré
What the Night Is For
Who's Afraid of Virginia Woolf?
You Say Tomatoes

CANADIAN
Anne of Green Gables

FRENCH

Calico
Camille
Don't Dress for Dinner
Every Other Evening
Germinal
Gigi
Madame Melville
Les Misérables
Picasso at the Lapin Agile
Rehearsal
Rise in the Market
Strictly Murder
Tower
Visions of Simone Machard

Winner Takes All
Wolf at the Door
(*See also* Feydeau, Marivaux, Molière)

IRISH

Comedies
Alone It Stands
Suburb of Babylon

Costume
Making History
Translations

Plays
Blind Fiddler
Cripple of Inishmaan
Dolly West's Kitchen
Home Place
I Dreamt I Dwelt ...
Lieutenant of Inishmore
Life
Lonesome West
Lovers
Loves of Cass McGuire
Moving (Leonard)
Night Season
Philadelphia, Here I Come!
Pizzazz
Same Old Moon
Skull in Connemara
Spokesong
Summer
There Came a Gypsy Riding
Women on the Verge of HRT

Serious Plays
After Easter
Aristocrats
Beauty Queen of Leenane
Bold Girls
Dancing at Lughnasa
Faith Healer
Freedom of the City
Gentle Island
Give Me Your Answer, Do!
Juno and the Paycock
Living Quarters
Paddywack
Plough and the Stars
Remembrance
Steward of Christendom
Suburb of Babylon
Sword Against the Sea

INDIAN
Indian Ink
Invisible River
Ramayana

ITALIAN

Accidental Death of an Anarchist
Filumena
God Only Knows
Grand Magic
Local Authority
Pope and the Witch
Saturday, Sunday, Monday
Scapino
Servant to Two Masters
Talented Mr Ripley
That Good Night
Yard of Sun

RUSSIAN

Black Snow
Breaking the Silence
Cherry Orchard
Coast of Utopia
Fathers and Sons
Fools
Fortune's Fool
Ivanov
Month in the Country
Parasol
Promise
Sarcophagus
Seagull
Sneeze
Three Sisters
Three Sisters Two
Uncle Vanya

SPANISH

Yerma

SCOTS

Costume
Maiden Stone

Plays
Gagarin Way
Men Should Weep
When I Was a Girl, I Used To Scream and
   Shout ...
Winter Guest

Serious
Rents

WELSH
(in English)

All's Fair
August
Biting the Bullet
Child's Christmas In Wales
Corn Is Green
Kiss on the Bottom
Loose Ends
Roots and Wings
Trivial Pursuits
Under Milk Wood

NORTH COUNTRY

Accrington Pals
All in Good Time
And a Nightingale Sang
Billy Liar
Caravan
Close the Coalhouse Door
Cracked Pot
Different Way Home
Fifteen Streets
Fur Coat and No Knickers
Happy Families
Happy Jack
Hobson's Choice
Home Before Dark
Last Tango in Whitby
Mail Order Bride
Men of the World
Not With a Bang
Pratt of the *Argus*
Road
Rutherford and Son
Salt of the Earth
Second From Last in the Sack Race
September in the Rain
Up 'n' Under
Up 'n' Under II
When We Are Married
York Realist

RURAL

Adam Bede
Candleford
Cider with Rosie
Cold Comfort Farm
Cracked Pot
Darling Buds of May

Lark Rise
Tess of the d'Urbervilles
York Realist

MYSTERY AND SUSPENSE PLAYS

Anagram of Murder
And Evermore Shall Be So
And Then There Were None
Anybody for Murder?
Appointment With Death
At the Sign of "The Crippled Harlequin"
Audience With Murder
Bad Blood
Black Coffee
Blood Money
Bonaventure
Bone-Chiller
Business of Murder
Busybody
Cards on the Table
Checkmate
Corpse!
Crucifer of Blood
Curtain Up on Murder
Dangerous Obsession
Dead Guilty
Dead Man's Hand
Dead of Night
Dead-Lock
Deadly Embrace
Deadly Nightcap
Death is Catching
Death Walked In
Deathtrap
Devil at Midnight
Deliver Us From Evil
Dial 'M' for Murder
Double Double
Edge of Darkness
Fatal Attraction
Fatal Encounter
Gaslight
Gentle Hook
Ghost Train
Hollow
Holmes and the Ripper
Hound of the Baskervilles
House Guest
House of Secrets
I'll Be Back Before Midnight!
In for the Kill
In Two Minds
Inside Job

It Could Be Any One of Us
Jekyll and Hyde
Killing Time
Kiss of Death
Lady Audley's Secret
Late Edwina Black
Love from a Stranger
Mindgame
Murder at Rutherford House
Murder by Misadventure
Murder Game
Murder Has Been Arranged
Murder in Company
Murder in Play
Murder is Announced
Murder of Maria Marten
Murder on the Nile
Murder Room
Murder Weekend
Murder With Love
Murderer
Mysterious Mr Love
Mystery of Irma Vep
Natural Causes
Night Watch
Nightmare
Nightmare: The Fright of Your Life
Out of Sight.....Out of Murder
Party to Murder
Perfect Murder
Portrait of Fear
Prescription for Murder
Recipe for Murder
Red in the Morning
Rope
Shock!
Silhouette
Sleuth
Small Hours
Spider's Web
Spygame
Star-Spangled Girl
Strangers on a Train
Strictly Murder
Suddenly at Home
Summer End
Suspects
Sweet Revenge
Talented Mr Ripley
Take Away the Lady
That Good Night
Theft
Time to Kill
Touch of Danger
Unexpected Guest
Verdict
Veronica's Room

Wait Until Dark
When the Reaper Calls
Who Dies Wins
Whodunnit
Without Trace
Witness for the Prosecution

PLAYS CONCERNING GHOSTS, WITCHCRAFT AND THE SUPERNATURAL

Blithe Spirit
Clothes for a Summer Hotel
Exorcism
Haunted
I Have Been Here Before
Inspector Calls
Invisible Man
Late Mrs Early
Laughter in the Dark
Laying the Ghost
Man Alive
Murder Has Been Arranged
Mystery of Irma Vep
Pictures of Clay
Salonika
They Came to a City

VERSE PLAYS

Cracked Pot
Curtmantle
Cyrano de Bergerac
Dark is Light Enough
Firstborn
Hiawatha
Lady's Not For Burning
Peer Gynt
Ramayana
Roundheads and Peakheads
Secret Love Life of Ophelia
Yard of Sun

PLAYS WITH MUSIC

And a Nightingale Sang
Animal Farm
Baal
Back to the Land (*music not supplied*)
BoyBand (*music not supplied*)
Brassed Off (*music not supplied*)

Canterbury Tales
Caucasian Chalk Circle
Child's Christmas in Wales
Close the Coalhouse Door
Days of the Commune
Dick Barton – Special Agent (*music not supplied*)
Drunkard (Burton)
East Lynne (Burton)
Fear and Misery of the Third Reich
Flint Street Nativity
Ghetto
Good Doctor
Good Person of Szechwan
Happy Wizard
Hiawatha
Hollow Crown
Invisible Man
Jack the Lad
Jack the Ripper
Lady Audley's Secret (Burton)
Lend Me a Tenor
Life of Galileo
Little Women (adapt. Reeves)
Man Is Man
Micky Salberg … Band
Mother
Mother Courage
Mr Puntila and his Man Matti
Murder at Rutherford House
Murder of Maria Marten (Burton)
Pied Piper
Privates on Parade
Prodigious Snob
Resistible Rise of Arturo Ui
Robin Hood
Rough Crossing
Round Heads and Pointed Heads
Roundheads and Peakheads
Schweyk in the Second World War
Secret Diary of Adrian Mole Aged 13¾
Serious Money
Sing On!
Spokesong
St Joan of the Stockyards
Sweeney Todd the Barber (Burton)
Tess of the d'Urbervilles
They're Playing Our Song
Thieves' Carnival
Trumpets and Drums
Turandot
Under Milk Wood
Vinegar Tom
Wind in the Willows
Women on the Verge of HRT
Word from Our Sponsor

RELIGIOUS AND MORALITY PLAYS

Easter
Son of Man

Biblical
Firstborn

Morality
Inspector Calls

Religious Interest
Agnes of God
Becket
Bonaventure
Devils
Exit the King
Francis
God's Favorite
Lark
Man for All Seasons
Messiah
Our Town
Physicists
Racing Demon
Ramayana
Royal Hunt of the Sun
Samson Riddle
Skin of Our Teeth
They Came to a City
Two Planks and a Passion
Waiting for Godot
Wayward Spirit

ALL FEMALE

Agnes of God
Bazaar and Rummage
Bold Girls
Breath of Life
Curtain Up!
Effect of Gamma Rays …
Female Parts
House of Bernarda Alba
If We Are Women
Killing of Sister George
Kiss on the Bottom
Love in the Title
Low Level Panic
Mrs Klein
My Brilliant Divorce
My Mother Said I Never Should
My Sister In This House
New Anatomies
One Last Card Trick
Passing-Out Parade

Playhouse Creatures
Princess Ascending
Rose
Shirley Valentine
Skirmishes
Snake in the Grass
Spoonface Steinberg
Steaming
Steel Magnolias
Top Girls
Vita and Virginia
Whale Music
Women

ALL MALE

American Buffalo
Anorak of Fire
Another Country
Bent
Birdy
Blue/Orange
Boys In The Band
Brief Lives
Bullet
Caretaker
Comedians
Dealer's Choice
Democracy
English Game
Gagarin Way
Glengarry Glen Ross
Hamp
Heroes
Journey's End
Life in the Theatre
Long and the Short and the Tall
Mystery of Irma Vep
Neville's Island
No Man's Land
Not About Heroes
Observe the Sons of Ulster ...
One Fine Day
Orphans
Our Boys
Painting By Numbers
Rents
Sleuth
Some Voices
Someone Who'll Watch Over Me
Staircase
Thyestes
Treasure Island
Twelve Angry Men
Waiting for Godot
Wild Turkey

Authors' Index

Entries in italics refer to novels by well-known authors which have been dramatized either under their own name or under another title which is given in parenthesis.

Abbot, Rick
Play On!
Sing On!

Ackland, Rodney
Absolute Hell
After October
Dark River

Adamson, Samuel
Cherry Orchard (adapt.)
Clocks and Whistles
Doll's House (adapt.)
Grace Note
Mrs Affleck (adapt.)
Pillars of the Community (adapt.)
Three Sisters (adapt.)

Albee, Edward
Delicate Balance
Who's Afraid of Virginia Woolf?

Alcott, Louisa M
Little Women

Allen, Jay Presson
Prime of Miss Jean Brodie (adapt.)

Allen, Paul
Brassed Off (adapt.)

Allen, Woody
Don't Drink the Water
Play It Again, Sam

Anouilh, Jean
Antigone
Becket
Lark
Léocadia
Rehearsal
Ring Round the Moon
Thieves' Carnival

Antrobus, John
(*see* Galton, Ray)

Arbuzov, Aleksei
Promise

Archer, Jeffrey
Beyond Reasonable Doubt
Perfect Murder

Ardito, Carlo
Grand Magic (trans.)

Local Authority (trans.)

Arthur, Dave and Toni
(*see* Wood, David)

Aron, Geraldine
My Brilliant Divorce
Same Old Moon

Ashby, Sylvia
Anne of Green Gables (adapt.)

Atkins, Eileen
Vita and Virginia

Aubrey, John
Brief Lives

Auburn, David
Proof

Austen, Jane
Mansfield Park
Northanger Abbey
Sense and Sensibility

Ayckbourn, Alan
Absent Friends
Absurd Person Singular
Bedroom Farce
Body Language
Chorus of Disapproval
Comic Potential
Communicating Doors
Confusions
Damsels in Distress
Drowning on Dry Land
Family Circles
FlatSpin
GamePlan
Henceforward ...
House & Garden
How the Other Half Loves
If I Were You
Improbable Fiction
Intimate Exchanges
It Could Be Any One of Us
Joking Apart
Just Between Ourselves
Man of the Moment
Mr Whatnot
My Wonderful Day
Norman Conquests
Private Fears in Public Places
Relatively Speaking
Revengers' Comedies
RolePlay

A

Season's Greetings
Sisterly Feelings
Small Family Business
Snake in the Grass
Sugar Daddies
Taking Steps
Ten Times Table
Things We Do for Love
Time and Time Again
Time of My Life
Tons of Money (revisor)
Way Upstream
Wildest Dreams
Wolf at the Door (adapt.)
Woman in Mind
Word from Our Sponsor

Bailey, Lucy
Baby Doll (adapt.)

Barlow, Patrick
39 Steps

Barnes, Peter
Corpsing
Dreaming

Barret, Earl
(*see* Sultan, Barret, Cooney)

Barry, Sebastian
Steward of Christendom

Barton, John
Hollow Crown

Bates, H. E.
Darling Buds of May

Beaton, Alistair
Arsonists (adapt.)
Government Inspector (adapt.)

Bean, Richard
English Game
Honeymoon Suite

Beckett, Samuel
Waiting For Godot

Becque, Henry
Les Corbeaux (*see* Wolf at the Door)

Beevers, Geoffrey
Adam Bede (adapt.)
Silas Marner (adapt.)

Benfield, Derek
Anyone for Breakfast?
Bedside Manners
Beyond a Joke
Caught on the Hop
Don't Lose the Place!
First Things First
Fish Out of Water
Fly In The Ointment
Flying Feathers
Funny Business
In at the Deep End
In for the Kill
Look Who's Talking!
Over My Dead Body
Panic Stations
Second Time Around
Toe in the Water
Touch and Go
Two and Two Together
Up and Running

Bennett, Alan
Enjoy
Forty Years On
Getting On
Habeas Corpus
History Boys
Kafka's Dick
Lady in the Van
Madness of George III
Office Suite
Old Country
Single Spies
Wind in the Willows

Benson, E.F.
(see *Make Way for Lucia*)

Bent, Simon
Bad Company

Bentley, Eric
(*see* Schnitzler, Arthur and Brecht, Bertolt)

Berkoff, Steven
Acapulco
Dahling You Were Marvellous
Decadence
East
Fall of the House of Usher (adapt.)
Greek
Kvetch
Messiah
Metamorphosis (adapt.)
Oedipus

A

Ritual in Blood
Secret Love Life of Ophelia
Sink the Belgrano!
Trial (adapt.)
West

Bettinson, Rob
Fifteen Streets (adapt.)

Bill, Stephen
Curtains

Bingham, Charlotte
(*see* Brady, Terence)

Birch, Michael
Pratt of the *Argus* (adapt.)
Second From Last in the Sack Race (adapt.)

Blackwell, Vera
Increased Difficulty of Concentration (trans.)
Vanek Plays (trans.)

Blakeman, Helen
Caravan

Blamire, Larry
Robin Hood

Bogdanov, Michael
Hiawatha

Bolt, R. R.
Resistible Rise of Arturo Ui (trans.)
Sisterhood

Bolt, Robert
Man for All Seasons
Vivat! Vivat Regina!

Bolton, Guy
Anastasia (adapt.)
(*see also* Wodehouse, P. G.)

Bond, C. G.
Sweeney Todd

Bond, Nelson
Animal Farm (adapt.)

Bowen, John
After the Rain

Bradbury, Malcolm
Inside Trading (adapt.)

Braddon, Mary
Lady Audley's Secret

Brady, Terence and Bingham, Charlotte
Shell Seekers

Bray, Barbara
Antigone (trans.)

Brecht, Bertolt
Antigone
Baal
Caucasian Chalk Circle
Coriolanus
Days of the Commune
Don Juan
Drums in the Night
Fear and Misery of the Third Reich
Good Person of Szechwan (Good Woman of
    Setzuan, Good Person of Sichuan)
In the Jungle of the Cities (In the Cities' Jungle)
Life of Galileo
Man Is Man (Man Equals Man)
Mother
Mother Courage and her Children
Mr Puntilla and his Man Matti
Resistible Rise of Arturo Ui
Round Heads and Pointed Heads (Money
    Calls to Money)
Roundheads and Peakheads (Rich and Rich)
Schweyk in the Second World War
St Joan of the Stockyards
Trumpets and Drums
Turandot
Tutor
Visions of Simone Machard

Breen, John
Alone It Stands

Brenton, Howard
Bloody Poetry

Brett, Simon
Bad Dream
Mr Quigley's Revenge
Murder In Play
Silhouette

Brighouse, Harold
Hobson's Choice
Zack

Briggs, Raymond
When the Wind Blows

Briggs, Stephen
Carpe Jugulum (adapt.)
Making Money (adapt.)
Maskerade (adapt.)

Brock, Jeremy
Oliver Twist

Brontë, Charlotte
Jane Eyre

Brontë, Emily
Wuthering Heights

Brooks, Jeremy and Mitchell, Adrian
Child's Christmas in Wales

Brown, Ben
All Things Considered

Brown, Irana
Lords and Ladies (adapt.)

Browne, Felicity
Family Dance

Bruce, Lesley
My Own Show

Buchan, John
39 Steps

Buchner, Georg
Woyzeck

Buffini, Moira
Dinner

Bulgakov, Mikhail
Black Snow

Burke, Gregory
Gagarin Way
Straits

Bullmore, Amelia
Mammals

Burney, Fanny
Busy Day

Burrows, John
(*see* Harding, John)

Burton, Brian J.
Drunkard
East Lynne

Lady Audley's Secret
Murder of Maria Marten
Sweeney Todd the Barber

Butler, Caroline
(*see* Goold, Rupert)

Calderon de la Barca, Pedro
Life Is a Dream
Surgeon of Honour
Three Judgements in One

Caldwell, Lucy
Leaves

Callan, Edward
I Am of Ireland

Camoletti, Marc
Ding Dong
Don't Dress for Dinner
Happy Birthday

Carmichael, Fred
Out of Sight, Out of Murder

Carpenter, Paul and Gower, Ian
Hi-de-Hi

Cartwright, Jim
Bed
Rise and Fall of Little Voice
Road
Two

Cary, Falkland L. and King, Philip
Big Bad Mouse
Sailor, Beware!

Chambers, John
Tales of King Arthur

Chapman, John
Kindly Leave the Stage
Nil by Mouth

Chapman, John and Freeman, Dave
Key for Two

Chapman, John and Lloyd, Jeremy
Keeping Down with the Joneses

Chapman, John and Marriott, Anthony
Shut Your Eyes and Think of England

Chapman, John and Pertwee, Michael
Holiday Snap
Look, No Hans!

Chappell, Eric
Double Vision
Father's Day
Fiddlers Three
Haunted
Haywire
Heatstroke (Snakes and Ladders)
It Can Damage Your Health
Natural Causes
Rising Damp
Something's Burning
Summer End
Theft
Up and Coming
Wife After Death

Charman, Matt
Five Wives of Maurice Pinder

Chaucer, Geoffrey
Canterbury Tales

Chekhov, Anton
Cherry Orchard
Ivanov
Three Years (see *Parasol*)
Seagull
Three Sisters
Uncle Vanya
(*see also* August)
Wild Honey
(*see also* Sneeze)

Chibnall, Chris
Kiss Me Like You Mean It

Chinn, Jimmie
Albert Make Us Laugh
Different Way Home
Home Before Dark
Something To Remember You By
Straight and Narrow
Sylvia's Wedding
Take Away the Lady

Chinn, Jimmie and Wyld, Hazel
Garden Party

Chiodo, Tom and DePietro, Peter
Murder at Rutherford House

Christie, Agatha
And Then There Were None
Appointment With Death
Black Coffee
Cards on the Table
Hollow
Love from a Stranger
Murder is Announced
Murder on the Nile
Spider's Web
Unexpected Guest
Verdict
Witness for the Prosecution

Christopher-Wood, John
Elsie and Norm's "Macbeth"

Churchett, Stephen
Tom and Clem

Churchill, Caryl
Blue Heart
Cloud Nine
Dream Play (adapt.)
Far Away
Fen
Icecream
Light Shining In Buckinghamshire
Mad Forest
Number
Serious Money
Thyestes (trans.)
Top Girls
Traps
Vinegar Tom

Churchill, Donald
Decorator
Mixed Feelings
Moment of Weakness
(*see also* Yeldham, Peter)

Clapham, Peter
Little Women (adapt.)

Clark, Brian
Can You Hear Me at the Back?
Petition
Whose Life is it Anyway?

Clark, Stephen
Making Waves

Clarke, T. E. B.
Titfield Thunderbolt

A

Cleese, John and Booth, Connie
Fawlty Towers

Clemens, Brian
Devil at Midnight
Edge of Darkness
Holmes and the Ripper
Inside Job
Shock!
Strictly Murder
Without Trace

Clemens, Brian and Spooner, Dennis
Anybody for Murder?
Will You Still Love Me in the Morning?

Clepper, P.M.
Joseph Andrews

Coburn, D.L.
Gin Game

Cogo-Fawcett, Robert and Murray, Braham
Keep An Eye on Amélie (trans.)

Coke, Peter
Breath of Spring

Coleman, Martyn
Cranford (adapt.)

Colley, Peter
I'll Be Back Before Midnight!
When the Reaper Calls

Collins, Wilkie
Woman in White

Colvill, Bill
See Can't Pay? Won't Pay!

Conan Doyle, Arthur
Hound of the Baskervilles
Sign of Four (see Crucifer of Blood)

Cooke, Brian
(*see* Mortimer, Johnnie)

Cookson, Catherine
Fifteen Streets

Cooney, Michael
Cash on Delivery

Cooney, Ray
Caught in the Net
Funny Money
It Runs in the Family
Out of Order
Run for Your Wife
Two into One
(*see* Stone, Gene)
(*see* Sultan, Barret, Cooney)

Cooney, Ray and Michael
Tom, Dick and Harry

Coveney, Alan
Busy Day (adapt.)

Coward, Noël
Blithe Spirit
Hay Fever
I'll Leave it to You
Nude with Violin
Present Laughter
Private Lives
Relative Values
Semi-Monde
Star Quality
This Happy Breed
Waiting in the Wings

Cox, Constance
Lord Arthur Savile's Crime (adapt.)
Murder Game
Woman in White (adapt.)

Crimp, Martin
Attempts on Her Life
City
Country
Cruel and Tender
Dealing with Clair
False Servant (adapt.)
Fewer Emergencies
Getting Attention
Misanthrope (adapt.)
Play With Repeats
Seagull (trans.)
Treatment

Crisp, N. J.
Dangerous Obsession
Fighting Chance
That Good Night

Croft, David
(*see* Lloyd, Jeremy)
(*see* Perry, Jimmy)

A

Cross, Beverley
Happy Birthday (adapt.)
Scarlet Pimpernel (adapt.)

Crowley, Mart
Boys In The Band

Crowther, Colin and Mary
Untimely Frost

Curry, Neil
Bacchae (trans.)

Dale, Jim
Scapino!

Daniels, Sarah
Gut Girls

Darbon, Leslie
Cards on the Table (adapt.)
Murder is Announced (adapt.)
(*see also* Harris and Darbon)

Day, Julie
Come Back for Light Refreshments After
the Service

De Angelis, April
Laughing Matter
Playhouse Creatures
Positive Hour
Warwickshire Testimony

de Fillipo, Eduardo
Filumena
Grand Magic
Local Authority
Napoli Milionaria
Saturday, Sunday, Monday

de Jongh, Nicholas
Plague Over England

DePietro, Peter
(*see* Chiodo, Tom)

De Marne, Denis
(*see* Pember, Ron)

De Wet, Reza
Three Sisters Two

Deegan, Denise
Daisy Pulls it Off

Delaney, Sheila
Taste of Honey

Desvalliere, Maurice
(*see* Feydeau and Desvalliere)

Devlin, Anne
After Easter

Dewhurst, Keith
Black Snow (adapt.)
Candleford
Lark Rise

Dickens, Charles
Christmas Carol
David Copperfield
Great Expectations
Hard Times
Oliver Twist
Tale of Two Cities

Dighton, John
Happiest Days of Your Life

Dinner, William and Morum, William
Late Edwina Black

Dinsdale, Stephen
Anorak of Fire

Donnellan, Declan
Vanity Fair (adapt.)

Donoghue, Mary Agnes
Me and Mamie O'Rourke

Dorfman, Ariel
Death and the Maiden
Purgatorio
Widows (with Tony Kushner)

Doust, Paul
Amphibious Spangulatos
Cold Comfort Farm (adapt.)

Downing, Martin
House of Dracula
House of Frankenstein!

Dryden, Ellen
Power of the Dog

Dudzick, Tom
Greetings!

A

du Maurier, Daphne
My Cousin Rachel
Rebecca
September Tide

Dumas
La Dame aux Camélias (see *Camille*)
Three Musketeers

Dumas (Père)
Tower

Dunai, Frank
Parasol (adapt.)

Dunlop, Frank
Scapino!

Dunn, Nell
Steaming

Dunne, Peter
Geometry of Love

Durang, Christopher
Baby with the Bathwater
Beyond Therapy
Laughing Wild
Sister Mary Ignatius Explains It All For You
    and Actor's Nightmare

Durbridge, Francis
Deadly Nightcap
Fatal Encounter
Gentle Hook
House Guest
Murder With Love
Small Hours
Suddenly at Home
Sweet Revenge
Touch of Danger

Dürrenmatt, Friedrich
Physicists
Visit

Dyer, Charles
Staircase

Edgar, David
Entertaining Strangers
Strange Case of Dr Jekyll and Mr Hyde

Edwards, Gwynne
Life Is a Dream (trans.)
Surgeon of Honour (trans.)
Three Judgements in One (trans.)

Elice, Eric and Rees, Roger
Double Double

Eliot, George
Adam Bede
Silas Marner

Elton, Ben
Gasping
Popcorn
Silly Cow

Emery, Ed
Mistero Buffo (trans.)
Pope and the Witch (trans.)

Erdman, Nikolai
Suicide

Euripides
Bacchae
Ion

Evans, Will and Valentine
Tons of Money

Everett, Richard
Entertaining Angels

Farmer, Jennifer
Compact Failure

Farr, David
Elton John's Glasses

Feinsod, Arthur
Sword Against the Sea

Ferris, Monk
Bone-Chiller

Feydeau, Georges
Absolute Turkey
Cat Among the Pigeons
Flea in Her Ear
Keep an Eye on Amélie
Winner Takes All

Feydeau, Georges and Desvalliere, Maurice
Hotel Paradiso
Little Hotel on the Side

Fielding, Henry
Joseph Andrews
Tom Jones

Fierstein, Harvey
Torch Song Trilogy

Fillinger, Johan
Peer Gynt (trans.)

Firth, Tim
Calendar Girls
End of the Food Chain
Flint Street Nativity
Neville's Island
Safari Party

Fitzgibbons, Mark
Tale of Two Cities

Fletcher, Lucille
Night Watch

Fo, Dario
Abducting Diana
Accidental Death of an Anarchist
Can't Pay? Won't Pay!
Elizabeth: Almost by Chance a Woman
Mistero Buffo
Pope and the Witch
Trumpets and Raspberries

Fodor, Ladilaus
(*see* Wodehouse, P. G.)

Foley, David
Sad Hotel

Foot, Alistair
(*see* Marriott, Anthony)

Fowles, John
Collector

Foxton, David
Real Story of Puss in Boots

Ford Davies, Oliver
King Cromwell

Forster, E. M.
Passage to India

Francis, Matthew
Adventures of Huckleberry Finn (adapt.)
David Copperfield (adapt.)
Northanger Abbey (adapt.)
Prisoner of Zenda (adapt.)
Tale of Two Cities (adapt.)

Frayn, Michael
Alarms and Excursions
Alphabetical Order
Balmoral
Benefactors
Cherry Orchard (trans.)
Copenhagen
Democracy
Donkeys' Years
Make and Break
Noises Off
Now You Know
Seagull (trans.)
Sneeze (trans., adapt.)
Three Sisters (trans.)
Two of Us
Uncle Vanya (trans.)
Wild Honey (trans.)

Freeman, Dave
Bedfull of Foreigners
Kindly Keep It Covered
(*see also* Chapman, John)

Frei, Nicki and Hall, Peter
Absolute Turkey

Friel, Brian
Aristocrats
Dancing at Lughnasa
Faith Healer
Fathers and Sons
Freedom of the City
Gentle Island
Give Me Your Answer, Do!
Home Place
Living Quarters
Lovers
Loves of Cass McGuire
Making History
Month in the Country (trans.)
Philadelphia, Here I Come!
Three Sisters (trans.)
Translations
Uncle Vanya (trans.)

Frisby, Terence
Funny About Love

Frisch, Max
The Arsonists

Fry, Christopher
Curtmantle
Dark is Light Enough
Firstborn

Lady's Not For Burning
Lark (trans.)
Peer Gynt (trans.)
Ring Round the Moon (adapt.)
Yard of Sun

Fry, Michael
Tess of the d'Urbervilles (adapt.)

Galantière, Lewis
Antigone (trans.)

Gallagher, Bryan
I Dreamt I Dwelt ...

Galsworthy, John
Forsyte Saga

Galton, Ray and Antrobus, John
When Did You Last See Your Trousers?

Gardner, Herb
I'm Not Rappaport

Garland, Patrick
Brief Lives (adapt.)

Gaskell, Mrs
Cranford

Gates, Tudor
Ding Dong (trans.)
Ladies Who Lunch

Gee, Shirley
Warrior

Gems, Pam
Camille

Gershe, Leonard
Butterflies Are Free

Gibbons, Stella
Cold Comfort Farm

Gibson, William
Miracle Worker

Gill, Peter
York Realist

Giovanni, Paul
Crucifer of Blood

Giugni, A. M., and McAvoy, R. C.
Trumpets and Raspberries (trans.)

Glass, Joanna McClelland
If We Are Women

Glenny, Michael
Sarcophagus (trans.)

Glenville, Peter
Hotel Paradiso (adapt.)

Godber, John
April In Paris
Blood Sweat and Tears
Christmas Crackers
Crown Prince
Departures
Going Dutch
Gym and Tonic
Happy Families
Happy Jack
It Started with a Kiss
Lucky Sods
Men of the World
Our House
Passion Killers
Perfect Pitch
Salt of the Earth
September in the Rain
Sold
Teechers
Unleashed
Up 'n' Under
Up 'n' Under II
Weekend Breaks

Goldman, James
Lion in Winter

Goldoni, Carlo
Servant of Two Masters

Gogol, Nikolai
Government Inspector

Gooch, Steve
Female Transport

Goodrich, Frances
(*see* Hackett, Albert and Goodrich, Frances)

Goodrum, John
Comedy of Terrors!
Sorry, I Love You ...

Goold, Rupert and Butler, Caroline
End of the Affair (adapt.)

Goulding, Philip
Titfield Thunderbolt

Gower, Ian *see* **Carpenter, Paul**

Graczyck, Ed
Come Back to the 5 and Dime, Jimmy Dean,
  Jimmy Dean

Graham, Andy
(*see* Parsley, Roger)

Graham, John
(*see* Taylor, Edward)

Grahame, Kenneth
Wind in the Willows

Gray, Simon
Butley
Common Pursuit
Hidden Laughter
Holy Terror
Just the Three of Us
Old Masters
Otherwise Engaged
Quartermaine's Terms
Stage Struck

Greene, Graham
End of the Affair
Travels With My Aunt

Greer, Germaine
Lysistrata – Sex Strike

Greig, David
Architect
Pyrenees
Yellow Moon

Greig, Noël
At Break of Day

Griffiths, Trevor
Comedians

Gubaryev, Vladimir
Sarcophagus

Gurney, A. R.
Cocktail Party
Dining Room
Perfect Party

Hackett, Albert and Goodrich, Frances
Diary of Anne Frank

Hall, Lee
Cooking with Elvis
Good Hope (adapt.)
Mother Courage and Her Children (adapt.)
Mr Puntila and His Man Matti (adapt.)
Servant to Two Masters (adapt.)
Spoonface Steinberg

Hall, Nick
Accommodations

Hall, Peter
Animal Farm (adapt.)
See Frei, Nicki

Hall, Roger
Conjugal Rites

Hall, Willis
Jane Eyre (adapt.)
Long and the Short and the Tall
Mansfield Park (adapt.)
Three Musketeers
(*see* Waterhouse and Hall)

Hamilton, Patrick
Gaslight
Rope
Slaves of Solitude (see *Miss Roach's War*)

Hampton, Christopher
Art (trans.)
Conversations After a Burial (trans.)
Doll's House (trans.)
Hedda Gabler (trans.)
Les Liaisons Dangereuses (trans., adapt.)
Life X 3 (trans.)
Philanthropist
Savages
Tales from Hollywood
Talking Cure
Tartuffe (trans.)
Three Sisters (adapt.)
Total Eclipse
Unexpected Man (trans.)
Wild Duck (trans.)

Hanna, Gillian
Accidental Death of an Anarchist (trans.)
Elizabeth: Almost By Chance a Woman
  (trans.)

Hanff, Helene
84 Charing Cross Road

Harding, John and Burrows, John
Golden Pathway Annual

Harding, Mike
Comfort and Joy
Fur Coat and No Knickers
Last Tango In Whitby
Not With a Bang

Hardy, Carey Jane
Let It Be Me

Hardy, Thomas
Far from the Madding Crowd
On the Western Circuit (see *Day After the Fair*)
Tess of the d'Urbervilles

Hare, David
Amy's View
Blue Room (adapt.)
Breath of Life
Ivanov (adapt.)
Life of Galileo (adapt.)
Mother Courage and her Children (adapt.)
Murmuring Judges
My Zinc Bed
Racing Demon
Secret Rapture
Skylight
Vertical Hour

Harling, Robert
Steel Magnolias

Harris, Richard
Business of Murder
Dead Guilty
Ghosts (adapt.)
Going Straight
In Two Minds
Local Affairs
Outside Edge
Party Piece
Stepping Out
Visiting Hour

Harris, Richard and Darbon, Leslie
Two and Two Make Sex

Harrower, David
Blackbird

Hart, Moss
(*see* Kaufmann, George)

Harvey, Frank
Day After the Fair

Harwood, Ronald
Another Time
Dresser
Equally Divided
Interpreters
Mahler's Conversion
Quartet
Taking Sides

Hastings, Charlotte
Bonaventure
Restless Evil
So What Do We Do About Henry?
Soft September Air

Hastings, Michael
Calico
Tom and Viv

Havel, Vaclav
Increased Difficulty of Concentration
Largo Desolato
Redevelopment
Temptation
Vanek Plays

Havergal, Giles
Travels With My Aunt

Hawdon, Robin
Birthday Suite
Don't Dress for Dinner (adapt.)
Perfect Wedding
Shady Business

Hawthorne, Nathaniel
Scarlet Letter

Hay, Ian and Woodhouse, P. G.
Leave It To Psmith

Hayes, Catherine
Skirmishes

Hayman, Ronald
Playing The Wife

Healy, Mark
Collector

Heather Brothers
Blood Money

Hecht, Ben and MacArthur, Charles
Front Page

A

Heijermans, H
Good Hope

Henley, Beth
Crimes of the Heart

Herman, Mark
Brassed Off

Highsmith, Patricia
Strangers on a Train
Talented Mr Ripley

Hill, Lucienne
Becket (trans.)
It's Later Than You Think (trans.)
Thieves' Carnival (trans.)

Hill, Ken
Invisible Man

Hoddinott, Derek and Pat
Forsyte Saga

Hodges, Adrian
Life Goes On

Hodges, Alan
Alan Turing: the Enigma (see Breaking the
Code)

Holland, Norman
To Meet Oscar Wilde

Holland, Vyvyan (adapt.)
Importance of Being Earnest (4 act version)

Holliday, Graham
Scottish Play

Holloway, Jonathan
Darkness Falls
Les Misérables (adapt.)

Home, William Douglas
Kingfisher

Hope, Anthony
Prisoner of Zenda

Horowitz, Anthony
Mindgame

Horsler, Peter
Cut and Run

Howe, Tina
Painting Churches

Hughes, Doug
(*see* Kash, Marcia)

Hugo, Victor
Les Misérables

Husson, Albert
Cuisine des Anges (see My Three Angels)

Hutchison, Ron
Moonlight and Magnolias

Huxley, Aldous
Devils of Loudun (see Devils)

Ibsen, Henrik
Doll's House
Ghosts
Hedda Gabler
Little Eyolf (see Mrs Affleck)
Peer Gynt
Pillars of the Community
Wild Duck

Iliffe, David
Seagull (trans.)

Ingham, Richard
Ski Whizz

Ionesco, Eugene
Exit the King

James, Henry
Turn of the Screw

Jackson, D. C.
My Romantic History

Janes, Hugh
Dead-Lock
Perfect Murder (adapt.)
Two of a Kind

Jeffreys, Stephen
Hard Times (adapt.)
Valued Friends

Jellicoe, Ann
Knack

Johnson, Terry
Cleo, Camping, Emmanuelle and Dick
Dead Funny

Graduate
Hitchcock Blonde
Hysteria
Insignificance
Piano/Forte

Jones, Charlotte
Humble Boy
In Flame
Lightning Play
Martha, Josie and Chinese Elvis

Jones, Glyn
Red in the Morning

Jones, Marie
Blind Fiddler
Women on the Verge of HRT

Kafka, Franz
Metamorphosis
Trial

Kane, Richard
Miss Roach's War (adapt.)

Kash, Marcia and Hughes, Doug
Party to Murder
Who's Under Where?

Kaufmann, George and Hart, Moss
Once in a Lifetime

Keatley, Charlotte
My Mother Said I Never Should

Keeler, Dawn (adapt.)
House of Mirth

Kelly, Dennis
Taking Care of Baby

Kelly, Tim
Frankenstein (adapt.)
Hound of the Baskervilles
It Was a Dark and Stormy Night

Kember, Paul
Not Quite Jerusalem

Kempinski, Tom
Duet for One
Separation

Kesey, Ken
One Flew Over the Cuckoo's Nest

Kesselman, Wendy
My Sister In This House

Kessler, Lyle
Orphans

King, Philip
I'll Get My Man
On Monday Next!
See How They Run
(*see also* Cary and King)

King, Philip and Boland, John
Murder in Company

Kirkup, James
Physicists (trans.)

Kleist, Heinrich von
Der Zerbrochene Krug
(*see* Cracked Pot)

Knott, Frederick
Dial 'M' for Murder
Wait Until Dark

Kopit, Arthur
Wings

Kramer, Larry
Normal Heart

Kuhn, Tom
Round Heads and Pointed Heads (Money
    Calls to Money) (trans.)

Kushner, Tom
(*see Ariel Dorfman*)

LaBute, Neil
Bash
Distance from Here
Fat Pig
Gaggle of Saints
Mercy Seat
Shape of Things
Some Girls

Lan, David
Cherry Orchard (trans.)
Ghetto (trans.)
Ion (trans.)

Lapworth, Paul
(*see* Turner, David)

A

Larbey, Bob
Building Blocks
Month of Sundays
Sand Castles

Laurence, Charles
About Alice
My Fat Friend
Ring Sisters

Lavery, Bryony
Frozen
Wedding Story

Leach, Karoline
Mysterious Mr Love

Leach, Roger and Wakefield, Colin
Audience With Murder

Lee, Laurie
Cider With Rosie

Leigh, Mike
Abigail's Party
Smelling a Rat
Two Thousand Years

Lenkiewicz, Rebecca
Her Naked Skin
Night Season

Leonard, Hugh
Great Expectations (adapt.)
Life
Love in the Title
Pizzazz
Suburb of Babylon
Summer

Levin, Ira
Deathtrap
Veronica's Room

Lewis, Jonathan
Our Boys

Lloyd, Jeremy
(*see* Chapman, John)

Lloyd, Jeremy and Croft, David
'Allo 'Allo
Are You Being Served?

Logan, John
Never the Sinner

Lonsdale, Frederick
Aren't We All?
On Approval

Lorca, Federico García
House of Bernarda Alba
Yerma

Lucas, Victor
Laughter in the Dark

Luce, Clare Booth
Women

Lucie, Doug
Hard Feelings
Progress

Luckham, Clare
Choice

Ludlam, Charles
Mystery of Irma Vep

Ludwig, Ken
Lend Me A Tenor
Over the Moon (Moon Over Buffalo)

Luke, Peter
Yerma (trans.)

Lumborg, Dennis
One Fine Day

Luscombe, Christopher
Star Quality (adapt.)

Macalpine, Joan
Tom Jones

MacArthur, Charles
(*see* Hecht, Ben)

MacDonald, Robert David
Britannicus (adapt.)
Chinchilla
Summit Conference
Webster

Macdonald, Sharman
Borders of Paradise
When I Was Girl, I Used to Scream and
    Shout …
Winter Guest

MacDonald, Stephen
Not About Heroes

MacIlwraith, Bill
Anniversary

Mackendrick, John
Woyzeck (trans)

Magee, Daniel
Paddywack

Malleson, Miles
Imaginary Invalid (adapt.)
Miser (adapt.)
Tartuffe (adapt.)

Mamet, David
American Buffalo
Cherry Orchard (adapt.)
Edmond
Glengarry Glen Ross
Life In The Theatre
Speed-the-Plow
Uncle Vanya (adapt.)

Manhoff, Bill
Owl and the Pussycat

Mankowitz, Wolf
Samson Riddle

Manktelow, Bettine
Curtain Call
Curtain Up on Murder
Death Walked In
Murder Weekend
Proscenophobia
Spygame
They Call it Murder
White Cliffs

Marber, Patrick
After Miss Julie
Closer
Dealer's Choice
Don Juan in Soho
Howard Katz

Marcus, Frank
Killing of Sister George

Marivaux
Les Fausses Confidences (*see* False Admissions)
False Servant

Marriott, Anthony and Chapman, John
Shut Your Eyes and Think of England

Marriott, Anthony and Foot, Alistair
No Sex, Please – We're British!

Marriott, Anthony and Grant, Bob
Darling Mr London
(*see also* Chapman, John)

Martin, Steve
Picasso at the Lapin Agile

Mastrosimone, William
Extremities

Matthews, Seymour
Anagram of Murder
Dead Man's Hand
Who Dies Wins

Maurette, Marcelle
Anastasia

Mawdsley, Simon
Audacity
Painting By Numbers

McAvoy, R. C. and Giugni, A. M.
Trumpets and Raspberries (trans.)

McConnell, Jean
Café Brosse

McConnell, Jean and Tripp, Miles
Death is Catching

McDonagh, Martin
Beauty Queen of Leenane
Cripple of Inishmaan
Lieutenant of Inishmore
Lonesome West
Pillowman
Skull in Connemara

McGillivray, David and Zerlin Jr, Walter
Chase Me Up Farndale Avenue
Farndale Avenue/*A Christmas Carol*
Farndale Avenue/*Macbeth*
Farndale Avenue/*Murder Mystery*
Haunted Through Lounge … Farndale Castle
They Came from Mars …
We Found Love … SS Farndale Ave

McGuinness, Frank
Dolly West's Kitchen

A

Observe the Sons of Ulster ...
Someone Who'll Watch Over Me
There Came a Gypsy Riding

McIntyre, Clare
Low Level Panic
Maths Tutor
My Heart's a Suitcase

Medoff, Mark
Children of a Lesser God

Mellor, Kay
Passionate Woman

Melly, George et al.
Mixed Doubles

Menchell, Ivan
Cemetery Club

Miles, Bernard; Coe, P and Wilson, J
Treasure Island

Minghella, Anthony
Made in Bangkok
Two Planks and a Passion
Whale Music

Mitchell, Adrian
Francis
(*see also* Brooks, Jeremy)

Mitchell, Julian
Another Country
August

Moffat, Peter
Nabokov's Gloves

Molière
Les Femmes Savantes (*see* Sisterhood)
Malade Imaginaire (*see* Imaginary Invalid)
Misanthrope
Miser
Tartuffe

Molnar, Ferenc
Rough Crossing

Montgomery, L. M.
Anne of Green Gables

Moon, Gerald
Corpse!

Morgan, Diana
My Cousin Rachel

Morley, John
Pinocchio
Wind in the Willows

Morris, Ade
I Dreamt I Dwelt ...
Micky Salberg ... Band

Morrison, Blake
Cracked Pot (adapt.)

Mortimer, John
Bells of Hell
Cat among the Pigeons (trans.)
Christmas Carol (adapt.)
Come As You Are
Flea in Her Ear (trans.)
Hock and Soda Water
Little Hotel on the Side (trans.)

Mortimer, Johnnie
Situation Comedy

Mortimer, Johnnie and Cooke, Brian
When the Cat's Away

Morum, William
(*see* Dinner, William)

Moss, Roger S.
Nightmare: The Fright of Your Life

Munro, Rona
Bold Girls
Maiden Stone

Murray, Braham
(*see* Cogo-Fawcett, Robert)

Nagy, Phyllis
Disappeared
Never Land
Scarlet Letter (adapt.)
Talented Mr Ripley

Naughton, Bill
Alfie
All in Good Time
Spring and Port Wine

Neilson, Anthony
Edward Gant ... Loneliness
Lying Kind
Wonderful World of Dissocia

A

Nelson, Richard
Madame Melville
New England

Nestroy, Johann
Einen Jux will er sich machen
(see *On the Razzle*)

Nichols, Peter
Blue Murder
Born in the Gardens
Day in the Death of Joe Egg
Lingua Franca
National Health
Passion Play
Privates on Parade
So Long Life

Nicholson, William
Katherine Howard
Map of the Heart
Shadowlands

Nicolaeff, Ariadne (trans.)
Promise

Nobbs, David
Pratt of the *Argus*
Second From Last in the Sack Race

Norfolk, William
Caramba's Revenge

Norland, Joanna
Lizzy, Darcy and Jane

Nye, Simon
Accidental Death of an Anarchist (trans.)

Oakes, Meredith
Editing Process

O'Casey, Sean
Juno and the Paycock
Plough and the Stars

Ogilvy, Ian
Slight Hangover

Oglesby, Tamsin
US and Them

Oliver, Reggie
Imaginary Lines
Winner Takes All

O'Malley, Mary
Once A Catholic

Orczy, Baroness
Scarlet Pimpernel

Orton, Joe
Entertaining Mr Sloane
Erpingham Camp
Fred and Madge
Funeral Games
Good and Faithful Servant
Loot
Ruffian on the Stair
Visitors
What the Butler Saw

Orwell, George
Animal Farm

Osborne, John
Entertainer
Hedda Gabler (adapt.)
Look Back in Anger
Picture of Dorian Gray (adapt.)

Osment, Philip
Buried Alive
Dearly Beloved
Undertaking

Oswald, Peter
Mary Stuart (adapt.)
Ramayana (adapt.)

Page, Louise
Real Estate

Paice, Eric
Deadly Embrace

Palin, Michael
Weekend

Parker, Michael
Amorous Ambassador

Parker, Stewart
Spokesong

Parsley, Roger
Brideshead Revisited (adapt.)

Parsley, Roger and Graham, Andy
Sense and Sensibility (adapt.)

Patrick, Robert
Kennedy's Children

Pember, Ron and De Marne, Denis
Jack the Ripper

Penhall, Joe
Blue/Orange
Bullet
Landscape With Weapon
Love and Understanding
Pale Horse
Some Voices
Wild Turkey

Permutt, Stewart
One Last Card Trick

Pernak, Adam
Killers

Perry, Jimmy and Croft, David
Dad's Army
Hi-de-Hi

Pertwee, Michael
(*see* Chapman, John)

Pielmeier, John
Agnes of God

Pilcher, Rosamunde
Shell Seekers

Pinter, Harold
Betrayal
Birthday Party
Caretaker
Homecoming
Hothouse
Moonlight
No Man's Land
Old Times

Pirandello
Henry IV

Plater, Alan
Close the Coalhouse Door
Peggy for You

Plowman, Gillian
Me and My Friend

Poe, Edgar Allan
Fall of the House of Usher

Poliakoff, Stephen
Blinded by the Sun
Breaking the Silence
Sweet Panic

Pomerance, Bernard
Elephant Man

Poole, Alan
Bottom's Dream

Potter, Dennis
Blue Remembered Hills
Brimstone and Treacle
Son of Man

Poulton, Mike
Cherry Orchard (adapt.)
Fortune's Fool (adapt.)
Seagull (adapt.)
Uncle Vanya (adapt.)

Pratchett, Terry
Carpe Jugulum
Lords and Ladies
Making Money
Maskerade

Prebble, Lucy
Enron
Sugar Syndrome

Price, Stanley
Why Me?

Priestley, J. B.
Dangerous Corner
I Have Been Here Before
Inspector Calls
They Came to a City
Time and the Conways
When We Are Married

Quilter, Peter
BoyBand
Curtain Up!
Duets
Glorious!
Respecting Your Piers
  (*see* Curtain Up!)

Racine
Britannicus

Raja, Gautam
Invisible River

Raphael, Frederic and Stephen
Becket (trans.)

Rattigan, Terence
Cause Célèbre
Deep Blue Sea
Flare Path
French Without Tears
In Praise of Love
Less Than Kind
Love in Idleness
Man and Boy
Separate Tables
Who Is Sylvia?
Winslow Boy

Rayment, Mark (adapt.)
September Tide

Rayson, Hannie
Life After George

Rees, Roger
(*see* Elice, Eric)

Reeves, Emma (adapt.)
Little Women

Reid, Georgina
Falling Off a Log

Reid, Graham
Remembrance

Reza, Yasmina
Art
Conversations After a Burial
Life X 3
Unexpected Man

Richards, Gavin
Accidental Death of an Anarchist (trans.)

Ridley, Arnold
Ghost Train

Robbins, Norman
And Evermore Shall Be So
At the Sign of "The Crippled Harlequin"
Late Mrs Early
Nightmare
Prepare to Meet Thy Tomb
Prescription for Murder
Pull the Other One
Rumpelstiltzkin
Tiptoe Through the Tombstones

Tomb with a View
Wedding of the Year

Robins, J. D.
Deliver Us From Evil
Recipe for Murder

Robson, James
Falling Short
Mail Order Bride
Mr Wonderful

Roose-Evans, James
Cider With Rosie (adapt.)
84 Charing Cross Road (adapt.)

Rose, Reginald
Twelve Angry Men

Rosenthal, Amy
On the Rocks
Sitting Pretty

Rosser, Austin
Sweeney Todd, the Demon Barber of Fleet
    Street

Rushforth, Tony
Kerry Dance

Russell, Willy
Breezeblock Park
Educating Rita
One for the Road
Shirley Valentine
Stags and Hens

Ryton, Royce
Anastasia File
Royal Baccarat Scandal

Sackville-West, Vita
Vita and Virginia

Samad, Sharif
Pictures of Clay

Sams, Jeremy
Rehearsal (trans.)

Sands, Leslie
Checkmate

Saunders, James
After Liverpool
Games

Next Time I'll Sing to You
Redevelopment (trans.)
Scent of Flowers

Schiller, Friedrich
Mary Stuart

Schnitzler, Arthur
Das weite Land
  (Undiscovered Country)
La Ronde
See also Blue Room

Seneca
Thyestes

Shaffer, Anthony
Murderer
Sleuth
Whodunnit

Shaffer, Peter
Amadeus
Equus
Five Finger Exercise
Gift of the Gorgon
Lettice and Lovage
Royal Hunt of the Sun

Sharkey, , Jack
Murder Room

Shaw, Do
Back to the Land

Shelley, Mary
Frankenstein

Shepherd, Jack
Chasing The Moment

Sherman, Martin
Bent
Cracks
Madhouse in Goa
Messiah
Passage to India (adapt.)
Rose
Some Sunny Day

Sherriff, R. C
Journey's End

Sibleyras, Gerald
Les Vents des Peupliers
(*see* Heroes)

Simon, Neil
Barefoot in the Park
Biloxi Blues
Brighton Beach Memoirs
Broadway Bound
California Suite
Come Blow Your Horn
Fools
Gingerbread Lady
God's Favorite
Good Doctor
Last of the Red Hot Lovers
London Suite
Lost In Yonkers
Odd Couple
Odd Couple (female)
Plaza Suite
Prisoner of 2nd Avenue
Rumours (British version)
Star Spangled Girl
Sunshine Boys
They're Playing Our Song

Simpson, N. F.
One Way Pendulum

Skinner, Penelope
Eigengrau

Slade, Bernard
Fatal Attraction
Romantic Comedy
Same Time, Next Year
You Say Tomatoes

Smith, Stevie
Stevie

Snelgrove, Michael
Bums on Seats

Sobel, Joshua
Ghetto

Sophocles
Trachiniae (*see* Cruel and Tender)

Sorkin, Aaron
Few Good Men

Sowerby, Githa
Rutherford and Son

Spark, Muriel
Prime of Miss Jean Brodie

Spewack, Sam and Bella
My Three Angels (adapt.)

Spooner, Dennis
(*see* Clemens, Brian)

Steel, Gordon
Like a Virgin

Stenham, Polly
That Face
Tusk Tusk

Stenning, Stephen
Abducting Diana (adapt.)

Stephens, Simon
On the Shore of the Wide World
Punk Rock

Stephenson, Shelagh
Ancient Lights
Enlightenment
Experiment with an Air Pump
Mappa Mundi
Memory of Water

Sterner, Jerry
Other People's Money

Stevenson, Robert Louis
Jekyll and Hyde (*see also* Strange Case of ...)
Treasure Island

Stewart, Ena Lamont
Men Should Weep

Stockwell, Richard
Bad Blood
Killing Time

Stoker, Bram
Dracula (see *Count Dracula*)

Stone, Gene and Cooney, Ray
Why Not Stay For Breakfast?

Stoppard, Tom
Arcadia
Artist Descending a Staircase
Coast of Utopia
Dirty Linen and Newfoundland
Dogg's Hamlet, Cahoot's Macbeth
Enter a Free Man
Hapgood
Henry IV (trans.)
Heroes (trans.)

Indian Ink
Invention of Love
Jumpers
Largo Desolato (trans.)
Night and Day
On the Razzle
Real Thing
Rock 'N' Roll
Rosencrantz and Guildenstern are Dead
Rough Crossing
Salvage
Seagull (trans.)
Shipwreck
Travesties
Undiscovered Country
Voyage

Storey, David
Home
Stages

Stott, Mike
Lenz

Strindberg, August
Dream Play

Sullivan, Daniel
Inspecting Carol

Sultan, Arne; Barret, Earl and Cooney, Ray
Wife Begins at Forty

Sutton, Shaun
Christmas Carol (adapt.)

Taylor, C. P.
And a Nightingale Sang

Taylor, Don
Exorcism
Retreat from Moscow
Road to the Sea
Roses of Eyam

Taylor, Edward
Murder by Misadventure
No Dinner For Sinners
Portrait of Fear
Rise in the Market

Taylor, Edward and Graham, John
Pardon Me, Prime Minister

Tegel, Peter
Suicide (trans.)

A

Terson, Peter
Pied Piper

Thackeray, William Makepeace
Vanity Fair

Thain, Paul
Black Widow

Theiner, George
Temptation (trans.)

Thomas, Brandon
Charley's Aunt

Thomas, Dylan
Child's Christmas in Wales
Under Milk Wood

Thompson, Flora
Candleford
Lark Rise

Tiller, Ted
Count Dracula

Tinniswood, Peter
Napoli Milionaria (adapt.)
You Should See Us Now

Townsend, Sue
Bazaar and Rummage
Groping for Words
Secret Diary of Adrian Mole Aged 13¾
Ten Tiny Fingers, Nine Tiny Toes

Travers, Ben
Rookery Nook

Tripp, Miles
See McConnell, Jean

Tristram, David
Bolt from the Blue
Forget-Me-Knot
Ghost Writer
Inspector Drake and the Black Widow
Inspector Drake and the Perfekt Crime
Inspector Drake and The Time Machine
Inspector Drake's Last Case
Opposite Sex
Searching for Dr Branovic
Secret Lives of Henry and Alice
sex, drugs & rick 'n' noël
Unoriginal Sin

Turgenev, Ivan
Fathers and Sons
Fortune's Fool
Month in the Country

Turner, David and Lapworth, Paul
Servant of Two Masters

Twain, Mark
Adventures of Huckleberry Finn

Valency, Maurice
Visit (adapt.)

Valentine
(*see* Evans and Valentine)

Valentine, Pam
Day of Reckoning

Valery, Anne
Passing Out Parade

van Druten, John
I Remember Mama
Make Way for Lucia (adapt.)

Vance, Charles
Jane Eyre (adapt.)
Wuthering Heights (adapt.)

Vickery, Frank
All's Fair
Biting the Bullet
Family Planning
Kiss On The Bottom
Night on the Tiles
One O'Clock From the House
Pullin' the Wool
Roots and Wings
Trivial Pursuits

Vosper, Frank
Love from a Stranger (adapt.)

Wade, Laura
Alice
Breathing Corpses
Colder Than Here
Other Hands
Posh

Wakefield, Colin
see Leach, Roger

Walker, David
Wolf at the Door (trans.)

Walker, Robert
Can't Pay? Won't Pay! (adapt.)

Wall, Michael
Amongst Barbarians
Women Laughing

Wallace, Naomi
Birdy (adapt.)

Warner, Craig
Strangers on a Train (adapt.)

Wasserman, Dale
One Flew Over the Cuckoo's Nest

Wasserstein, Wendy
Sisters Rosensweig

Waterhouse, Keith
Good Grief
Jeffrey Bernard Is Unwell
Our Song

Waterhouse, Keith and Hall, Willis
Billy Liar
Celebration
Children's Day
Filumena (adapt.)
Saturday, Sunday, Monday (adapt.)

Watson, Donald
Exit the King (trans.)

Waugh, Evelyn
Brideshead Revisited

Webb, Charles
Graduate

Weldon, Fay
Action Replay

Weller, Michael
What the Night Is For

Wells, H. G
Invisible Man

Wertenbaker, Timberlake
After Darwin
Ash Girl
Break of Day
Credible Witness

False Admissions (trans.)
Grace of Mary Traverse
Léocadia (trans.)
Love of the Nightingale
New Anatomies
Our Country's Good
Three Birds Alighting on a Field

Wesker, Arnold
Roots

Whalley, Peter
Dead of Night

Wharton, Edith
House of Mirth
Roman Fever
(*see* Pizzazz)

Wharton, William
Birdy

Wheeler, Paul
Deceptions

Whelan, Peter
Accrington Pals
Russian in the Woods

Whitby, Nick
To the Green Fields Beyond

White, Matthew
Far from the Madding Crowd (adapt.)

Whitemore, Hugh
Best of Friends
Breaking the Code
Disposing of the Body
God Only Knows
It's Ralph
Letter of Resignation
Pack of Lies
Stevie

Whitmore, Ken
Turn of the Screw

Whiting, John
Devils

Wilcox, Michael
Accounts
Lent
Massage
Rents

Wilde, Oscar
Importance of Being Earnest
Lord Arthur Savile's Crime
Picture of Dorian Gray

Wilder, Thornton
Matchmaker
Our Town
Skin of Our Teeth

Williams, Clifford
Rebecca (adapt.)

Williams, Emlyn
Corn is Green
Month in the Country (trans.)
Murder Has Been Arranged
Night Must Fall
Someone Waiting

Williams, Roy
Fallout
Sing Yer Heart Out for the Lads

Williams, Simon
Double Death
Kiss of Death
Laying the Ghost
Nobody's Fool
Nobody's Perfect

Williams, Tennessee
Baby Doll
Battle of Angels
Camino Real
Cat on a Hot Tin Roof
Clothes for a Summer Hotel
Eccentricities of a Nightingale
Glass Menagerie
In the Bar of a Tokyo Hotel
Kingdom of Earth
Milk Train Doesn't Stop Here Any More
Night of the Iguana
Not About Nightingales
Orpheus Descending
Period of Adjustment
Rose Tattoo
Slapstick Tragedy
Streetcar Named Desire
Summer and Smoke
Sweet Bird of Youth
Vieux Carré

Williamson, David
Up For Grabs

Willmott, Phil
Dick Barton – Special Agent
Dick Barton II
Dick Barton III
Lysistrata – Sex Strike
Treasure Island (adapt.)

Wodehouse, P. G. (based on Fodor, L)
Good Morning, Bill

Wodehouse, P. G. and Bolton, Guy
Come On, Jeeves

Wodehouse, P. G. and Hay, Ian
Leave It To Psmith

Wood, Charles
Tower (adapt.)

Wood, David, and Arthur, Dave and Toni
Jack the Lad
Robin Hood

Wood, Mrs Henry
East Lynne

Woods, Phil
Canterbury Tales

Woolf, Virginia
Vita and Virginia

Wright, Nicholas
Mrs Klein

Wyld, Hazel
(*See* Chinn, Jimmie)

Wymark, Olwen
Find Me

Yeats, W. B.
Cuculain Plays
(*see* Sword Against the Stone)

Yeldham, Peter and Churchill, Donald
My Friend Miss Flint

Young, Gail
Cheshire Cats

Zerlin Jnr, Walter
(*see* McGillivray, David)

Zindel, Paul
Effect of Gamma Rays On Man-in-the-Moon
    Marigolds

Full Length Plays

Abducting Diana. Play. Dario Fo adapted by Stephen Stenning
M5 F2. An apartment, a warehouse. Fee code M

A

Abigail's Party. Play. Mike Leigh
M2 (30s) F3 (30s, 40). A living-room and kitchen. Fee code M

First performed at Hampstead Theatre, London, and subsequently produced for BBC TV, this sharply wicked social satire on lower-middle-class suburbia starred Alison Steadman in an award-winning role as the formidable hostess, Beverly, entertaining new neighbours. The evening's initial good-will, clichés and fatuous small-talk only serve to create a rising tension which finally snaps with a dramatic denouement.
ISBN 978 0 573 11016 0

About Alice. Play. Charles Laurence
M2 (31, 60) F2 (31, 48). A sitting-room. Fee code M

Alice, the second wife of a famous sculptor, has indomitable humour and a lusty spirit that never let her down. So, when Peggy, a businesslike publisher, arrives with a sexy young gigolo in tow and a proposal to publish the renowned sculptor's memoirs, Alice has no trouble in dispatching the publisher but retaining the young man. That is, until Peggy returns with some news which will stun Alice. An ingenious comedy thriller which twists and turns and maintains the suspense until the very end.
ISBN 978 0 573 62632 6

Absent Friends. Play. Alan Ayckbourn
M3 (young, middle-age) F3 (20s, 30s). A living-room. Fee code M

Colin's friends are determined to comfort him in his grief over the death of his fiancée – a girl they have never met. They arrange a tea-party for him and are understandably on edge wondering what to say to him as they await his arrival. Their unease, however, has deeper roots as they are all kept together by a mixture of business and cross-marital emotional ties and by the time Colin arrives their tension contrasts dramatically with his cheerfully relaxed air.
ISBN 978 0 573 01331 7

Absolute Hell. Play. Rodney Ackland
M11 F10. Extras. A drinking club. Fee code M

This fascinating evocation of Bohemian life in London in 1945 was presented at the Orange Tree, Richmond, in 1988 and is a revision of the play *The Pink Room* originally staged at the Lyric Theatre, Hammersmith, in 1952. A world-weary hostess runs a drinking-club where the members gather to drink and, variously, escape, dream, seek, bitch, mock and destroy. 'This is not only an archaeologist's treasure, but is among the most convincing, moving pieces to hit London yet this year.' *Independent*

◆ **A bullet mark next to a title indicates that it is new to this edition of the Guide.**

A

♦ **An Absolute Turkey.** Farce. Georges Feydeau, adapted from *Le Dindon* by Nicki Frei and Peter Hall
M10 F8 (with doubling). A drawing room, a hotel room, a study. Fee code M

Georges Feydeau's elegantly complex play is brought to life in this witty, seamless and acutely funny translation by Peter Hall and Nicki Frei. Feydeau, the supreme master of farce, displays all his dramatic tricks as his characters are pulled back and forth spinning dizzily in a surrealistic climax of complications.

Absurd Person Singular. Play. Alan Ayckbourn
M3 (30s, 40s) F3 (30s, 40s). Three kitchen settings. Fee code M

We visit three couples in their three kitchens on the Christmas Eves of three successive years: the lower-class Hopcrofts; their bank manager and his wife and their architect neighbour with a suicidal wife. Running like a darker thread through the wild comedy of behind-the-scenes disasters at Christmas parties is the story of the advance of the Hopcrofts and the declines of the others. ISBN 978 0 573 01023 1

Acapulco. Play. Steven Berkoff
M5 F1. Fee code L

Bit-part players in *Rambo Two* sit along a bar and recount their stories. Says Berkoff: "I started writing down the actual dialogue of the actors ... and weaving a kind of docu-play. These actors fascinated me and were full of the joys of life... This is their story as I heard it."

Accidental Death of an Anarchist. Comedy. Dario Fo, translated by Simon Nye
M5 F1. Two offices. Fee code M

Dario Fo's controversial farce has been seen by over half a million people. It has been performed all over the world, and has become a classic. A sharp and hilarious satire on political corruption, it concerns the case of an anarchist railway worker who, in 1969, "fell" to his death from a police headquarters window. Simon Nye's witty translation updates and relocates the play close to contemporary England. It premièred at the Donmar Warehouse, London, in 2003.

Accidental Death of an Anarchist. Farce. Dario Fo, adapted by Gavin Richards from a translation by Gillian Hanna
M5 F1. Two offices. Fee code M

Dario Fo has always put a premium on entertainment and this sharp and hilarious satire on police corruption in Italy is no exception. This translation and adaptation was first seen in 1979 and enjoyed a very successful run at Wyndham's Theatre, London, in 1980. 'The brothers Marx, Karl and Groucho, have been working in unison ... when broad farce and social protest miscegenate the offspring is a real cracker.' *Guardian*

Accommodations. Comedy. Nick Hall
M2 (young, 30s) F2 (young, 30s). An apartment room. Fee code L

Lee decides to leave her husband and suburban home for six weeks to assert her independence and moves into a New York apartment with two roommates. One is an aspiring actress, never out of character or costumes; the other, due to an agency mix-up is a serious, young, graduate student called Tracy – but male! The ensuing complications make for an hysterical evening. ISBN 978 0 573 60560 4

Accounts. Play. Michael Wilcox
M4 F1. Various simple interior and exterior settings. Fee code L

A

Mary, a widow, and her two sons have moved to a new farm in the Scottish Borders where, for the first time, they are landowners. The play's action is spread over the first year in the new place and details the family's daily routine, their attempts to make the farm pay, Mary coming to terms with widowhood, the boys growing up without a father and the exploration of their own awakening sexuality – in the case of Donald, emerging homosexuality.

The Accrington Pals. Play. Peter Whelan
M5 (teenage, 30s) F5 (20s, 30s). Simple settings on an open stage. Fee code M

This lyrical, absorbing play, premièred by the RSC, is set in Accrington during 1914-16. The 'Pals' are the men from the local volunteer battalion who march high-spiritedly off to the Great War with their experiences in the trenches contrasted with those of the women left behind. At times funny, at times sad, it paints a moving and powerful picture of the changes in civilian life during wartime.
ISBN 978 0 573 11009 2

Action Replay. Play. Fay Weldon
M3 F3. A flat and elsewhere. Fee code L. ISBN 978 0 573 11001 6

Adam Bede. Play. Geoffrey Beevers, adapted from the novel by George Eliot
Flexible cast of up to 30 characters, can be played by M3 F3. Various interior and exterior settings. Fee code M. ISBN 978 0 573 11049 8

The Adventures of Huckleberry Finn. Play. Adapted by Matthew Francis from the novel by Mark Twain
M22 F8 (doubling possible). Various interior and exterior settings. Fee code M

Huckleberry Finn's adventurous journey along the Mississippi is skilfully captured in Matthew Francis' superb adaptation of Mark Twain's classic novel. First produced at the Greenwich Theatre, this exciting approach to Twain's epic thrives on the use of minimal set and prop devices to illustrate the many locations. A truly imaginative, both moral and humorous, tale of discovery with flexible casting opportunities. Period 19th century
ISBN 978 0 573 01779 5

After Darwin. Play. Timberlake Wertenbaker
M5 F1 or M3 F1. Simple settings. Fee code M

It's 1831 and the naturalist Charles Darwin is to travel with Robert FitzRoy into uncharted waters off the coast of South America aboard *The Beagle*. So far, so factual. But for Millie, Ian and Tom, getting to grips with a 1998 stage version of events includes uncovering the polarities both in and between their own lives. The exploration of nineteenth-century philosophical tensions, with the staunch solidity of FitzRoy's Christian ideals sparring with Darwin's slowly dawning radical vision, provokes unsuspected emotions in the present-day director and actors.

◆ **A bullet mark next to a title indicates that it is new to this edition of the Guide.**

After Easter. Play. Anne Devlin
M7 (20s, 30s, old) F7 (30s, old). Various simple settings. Fee code M

Greta, married to a Marxist and living in Oxford, has turned her back on her Catholic Belfast background. Suffering post-natal depression, she goes to stay with her sister Helen in London, where she reveals she is experiencing religious visions. When their father suffers a heart attack they are called back to the family home in Belfast and all the old grievances and jealousies are bared. Greta finds herself confronting the identity that she has wilfully excluded for so long.

After Liverpool. Play. James Saunders
Any number of characters. Fee code F. (Published with *Games*.) Playing time one to one and a half hours according to use made of material

A note on *After Liverpool* by the Author: '*After Liverpool* is not a play but a suite of pieces, to be performed by one or more actors and one or more actresses. The order in which the pieces are played is not specified. Using a musical analogy the script gives some themes, within and between which any number of variations are possible.'
ISBN 978 0 573 02501 3

After Miss Julie. Play. Patrick Marber
M1 (30) F2 (25, 35). A kitchen. Fee Code M

Patrick Marber's *After Miss Julie* is not a translation of Strindberg's classic *Miss Julie* but a version of it, moving the action from the original 19th Century Sweden to the England of 1945. Class suspicions and resentments, the erotic collusion of antagonists, the struggle against repressive social mores – all feature in this sharp, tense drama which combines Strindberg's original vision with Patrick Marber's own consummate skill in drawing believable and psychologically astute characters whose every word has point and deadly meaning. Period 1945
ISBN 978 0 573 11577 6

After October. Play. Rodney Ackland
M5 F6. A living-room. Fee code M

After October is Ackland's most autobiographical play. It shows a feckless family in the grip of poverty, with a young playwright, Clive, scenting the possibilities of escape to affluence and extravagance. But Clive's play is a failure and his beloved Frances opts for his rival Brian. A loan helps Clive until his novel will be completed and everything will be all right 'after October'. The mood lightens – only the creditors are heavy.

After the Rain. Play. John Bowen
M9 F3. A bare stage. Fee code M

The time is '200 years after the Rain of 1969' and the action is a paraphrase of the Bible, commencing with the ark and the flood and ending with the sacrifice of the god-figure. A vital youth and a girl are introduced to the rituals of the community led by Arthur, who believes himself divine. Another man becomes his priest and establishes a ritual – ablutions, confession, audiences, sacrifices, etc. But Arthur is disabused of his godly notions and convinced that he was only possessed by God and was only his vicar. It is he who must be sacrificed.

◆ **A bullet mark next to a title indicates that it is new to this edition of the Guide.**

Agnes of God. Play. John Pielmeier
F3 (21, middle-age). An open stage. Fee code M.for play, code B for music

A

Dr Livingstone, a court-appointed psychiatrist, is asked to determine the sanity of a nun accused of murdering her own baby. The Mother Superior seems bent on protecting Sister Agnes from Livingstone whose suspicions are immediately aroused. In searching for solutions to various mysteries Livingstone forces all of them to face some harsh realities in their own lives. This powerful drama was an outstanding success on Broadway and was filmed with Jane Fonda and Anne Bancroft.
ISBN 978 0 573 63022 4

Alarms and Excursions. Eight short plays. Michael Frayn
M16 F14 can be played by M2 (35, 45) F2 (35, 45). Various simple settings. Fee code M

These eight plays examine the difficulties modern technology has added to life – with hilarious results.

Alarms. (M2 F2) Fee code D
Two couples embark on a dinner party which is doomed to failure as labour-saving devices and furniture become hostile.

Doubles. (M2 F2) Fee code E
Two couples in adjacent hotel rooms have similar problems to those in *Alarms*.

Leavings. (M2 F2) Fee code B
The dinner-party is revisited.

Look Away Now. (M2 F2) Fee code A
Passengers ignore their airliner's safety lecture.

Heart to Heart. (M2 F1) Fee code A
Deals with the impossibility of communication at a noisy drinks party.

Glassnost. (F1) Fee code A
Presents us with a political speech sabotaged by a harassed autocue operator.

Toasters. (M2 F2) Fee code A
Shows the problems of trying to eat and work standing up at a function.

Immobiles. (M2 F2) Fee code C
This is acted out entirely over the phone, as a couple try to decide where they should be meeting their German guest.
ISBN 978 0 573 01808 4

Albert Make Us Laugh. Play. Jimmie Chinn
M6 F8 or M4 F5 (with doubling). Various simple interior and exterior settings. Fee code M

Some would say Albert Nuttall, aged eleven, is backward – but he is special. He is a poet and a visionary who, as he grows into manhood, inspires unexpected depths of emotion in other people, notably his classmate Primrose, whose glorious future as an actress fails to materialize, and the lost and lonely young schoolteacher, Janet Partington. This strange, touching and uplifting story – written to be enacted *entirely* by adults – is engaging and theatrically innovative. Period 1940s-1950s.
ISBN 978 0 573 01719 3

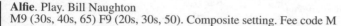

A

Alfie. Play. Bill Naughton
M9 (30s, 40s, 65) F9 (20s, 30s, 50). Composite setting. Fee code M

With sublime amorality Alfie swaggers and philosophizes his way through the play, chattily allowing the audience to eavesdrop as he goes from one 'bird' to another, trying hard to communicate his own brand of determined hedonism and carefully rejecting anyone or anything that might touch him too deeply. Premièred at London's Duchess Theatre, the stage play was later successfully filmed with Michael Caine in the role of the ebullient Cockney Alfie.
ISBN 978 0 573 01008 8

All in Good Time. Comedy. Bill Naughton
M7 (20s, 40s, 50s) F4 (20s-50). Three interiors, one exterior. Fee code M
ISBN 978 0 573 01011 8

♦Alice. A play. Laura Wade
M7 or 8, F3 or 4 with doubling. 2 boys, 1 girl, extras M or F. Simple settings. Fee Code L

The White Rabbit is late for the Duchess. The Cheshire Cat won't stop grinning. And the Hatter is, well, mad. Follow Alice as she escapes her Sheffield home and less than perfect family life to find adventure in a topsy-turvy world. Sheffield-born Laura Wade brings you Wonderland as you've never seen it before. First presented at the Crucible, Sheffield in 2010.
ISBN 978 1 84943 067 8

All Things Considered. Play. Ben Brown
M4 (49, middle-age) F3 (young, late 20s, 40s). A living-room. Fee code M

David Freeman, a Professor of Philosophy about to reach fifty, is tired of life. His only desire now is to control the timing and manner of his death. His plans for 'self-deliverance', however, are disrupted by the earthly demands of people around him. Alone at last he carries out his plan, but is saved by the college electrician. Returning from hospital, David hears news that may change his mind – yet ultimately the vagaries of chance would have it otherwise.
ISBN 978 0 573 01720 9

All's Fair. Play. Frank Vickery
M2 (20s) F4 (14, 20s, middle-age). A living-room. Fee code L. ISBN 978 0 573 01675 2

'Allo 'Allo. Comedy. Jeremy Lloyd and David Croft
M8 F5. Extras. Various interior and exterior settings. Fee code M

The stage version of TV's *'Allo 'Allo* follows the adventures of René, the hapless café owner in war-torn occupied France, as he and his wife, Edith, struggle to keep for themselves a priceless portrait stolen by the Nazis and endeavour to repatriate two British airmen with the help of the Resistance. The Führer is to visit the town. René will need all the wit he can muster to save his café and his life ...! Period 2nd World War
ISBN 978 0 573 01878 7

♦ **A bullet mark next to a title indicates that it is new to this edition of the Guide.**

Alone It Stands. Comedy. John Breen
M5 F1 play multiple characters. Various simple settings. Fee Code M

October 31st 1978. Thomond Park, Limerick. The mighty New Zealand All Blacks, on an Irish tour, take on the none-too-mighty Munster team – and, to everyone's surprise, they lose 12-0. From this piece of Irish sporting history John Breen has fashioned a funny, lively play in which both teams, plus fans, children, relatives and even a dog, are portrayed by a cast of six, with no props and only a half-time change of shirt. Period 1978.
ISBN 978 0 573 01988 3

Alphabetical Order. Play. Michael Frayn
M4 (30s-60s) F3 (20s, 30s, 50s). A library. Fee code M

The library office of a provincial newspaper is a scene of utter confusion – the cluttered chaos of the room matching the lives of its staff. It is also a scene of warmth and light-heartedness. In comes Leslie, a new young assistant with a passion for organization who transforms the office and the lives of its inhabitants into something orderly and neat – and also arid and colourless. An announcement that the paper is to close leads to a struggle between chaos and order.
ISBN 978 0 573 01600 4

Amadeus. Play. Peter Shaffer
M12 (30s-70) F3 (20s, 30s). Extras. Interior and exterior settings. Fee code M

In old age, Salieri recalls his successful career as Court Composer, his hatred of Mozart, and how he contrived the brilliant young composer's demise. A musical genius, Mozart died neglected and impoverished while the mediocre Salieri lived in a blaze of fame and praise. Period 1823 Vienna and in recall, 1781-1791. First presented at the Royal National Theatre.
ISBN 978 0 573 11015 3

American Buffalo. Drama. David Mamet
M3 (young, 40s). A junk shop. Fee code M

In a Chicago junk shop three small-time crooks plot to rob a man of his coin collection which came to light when the collector found a valuable 'buffalo nickel' in the shop. The three plotters fancy themselves as businessmen pursuing the genuine concerns of free enterprise. In reality, they are Donny, the stupid junk shop owner; Bobby, a spaced-out young junkie Donny has befriended; and Teacher, a violent, paranoid braggart. But their plans come to naught and are futile, vulgar verbal exercises.

Amongst Barbarians. Play. Michael Wall
M5 (young (1 Malay/Chinese), 20s (1 Sikh), 40s) F4 (17-19, 30s (1 Tamil), 40s). 2 hotel bedrooms, a prison cell. Fee code M

Set in Penang, Malaysia, and based on a true story, this powerful, gripping and unnervingly funny play focuses on two young Englishmen facing the death sentence for drug-trafficking. Their bewilderment and inadequacy in dealing with the experience, and their reactions to an alien culture, together with those of their families, only serve to make matters worse.
ISBN 978 0 573 01928 9

A

The Amorous Ambassador. American farce. Michael Parker
M4 (20-30, 25-45, 50+, 45-65) F4 (20-25, 25-40, 50+). A living-room. Fee code M

When Harry Douglas, the new American Ambassador to Great Britain, tells his family he is
going to Scotland to play golf, his wife Lois and daughter Debbie announce plans of their own.
Their newly hired butler, Perkins, watches stoically as each leaves and secretly returns for a
romantic rendezvous in the empty house. In the wake of a bomb threat, the Embassy is sealed
off – with hilarious results.
ISBN 978 0 573 67040 4

Amphibious Spangulatos, or Newt on Your Nellie! Farce. Paul Doust
M13 F21. Doubling possible. A sports changing-room in a village hall. Fee code L

Cherry Hellingsworth is fulfilling her Community Service stint by working at a Village Hall
as the Functions Manager. But she's not terribly good at it. On one evening she manages to
to hire out the hall to the Village Drama Society, the Cricket team, a Singing Telegram and a
Country and Western group called the Southern Fried Chickens. A frenzied, door-slamming
farce, suitable for adults or youth groups.
ISBN 978 0 573 01717 9

Amy's View. Play. David Hare
M3 (20s, early 50s) F3 (23-39, 49-66, late 70s-mid 80s). A living-room, a dressing-room. Fee
code M

1979. Esme Allen is a well-known West End actress at just the moment when the West End is
ceasing to offer actors a regular way of life. The visit of her daughter, Amy, with a new boyfriend
sets in train a series of events which only find their shape sixteen years later. David Hare mixes
love, death and the theatre in a heady and original way. Period: 1979, 1995.

Anagram of Murder. Thriller. Seymour Matthews
M3 (40s, 50s) F3 (20s-40s). A living-room. Fee code L

This tense, dramatic thriller contains plenty of twists to keep your audience guessing. Beautiful
Veronica plots to murder her writer husband, Gus, but becomes alarmed when Gus discusses
the plot of his new novel, which is uncomfortably close to her murder plans. She presses ahead,
however, but things do not run entirely smoothly. Next day the police report the finding of a
body – but is it Gus? The final denouement contains several surprises before the guilty are
brought to justice.
ISBN 978 0 573 11487 8

Anastasia. Play. Marcelle Maurette. Adapted by Guy Bolton
M8 (30s-50s, elderly) F5 (30s, 40s, 70, 84). A room in a mansion. Fee code M
ISBN 978 0 573 60529 4

◆ **A bullet mark next to a title indicates that it is new to this edition of the Guide.**

The Anastasia File. Play. Royce Ryton
M2 F2. Various simple settings. Fee code M

Did the Grand Duchess Anastasia actually die with the rest of the Imperial family at Ekaterinburg in 1918? Using only four characters – Mrs Manahan, a police Inspector and an actor and actress (playing between them forty parts) – this brilliantly structured drama presents in flashback the life of the lady found in an asylum in 1920. Is Anastasia genuine? Why did some of the closest relatives reject her? Your audience will be held by his compelling play until the final surprising twist.
ISBN 978 0 573 01642 4

Ancient Lights. Play. Shelagh Stephenson
M2 (40, 50) F4 (teenage, 30s, 40). A living-room. Fee code L

Tom Cavallero, Hollywood actor, and his girlfriend Iona are spending Christmas in England with his oldest friends, Bea and Kitty. Bea's new lover, Tad, would rather hole up with his copy of *Pathology for Beginners*. Her daughter would rather be in Shepherd's Bush. Northumberland in a blizzard isn't what Tom was expecting. And how can anyone relax when Iona's filming their every move? Tom, Kitty and Bea have known each other since they were young and unformed. But who have they become and at what price?

And a Nightingale Sang. Play. C. P. Taylor
M4 (20s, 30s, 50s, 70) F3 (22, 30s, 50s). An open stage. Fee code M

This play follows the course of World War II as experienced by a working-class family in Newcastle, each scene being opened by a member of the family addressing the audience or singing a song of the period. In wartime there are no public worries, only private worries, and this story of the family's personal relationships, preoccupations, troubles and joys suggests, perhaps, the reason why – with all the perils and troubles besieging it – the human race will continue to survive.
ISBN 978 0 573 11020 7

♦ **And Evermore Shall Be So.** Thriller. Norman Robbins
M5 (30s, 40s, 50s) F5 (30s, 40s, 60s). A living-room. Fee code L

A murder mystery with more than a touch of humour, exploring the events surrounding a murder which took place four years previously. An author arrives, having been encouraged to write a book about the murder. Old tensions and suspicions are brought to the surface as not everyone is in favour of raking up the past. Offering ten good acting roles, the story twists and turns, leaving your audience guessing until the very last speech of the play.
ISBN 978 0 573 11021 4

And Then There Were None. Play. Agatha Christie
M9 (20s, 30s, middle-age, elderly) F3 (25, middle-age). A living-room. Fee code M

Ten people are invited by unknown hosts to a lonely house on a remote island. A mysterious voice indicts each of them of murder. First one and then another dies, and the tension grows as they realize that the killer is one of themselves. With only two people remaining, it becomes apparent that one of the deaths was feigned; the real killer appears and they are able to outwit him.
ISBN 978 0 573 01441 3

Animal Farm. Fable. Adapted by Nelson Bond from the book by George Orwell
M5 F2. No setting. Fee code M. NB. This is a staged reading version.

Orwell's biting satire is a fable with a sting, revealing how an idealistic Communist dream
was converted into a nightmare. This simply staged dramatic reading begins with the creatures
who have emancipated themselves from their cruel human masters, only to find themselves
subjected to even more ruthless autocrats: the greedy, cunning pigs. Eventually, the animals
numbly accept that 'All animals are equal but some are more equal than others.'
ISBN 978 0 573 60538 3

Animal Farm. George Orwell, adapted by Peter Hall, with lyrics by Adrian Mitchell and
music by Richard Peaslee
M9 F6, 1 boy. Extras. Various simple settings. Fee code M

This much-acclaimed dramatization of George Orwell's classic, allegorical novel was first seen
at the National Theatre in 1984. The play starts with a schoolboy sitting down to read the novel
by a toy farmyard. As he reads, the farmyard comes to life around him, enacting the animals'
rebellion. The dialogue is complemented by Mitchell's witty lyrics and Peaslee's music, jaunty
at first, but increasingly threatening and dissonant.

Anne of Green Gables. Play. Sylvia Ashby, from the novel by L.M. Montgomery
M4 (30s, middle-age). F5 (20s, middle-age). 3 boys, 4 girls (12). Some doubling possible.
Various interior and exterior settings. Fee code L

Mathew Cuthbert and his sister Marilla decide to adopt a boy to work on their farm, Green
Gables, but the orphanage sends a girl by mistake – the young, befreckled, warm, witty and
charitable Anne Shirley – and their lives are changed forever. This concise yet detailed adaptation
is humorous and bittersweet; a refreshing, contemporary telling of a classic story.

The Anniversary. Play. Bill MacIlwraith
M3 (20s, 30s) F3 (19, 30s, 50s). A living-room. Fee code M

Mother keeps a tight hold on all three of her sons with gifts, threats and ruthless exploitation of
their weaknesses. But as the family is unwillingly brought together to celebrate Mum's wedding
anniversary (regardless of deceased Dad), revolt is in the air. One son gathers the courage to
tell Mum he is moving to Canada; another breaks the news of his impending marriage. Mum
finds her long ascendancy is broken at last. The play was filmed starring Bette Davis and
Sheila Hancock.
ISBN 978 0 573 11007 8

Anorak of Fire. The Life and Times of Gus Gascoigne, Trainspotter. Play. Stephen Dinsdale
M1 (20s). A railway station platform. Fee code H

'I was born a spotter.' Thus we are introduced to Gus Gascoigne, young, spotty, perpetually
cheerful and completely bemused by anything that isn't involved with his sole interest –
trainspotting. Touching, ironic and consistently hilarious, *Anorak of Fire*, which enjoyed a long
run at London's Arts Theatre, after the Edinburgh Fringe, is a guaranteed audience-pleaser.
Running time approximately one hour.
ISBN 978 0 573 14201 7

Another Country. Play. Julian Mitchell
M9 (17, 40s). 1 boy. A public school library, study, dormitory, cricket field. Fee code M

Julian Mitchell's much-acclaimed play is set in an English public school in the early 1930s. The two central characters are outsiders: Guy Bennett, coming to terms with homosexuality, and Tommy Judd, a committed Marxist. 'In this subtle, absorbing and deceptive play, Julian Mitchell persuasively examines the seeds of tribal snobberies sown in the pre-war heyday of the British public school and reaped today in a harvest of spy scandals in top places.' *Daily Mail*

Another Time. Play. Ronald Harwood
M3 F2 (some characters age over 35 years). A pentagonal hall of a small ground-floor flat, a recording studio. Fee code M

In early 1950s Sea Point Town, Ike and Belle live with their son, Leonard, already a brilliantly gifted pianist who needs to study in Europe. When Ike dies, Belle is determined to further Leonard's studies whatever the cost. In Act II it is thirty-five years later in London where Leonard is a famous concert pianist. Belle and her brother and sister have travelled to London to see him, but Leonard has some shattering news for Belle.

Antigone. Play. Jean Anouilh
M8 (20s, middle age, 60s) F4 (19, 20s, 60s). An open space. Fee code M

Versions: Lewis Galantière
         Barbara Bray

This play was first performed in German-occupied France and its theme is resistance to oppression. It is based on the Greek tragedy of Antigone, who tried to bury her brother's corpse against the diktat of her uncle, Creon. Creon is a dictator, but defends his position on practical grounds. In spite of her love for Creon's son, she chooses her part: to bury her brother and die.

Antigone. Play. Bertolt Brecht
Translations: K. I. Porter
             Robert Cannon
Fee code M

A prologue set in 1945 Berlin shows two sisters whose brother has deserted from the German army and is found hanged: should they risk being seen by the SS cutting his body down? In the play itself Creon becomes a brutal aggressor, who has attacked Argos for the sake of its iron ore. Tiresias, instead of prophesying the future, becomes a pessimistic analyst of the present; while the chorus of elders, always reserved in its attitude, eventually turns against Creon too.

Anybody for Murder? Play. Brian Clemens and Dennis Spooner
M3 (30s, 40s) F3 (30s, 40s). A converted farmhouse on a Greek island. Fee code M

Max and his lover Suzy have concocted a plot to kill Max's wife Janet, with ten thousand pounds insurance money as an added bonus. Their plan is for Janet to have a sailing 'accident'. Then two unexpected visitors arrive, in the shape of George and Mary Ticklewell, who have an eye on the money, with murder plans of their own. Thus begins an intriguing round of plot and counter-plot, with a final, unexpected twist.
ISBN 978 0 573 01713 1

Anyone for Breakfast? Comedy. Derek Benfield
M3 (20, 40s) F3 (20, 40s) A living-room. Fee code L

In this merry comedy of marital mishaps the scene is set for an evening and morning of riotous misunderstandings and mistaken identities as the guilty parties in question try desperately to keep their romantic secrets secret! Your audience will be kept on a roar for two hours and at the end of the play we realize that the complications and confrontations – far from ending – are only just beginning ...
ISBN 978 0 573 01715 5

April in Paris. Comedy. John Godber
M1 (30s) F1 (30s). Various simple settings. Fee code M

Bet and Al lead a quiet, humdrum life in their small Yorkshire home until Bet wins a 'Romantic Breaks' competition in a magazine. The prize, a holiday in Paris, represents their first experience abroad and has profound effects on the way they look at the world around them once they return home. They sort out French cuisine, wrestle with their phrase book, and fend off would-be muggers on the Métro in this hilarious depiction of the English abroad.
ISBN 978 0 573 01714 8

Appointment With Death. Play. Agatha Christie
M9 F7. 1 interior. 1 exterior. Fee Code M

The King Solomon Hotel in Jerusalem has seen strange travellers in its time but none so strange as those who are now staying there to see the sites of the city and to visit Petra. The Boynton family, presided over by the invalid Mrs Boynton, appear to be a close-knit group. But when Mrs Boynton is discovered, dead, supposedly of a heart attack, suspicion falls on each of her step-children. But only when the death is proved to be suicide can the family feel free at last.
Period 1945
ISBN 978 0 573 11019 1

Arcadia. Play. Tom Stoppard
M8 (15, 20s, 30s, middle-age) F4 (teenage, 30s). A room. Fee code M

In 1809 at Sidley Park, the orderly classicism of Lady Croom's Capability Brown grounds is being turned into picturesque romantic chaos, as fashion dictates. In a Regency room overlooking the work is Lady Croom's brilliant adolescent daughter, Thomasina Coverly, with her tutor. They are interrupted by, among others, the amorous Lady Croom and Ezra Chater, a cuckold and minor poet, determined on satisfaction. 180 years later, in the same room, a corresponding group try to unravel the events of 1809 – with spectacularly wrong results.
ISBN 978 0 573 01718 6

The Architect. Play. David Greig
M4 (20s, 40s, 50s) F3 (20s, 40s, 50s). Various simple settings. Fee code M

Leo Black was an architect of his time, a builder of buildings, an idealistic designer, but these days he has an executive role in designing car parks. Has he really sunk so low? His family are falling apart and his buildings are falling down, leaving Leo struggling with the grubby reality of his once magnificent visions. The play was premièred at Edinburgh's Traverse Theatre in 1996.

Are You Being Served? Comedy. Jeremy Lloyd and David Croft
M10 (young to elderly) F6 (young to middle age), or M7 F4, 1M extra with doubling. A
department store and hotel settings. Fee code M

To the delight of its fans everywhere, this popular TV comedy series is brought to the stage
by its creators in all its original glory. Double entendres non-stop as the motley crew of the
Grace Brothers department store prepare for a sale of German goods, then depart for their staff
holiday at a one-star hotel in Spain.
ISBN 978 0 573 01963 0

Aren't We All? Comedy. Frederick Lonsdale
M8 (young, 30s, middle-age, 59) F4 (20s, middle-age). Two drawing-rooms. Fee code M

Willie is a devoted husband but falls prey to the charms of a beautiful young woman while
his wife, Margot, is on holiday. Margot is furious when she discovers the affair, but becomes
terrified when Willie's father finds out about her own holiday romance. Eventually she realizes
that Willie still loves her and confesses her infidelity. Forgiveness is mutual.
ISBN 978 0 573 61987 8

Aristocrats. Play. Brian Friel
M6 (30s, 50s, 70s) F3 (20s, 30s). A lawn and a small room. Fee code M

Set in the mid-1970s in a crumbling Georgian mansion in County Donegal, this is a portrait of
an upper-class Catholic family which, over four generations, has declined from a position of
social power to one of genteel poverty. The characters find themselves attending the patriarch's
funeral, and sit about the lawn drinking and quarrelling. ' ... sad, enchanting play ... a heartaching
world of crushed hopes and futile longings.' *Evening Standard* ' ... Friel's eloquence and piquant
irony speaks volumes.' *Time Out*

The Arsonists. Play. Max Frisch, translation by Alistair Beaton
M4 F4, chorus. Various simple settings. Period 1930-50s. Fee code L

Fires are becoming a problem, but Biedermann, a respected member of the community with
a loving wife and flourishing business, believes nothing can get to him. Being the great
philanthrope, he happily fulfils his civic duty, giving shelter to two new houseguests and when
they start filling the attic with petrol drums he'll help them wire the fuse. Beaton's translation
of Max Frisch's parable about accommodating the very thing that will destroy us premièred
at the Royal Court in 2007.

Art. Play. Yasmina Reza, translated by Christopher Hampton
M3 (30s-50s). A room. Fee code M

Serge has bought a hugely expensive modern painting. Marc hates it and cannot believe that a
friend of his could possibly want such a work. Yvan attempts, unsuccessfully, to placate both
sides. If your friendship is based on tacit mutual agreement what happens when one person does
something completely different and unexpected? *Art*, winner of the Evening Standard Award
for Best Comedy of the Year received its British première at Wyndham's Theatre, London, in
1994 starring Albert Finney, Tom Courtenay and Ken Stott. Running time 80 minutes.

♦ **A bullet mark next to a title indicates that it is new to this edition of the Guide.**

A

Artist Descending a Staircase. Play. Tom Stoppard
M6 (20s, 70s) F1 (22). An attic studio, a room, in the open air. Fee code M

Donner, Beauchamp and Martello, three elderly avant-garde artists, have co-existed for over fifty years. The play opens with Beauchamp and Martello accusing each other of the murder of Donner. In a series of flashbacks from 1972 to 1914, the bickering trio are contrasted with their young counterparts. The pivot is Sophie, loved by each of them in different ways. In the play's final moments, the reality of Donner's death is revealed.
ISBN 978 0 573 01687 5

Arturo Ui . See **Resistible Rise of Arturo Ui**

The Ash Girl. Play. Timberlake Wertenbaker
M4 F6, 8 M or F (with doubling). A house, a palace, a forest. Fee code M

When an invitation to the Ball, addressed to all the daughters of the house, arrives from Prince Amir, the Ash Girl can't believe she has been invited as well as her stepsisters. With her friends' help she gets the strength to go. She finds fleeting happiness in the arms of the Prince; to regain it, she discovers, she must fight the monsters who have insinuated their way into her heart and mind. (**Slightly restricted**)

At Break of Day. Play. Noël Greig
17 characters. Various interior and exterior settings suggested on a bare stage. Fee code K

Please see the entry in Section C.

At the Sign of "The Crippled Harlequin". Thriller. Norman Robbins
M3 (30s, 40s, 50s) F5 (20s-70s). The lounge of a guest house. Fee Code L

In a snowbound guest house in the Peak District, Marjory Pike is wrongly identified by another guest as the author of a book declaiming certain mediums, one of whom had committed suicide as a result. When Marjory is found dead, it sets off a chain of events that sees the audience's expectations subverted at every turn. This gripping thriller is rich with shocks and laughs as it races towards its unexpected close.
ISBN 978 0 573 11631 5

Attempts on Her Life. 17 Scenarios for the Theatre. Martin Crimp
M4 F4. Various simple settings Fee Code M

Seventeen scenes make up this ambitious and highly original work, ranging from just a page to much longer dialogues. A woman with various identities links all the scenes: she is the heroine of a film in one, a victim of civil war in another, an international terrorist, a porn star, and the subject of a conversation among friends. She is the living embodiment of Crimp's underlying declaration that coherent identity in the modern world is little more than myth.
ISBN 978 0 571 22552 1

◆ **A bullet mark next to a title indicates that it is new to this edition of the Guide.**

A

Audacity. Play. Simon Mawdsley
M3 (30s-40s) F2 (20s, 40s). A bcdsit. Fcc code L

Philip is going through a messy divorce. To make some money and give himself a boost, he devises a cunning scheme to steal the daily takings from a London department store. He enlists the help of John, an ex-stationery salesman sacked for fiddling his expenses, and Dave, another salesman with a hugely expensive lifestyle. The plot seems to be going well – until John's and Dave's wives start investigating their husbands' odd behaviour … " … crisp dialogue … skilful plotting … gripping and amusing … " *The Times*
ISBN 978 0 573 11039 9

Audience with Murder. Thriller. Roger Leach and Colin Wakefield
M2 (25, 55) F2 (25, 55) play multiple characters. 1 male voice. Living-room. Fee Code L

This intriguing, multi-layered and witty thriller is full of unexpected twists. A Russian doll of a play, it moves from a seemingly innocuous domestic play reading, through a murder mystery in the classic style, to a final terrifying and violent climax. It was first produced at the Edinburgh Festival in 2004 and subsequently presented to critical acclaim at the Jermyn Street Theatre, London, in 2006.
ISBN 978 0 573 11003 0

August. Play. Julian Mitchell, adapted from *Uncle Vanya* by Anton Chekhov
M7 (middle-age, old) F4 (20s, old). A terrace, a dining-room, a drawing-room, a bedroom. Fee code M

Chekhov's eloquent study of languid Russian landowners has been transposed by Julian Mitchell to Victorian north Wales in this stunning adaptation, which dispenses with many of the alienating Russian principles – confusing patronymics – and theatrical clichés – birch forests and samovars – that characterize most modern British productions. Anthony Hopkins played Ieuan Davies in the acclaimed original production for Theatr Clwyd in 1994.

Baal. Play. Bertolt Brecht
Translations: Peter Tegal
　　　　　　　Christopher Logue
　　　　　　　William E. Smith and Ralph Manheim
M18 F12. Extras. Interior and exterior settings. Fee code M (for play), code A (for music)

Baal, a poet and singer, drunk, lazy, selfish and ruthless, seduces (among others) a disciple's seventeen-year-old mistress, who drowns herself. He mixes with tramps and drivers and sings in a cheap nightclub. With his friend the composer Ekart he wanders through the country, drinking and fighting. Sophie, pregnant by him, follows them and likewise drowns herself. Baal seduces Ekart's mistress, then kills him. Hunted by the police and deserted by the woodcutters, he dies alone in a forest hut.

Baby Doll. Tennessee Williams. A new stage version devised and originally directed by Lucy Bailey
M15 (4 Black) F2. Extras. Composite set: house and yard; doctor's surgery; café. Fee code M

Archie Lee Meighan's Mississippi cotton gin business is foundering in the face of Silva Vacarro's Syndicate Gin; to this frustration is added the sexual unavailability of his voluptuous young wife Baby Doll. Lucy Bailey's adaptation of Tennessee Williams' notorious screenplay, with an ingenious three-storey house setting by Bunny Christie, played at the Birmingham Repertory Theatre in 1999 and the National Theatre, London, in 2000, garnering rave reviews in both venues. Period 1950s
ISBN 978 0 573 01970 8

Baby with the Bathwater. Comedy. Christopher Durang
M2 F8 or M2 F3. Composite set. Fee code H

This bitingly satiric black comedy, which enjoyed a long off-Broadway run, begins with Helen and John deciding their newly born child is a girl and naming it Daisy – which leads to all manner of future emotional and personality problems because Daisy is actually a boy. Brilliantly theatrical and wildly hilarious, the play charts the saga of Daisy's struggle to establish his identity.

The Bacchae. Play. Euripides, translated by Neil Curry
M7 F1, chorus of women. An open stage. Fee code J

A lively, modern English translation of Euripides' last and greatest play which depicts the turbulent arrival of the Dionysiac religion in Greece.

Back to the Land. Community play. Do Shaw
M9 F17. Various simple settings. Fee code L

This takes a warm-hearted look at the lives of a group of Women's Land Army girls in the 1940s, making the best of life in a billet in the North East of England. With a cast of over twenty characters, and based on the recollections of former Land Girls, this lively and touching play is punctuated with the songs and music of World War II as well as BBC radio broadcasts of the period. (Music and songs are not included in the text.) Period 1940s

Bad Blood. Thriller. Richard Stockwell
M3 (19, 40s) F2 (19, 40). A living-room. Fee code M

Years ago, Tom had an affair with Catherine who became pregnant and had an abortion – or so he thinks. Now he is married to Vic and is desperate to be a father. Enter Smokey, a tearaway whose girlfriend is none other than – Catherine's and Tom's daughter Belinda. Tom's wish to be a father is fulfilled, but remember the saying: be careful what you wish for – you might just get it. Tom's philandering past catches up with him in this fast-moving, bloody and savage modern thriller.
ISBN 978 0 573 01994 4

Bad Company. Play. Simon Bent
M6 (20s) F2 (20s). Various simple scenes. Fee code M

A group of twentysomethings hangs out on the seafront of a northern resort at the end of the summer season, finding little to relieve the futility and boredom of their lives: they gamble in amusement arcades, bicker in cafés, lust on the beach ... Casual sex, mindless violence and comic clashes of outlook permeate this entertaining, contemporary and humane play which paints a believable, touching portrait of modern youth.
ISBN 978 0 573 01723 0

A Bad Dream. Play. Simon Brett
M8 F12. A Committee Room. Fee code L

Between June and November 1902, the year of Edward VII's coronation Bellingford Amateur Dramaticks Society is rehearsing *A Midsummer Night's Dream*. It has the usual range of different personalities – stalwart group members, young lads about town, daughters of local businessmen and the wealthy diamond-trade man, a devotee of Henry Irving, who is underwriting the production. This man's murder, set against Queen Victoria's golden jubilee, a new ping-pong craze and the invention of finger-printing, broadens the plot and develops the characters. Commissioned to commemorate Sutton Amateur Dramatic Club's centenary in 2002.
ISBN 978 0 573 01992 0

A

Balmoral. Comedy. Michael Frayn
M6 (20s, 50s, 60) F2 (20, 40). A room in Balmoral Castle. Fee code M

It is 1937. Twenty years earlier the Revolution took place in Britain instead of Russia and the Soviet Republic of Great Britain is at the height of the purges. The royal residence of Balmoral is now a State Writers' Home with Godfrey Winn, Warwick Deeping, Enid Blyton and Hugh Walpole among its current inmates. Upon this very entertaining premise, Michael Frayn has constructed a witty, ingenious farce which was presented at the Bristol Old Vic in 1987.

Barefoot in the Park. Comedy. Neil Simon
M4 (26, 30, 58, 60) F2 (young, 60). New York apartment. Fee code M

Corrie and Paul are newly-weds who have just moved into their cold eyrie of an apartment. Corrie is starry-eyed, Paul less so after staggering up five flights. Their house seems to be populated by unusual people, the most bohemian being Victor whom Corrie finds entertaining. Corrie tries matchmaking between Victor and her lonely mother but after a disastrous dinner party she learns that walking barefoot in the park may not necessarily denote *joie de vivre* – in February it is simply silly! **(Slightly restricted)**
ISBN 978 0 573 01551 9

Bash. Three plays. Neil LaBute
M1 F1, or M2 (young, early 30s) F2 (young, late 20s). Simple settings. Fee code M for triple bill

A collection of three raw, dark yet lyrically intense one-act plays which won the *Time Out* Critics' Choice Award after its successful run at the Almeida.

   Iphegenia in Orem. Fee code E
M1 (early 30s)

A Utah businessman, in a Las Vegas motel room, confesses an especially chilling crime to a complete stranger.

   A Gaggle of Saints. Fee code E
M1 (young) F1 (young)

A young couple separately describe the events of an anniversary weekend spent in New York. As the events described entwine, the girl is blissfully unaware of the violence perpetrated by her fiancé.

   Medea Redux. Fee code E
F1 (late 20s)

A tragic tale in which a woman recounts her relationship with a high school teacher and the lengths she goes to in order to exact revenge.

Battle of Angels. Play. Tennessee Williams
M11 F11. Fee code M

As in its later, and substantially re-written version (entitled *Orpheus Descending*) the play deals with the arrival of a virile young drifter, Val Xavier, in a sleepy, small town in rural Mississippi. Taking a job in a store his smouldering animal magnetism draws out the latent sexual passion in the love-starved store keeper, whilst her husband lies dying upstairs. A sense of inevitable tragedy grows and there is a denouement of overwhelming and chilling intensity.

Bazaar and Rummage. Comedy. Sue Townsend
F6 (20s, 30s, middle-age). A multi-purpose church hall. Fee code J

Gwenda, an ex-agoraphobic, leads a self-help group of three who have been unable to leave their homes for a variety of reasons. She forces them to help at a local bazaar, enlisting the support of Fliss, a trainee social-worker. While sorting through the rummage their individual fears erupt but calm is restored by the ever-sensible Fliss. As they leave the hall it is apparent their agoraphobia is not cured but they have made the effort.

The Beauty Queen of Leenane. Play. Martin McDonagh
M2 (20, 40) F2 (40, 70s). A kitchen/living-room. Fee code M

In a dingy cottage in Leenane, a remote part of Galway, spinster Maureen lives with her self-pitying, ruthless, hateful mother, Mag. Constantly at her beck and call, Maureen takes revenge by feeding her lumpy Complan and hurling the occasional insult. Escape comes in the form of Pato Dooley, who is about to go to Boston. When Mag interferes once too often Maureen decides the time has come to break free – in a very violent way.

Becket, or The Honour of God. Play. Jean Anouilh. Translated by Lucienne Hill
M34 F5. Composite setting. Fee code H

As he waits to be scourged for his part in Becket's murder, King Henry II retraces his entire relationship with the saint, once his dearest friend and mentor. His catastrophic mistake was to create Becket Archbishop out of political expediency for Becket found a fulfilment lacking in his hitherto luxurious life and therefore guarded the honour of God as once he had, as Henry's Chancellor, guarded the honour of his King. Period 12th century
ISBN 978 0 573 01034 7

Becket. Play. Jean Anouilh, translated by Frederic Raphael and Stephen Raphael
M19 F4. Extras. Simple settings. Fee code M

When the Archbishop of Canterbury died, Henry II forced his companion and political lieutenant, Thomas Becket, to take his place. Becket told his King: "If I become archbishop, I shall cease to be your friend." Becket, who with Henry had fought the Church for the good of the State, now felt responsible for the honour of God. Conflict was inevitable and was followed, just as inevitably, by murder and remorse. This translation premièred at the Theatre Royal Haymarket, London, in 2004.

Bed. Play. Jim Cartwright
M4 F4. A giant bed. Fee code M

Seven elderly people share a vast bed, to dream, remember and reflect on a long past. The play, with a running time of 90 minutes, was acclaimed at the Royal National Theatre. 'Cartwright writes better about old people than anyone I know, except perhaps Beckett. This is an odd, harrowing and hilarious piece, entirely without sentimentality, sturdy but moving.' *Sunday Times*. 'Sophisticated of structure and mature in content ... brims with the confidence of a craftsman who can work as happily with surrealism as naturalism ...' *City Limits*

♦ **A bullet mark next to a title indicates that it is new to this edition of the Guide.**

A Bedfull of Foreigners. Comedy. Dave Freeman
M4 (30s, middle-age) F3 (20s, 30s). An hotel bedroom. Fee code M

On the eve of a local festival in a French village Stanley and Brenda, on a motoring trip, think themselves lucky to obtain a hotel room. But in less than an hour Stanley finds himself lowering an attractive girl, stark naked, from the window. The girl's husband arrives and by the second hour almost everybody is in the wrong bed, figures dressed as nuns and monks rush in and out, seductions and confrontations run rampant!
ISBN 978 0 573 11043 6

Bedroom Farce. Comedy. Alan Ayckbourn
M4 (young, 60) F4 (young, 50s). Three bedrooms in one set. Fee code M

Three bedrooms are presented simultaneously on stage and the action between three households flows in and out from one to the other during this hectic night. There are Ernest and Delia celebrating an anniversary with pilchards on toast after a disastrous meal out; Malcolm and Kate preparing a house-warming party and Nick and Jan, the former resting his injured back in bed. The marital disasters of Trevor and Susannah weave in out and out of the bedrooms.
ISBN 978 0 573 11047 4

Bedside Manners. Comedy. Derek Benfield
M3 (young, middle-age) F2 (young). A reception room and two bedrooms represented by the same set. Fee code L

Ferris is looking after his sister's seedy hotel. Two young couples arrive. Roger has arranged an assignation with Sally, leaving his wife Helen at home, but Helen and Geoff, Sally's husband, have also made plans for a naughty weekend together – at the same hotel. The mischievous Ferris discovers their guilty secrets and tries (at some financial reward to himself) to prevent the inevitable meeting of husbands, wives and lovers in assorted compromising situations.
ISBN 978 0 573 11030 6

Benefactors. Play. Michael Frayn
M2 F2. A bare stage. Fee code M

Michael Frayn's highly-acclaimed play was premièred at London's Vaudeville Theatre and won the *Standard*, *Plays and Players* and Laurence Olivier awards for the Best Play of 1984. Spanning fifteen years this complex, well-structured play traces the story of the destruction of David's architectural dream by the embittered Colin and Colin's marriage to the inept Sheila, contrasting those who help and those who are helped; those who create and those who destroy. '... a beautifully crafted play, economically written.' *Time Out*
ISBN 978 0 573 01643 1

Bent. Play. Martin Sherman
M11 (20s, 30s) with doubling. Various simple interior and exterior settings. Fee code M

In 1930s Berlin Max and his lover/flatmate Rudy begin a nightmare odyssey through Nazi Germany, which placed homosexuals on a lower scale than Jews. Max refuses to abandon Rudy and soon they're caught. *En route* to Dachau, Rudy is killed and Horst, another homosexual prisoner, warns Max to deny Rudy, which he does. Max opts for the label 'Jew' rather than 'queer' but he and Horst are attracted to each other; when Horst is callously killed Max declares himself before committing suicide.

The Best of Friends. Play. Hugh Whitemore, adapted from the letters and writings of Dame Laurentia McLachlan, Sir Sydney Cockerell and George Bernard Shaw
M2 F1. A sitting-room, a conservatory, a study. Fee code M

In 1924, when George Bernard Shaw was 68, his friend Sydney Cockerell, then Director of the Fitzwilliam Museum in Cambridge, introduced him to a Benedictine nun at Stanbrook Abbey in Worcestershire. Dame Laurentia McLachlan, later to be elected Abbess, enjoyed a lively friendship with both Shaw and Cockerell for over twenty-five years. Whitemore's play is based upon the letters and writings of the three friends.

Betrayal. Play. Harold Pinter
M2 (40s) F1(30s). Extra 1M. Various simple settings. Fee code M

Jerry is a literary agent; Emma runs an art gallery; Robert is a publisher. Emma and Robert are married and Jerry is Robert's best friend, but Emma and Jerry have had a seven-year affair. The play opens with Emma and Jerry meeting for lunch in 1977, two years after the affair has finished and by a brilliant device the relationship of the three is traced backwards nine years to the evening when it all began. First presented at the National Theatre in 1978.

Beyond a Joke. Comedy. Derek Benfield
M4 (young, 50) F4 (20, 40s, 50). A drawing-room and a garden. Fee code L

Six times fatalities have occurred in Jane and Andrew's country house. When daughter Sally's new young man, Geoff, arrives for the weekend he mistakenly gets the idea that the occurrences were due to something more sinister than 'accident'. When a visiting vicar passes peacefully away in the garden Andrew and Jane try to remove the body. Events are further confused by the unexpected arrival of Geoff's parents who are unaware that the body has been stowed in their car boot!
ISBN 978 0 573 11027 6

Beyond Reasonable Doubt. Play. Jeffrey Archer
M11 F3. The Central Criminal Court, a London house. Fee code M

Accused of the wilful murder of his terminally ill wife, Sir David Metcalf finds himself locked in legal combat with his old rival, Anthony Blair-Booth QC. After a tense and gripping courtroom scene, Act I ends just as we are about to hear the jury's verdict. Act II takes us back in time to the fateful night of Lady Metcalfe's death and ends with a surprising twist. This play enjoyed a successful run in London's West End, with Frank Finlay and Wendy Craig in the leading roles. 'I loved it ... it's much more than a courtroom drama. It's a compelling love story and it's got the lot – laughter, tears and tension ...' *TV-am.*
ISBN 978 0 573 01676 9

Beyond Therapy. Comedy. Christopher Durang
M4 (30) F2 (29, middle-age). Various interiors, may be simply suggested. Fee code M

Prudence's therapist is urging her to be more assertive; while Bruce's therapist urges him to meet someone of the opposite sex by placing a personal ad, not realizing that Bruce has a male lover named Bob. Having met each other Bruce doesn't know how to handle nervous Prudence; and Prudence doesn't know what to make of decidedly unpredictable Bruce. How they sort it all out is the story of this delightful comedy. '*Beyond Therapy* offers the best therapy of all: guaranteed laughter.' *Time*

Big Bad Mouse. Farce. Philip King and Falkland Cary. From an idea by Ivan Butler
M3 (19, 40, 50) F4 (18, 50). An office. Fee code M

A

In the Orders Office of Chunkibix Ltd, it is Mr Price-Hargreaves who gives the orders and Mr Bloome who obeys them. Until, that is, Mr Bloome is one day accused of chasing a young female person across Wandsworth Common making him the hero of every woman and girl in the office not least Miss Spencer. So glorious is Bloome's transformation, in fact, that when the young person in question discovers she has made a mistake in her identification, Bloome is the reverse of pleased, and determines to keep her quiet.
ISBN 978 0 573 01532 8

Billy Liar. Comedy. Keith Waterhouse and Willis Hall
M3 (19, 50s) F5 (17-19, 40s, 80s). A composite set. Fee code M

Less than dedicated to his job as undertaker's clerk, bored with his North Country family background, Billy Fisher takes refuge in his own invented world. For Billy, an energetic imagination makes life tolerable but well-nigh intolerable for all around him. He lies his way into and out of every situation, producing any explanation and making any promise that will extricate him from his present predicament, and thereby creating ever more tortuous entanglements for the immediate future.
ISBN 978 0 573 11142 6

Biloxi Blues. Comedy. Neil Simon
M7 (18-20) F2. Various interior and exterior settings. Fee code M

This sequel to *Brighton Beach Memoirs* won the 1985 Tony Award for Best Play and received its British première at the Library Theatre, Manchester, in 1991. When we last met Eugene, he was coping with adolescence in the 1930s in Brooklyn. Now it is 1943 and the saga of Eugene Morris Jerome, *alter ego* of the youthful Neil Simon, continues with him as a young army recruit during the Second World War. 'Joyous and unexpectedly rewarding.' *New York Times* (**Slightly restricted**)
ISBN 978 0 573 69040 2

Birdy. Play. Naomi Wallace, based on the novel by William Wharton
M6 (16,17, 21, 22, 50). Various simple settings. Fee code M

Naomi Wallace has skilfully transformed William Wharton's novel into a compelling, intimate piece of theatre. This is the journey of Birdy and his friend Al who are seen both as young men in Philadelphia in the years just before World War Two and as wounded soldiers bearing the mental and physical scars of war. Period 1930s, 1946 '… ingeniously conveys the essence of the book's attraction.' *Evening Standard*

The Birthday Party. Play. Harold Pinter
M4 (35, 50, 65) F2 (25, 65). A living-room. Fee code M

Goldberg and McCann arrive at a seaside boarding house where Meg and Petey live with their guest Stanley. They inquire about Stanley: we soon find out that McCann and Goldberg have a job to do. Learning it is his birthday they give Stanley a party at which Stanley is verbally bludgeoned into submission. The next day Stanley is removed. It is the collective impact of the dialogue which welds the seemingly inexplicable actions of Goldberg and McCann into a menacing whole.
ISBN 978 0 573 01042 2

A

Birthday Suite. Comedy. Robin Hawdon
M3 (30, 40) F2 (30). Two adjoining hotel rooms. Fee code M

Geoff Tippet has arranged a special birthday treat for his old friend, Bob. The treat is a hotel room for the night, a double-bed which folds up into the wall and an attractive girl called Mimi. Add a shy Kate who anxiously awaits her computer agency date – Dick, who has been shown into the wrong room; Bob's wife Liz, who believes she is dining with Geoff, and a connecting door between the two rooms and you have the recipe for a fast-moving and hilarious comedy.
ISBN 978 0 573 11509 7

Biting the Bullet. Play. Frank Vickery
M2 (late 20s, 55) F3 (young, middle-age, 58). A living-room. Fee code M

Ted, undergoing a mid-life crisis, leaves the house he and home-loving wife Beryl have shared for thirty-two years. At first Beryl is shattered, but gradually works back from the edge of despair, helped by her exuberant daughter Angie and down-to-earth neighbour Dawn. A holiday abroad, a complete make-over – not to mention a platonic friendship with the young handyman, who gives her new ways of looking at life – rescue her from the nightmare of separation.
ISBN 978 0 573 01920 3

Blackbird. Play. David Harrower
Ml (mid 50s) Fl (late 20s). A room.

Fifteen years ago, Una and Ray had a relationship which resulted in a jail sentence and new identity on his release for Ray, and psychotherapy for Una. They haven't set eyes on each other since.
Now she's found him again. A remarkable drama which poses serious questions about society and morality. The play won the Laurence Oliver Award for Best New Play.

Black Coffee. Play. Agatha Christie
M10 (30s, 60s) F3 (20s, 50s). A library. Fee code M

Lucia, wife of Sir Claude Amory's son Richard, Dr Carelli and Barbara are all having coffee when Sir Claude announces that a new explosive formula has been stolen from his safe and that he has sent for Hercule Poirot. To enable the thief to replace the formula he orders the lights to be turned out but when they are switched on again and as Poirot enters, Sir Claude is found poisoned. Poirot sets about his investigation, foils the murderer in a second attempt and cleverly tricks him into betraying himself.
ISBN 978 0 573 61885 7

Black Snow. Play. Keith Dewhurst, adapted from the novel by Mikhail Bulgakov
Large cast may be played by M10 F5 with extras. Various interior settings. Fee code M

This bitingly funny adaptation of Bulgakov's modern Russian classic novel of 1936 was premièred at the Royal National's Cottesloe Theatre in 1991. Set between 1924 and 1925 it is an hilarious send-up of Stanislavsky's famous 'Method' and the acting profession in general and was based on fact – the mutilation of Bulgakov's play *Molière*, for which Bulgakov blamed Stanislavsky. '... the funniest and cleverest new play I have seen for a very long time.' *Financial Times*

Black Widow. Play. Paul Thain
M4 (any age, 30s, 60s) F6 (teens, 30s-60s). Doubling possible. A bare stage. Fee code M
ISBN 978 0 573 01727 8

A

The Blind Fiddler. Play. Marie Jones
M2 F3. Multiple roles. Various simple settings. Fee Code M

The 1970s. Northern Ireland. Pat and Mary Gormley are an ill-matched couple: Pat is a laid-back publican, a storyteller and musician, whereas Mary is determinedly, upwardly mobile, nagging at their children to succeed and moving the family away from the pub as soon as she can. Looking back thirty years later, their daughter Kathleen tries to piece together the family story so that she can understand what drove them apart; in doing so, she uncovers an important family secret … Period 1970s
ISBN 978 0 573 11337 6

Blinded by the Sun. Play. Stephen Poliakoff
M4 (40, 41, 50s, 70s) F4 (20s, 40, 50s). Various simple settings. Fee code M

The retiring professor in a university chemistry department chooses Al, a mediocre scientist but a brilliant administrator, to succeed him as department head. Al begins reorganizing the department, but finds that Christopher, his peer and rival, and Elinor, his one-time teacher, are unwilling to change the isolated way they work. Christopher announces a major breakthrough, which should assure prosperity – but has disastrous results.
ISBN 978 0 573 01929 6

Blithe Spirit. Improbable Farce. Noël Coward
M2 (40, middle-age) F5 (young, 45, middle-age). A living-room. Fee code M

Charles Condomine, whose first wife Elvira has been dead for seven years, has been reasonably happy with his second wife Ruth. After he invites Madame Arcati, a local medium, to conduct a seance at their home, Elvira returns from the dead. Determined to get Charles to herself forever, she arranges several 'accidents', one of which culminates in Ruth joining Elvira. Now plagued by *two* jealous squabbling spirits, Charles bids them both farewell and his two wives are left petulantly tearing the house apart.
ISBN 978 0 573 01044 6

Blood Money. Thriller. The Heather Brothers
M1 (40s) F3 (20s-40s). 1F extra. 1M 2F voices only. A lounge. Fee code M

Seven years ago, Mike Mason, star of TV's 'Bargain Basement', and his wife Liz killed young Carol Mitchell in a hit-and-run car accident – and now it seems they have at last been found out. A mysterious telephone caller claims to be Carol Mitchell and her name appears in blood on the wall; Liz is certain she has been followed; then a car draws up outside the house and shots soon ring out ...
ISBN 978 0 573 01753 7

Blood Sweat and Tears. Play. John Godber
M2 (30s, 40s) F3 (20s). Composite set on 2 levels: a burger bar, a judo hall. Fee code M

Louise Underwood's life revolves around the hamburger restaurant where she works, and a night club: then she discovers judo. This inspiring play charts Louise's progress to Black Belt. Her personal journey involves numerous sacrifices, crises of confidence and battles with more experienced players who think she has no chance of success. A play about the opportunities given to ordinary people to be something special.
ISBN 978 0 573 01725 4

Bloody Poetry. Play. Howard Brenton
M3 (20-30s) F3 (18-20s). A bare stage. Fee code M

Staged to critical acclaim in both New York and London, first at the Hampstead Theatre in 1984 and subsequently in a revival at the Royal Court Theatre in 1988, this is a portrayal of the lives of Shelley, Mary Shelley and Claire Clairemont. Set between the summers of 1816 and 1822 the play opens with their flight from England to Switzerland and Italy where, for the first time, they encounter Lord Byron.

Blue Heart
A double bill by Caryl Churchill. M2 F7, with doubling. Child extras. Fee code M as a double bill. For separate fee codes see below

Two related short plays, both teasingly entertaining and brilliantly executed, one about a father and daughter, the other about a mother and son. In *Heart's Desire*, a family await the return of their daughter after a long sojourn in Australia. In *Blue Kettle* a middle-aged man and his girlfriend are involved in a con trick, making elderly women believe they are the man's long-lost mother. But neither play is what it seems. Something catastrophic is happening which disrupts and destroys them.

Heart's Desire
M2 F4 with doubling. Child extras. A kitchen. Fee code E if performed separately

Blue Kettle
M2 F6. Various simple settings. Fee code E if performed separately

Blue Murder. Double bill. Peter Nichols
M5 F2. FOREIGN BODIES: composite set: a study, a sitting-room A GAME OF SOLDIERS: an elegant room. Fee code M

Subtitled 'a play or two', Blue Murder opens with *Foreign Bodies*, where Swinging London meets bourgeois Shrewsbury in 1963 and the drinks are laced with cyanide. The second half, *A Game of Soldiers*, is a Whitehall farce taking place in St James's Palace. A dramatist has brought his completed play to be censored but the Lord Chamberlain's Men have a few shameful secrets of their own ... Period 1963 and 1967

Blue/Orange. Play. Joe Penhall
M3 (20s, 24 (black), 50s). A hospital consultation room. Fee Code M

In a London psychiatric hospital, an enigmatic patient claims to be the son of an African dictator – a story that becomes unnervingly plausible. An incendiary tale of race, madness and a Darwinian power struggle at the heart of a dying NHS. This multi-award-winning play premièred at the National Theatre in 2000 starring Bill Nighy, Chiwetel Ejiofor and Andrew Lincoln.

Blue Remembered Hills. Play. Dennis Potter
M5 F2. Composite setting: wood, field, barn. Fee code M

This apparently simple tale relates the activities of seven-year-olds on a summer afternoon during World War II. The children (all played by adult actors) and their world become a microcosm of adult interaction. Willie tags along as burly Peter bullies Raymond and is challenged by fair-minded John. Audrey is over-shadowed by Angela's prettiness and wreaks her angry frustrations on the boys. All of them gang up on the terrified 'Donald Duck' who, abused by his mother and ridiculed by his peers, plays his own dangerous game of pyromania which ends in tragedy.
ISBN 978 0 573 01699 8

The Blue Room. Play. Freely adapted from Arthur Schnitzler's *La Ronde* by David Hare
10 characters, minimum cast of M1 F1. Various simple settings. Fee code M

Reigen, Schnitzler's loose series of sexual sketches, became better known after they were filmed, as *La Ronde*, in 1950. David Hare has re-set these circular scenes of love and betrayal, transposing them from the Viennese original of 1898 to a modern city of 1998, creating a fascinating landscape of dream and longing. The ten couples, whose linked liaisons make up a sexual carousel, can be performed by just two actors.

Body Language. Play. Alan Ayckbourn
M5 (34, 41, 50, 84) F3 (30, 40). A terrace. Fee code M

There is an awful accident at a cosmetic surgery clinic; overweight reporter Jo and glamour model Angie are beheaded by a helicopter. But never fear, infamous surgeon Hravic knows exactly how to save them and as if by miracle, their heads are sewn back – on the wrong bodies. Will the women learn to cope with their new bodies? Or will Hravic be able to re-sew them correctly? The ending sees everything stitched up nicely.
ISBN 978 0 573 01957 9

Bold Girls. Play. Rona Munro
F4 (young, middle-age). A kitchen, a night club, a hilltop. Fee code M

The dramas of everyday life in Belfast are but off-stage events in this stirring play about the lives of three women whose men have been killed or imprisoned for their political activities, but where bread must still be bought between explosions. In spite of its chilling theme there are many humorous and heart-warming moments – a play about people, not politics, which offers excellent acting opportunities. Rona Munro received the *Evening Standard* Most Promising Playwright Award for 1991 for *Bold Girls*.
ISBN 978 0 573 13006 9

A Bolt from the Blue. Comedy. David Tristram
M2 F2 (minimum casting). Simple Settings. Fee Code L

Edward Jones was just an ordinary man, doing ordinary things- until the day before his 40th birthday. What happened next was, quite literally, incredible. It defies belief. It defies logic. It defies the fundamental laws of science and nature. But it happened. With his latest comedy, adapted from his novel of the same name, David Tristram brings his trademark hilarity to every page, but with a poignant and unusual story that tingles every nerve ending before reaching its extraordinary conclusion.

Bonaventure. Play. Charlotte Hastings
M3 (young, 35, 40) F8 (20-50, elderly). Two interiors. Fee code M
ISBN 978 0 573 01046 0

Bone-Chiller. Comedic Mystery-Thriller. Monk Ferris
M5 (20s, 30s, elderly) F8 (18, 20s, 30s, middle-age). Can also be M4 F9, or M6 F7. A parlour/library. Fee code M

On Friday the 13th, thirteen people gather for the reading of the late Josiah Travers's will. The will consists of a rebus which offers the lucrative estate to *anyone* who can solve the puzzle. To make things tougher, the lights keep going out and people keep being murdered. This is not only a very funny farce, it is also a superbly-crafted mystery.
ISBN 978 0 573 61985 4

Borders of Paradise. Play. Sharman Macdonald
M5 (young) F2 (young). A beach. Fee code M

Ellen and Rose have arrived from Scotland and set up their tent on a Devonshire cliff top.
Down on the beach Rob, David, Charlie, Cot and John are enjoying a surfing break. A touching
and humorous piece with seven excellent roles for young actors. 'No-one writes about the
mysteries of young adulthood with more truth … combines warm and funny naturalism with
an appropriate touch of the mystic.' *The Times*

Born in the Gardens. Play. Peter Nichols
M2 (45, 50) F2 (35, 70s). A living-room. Fee code M

Maud, a decidedly eccentric woman, lives in a dilapidated mock-Tudor Victorian house with
her son Mo. The other children, Hedley, an ineffectual Labour MP, and Queenie, an expatriate
in America, arrive and try to persuade Maud to go to a modern 'duplex' in London, and Mo to
join Queenie in California, but both prefer to remain as they are. Not all of us, Mo says, 'want
freedom. Captivity has its points as well.'
ISBN 978 0 573 11045 0

Bottom's Dream. Play. Alan Poole
M8 F6. Children: M or F5. Various simple settings on an open stage. Fee code K

Who dreamt the Midsummer Night's Dream? What were the reactions of the Artisans' relatives
to their play-acting activities? The author considers the play from the point of Bottom – and the
women as members of the audience. Bottom and his wife are discovered settling down for the
night – as twelve o'clock strikes, Bottom dreams a 'most rare vision'. All the Artisan scenes
are preserved intact – but here the women also have their say.
ISBN 978 0 573 12026 8

BoyBand. Peter Quilter
M7 (young, 30s) F3 (young, 20s) with doubling. Various simple settings. Fee code M
ISBN 978 0 573 01955 5

The Boys in the Band. Play. Mart Crowley
M9 (20s-30s, 1 Black). An apartment. Fee code M

Michael, a homosexual, has invited a number of friends to his birthday party. A straight friend
of his, Alan, rings up and wants to see him. Though anxious about the outcome, Michael agrees
to his joining them. Alan's presence acts as a catalyst to the emotions – never far from the
surface – of those at the party. The result is a mixture of bitter humour and physical violence.
Alan goes, leaving behind him the debris of the party.
ISBN 978 0 573 64004 9

Brassed Off. Play. Paul Allen, from the film by Mark Herman
M6+ F4+. Composite setting. Fee code M

Grimley Colliery is set to close as the accountants say there's more money in it shut than open,
even after redundancy payments. It means 1200 job losses, a dying town and the loss of its
brass band. But under the leadership of Danny, coughing with coal-dusted lungs, the band is
somehow transformed into British champions with local lass Gloria whipping up the money
needed to get them to the Albert Hall.
ISBN 978 0 573 01996 8

The Break of Day. Play. Timberlake Wertenbaker
M8 (20, 40s, 80, old) F5 (20s, 40) (with doubling). Various simple settings. Fee code M

Tess, Nina and April are old friends reunited one hot summer weekend to celebrate Tess's fortieth birthday. With their partners in tow, a feeling of dissatisfaction and unease seizes the group. Is it too late to have children? Were they wrong to focus so much on work? The second act finds Tess and Robert resorting to the fertility industry to conceive, while Nina and Hugh become embroiled in the corrupt bureaucracy of an East European country as they try to adopt a baby.

Breaking the Code. Play. Hugh Whitemore, based on the book *Alan Turing: The Enigma* by Alan Hodges
M7 (17, 20s, 40s, 60s) F2 (20s-50s, 60s). An open space. Fee code M

This compassionate play is the story of Alan Turing, who broke the code in two ways: he cracked the German Enigma code during World War II (for which he was decorated by Churchill) and also shattered the English code of sexual discretion with his homosexuality (for which he was arrested on a charge of gross indecency). Whitemore's play, shifting back and forth in time, seeks to find a connection between the two events.
ISBN 978 0 573 01656 1

Breaking the Silence. Play. Stephen Poliakoff
M5 (teenage, 20s-50s) F2 (30s, 40s). A railway carriage. Fee code M

Stephen Poliakoff's intriguing and moving play is inspired by his own family's experience in Russia. Father spends his time (and government money) in trying to record sound on to film. With the death of Lenin, however, the research must be abandoned and the family is forced to flee. The play follows the material and spiritual adjustments the upper-middle-class Pesiakoff family have to make when forced to live for years in a railway carriage.
ISBN 978 0 573 01617 2

The Breath of Life. Play. David Hare
F2 (60s). A flat. Fee Code M

Frances was the dutiful wife of Martin. Madeleine was his not-so-dutiful mistress of 25 years. Now Martin has moved to America with a younger woman, so the two enemies meet face to face at last, to discuss their relationships with the elusive man whom they refuse to be defined by. Together they explore the past, realizing they must learn to feel the breath of life again. This is a riveting play packed with electric tension, quick wit and raw humour.

Breath of Spring. Comedy. Peter Coke
M3 (young, middle-age, elderly) F5 (20s, middle-age). A living-room. Fee code M

Dame Beatrice houses a collection of middle-aged 'guests', plus Lily her maid. To repay Dame Beatrice for giving her a job despite her criminal past, Lily presents her with a mink stole filched from the next flat. The Brigadier deploys his 'troops' to return the fur. The whole campaign is so invigorating that they decide to retain this excitement in their lives by pinching furs and giving the proceeds to charities.
ISBN 978 0 573 01053 8

> ◆ **A bullet mark next to a title indicates that it is new to this edition of the Guide.**

A

Breathing Corpses. Play. Laura Wade
M4 (20s, 30, 45) F3 (19, 35, 46).Various simple sets. Fee Code L

Amy, a hotel chambermaid, has just found a dead body in the room she is cleaning – for the second time. Jim, the manager of a self-storage facility, has also discovered a dead body. Then there is Kate, a fiercely dedicated professional who comes across a dead body while walking her boyfriend's dog in the park. The theme of mortality casts a long shadow across this tense play as the storyline unfolds backwards and the audience need to piece together the clues.

Breezeblock Park. Play. Willy Russell
M5 (young, middle-age) F4 (young, middle-age). Two split-level sets: living-room and kitchen. Fee code M

Three married couples, 'superior' council-house dwellers, regard themselves as a close-knit family, a team, despite their generally concealed jealousies. When one of their daughters, Sandra, announces she is pregnant and intends to live unmarried with her student lover, Tim, the news explodes like an atom bomb. Tim himself is unhappy about the arrangement and tries to make Sandra realize she now has responsibilities, but she walks out on them all.
ISBN 978 0 573 11051 1

Brideshead Revisited. Play. Evelyn Waugh, adapted for the stage by Roger Parsley
M14 (late teens, 20s, middle-age) F8 (late teens, middle-age, elderly). M4 F3 with doubling. Characters age over 20 years. Various simple settings. Fee code M

This portrait of the interweaving relationships and fortunes of a desperately charming, if eccentric, aristocratic family and their influences upon Charles Ryder has been faithfully adapted for the stage, preserving all the sharp wit and candid social commentary of Waugh's narrative. Period 1943, and in flashback to the 1920s.
ISBN 978 0 573 01730 8

Brief Lives. John Aubrey. Adapted for the stage by Patrick Garland
M1 (71), M and F voices only. A Jacobean chamber. Fee code M

John Aubrey (1626-97) has come to be recognized as England's first serious biographer. Patrick Garland's adaptation of Aubrey's writings represents a day in the latter part of Aubrey's life. 'It is as if one is paying a visit to the house of an old man, who makes up for the absence of friends by bringing to life reminiscences of people, remembering them and telling stories about them.'
ISBN 978 0 573 04022 1

Brighton Beach Memoirs. Play. Neil Simon
M3 (teenage, 40) F4 (teenage, 30s, 40s). Various interior and exterior settings. Fee code M

This portrait of the writer as a Brooklyn teenager in 1937, living with his family in crowded, lower-middle-class circumstances, was first presented in London at the National Theatre in 1986. Eugene (the young Neil Simon) is the narrator and central character. The play's scenes consist of a few days in the life of a struggling Jewish household, of whom two have heart disease, one has asthma and two at least temporarily lose jobs needed to keep the straitened family afloat. It is a deeply appealing play that deftly mixes drama with comedy. (**Slightly restricted**)
ISBN 978 0 573 61941 0

Brimstone and Treacle. Play. Dennis Potter
M2 (young, middle-age) F2 (young, middle-age). A living-room. Fee code M

A clever and highly controversial play about the intrusion of a slick, satanic young man into the lives of a humdrum couple whose only deviation from the appalling norm to which they steadfastly adhere is that they have an attractive only daughter, reduced to a vegetable after a car accident. 'Dennis Potter is a mass of contradictions as a writer and in *Brimstone and Treacle* ... we see all his paradoxical drives coming fruitfully together.' *Guardian*
ISBN 978 0 573 01626 4

Britannicus. Play. Racine. A new version by Robert David Macdonald
M3 F3. Extras. A room. Fee code M

Broadway Bound. Play. Neil Simon
M4 (20s, 50, 75) F2 (50s). 2M 1F, voices only. Split set representing a house. Fee code M

Forming the third part of the famous Neil Simon autobiographical trilogy, this charming play about youthful ambition and parental regret is set in late 1940s Brooklyn. While their parents go through various conflicts which will ultimately end in divorce, Eugene and his brother Stanley struggle to become professional comedy writers. When a sketch based on their family life gets a radio broadcast it upsets the family but Eugene and Stan are now Broadway bound. (**Slightly restricted**)
ISBN 978 0 573 69053 2

Building Blocks. Play. Bob Larbey
M5 (young, 30s, 40s-50s) F1 (30s). A garden. Fee code M

Jim and Mary Baxter are in the middle of one of life's major traumas – they are having an extension built on to their house. A great deal of their time is taken up with negotiating with the builder, the charming but evasive David. By turns hilarious and touching, this well-observed comedy will bring smiles and groans of recognition to all those who have ever been involved in this situation – and a few rueful warnings to those who have not!
ISBN 0 573 11086 7

♦ **The Bullet**. Play. Joe Penhall
M1. Fee Code L

Two lovers return from a sun-kissed life in the Far East to a suburban London family in crisis. In a wry exploration of personal politics and family values, Penhall exposes the shifting loyalties and power struggles that startlingly follow.

Bums on Seats. Comedy. Michael Snelgrove
M6 (20s, 40s-60s, any age) F10 (20s-40s, any age) can be played by M3 F6 with doubling. Extras. A stage, an auditorium. Fee code L

In a tatty provincial theatre, a new play, *Fecund*, is being staged. *Bums on Seats* introduces us to everyone involved in the production: in a series of hilarious scenes, linked by a chorus of usherettes, we meet the stage manager, the leading actors, the lecherous, unscrupulous author, and others. In the second act, set in the auditorium, attention focuses on the audience, an equally mixed and unharmonious group.
ISBN 978 0 573 01756 8

Buried Alive. Play. Philip Osment
M5 (15, middle age, elderly) F4 (20s (1 black), middle age, elderly). Various simple settings.
Fee code M

Photo-journalist Stewart, who has won awards for his unflinching portrayals of Third World
conditions, has turned his back on his career and sought refuge in his Suffolk house, accompanied
by his young half-Brazilian son whom he hardly knows. Ammy, a young black reporter, is
sent to uncover his story and Stewart has at last to face up to his past. This fine, moving and
desperate story unfolds in two time zones – the 1970s and the present.

The Business of Murder. Play. Richard Harris
M2 (40s) F1 (20s). A first-floor flat. Fee code M

A psychological thriller on the theme of revenge centres on the interlocking triangular
relationship between Dee, a successful TV playwright, Hallett, a detective superintendent and
Stone, 'a humourless, rather prissy man', *The Business of Murder* had a very successful West
End run. 'How refreshing to welcome that rarity of the West End: a well-written, skilfully
crafted tale of mystery and suspense that pays dividends from start to finish.' *Sunday Express*
ISBN 978 0 573 11017 7

A Busy Day. Play. Fanny Burney, adapted Alan Coveney
M7 F7. Various settings. Fee code M

London, 1800. In the course of just one busy day we are tumbled gleefully into a world of
frustrated love, mistaken identity, snobbery and downright vulgar bad manners. Actor and
director Alan Coveney has streamlined and clarified the original, somewhat repetitive and
over-written script into a fast-moving, side-splittingly funny example of English theatrical
comedy. ' … constantly engaging … sharply observant of snobbery and the English class
system … ' *Daily Telegraph*

Butley. Play. Simon Gray
M4 (young, 20s, 30s) F3 (young, 30s, 40s). A university lecturer's study. Fee code M

This play concerns a university lecturer, Ben Butley, who shares his office and his flat with a
former star pupil, Joey, now also a teacher. On the day when the play takes place Butley faces
both the ultimate breakdown of his marriage and of his intense friendship with Joey. Butley's
painful discoveries are made against a background of petty university politics and unease about
student dissent. He greets them with a blistering torrent of repartee and rhetoric.

Butterflies Are Free. Comedy. Leonard Gershe
M2 (young, 20s) F2 (19, middle-age). A one-room apartment. Fee code M for play, code B
for music

Don, a young bachelor in his first apartment, is escaping from an overprotective mother; his
next-door neighbour is an actress who offers true friendship. We are well in to the play when
we discover, with the actress, that Don is blind. Mother does not like the girl and succeeds in
breaking up the match, but then realizes how demoralized her son is. Eventually the neighbour
returns and the young people can together face up to life.
ISBN 978 0 573 60644 1

◆ **Café Brosse.** Comedy. Jean McConnell
M3 (30-40s) F3 (20s, 30 40s, elderly) 2M or F. A café. Fee code L

George and Seraphine run a café in a small French town. Seraphine is fed up with the drudgery of her daily life, George seeks solace with his mistress, Yvette, but she too is becoming disgruntled. George's friend Aramis suggests that the two women should swap lives, but things don't work out. Seraphine returns home and she and Yvette agree that they were both better off where they were. As Aramis says, maybe George is the problem, but who should take his place ...?
ISBN 978 0 573 11542 4

◆ **Calendar Girls**. Comedy. Tim Firth. Available until 31st August 2013 only
M4 (middle-aged, young) F10 (30s-elderly). Composite set. Fee per performance £100 (to include a donation to Leukaemia Research)

When Annie's husband dies of leukaemia, she and best friend Chris resolve to raise money for a settee for the hospital's relatives' room. They persuade fellow W.I. members to pose nude with them for an "alternative" calendar. News of their charitable venture spreads - the calendar is a success - but Chris and Annie's friendship is put to the test. Based on a true story, the play has been seen world-wide and filmed.
ISBN 978 0 573 11067 2

Calico. Play. Michael Hastings
M4 (20s, 35, 46) F3 (21, 33, 44). Various simple settings. Fee code M

Paris, 1928. Samuel Beckett is introduced to the notorious novelist James Joyce and his family and soon becomes like a new son in the household. He finds himself drawn to Joyce's gifted but troubled daughter Lucia … What does *Calico* stand for? Calico is the coarse cotton wrapping of the mattress you lie on. It can also be the body restraints when you are sectioned off to an asylum. This is a carefully researched, strange love story.

California Suite. Comedy. Neil Simon
M2 (40s) plus M3. F2 (30s, 40s) plus F3. A hotel suite. Fee code M

This four-part play is Neil Simon at his best. In *Chicago* two couples go on vacation together, but wind up miserable and hating each other. *London* concernsa British star who returns from the Academy Awards ceremony without an Oscar. *Philadelphia* is about a wife who arrives at the hotel suite before her husband can get rid of the drunken hooker in his bed. In *New York* a magazine writer is visited by her ex-husband. (**Slightly restricted**)
ISBN 978 0 573 60664 9

Camille. Play. Pam Gems
M13 F6, a boy, M1(voice only), a pianist. Extras. Interior and exterior settings. Fee code M

Beautiful Marguerite Gautier, seduced at the age of fifteen by her Marquis employer, decides on a courtesan life. She meets Armand Duval, son of the Marquis, and the two fall desperately in love. Aware that she is in the initial stages of tuberculosis, Armand persuades her to settle in the country with him, but Marguerite is threatened by the Marquis and forced to return to Paris, dying and reviled by Armand. Period 1840s Paris
ISBN 978 0 573 01634 9

Camino Real. Play. Tennessee Williams
M21 F7. Extras. A plaza in a walled city. Fee code M

Aptly described both as an 'expressionist phantasmagoria' and 'an apocalyptic vision of the contemporary world', the play is set in a walled town in a police state from which various characters try to escape. Among the fictional people are famous literary and historical characters such as Don Quixote, Marguerite Gautier, Casanova and the mythical American Kilroy who 'was here'; they converse with one another in cryptic and soulful conversation in the midst of various extraordinary events happening around them.

Can You Hear Me at the Back? Play. Brian Clark
M3 (17, 40s) F2 (30s, 40s). A living-room, other small sets. Fee code M

Philip Turner, chief architect of Feltonly New Town, is disillusioned in the realization of what he has destroyed in planning and developing the town's sterile, inhuman tower and office blocks. He decides to plan nothing at all, to opt for spontaneity even in his private life. Margery, wife of his old friend, is willing to become his mistress, but Philip demurs. 'Can't you see you are just as ruthlessly planning spontaneity?' says his wife.

Can't Pay? Won't Pay! Farce. Dario Fo. Translated by Lino Pertile, adapted by Bill Colvill and Robert Walker
M6 F2 or M3 F2, with doubling. A living-room and kitchen area. Fee code M

This hilarious and critically acclaimed political farce centres on direct action by housewives against inflationary supermarket prices and struggles with their Communist trade unionist husbands who face unemployment and political crisis. 'It is rare to find a farce original enough to ... find jokes in rising prices and quips in unpaid bills and redundancy notices. This Dario Fo does with ease ... ' *Daily Telegraph*

Candleford. Play. Keith Dewhurst, from the book by Flora Thompson
M12 F6, with doubling. An open stage. Fee code M. (In a volume with *Lark Rise*)

A sequel to *Lark Rise*, *Candleford* is also performed with audience and players freely mingling, re-enacting a meeting of the local hunt in mid-winter. It concentrates on events in the Oxfordshire village where Flora Thompson worked in the post office-cum-blacksmith, includes music and song, and ends with a flash forward to her own unhappy married life, after which Company and audience perform the Grand Circle Dance. Period 1880s
ISBN 978 0 573 10011 6

Canterbury Tales. Chaucer made modern by Phil Woods. Music by Chris Barnes
Large cast may be played by M7 F5. An open space. The music is available on hire from Samuel French Ltd. Fee code M (play), B (music)

Phil Woods has updated Chaucer to recreate for a modern audience the spectacle, humour and bawdiness of the fourteenth-century original. Set in the present the tales are told in the form of an annual 'Geoffrey Chaucer Canterbury Tales-telling Competition', with the audience invited on stage between tales. 'Colourful, boozy, good-spirited, compelling entertainment.' *Stage and Television Today*

♦ **A bullet mark next to a title indicates that it is new to this edition of the Guide.**

A

Caramba's Revenge. Play. William Norfolk
M1 (late 30s) F6 (20, late 60s, 70s). A living-room. Fee code L

A highly entertaining and ingenious black comedy. Four elderly ladies have been sharing their lives in Violet's rented house, pooling their pension books and sharing chores. After a mugging Violet dies, but Marge, Lottie and Doris omit to tell the authorities and leave Violet's body peacefully in the cemetery. However, Violet's granddaughter, Ronnie, arrives from Australia in search of her relative ...
ISBN 978 0 573 01771 1

Caravan. Play. Helen Blakeman
M2 (20, 50) F3 (15, 19, 45) A caravan park. Fee code M. 978 0 573 01770 4

Cards on the Table. Play. Dramatized by Leslie Darbon from the novel by Agatha Christie
M7 (30s-50s) F7 (20s, 30s, middle-age, 63) or M5 F7, with doubling. Two drawing-rooms, a surgery, a patio, a flat. Fee code M

A dramatization, first presented at London's Vaudeville Theatre starring Gordon Jackson and Margaret Courtenay, of a classic Agatha Christie tale of murder and mystery, involving a wealthy collector, four murderers and two crime specialists, Superintendent Battle of the Yard and Mrs Oliver the novelist.
ISBN 978 0 573 11540 0

The Caretaker. Play. Harold Pinter
M3 (25, 35, old). A shabby room. Fee code M

Into his derelict household shrine Aston brings Davies, a tramp – but a tramp with pretensions, even if to the world he may be a pathetic old creature. All that is left of his past now is the existence in Sidcup of some papers, papers that will prove exactly who he is and enable him to start again. Aston, too, has his dreams: he has always been good with his hands and there is so much to do in the house. Aston's hopes are tied to his flash brother Mick's; he has aspirations to live in a luxurious apartment. Human nature is a great spoiler of plans, however ...
ISBN 978 0 573 04002 3

Carpe Jugulum. Terry Pratchett. Adapted for the stage by Stephen Briggs
M21 F15. Extras. Various simple settings. Fee code M

The de Magpyrs are the sort of vampires that would have Count Dracula spinning in his grave: modern, forward-looking and no longer afraid of holy water, garlic, religious symbols or, indeed, of anything else. This makes them very, very dangerous. Luckily for the Discworld, the three Lancre witches are on hand – and the battle is on!
ISBN 978 0 573 01776 6

Cash on Delivery. Farce. Michael Cooney
M6 F4. A living-room. Fee code M

Michael Cooney's riotous farce has all the ingredients for rib-tickling hilarity and offers a colourful selection of character roles. Eric Swan (aided by his Uncle George and unbeknown to his wife, Linda) has pocketed thousands of pounds through fraudulent DSS claims. When Norman Bassett (the lodger) opens the door to Mr Jenkins, the DSS Inspector, deceptive mayhem follows – as do the undertaker, bereavement counsellor, psychiatrist, Norman's fiancée, a corpse, the ominous *Ms* Cowper and a rather rebellious washing-machine!
ISBN 978 0 573 01752 0

Cat Among the Pigeons. Farce. Georges Feydeau. Translated by John Mortimer
M13 F7. A drawing-room, a bedroom, an apartment. Fee code M

Feydeau's lady this time has two lovers: a ne'er-do-well who has secretly affianced himself to a baroness's daughter, and a flamboyant Spanish general who challenges anyone who comes near her. Complications arrive with an amateur composer of a bad song which he hopes the lady will sing in the theatre ... This translation was presented at Wyndham's Theatre. 'A triumph of ingenuity, gaiety, absurdity and laughter.' *Daily Telegraph.* Period early 1900s
ISBN 978 0 573 60683 0

Cat on a Hot Tin Roof. Play. Tennessee Williams
M7 (young, 60, 2 black) F3 (young, 60). 2 small girls. Extras. A bedsitting-room. Fee code M

This award-winning play is set in a Mississippi plantation house where the family celebrate Big Daddy's birthday. '... a stunning drama ... It is the quintessence of life. It is the basic truth ... The tone is gay. But the mood is sombre. For a number of old evils poison the gaiety – sins of the past, greedy hopes for the future, a desperate eagerness not to believe in the truths that surround them ...' *New York Times*

The Caucasian Chalk Circle. Play. Bertolt Brecht
Translations: W. H. Auden and James and Tania Stern
                        Alistair Beaton
                        Ralph Manheim, music by Dessau
                        Eric Bentley, music by Durrent
                        John Holstrom, music by Griffiths
                        Frank McGuinness
M38 F11 with doubling possible. Various simple settings. Fee code M (for play), code C (for music)

In the heat of civil war, a cruel town governor is murdered. His wife escapes but abandons her baby, who is harboured by a kitchen-maid, Grusha. Later the governor's widow returns and a trial is ordered with the test: which woman can drag the child out of a chalk circle? In refusing to harm the child by pulling it, Grusha is ruled to be the 'true' mother. Period 1945

Caught in the Net. Comedy. Ray Cooney
M4 (16, 40s, 80s) F3 (15, 40s). Composite setting: two living-rooms. Fee code M

The sequel to *Run For Your Wife* finds our bigamist taxi-driver, John Smith, still keeping both his families (one in Wimbledon and one in Streatham) happy and blissfully unaware of each other. However, his teenage children – one girl and one boy by each wife – have met on the Internet and are determined to see each other in person. When it dawns on John that they are about to meet, he plunges into a hell-hole of his own making in order to keep them apart.
ISBN 978 0 573 01975 3

Caught on the Hop. Comedy. Derek Benfield. *Revised version*
M4 (30s, middle-age) F4 (20s, 37, middle-age). A sitting-room and patio. Fee code L
ISBN 978 0 573 11066 5

♦ **A bullet mark next to a title indicates that it is new to this edition of the Guide.**

Cause Célèbre. Play. Terence Rattigan
M15 (young, 18, middle-age, elderly) F5 (40, middle-age). 1 boy (9). Composite setting. Fee code M

When Alma Rattenbury, attractive wife of an elderly man, engages the handsome but uncouth Wood as odd-job boy it has tragic consequences, culminating in murder. The story follows the course of the trial, and also the lasting effect on a woman member of the jury. The play, first presented in London at Her Majesty's Theatre, was partly inspired by the facts of a well-known case. Period 1934-5
ISBN 978 0 573 11059 7

Celebration. Comedy. Keith Waterhouse and Willis Hall
M7 (19, 20s, 40s, middle-age) F7 (19, 20s, middle-age). A large room above a pub. Fee code M. If performed separately *The Wedding* and *The Funeral* are each fee code F

The Wedding and *The Funeral* make up the two parts of this comedy in which we are introduced to the same family, first making preparations for a wedding and subsequently, six months later, returning from the funeral of their Uncle Arthur, a lovable personality who provides the link between the two plays.
ISBN 978 0 573 11251 5

The Cemetery Club. Play. Ivan Menchell
M1 (late 50s-early 60s) F4 (late 50s- early 60s). A living-room, a cemetery. Fee code M

Ida, Lucille and Doris are part of a club – the cemetery club. Every month they meet at Ida's New York house for tea, then trundle off to the cemetery to remember the good times and gossip with their late husbands. Sam, a butcher, meets the widows at the cemetery while he is visiting his wife's grave and changes their lives forever. This touching play about three superannuated, feuding Jewish women is funny, wise and gloriously witty.

Charley's Aunt. Farce. Brandon Thomas
M6 (20s, 40s, 51) F4 (young, middle-age). Two interiors, one exterior. No fee
ISBN 978 0 573 01067 5

Chase Me Up Farndale Avenue, S'Il Vous Plaît! Comedy. David McGillivray and Walter Zerlin Jnr
M1 F4 (late 20s, 40s-50s). Two adjoining rooms. Fee code K

Le farce français est arrivée! Bubbling comme une glasse de champagne, ces femmes formidables and leur chef d'étage, Gordon, fizz leur way avec panache entre un plot unintelligible, un plethora de portes, et un grand range de characteurs. Oo-la-la, le show-stopping moment de Thelma ... mais pour dire quelque chose else would spoilé le surprise – ah quelle surprise! – Vive les dames de Farndale Avenue Housing Estate Townswomen's Guild Dramatic Society!
ISBN 978 0 573 01732 2

Chasing the Moment. Play. Jack Shepherd
M4 (young, 1 black, middle-age, old) F2 (young, 1 black). A basement club. Fee code M

This could be the last gig for Les Padmore and his jazz band. Wes, the founder of the club, is on life-support and there are rifts between the players. Les looks back to a golden age of jazz and is suspicious of the younger, more progressive band members, who are all are seeking a balance to the chaos of their lives. This is a gritty play, full of wry philosophy.

Checkmate. Play. Leslie Sands
M3 (40s, middle-age) F2 (20s, 40s). 1F voice only. 1 extra. A living-room. Fee code M

Subtitled *A Play on Murder*, this is a witty and theatrical thriller. The career of famous TV actor Peter Conway is in the doldrums, his financial state is parlous, he has a drink problem and his long-suffering wife Stella has had enough. Secretly, he has been having an affair with Lori, an American actress, and Stella's death brings the police to his up-market London home. It looks an open and shut case but is what we see real or unreal?
ISBN 978 0 573 69481 3

The Cherry Orchard. Play. Anton Chekhov
M9 (young, 20s, middle-age, 87) F5 (17, middle-age). Extras. A nursery, a drawing-room, open fields. Fee code M

Versions:
Samuel Adamson.. ISBN 978 0 573 01999 9
      Michael Frayn
      David Lan
      David Mamet

♦ **The Cherry Orchard.** Play. Anton Chekhov. New version by Mike Poulton
M9 F5. Extras. A nursery, a drawing-room, open fields. Fee code M. Period 1903

For Madame Ranevskaya, her cherry orchard is more than just land; it is her childhood, her memories and her life. Returning for the first time since her young son drowned there, she must come to terms with the fact that to pay off debts, the cherry orchard must be sold. This touching and often hilarious play exercises the perfect balance of comedy and tragedy, through the characters, relationships and observations of society.
ISBN 978 0 573 11069 6

The Cherry Orchard is the story of a mortgage, with the grounds and beautiful trees of the proud landowners going for sale at a public auctio to pay off their debts to the boorish son of a peasant who has risen in the world. Mme Ranevskaya's family departs to take up their lives anew, leaving the old and forgotten Firs to die alone as the woodsmen's axes thud ironically against the cherished trees.

♦ **Cheshire Cats**. A play. Gail Young
M1-3, F5-7. Extras. Various simple settings. Fee Code L

Grown women, aching feet, heaving bosoms! Follow the Cheshire Cats as they speedwalk their way to fundraising success in the London Moonwalk. A cross between a girls' night out and a real mission to support a cause , with plenty of laughs and a few tears along the way. Flexible casting - may be performed by a cast of five women and one man or a larger ensemble. ". . . moving, emotional, poignant and best of all it makes you laugh. . ." *Chester Chronicle*.
ISBN 978 0 573 11081 8

♦ **A bullet mark next to a title indicates that it is new to this edition of the Guide.**

Children of a Lesser God. Play. Mark Medoff
M3 (20s, 30s-40s) F4 (late teens, mid-20s, 30-40s). Various simple interior and exterior settings.
Fee code M

James joins a school for the deaf to teach lip-reading and meets the spirited Sarah, totally deaf
from birth and estranged from the world of hearing and from those who would compromise
to enter it. James tries to help Sarah, but gradually the two fall in love and marry. Discord
develops as Sarah militates for the rights of the deaf, but love and compassion hold the hope
of reconciliation.

Children's Day. Play. Keith Waterhouse and Willis Hall
M3 (30s, 40s) F4 (19, youngish, 30s). A kitchen. Fee code M

A hectic children's birthday party provides a noisy background to a series of domestic crises.
Robin has left Emma and Emma has become friendly with her solicitor, Tom; both Tom and
Robin arrive for the celebrations. The mishaps of the party spill over into the kitchen situation,
the behaviour of the young visitors affecting the adults. By the end of the party however, things
look a little brighter for Robin and Emma.
ISBN 978 0 573 01561 9

A Child's Christmas in Wales. Christmas musical. Jeremy Brooks and Adrian Mitchell. Based
on the poem by Dylan Thomas
M15 F7. Extras. Various simple settings. Fee code M

This enchanting play with music uses a variety of carols and well-known Welsh songs to
conjure up the pure magic of Christmas for the enjoyment of an audience of all ages. The main
course of events takes place on Christmas Eve itself, when the Thomas family are host to their
relatives. Apart from a potentially major hiccup, when the turkey catches fire, the traditional
Yuletide celebrations are enjoyed by all.

Chinchilla. Play. Robert David MacDonald
M11 F5. Simple settings. Fee code M

Subtitled *Figures in a Classical Landscape with Ruins*, this takes us into the world of the Ballet
Russe. On holiday in Venice, the impresario, Chinchilla, is longing for both love and money
amid the backstage drama of dancers, choreographers, designers and hangers-on. Autocratic,
splendid and world-weary, he is the creator and destroyer of what happens on his stage and
to his company. The play is divided into scenes marked 'Present' (taking place on a single
afternoon in June 1914) 'Past' and 'Future'.

The Choice. Play. Claire Luckham
M2 (30, 50s) F3 (30s, late 40s). A space. Fee code M

The choice is whether or not to abort a foetus after an amniocentesis test reveals that the unborn
child has a chromosome deficiency. Sal, a journalist in her thirties, is the mother, and she must
make the most difficult decision of her life in the midst of the conflicting opinions of those
around her. Sally's story is framed within Claire Luckham's own personal tale – she grew up
with a handicapped brother.

A

A Chorus of Disapproval. Play. Alan Ayckbourn
M7 (young, 30s-late 50s) F6 (young, 30s-50s). Extras. Various simple settings. Fee code M

Alan Ayckbourn skilfully draws parallels between John Gay's *The Beggar's Opera* and the day-to-day activities of the amateur dramatic society who are performing it, showing how painfully embarrassed are the British in the face of emotion and keeping us laughing in happy recognition. *A Chorus of Disapproval* played very successfully at the National Theatre in 1985. '... symmetrically shaped, psychologically acute and painfully, heartbreakingly funny ...' *Guardian*
ISBN 978 0 573 01620 2

A Christmas Carol. Play. Adapted by John Mortimer from the story by Charles Dickens
Large mixed cast, doubling possible. Various simple settings. Fee code M

Charles Dickens' famous tale of Ebenezer Scrooge's transformation from embittered skinflint to generous benefactor has been dramatized by John Mortimer with typical flair and wit in this definitive adaptation, first performed by the Royal Shakespeare Company. Retaining Dickens' own ironic point of view through the use of a Chorus, Mortimer has created a panoramic view of Victorian London with all the much-loved characters in place. There is plenty of scope for imaginative doubling, and the staging requirements are flexible.
ISBN 978 0 573 01733 9

A Christmas Carol. Christmas Play. Adapted by Shaun Sutton from the story by Charles Dickens.
M24 F15. Three interiors, one exterior. Fee code K

This adaptation follows its well-loved original in tracing Scrooge's conversion from miserliness to benevolence. We first see him in the counting house berating his unfortunate clerk Bob Cratchit and then receiving the visitations of the Spirits of Past, Present and Future. He learns to feel compassion for Tiny Tim and remorse for his avarice. Some scenes are introduced that elaborate a Christmas play into a simple form of pantomime. Period early Victorian
ISBN 978 0 573 01070 5

♦ **Christmas Crackers.** Play. John Godber
M10 (30s, 40s, 50s, 60s) F5 (20s, 40s), may be played by M3 F2. Simple settings. Fee code M

It's Christmas and A & E security guard Keith sees a cross-section of patients come and go. Recently widowed nurse Kath decides to take a younger nurse, Hollie, with her on a festive getaway. Keith fantasizes about reinventing himself and meeting them in Prague, sweeping Kath off her feet, but he is brought swiftly back to the reality that Kath doesn't know who he is other than as "Scary Keith".
"A festive fairy-tale for grown ups ... very funny." *The Times*

Cider with Rosie. Laurie Lee. Adapted for the stage by James Roose-Evans
24 roles, may be played by M5 F4. Various simple settings. Fee code M

Poet Laurie Lee was born in 1914 in a small Cotswold village and grew up during a time of change when the rural traditions of past centuries were being swept aside in the path of twentieth-century progress. His autobiography *Cider with Rosie*, a poetic evocation of his childhood, has become a modern classic both in the United Kingdom and in America and is here imaginatively adapted for the stage by James Roose-Evans.
ISBN 978 0 573 01735 3

A

◆ **The City.** Play. Martin Crimp
M1 (40s) F2 (30s, 40s). Various simple settings. Fee code M

Clair wants to be kissed – but not now – and certainly not by her husband. Chris wants to celebrate his new job by driving into the oncoming traffic. Jenny arrives to complain about the screaming children – but the garden's empty, and the key to the playroom's disappeared. Just what strange game is being played here? Three characters fight to make sense of a surreal and collapsing world. The play opened at the Royal Court Theatre, London, in April 2008.

Cleo, Camping, Emmanuelle and Dick. Comedy. Terry Johnson
M3 F3 A caravan. Fee code M

Filming's not as glamorous as it's cracked up to be. It's a miserable business if your caravan leaks, your co-star's a manic depressive, and those younger women aren't so young any more. Carrying on in the great British comedy tradition, this play takes some familiar faces and gets a bit familiar with them. It premièred at the National Theatre, London, in 1998 starring Geoffrey Hutchings as Sid, Adam Godley as Kenneth and Samantha Spiro as Barbara and was produced on TV under the title *Cor, Blimey!*. Period 1960s

Clocks and Whistles. Play. Samuel Adamson
M3 (25, late 40s-early 50s) F2 (26, late 30s). Various simple settings. Fee code M

Henry watches. He watches Anne – who is helped or hindered by the older man in her life, the enigmatic Alec – as she tries to make it as an actor. And he watches Trevor, who hangs out in seedy clubs and his flat in Paddington, as he tries to make it as a poet. As the lives of the three interlock, they drift into a world of sexual and emotional confusion.

Close the Coalhouse Door. Musical documentary. Alan Plater. From the stories by Sid Chaplin. Songs by Alex Glasgow
M7 F1. Various simple settings. Fee code M

A golden wedding party of an old pitman and his wife forms a springboard into reminiscence and reflection about the past. The historical material falls into a three-act pattern: nineteenth-century oppression as the Beginning, between-the-wars chaos as the Middle with post-Nationalization non-Utopia the ambivalent End. Originally written for the Newcastle Playhouse, the play is an outstanding documentary musical. This new edition contains the version memorably presented at Newcastle's Live Theatre in 1994.

Closer. Play. Patrick Marber
M2 (late 20s, 35) F2 (20, 30s). Various simple settings. Fee code M

This multi-award winning play of sexual passion and betrayal, which premièred at the Royal National Theatre in 1997, charts its characters' actions through nearly four years. Alice, a young stripper, falls in love with suburban journalist Dan. Then Dan meets Anna, a photographer, and brings her together with Larry, a young consultant dermatologist, via the Internet, before leaving Alice for Anna. NB. The play contains explicit language.

◆ **A bullet mark next to a title indicates that it is new to this edition of the Guide.**

Clothes for a Summer Hotel. Ghost Play. Tennessee Williams
M9-13 F7–14, doubling possible. An asylum. Fee code M

The play opens in an asylum where Zelda Fitzgerald is being treated for mental disorder. Her husband, Scott, visits her, and this leads to a series of flashbacks in which details of their lives, in particular those concerning Zelda's attempts to achieve self-expression, are enacted.

Cloud Nine. Play. Caryl Churchill
M4 F3. A veranda, a hut interior. Fee code M

Written for Joint Stock, this theatre company's workshop for the play was 'sexual politics', thus giving Caryl Churchill the idea for her parallel between colonial and sexual oppression. Act I takes place in Victorian Africa, whilst Act II is set in modern London. Much interplay is made of gender and colour: for example, Clive, the white settler, has a black servant, Joshua, who is played by a white because he wants to be what the whites want him to be. Hilarious and thought-provoking.
ISBN 978 0 573 01668 4

The Coast of Utopia. A trilogy. Tom Stoppard

This epic but intimate drama of romantics and revolutionaries in an age of emperors, comprises three sequential but self-contained plays. Set in the tumultuous years between 1833 and 1866 in Russia and Europe, the trilogy spans the lives of a group of friends who come of age under the Tsarist autocracy of Nicholas I. It premiered at the Olivier auditorium of the National Theatre in 2002. The three plays may be performed separately and for details please see the individual entries:
Voyage, Shipwreck and *Salvage*.

The Cocktail Hour. Comedy. A. R. Gurney
M2 (40s, 70s) F2 (40s, 60s). A living-room. Fee code M

With a mixture of gentle comic poignancy and dramatic tension, one of America's leading contemporary playwrights here examines the problems which arise when John, a leading playwright, returns home to ask his parents' permission to produce his latest work, a play about his family. *The Cocktail Hour* had a long and successful run in New York and successful tours in both the UK and Australia.
ISBN 978 0 573 01736 0

Cold Comfort Farm. Play. Paul Doust, adapted from the novel by Stella Gibbons
M9 (20s, middle-age) F6 (20s, middle-age, 60), doubling possible. Extras. A kitchen, an attic room, a garden. Fee code M

Orphan Flora Poste, heroine of Gibbons's tongue-in-cheek classic novel, likes everything to be tidy and comfortable so when she goes to live with her eccentric relatives at Cold Comfort Farm she tries to alter her surroundings and encourage others to greater things. But this proves difficult ... Period 1930s. 'Paul Doust's new adaptation embraces the book with a stylistic exuberance.' *Financial Times*
ISBN 978 0 573 01737 7

♦ **A bullet mark next to a title indicates that it is new to this edition of the Guide.**

Colder Than Here. Play. Laura Wade
M1 (57) F3 (27, 29, 57). Burial grounds, a living-room, a cemetery. Fee code L

Nobody can ignore the fact that Myra is dying, but in the meantime life goes on. There are boilers to be fixed, cats to be fed and the perfect funeral to be planned. As a mother researches burial spots and biodegradable coffins, her family are finally forced to communicate with her, and each other, as they face up to an unpredictable future. Laura Wade's beautifully poised family drama was first performed at the Soho Theatre, London, in 2005.

The Collector. Play. Mark Healy, from the novel by John Fowles
M1 (20s) F1 (19). A cellar, a lounge, a dining room. Fee Code L

Ever since he first saw her, Frederick Clegg has been obsessed with Miranda Grey. The repressed, introverted butterfly collector admires the beautiful, privileged art student from afar until he wins the Lottery and buys a remote country house, planning to bring her there as his "guest". Having abducted and imprisoned her in the cellar he soon finds reality is far from his fantasy and their tense, claustrophobic relationship leads to a devastating climax.
ISBN 978 0 573 11603 5

Come As You Are. Four Playlets. John Mortimer
M2 F2 or M8 F7. A bedroom, a living-room, a basement apartment, a flat. Fee code M

The characters in all four plays are in their twenties to forties and can either be played by the same four artists or by separate casts. The first, *Mill Hill*, calls for 2 Men and 1 Woman, the remainder, *Bermondsey*, *Gloucester Road* and *Marble Arch*, call for 2 Men and 2 Women each. These four plays are linked by their themes of sexual entanglements and by their central or suburban London settings.
ISBN 978 0 573 01052 1

Come Back for Light Refreshments After the Service. Play. Julie Day
M1 (any age) F5 (19, mid 30s, 40s, early 70s) Various simple interior and exterior settings. Fee code G

Beth is in the kitchen preparing food for her father's wake – real sandwiches, cakes, etc., that the audience are invited to partake of as they become the visiting mourners. After nursing her father for five years before he died, she plans to sell the house and go back-packing despite the disapproval of others. This play about relationships and understanding garnered rave reviews and an Edinburgh Fringe Award for excellence.
ISBN 978 0 573 60130 9

Come Back to the 5 & Dime, Jimmy Dean, Jimmy Dean. Comedy-drama. Ed Graczyck
M1 (17) F8 (17, 30s, middle-age). A five-and-dime store in Texas. Fee code M

In a small-town dime store in West Texas, the Disciples of James Dean, now middle-aged, gather for their tentieth reunion. The ladies' reminiscences mingle with flash-backs to their youth; then the arrival of a momentarily unrecognized woman sets off a series of upsetting and revelatory confrontations. The action takes place in 1975 and, in recall, 1955.
ISBN 0 573 60764 6

Come Blow Your Horn. Comedy. Neil Simon
M3 (21, 33, 60) F4 (20s-50s). A bachelor apartment. Fee code M

Harry Baker should be a happy man, but his sons are a daily trial. Alan is a playboy with a penchant for beautiful girls and now Buddy, formerly so timid and obedient, has joined his brother in dissipation, unsuccessfully experimenting with the fair sex while his parents become more mystified and irate. Alan suddenly redeems himself by settling down, and Buddy, having learned how to handle women, determines to take over Alan's role as the family playboy. **(Slightly restricted)**
ISBN 978 0 573 60713 4

Come On, Jeeves. Farcical comedy. P. G. Wodehouse and Guy Bolton
M5 F4. A living-room. Fee code L

Comedians. Play. Trevor Griffiths
M11 (20 -50s, middle age). A classroom. Fee code M

The setting is a schoolroom near Manchester where an evening class of budding comics congregate for a final briefing from their tutor before facing an agent's man from London. Telling jokes for money offers an escape from the building site or the milk round. But the humour is a deadly serious business that also involves anger, pain and truth. How and why are laughter engineered? What dark secrets within us trigger mirthful responses to shaped remarks about sex, ethnic groups and physical disabilities?

The Comedy of Terrors! Play. John Goodrum
M1(30s) F1(30s). A theatre stage. Fee code L

Jo Smith arrives for an audition with director Vyvian Jones, but it transpires that she has been invited by Beverley, Vyvian's twin brother, who wants her to impersonate her own twin sister Fiona to scotch the rumour that Beverley has slept with Fiona. Jo reluctantly agrees, but then the real Fiona arrives … Only the intervention of a policeman, Janet Jones (the Joneses' identical younger brother) can save the day. One actor and one actress play all the Joneses and Smiths respectively in this fast-moving madcap comedy of multiple mistaken identity.
ISBN 978 0 573 11060 3

Comfort and Joy. Comedy. Mike Harding
M6 (20s, 50s, elderly, 70s) F6 (late 20s-early 30s, 50s, elderly) or M5 F5 with doubling. A front room. Fee code M

It's Christmas. Relatives you hardly ever see and who are now very different from you arrive at your house for the festivities. No-one receives a present that is at all appropriate. Culinary disasters abound. Long-buried resentments rear their ugly heads as the alcohol flows and tongues are loosened. *Comfort and Joy,* Mike Harding's comedy, is painfully – but always amusingly – familiar.
ISBN 978 0 573 01772 8

♦ **A bullet mark next to a title indicates that it is new to this edition of the Guide.**

Comic Potential. Comedy. Alan Ayckbourn
M5 (20s, 40s, 50s, 80s) F5 (20s, 30s, 40s) with doubling. A TV studio and various simple hotel settings. Fee code M.

This hilarious and heartbreaking play was seen at the Lyric Theatre, London in 1999. It is set in the foreseeable future when everything has changed except human nature; a future where TV daytime soaps are performed by android actors emotionally programmed by the control room. One, JC 31333, finds herself humanized as Jacie Triplethree, complete with a sense of humour and Adam, a young scriptwriter, falls for her.
ISBN 978 0 573 11061 0

The Common Pursuit. Play. Simon Gray
M5 F1 (all young, ageing 15 years). Various interior settings. Fee code M

A very English modern play, reeking of real tragedy, real humour and real life. *The Common Pursuit* chronicles the erosion of the ambitions of a smug, eliist group of Cambridge friends. Stuart is editor of a literary magazine and the pursuit of excellence is shown to be economically a bad proposition in this world. The magazine collapses and the characters' fates vary as the play proceeds. An ironic epilogue returns to the early days in Cambridge with the young people planning their futures.
ISBN 978 0 573 01696 7

Communicating Doors. Comedy. Alan Ayckbourn
M3 (30s-70) F3 (25-45). A hotel suite. Fee code M

An ingenious time-warp comedy which begins in the year 2014 when a prostitute, Poopay, is summoned to a deluxe London hotel suite by an infirm elderly businessman to witness a document detailing the murder of his two wives by his psychopathic business associate. Poopay finds herself in the year 1994 confronting Ruella, the second wife, and when Ruella finds herself in 1974 with the first wife she decides to rewrite the future!
ISBN 978 0 573 01740 7

Compact Failure. Play. Jennifer Farmer.
M1 (45) F6 (20s, 56), 1M or F. Simple settings. Fee Code K

Compact Failure explores the relationships between three women prisoners: Chelle, Ruthie and Maya. Old-timer Chelle is lonely. Maya is missing her children. Ruthie is a breath of fresh air for Chelle who thought she was done with friendship. The sharp and richly textured narrative is about the hierarchy of prison life, its impact on families and visitors, challenges of release and resettlement and, ultimately, redemption.

Confusions. Five interlinked one-act plays. Alan Ayckbourn
M3 F2 (minimum cast). A living-room, a bar, a restaurant, a marquee, a park. Fee code M

These five short plays deal riotously, but with sharply pointed undertones, with the human dilemma of loneliness; a mother unable to escape from baby talk (*Mother Figure*), a disastrous fête (*Gosforth's Fête*), an unsuccessful seduction attempt (*Drinking Companion*), a fraught dinner encounter (*Between Mouthfuls*) and the final play, *A Talk In The Park*, sums up, with five self-immolated characters on park benches.
ISBN 978 0 573 11073 3

Conjugal Rites. Play. Roger Hall
M1 (late 40s) F1 (mid 40s). A bedroom. Fee code M

A middle-aged couple, Barry and Gen, are celebrating their twenty-first anniversary – in bed. It begins amiably enough – it's a time for reflection and celebration, after all. But the rewards of middle-aged married life are doubtful, and gradually, the picture darkens as they confront the spectres of death, physical decline and adultery that surround them.

Conversations After a Burial. Play. Yasmina Reza. Translated by Christopher Hampton
M3 (40s, 65) F3 (35, 45, 64). An open space. Fee code M

From the award-winning author of *Art*, *Conversations After a Burial* explores that ineffable moment of mourning, when the newly deceased is still almost palpable, the intense pause between absence and the return to everyday existence, between loss and life. Christopher Hampton's superb translation of Yasmina Reza's savage but richly comic play uncovers love and its inevitable betrayals. It premièred at the Almeida Theatre, London, in 2000.

Cooking with Elvis. Play. Lee Hall
M2 (26, 39) F2 (14, 38). Various simple settings. Fee code M

When an amateur Elvis impersonator is paralysed in a car crash, his wife and daughter are forced to cope with the aftermath. Jill tries to replace him with cooking. Mam tries to replace him with sex. Unfortunately, they both try out their talents with the same man. Part knockabout farce, part cookery course, part philosophical investigation, this play is a provocative and outrageously funny look at disability while enjoying the three greatest pleasures in the world – sex, food and the King.

Copenhagen. Play. Michael Frayn
M2 (40s, 50s) F1 (50s). Simple setting. Fee code M

In 1941 the German physicist Werner Heisenberg made a strange trip to Copenhagen to see his Danish counterpart and old friend, Niels Bohr. Together, they had revolutionized atomic physics, but now the two men were on opposite sides in a world war. The meeting was fraught with embarrassment and ended in disaster. In *Copenhagen* Heisenberg meets Bohr and his wife Margrethe once again to look for the answers and to work out how we can ever know why we do what we do. Period 1941

Coriolanus. Play. Bertolt Brecht. Translated by Ralph Manheim
M11 F3. Extras. Numerous settings on an open stage. Fee code M

The Corn Is Green. Play. Emlyn Williams
M10 (12-16, 40s) F5 (14, 30s-middle-age). Extras. A living-room. Fee code M

Miss Moffat settles in a remote Welsh mining village and starts a school for the local boys, one of whom, Morgan Evans, shows great promise. Miss Moffat determines to do everything to help Morgan's application for a scholarship to Oxford. But Morgan rebels against help from a woman and falls prey to the flashy charms of Bessie Watty. His chances of success are almost destroyed but Miss Moffat's courageous wisdom and her affection for him win the day and Morgan wins the scholarship. Period late nineteenth century.
ISBN 978 0 573 01738 4

Corpse! Comedy thriller. Gerald Moon
M4 (middle-age) F1 (middle-age). A basement flat, an elegant flat. Fee code M

Evelyn, an out-of-work actor, engages Powell, with a shady past, to do away with his suave, sophisticated, moneyed twin. As with most 'fool-proof' plans things do not go as they should and people are not what they seem. *Corpse!* is not so much a whodunit as a whodunit to whom! 'If *The Mousetrap* is the thriller for the fifties; *Sleuth* for the sixties; *Deathtrap* for the seventies; *Corpse!* is surely the thriller for the eighties...' *Los Angeles Times*. Period 1936
ISBN 978 0 573 11014 6

Corpsing. Four one-act plays. Peter Barnes
M6 (20s-30s, elderly) F3 (20s-30s, elderly). Various simple settings. Fee code M

This collection of plays – three duologues and one three-hander – on a strong theatrical theme, may be presented individually (see the separate listings in Section B) or in one programme as a complete evening's entertainment under the title *Corpsing*. Together they encapsulate Peter Barnes' consummate skill of contrasting opposites and simultanously combining 'the absurdly tragic and the tragically absurd'.
ISBN 978 0 573 10006 2

Count Dracula. Play based on Bram Stoker's novel *Dracula*. Ted Tiller
M7 (young, 50) F2 (young, 40). Living quarters and crypt of an asylum for the insane. Fee code M

This is a new witty version of the classic story of a suave vampire whose passion is sinking his teeth into the throats of beautiful young women. There are many surprising but uncomplicated stage effects (full details are given) including secret panels, howling wolves, bats that fly over the audience, and Dracula vanishing in full view of the audience.
ISBN 978 0 573 60729 5

The Country. Play. Martin Crimp
M1 (40) F2 (25, 40). A room. Fee Code M

Richard and his wife Corinne have moved to the country to start a new life, but for Richard this also means kicking his crippling drug addiction. One night he brings home a young American, Rebecca, claiming to have found her unconscious by the roadside, but Corinne is justifiably suspicious and takes the first opportunity to interrogate the girl. It gradually emerges that all is not as it seems, and so begins a chain of events that sees their rural idyll smashed by adultery and alienation.

The Cracked Pot. Play. Blake Morrison. Translated and adapted from Heinrich von Kleist's *Der Zerbrochene Krug*
M5 F4. A courtroom. Fee code M

The Cracked Pot is more than a translation of Heinrich von Kleist's *Der Zerbrochene Krug*, as the action now takes place in Skipton, Yorkshire, in 1810, with Kleist's German verse transformed into tough Yorkshire dialect. Funny, earthy and satirical, the play concerns Judge Adam, Skipton's sole agent of justice, who is far from happy to be visited by the investigating magistrate Walter Clegg, seeking out signs of malpractice.
ISBN 978 0 573 01734 6

A

Cracks. Play. Martin Sherman
M5 (20s-40s) F4 (17, late 20s, 42). Composite setting: a living-room, study and garden. Fee code M. ISBN 978 0 573 11089 4

Cranford. Play. Martyn Coleman, adapted from the novel by Mrs Gaskell
M2 (20s, middle age) F8 or 9 (20s, middle age). A parlour. Period 1830. Fee code K

An adaptation in three acts of Mrs Gaskell's classic novel which was first staged in 1951. Necessarily condensed to play under three hours, some elements of the story have been lost, but the action focuses on the ladies of Cranford and their love of gossip. Mrs Gaskell appears as a narrator at the beginning of each act to introduce the scene, although her appearance is not necessary and she may be omitted.

Credible Witness. Play. Timberlake Wertenbaker
M8 F3. Varying ages and nationalities. Simple settings. Fee code K

A Macedonian woman arrives in London seeking her son Alexander who claimed political refuge three years earlier. Sent to a detention centre, she meets other refugees, including a Somalian woman and a Tamil doctor. In juxtaposed scenes we see Alexander losing his old sense of identity. When the two are finally reunited events take an unexpected turn. In this story of love and loss Wertenbaker explores passions simmering in contemporary Britain.

Crimes of the Heart. Comedy. Beth Henley
M2 (30) F4 (20s, 30). A kitchen. Fee code M

Three sisters have gathered in their small Mississippi hometown awaiting news of their grandfather who is dying in a local hospital; Lenny, unmarried, Meg, a failed singer and Babe, on bail having shot her husband. Their troubles, which are grave yet somehow hilarious, are highlighted by their cousin Chick, Doc Porter and Babe's lawyer who is trying to keep her out of jail while waging a personal vendetta against her husband. But the play ends on a joyful note with the three sisters re-united celebrating Lenny's birthday.

The Cripple of Inishmaan. Play. Martin McDonagh
M5 F4. Various simple interior and exterior settings. Fee code M

Set on a remote island off the west coast of Ireland in 1934, this is a strange comic tale in the great tradition of Irish storytelling. As word arrives on Inishmaan that the Hollywood director Robert Flaherty is coming to the neighbouring island of Inishmore to film 'Man of Aran', the one person who wants to be in the film more than anybody is young Cripple Billy, if only to break away from the bitter tedium of his daily life.

♦ **Crown Prince.** Play. John Godber
M4 (27, 61) F2 or 3 (17, 61, 68). A bowling club. Fee code M

Crown Prince takes us from the present day twenty years into the future at the bowling club, whose members Jack, May, Ted, Ronnie and Caroline age from their sixties to their eighties. Initially sceptical about the effects of global warming being forecast by Jack's granddaughter, Faye, they are soon forced to confront the reality of climate change. By 2027, Hull has been flooded and its residents are forced to seek refuge on the bowling club hill.

The Crucifer of Blood. Play. Paul Giovanni, based on characters created by Sir Arthur Conan Doyle
M10 (20, 30, 50, black pygmy) F1, with doubling. Three exterior, two interior settings. Fee code M

A Sherlock Holmes pastiche based mainly on *The Sign of Four*, though with some fundamental differences (the lady in the case proves to be far from Dr Watson's true love), and bringing in elements from other stories. The action starts in India with the theft of the Agra Treasure, moves forward thirty years to deal with the exciting events resulting from the crime and concludes with a tantalizing hint of one of Watson's most famous unwritten adventures – 'The Giant Rat of Sumatra'. Period 1857 and 1887
ISBN 978 0 573 60757 8

Cruel and Tender. Play. Martin Crimp after Sophocles' *Trachiniae*.
M6 (6, teens, 30s, 40s, 50s) F5 (18, 40s). A room. Fee Code M

Far away a battle rages and an entire city is turned to dust. Meanwhile Amelia waits for news of her husband, the great General. But when the motives for the war start to look disturbingly personal, his wife becomes desperate to hold on to his love. Martin Crimp takes Sophocles' ancient story of marriage and violence and propels it into a modern world of political hypocrisy and emotional terrorism.

Curtain Call. Comedy. Bettine Manktelow
M3 (35, 50, middle age) F5 (25-30, 30s-50s) An office. Fee code L

An amusingly chaotic day in the life of Alec Partridge, Manager of the Thurlow Playhouse. The director of an amateur production of *Oklahoma* demands real horses in the show; an Arts Council agent arrives to assess the theatre's eligibility for a grant; the Front of House manager's flirty ways upset Alec's secretary and, worst of all, the Chairman of the Board of Trustees appears on the scene ... All ends happily – for most of them.
ISBN 978 0 573 01918 5

Curtain Up! (formerley **Respecting Your Piers**). Comedy. Peter Quilter
F5 (20s, 30s, 50s, 70s). A seaside theatre. Fee code L

Five women inherit equal shares in a dilapidated theatre and are forced to settle their differences in order to get it operational again. This farcical comedy takes its humour from the culture clashes between the women, two of whom are sworn enemies! The comedy moves through the rigours of aerobics classes and exploding candyfloss machines until it culminates in a fund-raising concert where the celebrity guest cancels at the last minute. This play is the perfect vehicle for five comedy actresses.
ISBN 978 0 573 13014 4

Curtain Up on Murder. Thriller. Bettine Manktelow
M3 (35, 40, elderly) F5 (18, 20, 28, 40, 50s). A stage. Fee code L

An amateur drama company is rehearsing in the theatre at the end of the pier. Storms rage overhead and the doors are locked – they are trapped! Then a mysterious, ghostly presence passes across the stage, and when the Assistant Stage Manager falls to certain death through a trapdoor, the remaining actors are thrown into disarray. Their panic increases when one of the actresses is poisoned and it becomes evident that a murderer is in their midst ...
ISBN 978 0 573 01769 8

Curtains. Play. Stephen Bill
M3 (30, 48, 63) F5 (43, 50s, 70, 86). A living-room. Fee code M. ISBN 978 0 573 01686 8

Curtmantle. Play. Christopher Fry
M24 F7. Extras, doubling possible. Various simple settings. Fee code M

Cut and Run. Comedy. Peter Horsler
M4 F5. A doctor's surgery. Fee code L

The young, altruistic Dr Glow is perturbed when his National Health Clinic is hired out to Dr Boxclever, a private consultant who extorts outrageous fees from his patients by prescribing unnecessary treatments and useless medicines. Boxclever persuades Dr Glow to impersonate an eminent specialist and so begins a slide into malpractice. The denouement, though, is not as straightforward as it would appear for, by another twist of the plot, all ends happily. This is an hilarious comedy painting large the dangers in private health care.
ISBN 978 0 573 01768 1

Dad's Army. Three comedies. Jimmy Perry and David Croft
Large, flexible cast. A church hall and office, other simple settings. Fee code M for complete play, code E for individual plays, code C for sketch

This classic BBC TV comedy series of the Home Guard of Walmington-on-Sea who battle daily against the Germans and local ARP Warden Hodges, comes to the stage complete with all the well-loved characters: "stupid boy" Pike, "Don't panic, don't panic" Jonesey, "Doomed, we're all doomed!" Fraser, "May I be excused, sir?" Godfrey, the redoutable Captain Mainwaring and his effacing deputy Sergeant Wilson

> **The Deadly Attachment**
> **The Godiva Affair**
> **Mum's Army**.
> **Floral Dance** Sketch

Please see Section B for separate entries.
ISBN 978 0 573 10014 7

Dahling You Were Marvellous. Play. Steven Berkoff
Large mixed cast. Fee code L

Actors, producers and hangers-on gather at a good London restaurant after a first night at the theatre. *Dahling You Were Marvellous* parodies "those utterly self-important creatures whose lives desperately depend on the outside world to give them form and shape, adulation and importance, having very little substance of their own."

♦ **A bullet mark next to a title indicates that it is new to this edition of the Guide.**

Daisy Pulls It Off. Comedy. Denise Deegan
M2 F14, may be played by M2 F11. Extras. A school. Fee code M

Daisy Pulls it Off is about the attempts of Daisy Meredith to find acceptance in the snobby confines of Grangewood School for Young Ladies. After undergoing a number of tribulations all comes right in the end with Daisy saving the lives of her arch-enemies, discovering the treasure of Grangewood, scoring the winning goal at hockey and finding her long-lost father! This witty comedy enjoyed a long and very successful run in the West End at the Globe Theatre. Period 1927
ISBN 978 0 573 11117 4

Damsels in Distress. Trilogy of plays. Alan Ayckbourn

The trilogy comprises *FlatSpin*, *GamePlan* and *RolePlay* and was first seen at the Stephen Joseph Theatre, Scarborough and later at the Duchess Theatre, London. Each is self-contained, the common themes linking them being that the setting is the same London Docklands apartment and that all three concern young women in various states of distress. Please see the individual titles in Section A for details.

Dancing at Lughnasa. Play. Brian Friel
M3 (30s, 53) F5 (26, 30s). Composite set: a kitchen and garden. Fee code M

Premièred at Dublin's Abbey Theatre, this multi-award-winning play is about five impoverished spinster sisters in a remote part of County Donegal in 1936. With them live Michael, seven-year-old son of the youngest sister, and Jack, the sisters' elder brother, a missionary priest newly returned from Africa. The events of that summer are narrated in recall by the adult Michael, unfolding a tender study of these women's lives.
ISBN 0 573 01742 1

Dangerous Corner. Drama. J. B. Priestley
M3 (25-40) F4 (20, 47). A drawing-room. Fee code M

Robert Caplan and his wife are entertaining her brother and sister-in-law. Because Robert insists on uncovering the truth about his brother Martin's 'suicide', many unpalatable revelations ensue which cause Robert to shoot himself. At this point, the opening scene is repeated, but this time they bypass the dangerous corner at which the truth is demanded, thus averting the disaster. Written in 1932 this forms one of the three 'time plays'.
ISBN 978 0 573 01088 0

Dangerous Obsession. Play. N. J. Crisp
M2 (30, 40) F1(20). A conservatory. Fee code M. ISBN 978 0 573 01682 0

The Dark Is Light Enough. Play. Christopher Fry
M13 F3. A room and a great staircase, stables. Fee code M

◆ **A bullet mark next to a title indicates that it is new to this edition of the Guide.**

The Dark River. Play. Rodney Ackland
M5 F3 1 boy. A room in an old house. Fee code M

It is 1937; there are warning signs of World War Two. Catherine Lisle, recently divorced and with her hopes of a dancing career dashed, moves into the house of her old school-teacher. Like nearly everyone else in the house, Catherine is attempting to evade the present by living entirely in the past, and is hopelessly torn between her infantile ex-husband Chris and her lover Alan, who is passionately aware of the dangerous political situation surrounding them.

Darkness Falls. Double bill. *The Monkey's Paw*, adapted by Jonathan Holloway from the short story by W. W. Jacobs. *The Dark* by Jonathan Holloway
M4 F1, or M3 F1, with doubling. A kitchen/living-room, an elegant living-room. Fee code L

The perils of ambition lie at the heart of this double-bill of supernatural tales. In *The Monkey's Paw* a working-class family is granted three wishes, all of which come true, but in a macabre and unexpected way. In *The Dark* a successful and ambitious novelist meets his Mephistopheles and is dispatched to a sinister fate. Period 1940s / today
ISBN 978 0 573 10002 4

The Darling Buds of May. Comedy. H. E. Bates
M5 (15, 24, 40s, middle-age, 60) F6 (17, 19, 37, 45). 1 boy, 4 girls. A kitchen/living-room and yard. Fee code M

Pop Larkin, who makes a fortune from scrap-iron deals but has never paid income tax, lives in rural idyllic bliss with generous-hearted Ma and their six children. When a young, earnest tax official, Mr Charlton, turns up one hot May afternoon in 1957 to investigate he is bewitched immediately by eldest daughter Mariette and it isn't long before he succumbs to the boisterous Larkin family charm and largesse. Period 1950s
ISBN 978 0 573 01751 3

Darling Mr London. Farce. Anthony Marriott and Bob Grant
M3 (20-40) F6 (20, 30, 50). A living-room. Fee code L

Mild Edward works at the Continental Telephone Exchange and has been in the habit of chatting up his co-telephonists, all female, in various Continental exchanges. These affairs-by-proxy have caused no complications until the occasion of a Miss Europhone Contest brings the girls to London. Four of the most glamorous turn up at his home anxious to meet the flirtatious 'Mr London' in the flesh. The complications that ensue result in an evening he will never forget!
ISBN 0 573 11113 6

David Copperfield. Play. Matthew Francis, adapted from the novel by Charles Dickens
M19 F10. Extras. Minimum cast of 13. Various interior and exterior settings. Fee code M

Following the adventures of its eponymous hero from birth through three decades, this acclaimed stage adaptation presents a plethora of brilliant characters from the original novel: the Peggottys; 'umble Heep; eccentric Aunt Betsey and Steerforth, young David's champion. Two actors play David Copperfield: one the young David, the other David's older self, each interacting throughout. This clever device moves the play effortlessly from scene to scene, ensuring a vigorous momentum for the narrative. Period 1820s-1840s
ISBN 978 0 573 01775 9

The Day After the Fair. Play. Frank Harvey, from a short story by Thomas Hardy
M2 (young, 50s) F4 (young, 35, 60). A living-room and hall. Fee code K. Period late nineteenth century
ISBN 978 0 573 01554 0

A Day in the Death of Joe Egg. Play. Peter Nichols
M2 (30s) F3 (30s, 60s), 1 child (10, non-speaking). A living-room. Fee code M

Joe Egg is the name given by Bri and Sheila to their spastic child. To make their lives bearable they have evolved an elaborate series of fantasy games about Joe. Yet ten years of devotion to a human vegetable have created terrible strains on their marriage and when Bri sees an opportunity of allowing Joe to die, he takes it. The attempt fails; Joe's living death will continue. Although the theme is deeply serious the tone is one of biting, ironic comedy, giving the work enormous theatrical effectiveness and compassion.
ISBN 978 0 573 01084 2

Day of Reckoning. Play. Pam Valentine
M1 (50s) F7 (20s-50s, 83). A village hall. Fee code L

A committee meets on a winter's night to arrange the summer village fête. As protocol gives way to bickering and gossip, the personalities of those present emerge – busybody Ethel; Pauline, the vicar's long-suffering wife; careworn Gloria; horsy Marjorie who is very attentive to the shy new teacher, Angela; elderly Mavis and Sally, the brisk Army wife. Six months on, the cathartic events of the fête are related with humour and pathos, and the upbeat ending affirms the enduring value of village life.
ISBN 978 0 573 01806 0

The Days of the Commune. Play. Bertolt Brecht
Translations: Clive Barker and Arno Reinfrank, music by Hanns Eisler
           Jean Benedetti
           Ray Herman
M42 F12, 2 children. Extras. Interior and exterior settings. Fee code M (for play), code C (for music)

The story of the Paris Commune is told through fictional Men in the Street grouped round a Montmartre café, and a number of historical personages. The Men in the Street resist Thier's attempt to disarm the National Guard and watch its Central Committee seize power at the Hôtel de Ville. The Men in the Street put up a barricade, on which they fight and die. Set in Paris between January-April 1871.

Dead Funny. Comedy. Terry Johnson
M3 (36, 59) F2 (33, 39) A living-room. Fee code M

The death of Benny Hill provides the impetus for this award-winning comedy about impotence, sex therapy and the English sense of humour. Eleanor wants what her husband Richard won't give her. Richard wants to be left in peace. Benny would rather rest in peace, but for tonight at least, his fans won't let him. '... a shatteringly good play, as hilarious as it is heartbreaking ...' *Daily Telegraph*

A

Dead Guilty. Play. Richard Harris
M1 (20s), F3 (30s, 40s-60s). 1 male voice A sitting-room. Fee code M

When John Haddrell dies of a heart attack at the wheel of his car, the woman at his side is not his wife Margaret but his lover, Julia. Recovering from the injuries she sustained in the ensuing crash, Julia is visited by Margaret, who apparently knows nothing of the affair. Events take a sinister turn when Margaret begins to encroach on Julia's life. Left alone in the house together, Julia and Margaret are locked in deadly combat ...
ISBN 978 0 573 01750 6

Dead Man's Hand. Thriller. Seymour Matthews
M3 F3. A lounge. Fee code L

This captivating thriller employs a play within a play theme in a singularly exciting manner. At first it seems to be the usual Agatha Christie-type play – two couples lured to a remote Italian villa to be murdered one by one. It is only when this play is well advanced that we learn we are watching actors rehearsing their own murder mystery. An intriguing final twist unravels the real reason for the whole charade.
ISBN 978 0 573 01618 9

Dead of Night. Thriller. Peter Whalley
M2 (30s, 40s) F2 (20s, 30s). A living-room. Fee code M

Jack has just been acquitted of manslaughter, and regales his girlfriend Maggie and their neighbours with a disparaging account of the trial. According to the evidence (most of it Jack's), the victim, Philip Mercer, had broken in late at night, and, on being confronted by Jack, produced a gun which Jack got hold of during the ensuing struggle and then used to kill Mercer. A clear case of self-defence. Or was it?
ISBN 978 0 573 01743 8

Dead-Lock. Thriller. Hugh Janes
M3 (middle-age) F2 (30s, middle-age). A large country house. Fee code M

When her husband dies in a car crash, Diana is determined to succeed as the new head of his successful company. Her son Alec believes the position should be his, while her younger son demands more of the family fortune. When strange events start happening in the house and a voice haunts her, Diana's fears and uncertainties increase. Just as she feels she knows who is responsible, events take a dramatic turn as her real enemy is revealed.
ISBN 978 0 573 01744 5

Deadly Embrace. Thriller. Eric Paice
M1 (35) F3 (18, early 40s). Extras 1M 1F. A living-room with gallery bedroom. Fee code M

Angry and bitter after throwing out her unfaithful husband, Julia is only too ready to succumb to the good-looking Welshman who comes ostensibly to update her husband's computer. Julia enjoys playing games with the computer, particularly when it invites her to play the Murder Game and she can fantasize about how easy it would be to commit the perfect murder by computer with her errant husband as victim. However, stopping the program the next morning isn't so easy ...
ISBN 978 0 573 01745 2

Deadly Nightcap. Play. Francis Durbridge
M6 (30, 40, middle-age) F4 (young, 40s). A living-room. Fee code M

Murder and mystery abound in this ingenious play from the master of the genre. Initially the plot seems to concern a greedy husband plotting to kill his wife. Disposing first of his brother-in-law, Jack enlists the help of his girlfriend in his plan to murder Sarah. But his scheme goes horribly wrong and he, not his wife, ends up dead. There are so many possible suspects and motives that the truth eludes us all ... although Cliff seems to be on the right track.
ISBN 978 0 573 01627 1

Dealer's Choice. Play. Patrick Marber
M6 (20s-50s). A kitchen, restaurant, basement. Fee code M

Stephen, a restaurateur, has a weekly poker game in the basement. The stakes are high and the waiters often lose their paycheques. Stephen's son, Carl, is an obsessive gambler who has run up debts and when Ash, a professional gambler, threatens to kill Carl if he doesn't pay the £4000 he owes, Carl arranges for him to play in the weekly game. But Stephen can spot a professional and confronts Ash who asks where Carl acquired his addiction. Who is the real addict, Carl or Stephen?

Dealing with Clair. Play. Martin Crimp
M4 (20s, 30, 50s) F3 (17, 25, 30). Various simple settings. Fee Code M

A young estate agent, Clair, tries to sell a suburban house to James, a distinguished and disarming cash buyer. At first debonair, James becomes increasingly sinister, prying his way into Clair's private life. She is soon drawn to him. By the end James is in her flat, talking to Clair's mother on the phone. He tells her that Clair is taking a shower. But it becomes clear she is not, and just as the play's title promises, James has dealt with Clair for good. Period late 1980s

The Dearly Beloved. Play. Philip Osment
M4 (teenage, 40s) F5 (30s, 40s, 70). Simple interior and exterior settings. Fee code M

When Alaric, a successful London television producer, returns to his sleepy rural home town, his arrival heralds suffering and domestic turmoil in this sensitive, compelling depiction of a variety of family relationships. The play was critically acclaimed at Hampstead Theatre in 1993. '... exceptionally poignant, and there is no mistaking the overall richness of this play. Osment's penetrating observation of character and heartening generosity of spirit mark him out as a dramatist of exceptional and distinctive promise.' *Daily Telegraph*
ISBN 978 0 573 01746 9

Death and the Maiden. Play. Ariel Dorfman
M2 (45, 50) F1 (40). A dining/living-room. Fee code M

Set in a fragile new South American democracy, this piece concerns Paulina who, fifteen years ago, was picked up by the police, blindfolded and tortured. When Roberto stops to help Gerardo, whose car has broken down, and brings him home, Paulina is convinced he is one of her torturers. Husband and wife are caught in a gripping, passionate deadlock: one liberal and judicious, the other victimized and full of hatred, coming to grips with an oppressor. **NB. The text of the 1992 Broadway première must be used in all performances.**

Death Is Catching. Murder mystery. Jean McConnell and Miles Tripp. Based on *Kilo Forty* by Miles Tripp
M3 (40s) F1 (late 30s). A desert campsite. Fee code L

In this tense, psychological thriller set in a remote part of Egypt, French ex-pats, Hélène and Philippe, are on holiday with their English friend, Foster Smith, and Haik, an Armenian businessman. Foster Smith finds a woman's mutilated body on the beach and, with Hélène apparently missing, the scene is set for a game of bluff and double bluff that will leave two others dead and the hapless Foster Smith the fall guy yet again.
ISBN 978 0 573 01977 7

Death Walked In. Play. Bettine Manktelow
M3 (30, 60s) F4 (teens, 20, 30, 40). An hotel lounge. Fee code K

Celia, lonely and highly strung, is struggling to run her small country hotel. Her charming, rakish stepson, Rex, is no help. Joan and her tearaway sister, Eva, are staying at the hotel which represents something of a romantic pilgrimage for Joan who, after ten years, still believes herself in love with Rex. Events lead to a suicide (or is it murder?). The climax involves mistaken identity and mislaid cyanide!
ISBN 978 0 573 11127 3

Ira Levin's **Deathtrap**. Thriller
M3 (25, 50s) F2 (40, 50). A study. Fee code M

A hugely popular stage and screen success, this ingeniously constructed play offers a rare and skilful blending of two priceless theatrical ingredients – gasp-inducing thrills and spontaneous laughter. Unknown dramatist Clifford Anderson has sent his new thriller to award-winning Broadway author Sidney for comment – or has he? Without a success to his credit for some years, Sidney plots with his reluctant wife Myra about how best to plagiarize 'Deathtrap' and when Clifford turns up to discuss the play with the 'Master' events take a sinister turn.
ISBN 978 0 573 11121 1

Decadence. Play. Steven Berkoff
M1 F1. Fee code M

"A study of the ruling classes or upper classes, so called by virtue of strangulated vowel tones rather than any real achievement." – Steven Berkoff on *Decadence*. Two performers play two couples in this hilariously vitriolic play. Steven Berkoff starred in it with Linda Marlowe at the New End Theatre and with Joan Collins in the film version.

Deceptions. Play. Paul Wheeler
M1 (early 20s) F1 (early 40s). A consulting room, a bedsitter. Fee code M

Julia Smythe is a psychiatrist. A mysterious young man comes into her Mayfair consulting rooms for treatment for impotence and a tendency towards compulsive lying. Quickly, the psychoanalyst becomes hooked on the case of this strange young man, curing him to the point where he seemingly stops lying and falls in love with her. We are plunged into a complex, perverse situation right, it seems almost, out of Jacobean drama. '... intriguing ... neatly structured and snappily written.' *Independent*
ISBN 978 0 573 69287 1

The Decision. See **The Measures Taken** in Section B.

The Decorator. Comedy. Donald Churchill
M1 (53) F2. A flat. Fee code M

Marcia has a surprise visitor: Jane, the wife of the man with whom Marcia is having an affair, who has come to take her revenge by informing Marcia's husband of his wife's infidelity. Marcia is at her wits' end, then has a brilliant idea. It seems her housepainter is a part-time professional actor. Marcia hires him to impersonate her husband, Reggie, at the big confrontation later that day, when the wronged wife plans to return and spill the beans. From then on hilarity piles on hilarity ...
ISBN 978 0 573 69127 0

The Deep Blue Sea. Play. Terence Rattigan
M5 (young-50) F3 (young, 30, 50). A sitting-room. Fee code M

Hester Collyer's husband is a rich, talented lawyer; her lover, Freddie, is neither Hester's moral nor intellectual equal, but Hester loves him with an intensity that few, and especially not Freddie, are capable of matching. They are death to each other. Hester is driven to attempt suicide. Between the devil and the deep blue sea the latter looks very attractive. She is saved by Miller, a disbarred doctor, and through him learns how to transcend both hope and despair. Period 1950s
ISBN 978 0 573 01098 9

A Delicate Balance. Play. Edward Albee
M2 (60s) F4 (30-50s). A living-room. Fee code M

Agnes and Tobias arc long married and remain together out of habit. Agnes' sister, Claire, lives with them and takes refuge from life's perils in alcohol and self-lacerating wit. One night Julia, Agnes and Tobias' daughter, comes home, escaping from her fourth marriage. They are visited by Edna and Harry, their oldest friends, who are deeply disturbed by a great shock they have had. The door is locked and Tobias' family is made to recognize how they have lost love through undervaluing it. This stimulating play is distinguished by the award of a Pulitzer Prize.

Deliver Us from Evil. Thriller. J.D. Robins
M3 (all early 40s) F4 (early 40s, 1 elderly, 1 indeterminate age). A sitting-room Fee Code K

Ben Seaton is the new rector of Wychcombe Magna. His wife Diana feels decidedly out of place and increasingly threatened as a strange woman keeps walking into the house without any invitation and the church bells suddenly ring at odd times. Then the unthinkable happens – there is a murder at the rectory and it soon becomes apparent that not everyone in the village is who they say they are…
ISBN 978 0 573 11552 3

Democracy. Play. Michael Frayn.
M10. Various simple settings. Fee Code M

West Germany 1969. Willy Brandt begins his brief but remarkable career as the first left-of-centre Chancellor for nearly forty years. Always present but rarely noticed is Günter Guillaume, Brandt's devoted personal assistant – and no less devoted in his other role, spying on Brandt for the Stasi. Period 1969

A

Departures. Comedy. John Godber
M3 (40s) F6 (20s, 39, 43). Various simple settings. Fee code M

The departure lounges of ten airports across Europe and America provide a backdrop of delays, dangers and frustration as two business executives, Jim and Steve, embark on a journey of self-discovery. While the easy-going, unscrupulous Steve spends time on the mobile running a number of love interests, Jim is determined to remain faithful to his wife Claire. Young Zoë's arrival changes everything ... The anxiety of the departure lounge becomes all too personal for all involved, leading to a sad yet hopeful ending.
ISBN 978 0 573 01990 6

The Devil at Midnight. Thriller. Brian Clemens
M2 (20s, 40s) F2 (26, 40s). M2 F1 voices only. A living-room. Fee code M

Liz Burns, a psychoanalyst, receives an unexpected visitor – Nicki, a troubled young woman who is visited in her dreams by a devil who carries her away to a lonely, terrifying old house. Liz sees immediately that her visitor is a victim of child abuse and, as the details of Nicki's past life emerge, clues mount up that point to Liz's husband Jack as the perpetrator. And Nicki is out for revenge ...
ISBN 978 0 573 01758 1

The Devils. Play. John Whiting from a book by Aldous Huxley
M17 F6. Composite setting. Fee code L

The nuns of St Ursula's Convent, led by the Prioress, Sister Jeanne, accused Urbain Grandier, Vicar of Loudon, of sorcery. He was tried, tortured and burned. On this baldly terrible foundation, Whiting has built a powerful, complex play, interweaving the personal dilemmas of Jeanne and Grandier with the political necessities of the time. Period 1623-34, although essentially it is no more a period play than Miller's *The Crucible*.
ISBN 978 0 573 01101 6

Dial 'M' for Murder. Play. Frederick Knott
M4 (30s, 45) F1 (20). A living-room. Fee code M

Tony had quite blatantly married Sheila for her money. When it seems likely that she is in love with Max, Tony begins to plot her murder. Lesgate, the hired killer, enters the flat while Tony establishes his own alibi. But Sheila defends herself so ably that it is Lesgate who is killed. Tony callously plants evidence to suggest that Sheila had killed Lesgate because he was blackmailing her. She is convicted but fortunately the Inspector continues his investgations ...
ISBN 978 0 573 01102 3

The Diary of Anne Frank. Play. Dramatized by Frances Goodrich and Albert Hackett
M5 (16, middle-age-elderly) F5 (teenage, 20s-40). An attic. Fee code M

Few more poignant true stories emerged from World War II than the diary of young Anne Frank. Published long afterwards by her father, the only family survivor, it records the minutiae of twenty-five months that two Jewish families spent in hiding from the Gestapo in an Amsterdam warehouse attic. The constant secrecy, growing hunger and friction of living in such cramped conditions could not dull Anne's vibrant personality or her passion for living.
ISBN 978 0 573 01104 7

Dick Barton – Special Agent. Musical comedy. Phil Willmott
M9 F3, with doubling. Extras. Various simple settings. Fee code L

Based on the 1940s BBC serial, hilarious Dick Barton faces new stage adventures. When Britain's entire tea supply is threatened to be poisoned, he soon finds himself wrapped up in an adventure soaked with intrigue and mystery, as he faces off against arch enemies Marta Heartburn and Baron Scarheart – all the while finding the time to sing a few songs along the way – and saves the day! Musical material can be easily sourced or hired from the arranger.

♦ **Dick Barton Episode II: The Curse of the Pharaoh's Tomb.** Comedy. Phil Willmott
M13 F4. 2M or F. Various settings. Fee code L

In this follow up, the intrepid sleuth brings the body of Marta Heartburn back to London, having taken from her a cursed sapphire. Marta becomes reincarnated as the ancient Queen Nefatartie and charms Piggy into accompanying her back to Egypt. Dick Barton and his assistants Snowy and Jock must employ all their ingenuity to rescue Piggy and break the curse. A tongue-in-cheek musical rejuvenation of the iconic 1940s radio detective show. Period 1940s

♦ **Dick Barton Episode III: The Tango of Terror.** Comedy. Phil Willmott
M10 F9. Various settings. Fee code L

In the third musical comedy based on the BBC's 1940s radio serial, a mysterious "Johnny foreigner" has struck London, wooing women with his dance moves before stealing their jewels. Worse still, he has got hold of a dossier containing the whereabouts of Wilco and Rodger, Britain's finest secret agents. Fortunately DB is on hand to save the day with his faithful sidekicks, Snowy and Jock. This play works both independently of its predecessors and as the final part of a hilarious trilogy.

A Different Way Home. Play. Jimmie Chinn
M1 F1. A living-room. Fee code M

A deeply moving, astutely observed play which consists of two monologues from a middle-aged estranged brother and sister in a closely-knit, North of England town. Leslie, who has lived always with his mother, narrates the events leading up to his mother's death, unwittingly revealing the extent of his loss. From Maureen we hear that Leslie had succumbed to his grief, and we hear her side of the story: feeling rejected because she married a Jew, she also feels betrayed for not being asked to help.
ISBN 978 0 573 11092 4

Ding Dong. A comedy. Adapted by Tudor Gates from the French play by Marc Camoletti
M2 F4 1 interior setting. Fee Code M

Bernard has discovered that his wife is having an affair with Robert. Being a reasonable businessman Bernard give Robert two options to compensate for the affair: either he will sleep with Robert's wife or he will have him killed. Needless to say Robert chooses to let Bernard sleep with his wife. However Bernard engages a call girl to take the place of his wife but this later backfires when the real wife turns up!
ISBN 978 0 573 11108 2

♦ **A bullet mark next to a title indicates that it is new to this edition of the Guide.**

The Dining Room. Play. A. R. Gurney
57 characters played by M3 F3 (minimum). A dining-room. Fee code M. ISBN 978 0 573 11536 3

Dinner. Play. Moira Buffini
M4 F3. A dining area. Fee code M

"It's my creation – like Frankenstein's monster." An artist, a scientist and a sexpot are coming to dinner. Paige, hostess extraordinaire, is celebrating the publication of her husband's bestseller. The arrival of Mike, marooned in the foggy lane after crashing his van, provides an unexpected addition to the evening's entertainment. A silent waiter, sourced from an obscure website, completes the picture. Primordial Soup is first on the menu – let the dinner from hell begin. A wonderful comedy chiller, with blood on the carpet before bedtime.

Dirty Linen and **New-Found-Land.** Two plays. Tom Stoppard
M8 (young, middle-age) F2 (young, middle-age). A committee room in the House of Commons. Fee code K

Dirty Linen concerns the investigation of a Select Committee into the moral standards of the House of Commons – a somewhat unconventional investigation, rendered not less so by the presence of an ultra-sexy secretary whose clothes have a trick of whisking off in the hands of various members. *New-Found-Land* is a duologue between two Home Office officials, with a tour-de-force speech on America by one of them.
ISBN 978 0 573 11109 9

Disappeared. Play. Phyllis Nagy
M5 (20s, any age, middle-age, 40s) F3 (25, 30s, middle-age). Various simple settings. Fee code M

This starkly modern play concerns Sarah Casey, a twenty-five-year-old travel agent who has never been outside New York City. She goes missing after leaving a bar, where the last person to see her was Elston Rupp, a man who works in a thrift shop and dresses in his clients' clothes to assume different identities. Was Sarah killed, or did she merely 'disappear' to escape her anonymous existence in a big, lonely city?
ISBN 978 0 573 01747 6

Disposing of the Body. Play. Hugh Whitemore
M5 (20s, 40s, 50s) F3 (40s). Various simple settings. Fee code M

"All my life I've either been looking back at happy times that have gone or looking forward to the happiness to come." Thus speaks Henry Preece, embarking on early retirement. In Hugh Whitemore's elegant and tantalizing play, the mystery and excitement of an unexpected passion is given full rein, until Henry realizes that a door he's just flung open should have remained tightly shut.

The Distance From Here. Play. Neil LaBute
M5 (teenage, 33) F4 (teenage, 21, 38). Various simple settings. Fee code M

With little to occupy their time other than finding a decent place to hang out, Darrell and Tim are two American teenagers who lack direction and purpose. When Darrell's suspicion about the infidelity of his girlfriend is confirmed, and Tim comes to her defence, there is nothing to break their momentum as all three speed towards disaster. The play, which takes an intense look at the dark side of American suburbia, was seen at the Almeida Theatre, London, in 2002. Contains strong language.

Dogg's Hamlet, Cahoot's Macbeth. Double bill. Tom Stoppard
Up to 20 characters, much doubling possible. Fee Code M (when performed as a double bill).
Fee code F when performed separately

Tom Stoppard explains that the comma between the two titles serves to unite the plays: 'the first is hardly a play at all without the second which cannot be performed without the first. *Dogg's Hamlet* is a reworking of *Dogg's Our Pet*, an exercise in nonsense language which leads on to *The Fifteen Minute Hamlet* (published separately by Samuel French) which takes the most well-known lines from *Hamlet* and condenses them into 13 minutes. *Cahoot's Macbeth* ingeniously abbreviates Shakespeare and combines it with linguistic jokes, political comment and farce.

A Doll's House. Play. Henrik Ibsen, in a new version by Samuel Adamson
M3 F3, 1 boy, 1 girl. A living-room. Fee code L

Specially commissioned to celebrate the 10th anniversary of Southwark Playhouse, Samuel Adamson's new version brings zest to this classic play. Thus, the story of Nora, the delicate and over-protected wife of Torvald Helmer, who bravely walks away from her confined marriage in a quest for freedom and self-enlightenment, remains poignant and real for modern-day audiences. Period: late 19th century. "… the most exciting translator of his generation. [Samuel Adamson's] version is fluent, pointedly modern but never obtrusive." *What's On*
ISBN 978 0 573 01951 7

A Doll's House. Play. Henrik Ibsen, in a new version by Christopher Hampton
M3 (late 30s, 40s) F4 (30s, 35, old), 1 boy 1 girl (optional). A flat. Fee code M

Ibsen's classic play tells the story of Nora, beautiful, fragile wife of Torvald Helmer. Nora had secretly borrowed money for her husband by forging her father's signature. Krogstad, her creditor, threatens to ruin Helmer by exposing Nora's fraud. When Helmer finds out, he is not prepared to sacrifice his reputation to protect Nora; she realizes that she must close the door on her marriage and her husband to retain her self-respect.

Dolly West's Kitchen. Play. Frank McGuinness
M5 (20s, 30s, 40s) F4 (teens, 30s, 60s). A kitchen and part of a garden. Fee code M.

As the Second World War rages in Europe, in Donegal there is another war closer to home. In Dolly West's kitchen, the family has its own conflicts to face as their lives are transformed with the arrival of allied troops across the border in Derry. War changes everything – its tragedies and its survivals will alter the history of the West family for ever. Period 1943-45.

Don Juan. Play. Bertolt Brecht, adapted from Molière. Translated by Ralph Manheim
M15 F6. Fee code M

In this adaptation Don Juan, the legendary lover, is regarded as a means to ridicule the hypocrisy and pretentiousness of the world as he pursues his amorous ways, dodges and outwits his enemies until, in the form of the Statue of the Commander, he meets his inevitable emesis and is cast into hell fire. This is one of Brecht's less radical adaptations and one of those with which he apparently had least to do.

◆ **A bullet mark next to a title indicates that it is new to this edition of the Guide.**

Don Juan in Soho. Play. Patrick Marber after Molière
M7 F3. A hotel lobby, hospital A & E, Soho Square. Fee Code M

Patrick Marber's updating of Molière's Don Juan has transposed the action to today's London where this modern-day wastrel is let loose among the fleshpots of Soho. DJ is an utter cad, an aristocrat who will bed anything female and attractive without a thought for the consequences. In a demotic script full of foul language and irresistible filthy jokes Marber uses the character to lay into the idiocies of our age, notably our obsession with celebrity.

Donkeys' Years. Play. Michael Frayn
M8 F1. A college courtyard. Two studies. Fee code M

The occasion is a reunion dinner at a lesser college of an older university. Gathered together are a number of graduates now in their early forties and mostly in responsible, influential positions. All starts smoothly, with the usual conventional greetings, but as the night goes on the college port causes behaviour surprising in those positions of political, academic or spiritual authority. The play was seen at the Globe Theatre, London, with Peter Barkworth, Jeffrey Wickham and Penelope Keith.
ISBN 978 0 573 11097 9

Don't Dress for Dinner. Farce. Marc Camoletti, adapted by Robin Hawdon
M3 (35, any age) F3 (30s). A living-room. Fee code M

Bernard is hoping to weekend in the country with his chic Parisian mistress Suzy. He has arranged for a cordon bleu cook, is in the process of packing his wife Jacqueline off to her mother, and has invited along his best friend Robert as a suitable alibi. It's foolproof. What could possibly go wrong? Well ... Hilarious confusion piles upon hilarious confusion as Bernard and Robert improvise at breakneck speed!
ISBN 978 0 573 01748 3

Don't Drink the Water. Comedy. Woody Allen
M12 F4. An embassy. Fee code M

This hilarious affair takes place in an American Embassy behind the Iron Curtain. An American tourist, caterer by trade, and his family, rush into the embassy two steps ahead of the police who suspect them of spying and picture-taking. But it is not much of a refuge as the ambassador is absent and his son, now in charge, has been expelled from a dozen different countries. Nevertheless they carefully and frantically plot their escape and the ambassador's son and the caterer's daughter even have time to fall in love.
ISBN 978 0 573 60817 9

Don't Lose the Place! Comedy. Derek Benfield
M3 (young, late 30s, early 50s) F2 (young, 35). Composite setting: a sitting-room, patio and part of a kitchen. Fee code L

When Sylvia's boyfriend Robin walks out on her she decides on a rather unconventional method of finding a replacement. Determined not to be let down a second time, she has carefully arranged a timetable in order to 'try out' various assorted lovers and assess their suitability before making her final choice of a potential husband. But timetables have a way of going wrong ... A torrent of confusions and mistaken identities inevitably arise as Sylvia and her friend Jemma try, with unexpected and hilarious results, to prevent the final confrontation of the three trial husbands. A delightfully comic climax ensues.
ISBN 978 0 573 01749 0

Double Double. Play. Eric Elice and Roger Rees
M1 (40) F1 (30). A London apartment. Fee code M

A

Phillipa has picked up down-and-out Duncan. It is, she explains, purely a business arrangement based on Duncan's uncanny resemblance to her recently deceased husband, Richard, who stood to inherit a million-pound trust fund in a few weeks. All Duncan has to do for a half-share in the fund is impersonate Richard at a party. This clever thriller twists and turns until the stunning climax that leaves the audience gasping. 'A glossy romantic thriller – it should be seen to be believed.' *Sunday Times*
ISBN 978 0 573 01646 9

Double Death. Play. Simon Williams
M2 (30s, 50s) F2 (30s, 60s). 1M. A living-room. Fee Code L

In an isolated house on the cliffs of north Cornwall the sibling rivalry between identical twins Max and Ashley Hennessy is coming to a murderous climax. They both know one of them must die, but, trapped in his wheelchair, Ashley knows the odds are now against him and he is in mortal danger. Poor Lalla, the twins' aunt, is torn between the two boys: which of them is the victim and which is the psychopath?
ISBN 978 0 573 11098 6

Double Vision. Comedy. Eric Chappell
M2 (40, 50s) F1 (40s). A living-room. Fee code M

Ex-boxer Spinks is myopic, poor and lonely, his one companion being the alcoholic Kingsley with whom he has a rather tetchy, exasperated friendship. To gain attention, Spinks pretends to win the National Lottery and he starts receiving freebies and handouts from people hoping to get a share of his fortune. Plain Dawn Pringle who loves Spinks for himself not his money, warns against her maneater identical twin sister Donna, who then turns up and seduces him. Just in time he makes an important discovery about his new-found loves.
ISBN 978 0 573 01976 0

A Dream Play. Play. August Strindberg, in a new version by Caryl Churchill
Large cast may be played by M5 F5. Various simple settings. Fee code K

A young woman comes from another world to see if life is really as difficult as people make it out to be. In Strindberg's *A Dream Play*, written in 1901, characters merge into each other, locations change in an instant and a locked door becomes an obsessively recurrent image. Caryl Churchill's spare and resonant new version was first staged at the National Theatre, London, in a production by Katie Mitchell in 2005.

Dreaming. Play. Peter Barnes
Large cast may be played by M11 F4. Various simple settings. Fee code M (play). Details of the music available from Samuel French Ltd

In the bloody aftermath of the Wars of the Roses, Captain John Mallory leads a band of renegades across a war-torn landscape on a breathtaking quest in search of a dream – a dream of home. An apocalyptic vision packed with ravishing images, *Dreaming* is a haunting and brutally funny story of heroism and human values. Period 1471

The Dresser. Play. Ronald Harwood
M4 (30, 40, 60, old) F3 (young, middle-age, 50s). Composite set. Fee code M

Sir, the last of the great, but dying, breed of English actor-managers, is in a very bad way tonight. As his dresser tries valiantly to prepare him to go on stage as King Lear, Sir is having great difficulty remembering who and where he is, let alone Lear's lines. With a Herculean effort on the part of Norman, the dresser, Sir does finally make it on stage, and through the performance. Period 1942. During its long West End run the play starred Tom Courtenay and Freddie Jones.

Drowning On Dry Land. Comedy. Alan Ayckbourn
M4 (30s, 40s, 50s) F3 (20s, 30s) 2 girls (8, 10). A garden and folly. Fee Code M

Charlie Conrad is a celebrity. His talent? He hasn't got one; the nation took him to their hearts for very publicly being unable to do anything competently. One fateful day, however, Charlie meets Marsha, and his marriage and career go into freefall ... *Drowning on Dry Land* examines the current obsession with celebrity for its own sake and chillingly but hilariously demonstrates how celebrities can be destroyed as quickly as they are made.
ISBN 978 0 573 11224 9

Drums in the Night. Drama. Bertolt Brecht
Translations: John Willett
     Gerhard Nellhaus
     Richard Beckley
     Frank Jones
M9 F6. Interior and exterior settings. Fee code M

The soldier Andreas returns from a prison camp to find his fiancée Anna just engaged to the prosperous Murk. Against sounds and reports of the Spartacists storming the newspaper offices, Andreas quarrels in a bar with Anna's parents and the now drunken Murk. Lost in the street, he follows the rioting; Anna follows him. In desperation Andreas leads the (partly drunken) company to the newspaper offices. In the early morning he and Anna meet in the streets. He refuses to return to the fighting and the two go home together.

The Drunkard or Down with Demon Drink! Melodrama. Brian J. Burton
M7 (20s, middle-age, 60s, elderly) F8 (11, young, middle-age, 60). Extras. Interior and exterior settings. Fee code L

Edward, the penniless heir of his kind-hearted father, is a virtuous man. One day the villain Squire Cribbs lures Edward to drink in an inn, and the effect is instantaneous; he becomes a drunkard and his poverty increases. It is his foster brother William who finds out what Cribb is up to, discovers Edward in the slums of London and finds the true will hidden by the villain. Period Victorian

Duet for One. Play. Tom Kempinski
M1 (60s) F1 (33). A consulting room. Fee code M

Stephanie, an eminent violinist struck down by multiple sclerosis, consults Dr Feldmann to help her adjust to her new life. Under Dr Feldmann's quiet, probing questions layers of protective pretence are stripped from her, revealing dangerous depths of resentment and despair. She becomes aggressive towards the psychiatrist and finally decides to give up the treatment, but his last word is to ask her if 'the same time' will be convenient for her next appointment.
ISBN 978 0 573 11091 7

A

♦ **Duets.** Comedy. Peter Quilter
M1 to 4, F1 to 4. A living-room. Fee code M (for entire play)

Four sets of characters, four crucial moments. A gloriously funny examination of the chaotic world of love, relationships and why the grass is never greener and a hilarious tribute to the strength and madness of the human heart. Though written to be produced in its entirety with a cast of up to M4 F4, *Duets* may also be performed as four separate one-act plays, each with a cast of M1 F1 (see Section B).
"A warm and funny exploration of love and other bruises." *Daily Telegraph*
ISBN 978 0 573 11111 2

East. Play. Steven Berkoff
M4 F1. Fee code M

A razor-sharp, vibrant and funny portrait of life in London's East End seen through the eyes of tearaways Les and Mike. "Berkoff razzle-dazzles their lifestyle in a tumult of imagery; the language flashes from Shakespearian parody to the shatteringly profane ..." *Daily Mail*

East Lynne or Never Called Me Mother! Melodrama with music. Brian J. Burton, based on the novel by Mrs Henry Wood
M4 (20s, 30s, middle-age) F5 (young, 40s). 1 child (optional). A sitting-room. Fee code L

Lady Isabel is cunningly seduced by the villain into believing that the clandestine meetings of her husband and another woman are for romance rather than business. In despair, she abandons home and children, only to come back in later years disguised as a governess to her own children and to die in her husband's arms in heartbroken penitence and forgiveness. Period Victorian

The Eccentricities of a Nightingale. Play. Tennessee Williams
M5 (young, middle-age, 60s) F5 (young, middle-age, 60s). A small square with fountain, three interiors. Fee code M

Hemmed in by her parents, Alma Winemiller, afraid that she will always remain a spinster, has set her heart on the young Dr Buchanan. Though attached to Alma, he is guided by his socially ambitious mother and by his own uncertainties. Neither of them can break free from the influences that pull them apart. Period shortly before World War I

The Edge of Darkness. Play. Brian Clemens
M3 (30s-50s) F3 (20s, 50s). Extra 1M. A living-room. Fee code L

After her disappearance several years ago, Emma finds that her memory is damaged; there is much she does not recognize or understand. Why does she appear familiar with certain Russian phrases; why has she such a horror of a harmless silver bell, of a portrait on the wall, of knives? Is she, in fact, Emma Cranwell? Behind these questions looms a menacing mystery which finally erupts into violence and horror. Period 1900
ISBN 978 0 573 11118 1

♦ **A bullet mark next to a title indicates that it is new to this edition of the Guide.**

The Editing Process. Play. Meredith Oakes
M5 (20s, 30s, 60) F3 (20s, 50). Various offices. Fee code M

In publishing, little companies are often gobbled up by big ones. This scenario faces the staff of *Footnotes in History*, who find their old-fashioned magazine amalgamated into a large publishing consortium. What will happen to pedantic William, who has edited the magazine all his life? How does his long-suffering secretary feel about being 'rationalized'? And does the new company – satirically represented by designer 'image consultants' – really want William's magazine to continue?

Edmond. Play. David Mamet
M20 F8 (may be played by M6 F4). Simple interior and exterior settings. Fee code M

This is a brutal, probing, and controversial story of a man set morally adrift in a corrupt and violent world. Leaving a wife and marriage in which he finds no fulfilment, Edmond sets out to find sex, adventure and companionship but ultimately finds the meaning of his existence in a world where there seems to be no concern for others, only selfishness and self interest. What Edmond experiences is a nightmare odyssey through the underworld of New York City.

♦ **Edward Gant's Amazing Feats of Loneliness.** Play. Anthony Neilson
M3 F1 with doubling. Various simple settings. Fee code L

In 1881, famed impresario Mr Edward Gant presented his renowned travelling show for the final time. The opiate-addicted actor manager showcased his troupe, creating a spectacle of grotesquery, black comedy, mystery and magic realism. Over a century later, Anthony Neilson has reconstructed this historical event in a theatrical piece that reveals the melodrama, extravagance and painful loneliness of a Victorian freak show, offering a strange and beautiful exploration of sadness and mortality, probing even the nature of theatre itself. Period 1881

Educating Rita. Comedy. Willy Russell
M1 (middle-age) F1 (26). A first-floor room in a university. Fee code M

Frank is a tutor of English whose disillusioned outlook on life drives him to the bottle. Rita is a hairdresser hungry to find some meaning to life. With Frank as her tutor Rita embarks on an Open University course and her education process begins. The effects are both amusing and serious as her fresh, intuitive approach becomes clouded and stifled as she grapples with the problem of a formal education, while Frank also learns something – to believe in himself again. ISBN 978 0 573 11115 0

The Effect of Gamma Rays on Man-in-the-Moon Marigolds. Play. Paul Zindel
F5, or 2 women, 3 girls. A living-room. Fee code M

Encouraged by her teacher, Matilda undertakes a gamma ray experiment with marigolds which wins her a prize at high school – and brings on the shattering climax of the play. Proud, jealous, too filled with her own hurts to accept her daughter's success, Beatrice can only maim when she needs to love, and deride when she wants to praise. Yet, as Matilda's experiment proves, something beautiful can emerge from even the most barren, afflicted soil.

84 Charing Cross Road. Helene Hanff. Adapted for the stage by James Roose-Evans
M3 F4 or 5. Extra 1M. Split set: an apartment and bookshop. Fee code M

In 1949 a struggling American writer started a correspondence with a firm of British antiquarian
booksellers that was to last for twenty years. The warm, compassionate and very human
exchange of letters was published as a book and is here skilfully and lovingly adapted for the
stage. 'An evening of enchantment and charm the like of which is rarely encountered in the
theatre.' *What's On in London*
ISBN 978 0 573 11005 4

♦ **Eigengrau.** Play. Penelope Skinner
M2 F2. Voices. Various simple settings. Fee code L

Feminist activist Cassie is engaged in a fervent struggle against patriarchal oppression. Her
new flatmate Rose believes in true love and leprechauns. Across London, Mark believes in
the power of marketing. His flatmate Tim Muffin is engaged in a fervent struggle just to get
out of bed. Their lives become intertwined. In a city where Gumtree can feel like your closest
friend, looking for the right person sometimes leads you to all the wrong places. Premiered at
the Bush Theatre, London, in 2010.

The Elephant Man. Play. Bernard Pomerance
M5 F3, with doubling and trebling. Composite setting. Fee code M. Music fee code B

The true story of John Merrick, treated first as a fairground freak because of his hideously,
repulsively deformed body and later exploited more subtly by Victorian society. He is befriended
by a young doctor who provides him with a home in the London Hospital where Merrick is
shrewdly used for fund-raising. He is introduced to high society, and is trapped by Victorian
values so incongruous to his reality. Even those who love him can't help him and he dies from
his horrible affliction. Period 1884-90

Elizabeth: Almost by Chance a Woman. Farce. Dario Fo. Translated by Gillian Hanna
M4, with doubling, F2. A bedchamber. Fee code M

In 1601 Queen Elizabeth I of England, afraid of growing old and losing her lover, seeks help in
the remedies of Dame Grosslady, a bawdy dealer in patent medicines. The Dame is a licensed
jester who has an ability to see through to the truth of things, in contrast to the Queen's paranoid
fears and nightmares which come to their climax at the end of the play.

Elsie and Norm's "Macbeth". Comedy. John Christopher-Wood
M1 (late middle-age) F1 (late middle-age). Extra 1M. A living-room. Fee code L

Elsie and Norm have decided to have a bit of a bash at culture by staging a production of
Macbeth in their living-room. After a spot of judicious re-writing by Norm to make it snappier
and more punchy, and undaunted by the large cast, Elsie and Norm set out to act 'one of the
greatest pieces of literature what has ever been wrote in the English language', playing all the
characters between them. The hilarious results set Shakespeare spinning in his grave!
ISBN 978 0 573 01754 4

♦ **A bullet mark next to a title indicates that it is new to this edition of the Guide.**

Elton John's Glasses. Play. David Farr
M4 (21, 24, 30s) F2 (16, 35). A room. Fee code M

Bill is a fanatical supporter of Watford FC. Day after day he sits in his unfurnished flat, watching the 1984 Cup Final with an obsession verging on madness. The video replays the fatal moment when the Watford goalkeeper fumbles the ball and Everton take a two-nil lead. Bill blames the goalkeeper's mishap on the glare from Elton John's glasses. Reconciled to an agoraphobic existence, Bill laments the decline of his beloved team: 'It was there the dream died'.

The End of the Affair. Play. Graham Greene. Adapted for the stage by Rupert Goold and Caroline Butler
M9 F1, 1 boy or M4 F1, 1 boy, with doubling. Various simple settings. Fee code M

Henry Miles, a civil servant, suspects that his wife Sarah is having an affair, and asks his writer friend Maurice Bendrix to contact a private investigator on his behalf. Maurice has a secret, however: he was once Sarah's lover, and is equally keen to find out whether she was unfaithful to him too … An economical and intense adaptation. Period 1943-46
ISBN 978 0 573 01886 2

The End of the Food Chain. Play. Tim Firth
M5 (20s) F1 (20s). Composite set: 3 levels of a grocery distribution depot, plus the roof. Fee code M

Welcome to the 'animal shift' at Kale Moor grocery distribution depot. Under the guidance of Bruce, work here is an endless round of sports and juvenile humour. But a change is due, for their new colleague is not a born games player and is – even worse – a woman. Wildly funny, sharply observed and peopled with vivid, likeable characters, this is another comic gem from the author of *Neville's Island*.
ISBN 978 0 573 01755 1

♦ **The English Game**. A play. Richard Bean
M14. A cricket pitch. Fee Code L

The Nightwatchmen: an amateur London cricket team, making up in enthusiasm for what they lack in ability. As they gather on a sunny Sunday to face Bernard and his ethnically diverse, highly talented squad, Will and his mates spend the day smoking, drinking tea and discussing love, politics and the correct interpretation of the LBW law. ". . . a blinder that knocked me for six.. Catch it!" *Daily Telegraph*
ISBN 978 1 840 02853 9

Enjoy. Play. Alan Bennett
M6 (teenage, 20s, middle-age, 60s) M4 (non-speaking) F3 (20s, 60s). A living-room. Fee code M

Dad thinks everything will be better when the family moves. The social worker who calls to observe their lives turns out to be absent son Terry, idolized by Mam, in drag. Secretary daughter Linda, in reality a prostitute, breezes in, shattering Dad's illusions. The house is dismantled around them to be rebuilt in a park preserving the ideals of family life. Mam will be in a showcase whilst Dad is carted off to the geriatric ward.
ISBN 978 0 573 11129 7

A

♦ **Enlightenment**. A play. Shelagh Stephenson
M3 (20,40,60) F3 (30s, late middle-age). Various simple settings. Fee Code M

Five months since the disappearance of their son Adam, all Lia and Nick can cling to is a vague email mentioning Jakarta, and the possibility that somewhere he may still be alive. As they struggle with uncertainty, a spiritualist and a determined journalist seem to be their only hope. A powerful and timely study of parental grief and of hope amidst fear. First seen at the Peacock Theatre, Dublin.
ISBN 978 0 413 77521 4

♦ **Enron**. Play. Lucy Prebble
M11 F5 (with doubling) Extras. Simple settings. Period 1990s. Fee Code M

In *Enron*, one of the most infamous scandals in financial history is transformed into a theatrical epic. Mixing classical tragedy with savage comedy, the play follows a group of flawed people in a narrative of greed and loss reviewing the tumultuous 1990s and casting new light on the financial turmoil in which the world currently finds itself. " One of the most incisive, most grown-up political dramas of the past 10 years". *Observer*. Samuel French cannot supply any music for use in this play.
ISBN 978 1 40812 476 3

Enter a Free Man. Comedy. Tom Stoppard
M5 (young, 30s, 50s) F3 (18, 20s, 50s). Composite setting. Fee code M

George Riley refuses unemployment on the grounds that he is employed in inventing; unfortunately his inventions are slightly ahead of their time. Every Saturday he sweeps into his local declaring that he has left home to make his fortune. But this Saturday his long-suffering, pocket-money-providing daughter has had enough, and she too runs away, only to discover that her knight in shining motor-cycle gear is already married. Sunday finds them both back at home once again.

The Entertainer. Play. John Osborne
M5 (young, middle-age, 50s, 70s) F3 (young, 22, 60s). A living-room, a front cloth. Fee code M

Archie Rice is a failure as a comedian. News of his son's death while on military service arrives as the family is anticipating his return with a party. Archie tries to stage a comeback for his befuddled, has-been father who, mercifully, dies in the attempt. A prosperous brother offers to send the family to Canada but Archie cannot leave the decaying world of the music hall, where he is at home.
ISBN 978 0 573 11206 5

♦ **Entertaining Angels.** Comedy. Richard Everett
F4 (60s, 30s) M1 (60s). A rural English garden. Fee code L

Newly widowed clergy wife, Grace is at last enjoying the freedom to do and say as she pleases, usually to the new female vicar, Sarah. The return of Grace's eccentric sister prompts disturbing revelations, which force her to confront Bardolph's ghost and the truth of their marriage. Meanwhile, Sarah reveals some unclergy-like credentials of her own to Grace's therapist daughter Jo. Can God can be trusted to do anything right at all, "Or is the whole thing a divine exercise in trial and error?"

Entertaining Mr Sloane. Play. Joe Orton
M3 (young, elderly) F1 (middle-age). A room. Fee code M

A youth named Sloane comes in search of a room, and is then seduced by the landlady. Along comes her homosexual brother, who sets about capturing the affections of the youth for himself. Their father believes he witnessed the youth murder someone and, to silence him, Sloane kicks the old man to death. The landlady and her brother now have Sloane exactly where they want him: each of them will enjoy his company for six months of the year.

Entertaining Strangers. Play. David Edgar
59 characters. Various simple interior and exterior settings. Fee code M

Sarah Eldridge, a beer-brewing tradeswoman, embodies the free-thinking, bustling spirit of a community beginning to reap the rewards of the Industrial Revolution. The rise to commercial eminence runs parallel to the story of Reverend Henry Moule, a hardline fundamentalist who believes brewing to be a sinful trade. During the Dorchester cholera epidemic Moule, spiritually intolerant, proves socially altruistic, while self-interest keeps Sarah away from helping the infectious sick. Period Victorian

Equally Divided. Play. Ronald Harwood
M2 (50s) F2 (50s). Converted old railway carriages. Fee code M

The play begins shortly after the funeral of Edith's and Renata's mother. Edith, severe, embattled, unmarried, has sacrificed her life to nurse the bedridden old woman. Renata, glamorous and married several times, has spent her life doing what she pleases. When the contents of the will are made known, childhood rivalries re-emerge and the result is a moral tale both powerful and comic in this astute, intelligent play.

Equus. Play. Peter Shaffer
M5 (17, middle-age) F4 (20s, middle-age). Extras M. An open stage. Fee code M

Martin Dysart, a psychiatrist, is confronted with Alan Strang, a boy who has blinded six horses, although his parents insist he has always adored horses. Dysart finds the psychological puzzle turns into something far more complex and disturbing – a confrontation with himself as well as with Alan, in which he comes to an inescapable view of man's need to worship and the distortions forced on that need by so-called civilized society.
ISBN 978 0 573 01566 3

The Erpingham Camp. Play. Joe Orton
M6 (middle-age) F3 (young, middle-age). A camp office and bare stage. Fee code F

This is a camp for grown-ups, not for children, and certainly not for fun. In the midst of the activities there is a fight, or rather a free-for-all, during which the headmaster falls through the floor on to the heads of the dancers below, killing several of them. The action concludes with an elegy.

Exit the King. Play. Eugene Ionesco. Translated by Donald Watson
M3 F3. A throne room. Fee code M
ISBN 978 0 573 01123 8

The Exorcism. A Ghost Story. Don Taylor
M2 (38, 40) F2 (30s). A cottage. Fee code M

A

Dan and Margaret have come to spend Christmas with Rachel and Edmund in their renovated seventeenth-century labourer's cottage. Later, as Rachel plays the piano, she suddenly gets a sinister feeling of *déjà vu.* Shortly afterwards, the electricity fails and the phone is out of order too. It is the start of a series of macabre events which mount relentlessly to a bizarre and terrifying climax culminating in a tragic report coming from the TV into an empty brightly-lit room.
ISBN 978 0 573 11120 4

An Experiment with an Air Pump. Play. Shelagh Stephenson
M3 F4. A room. Fee code M

1799 – On the eve of a new century, the house buzzes with scientific experiments, furtive romance and farcical amateur dramatics. 1999 – In a world of scientific chaos, cloning and genetic engineering, the cellar of the same house reveals a dark secret buried for 200 years. Shelagh Stephenson's daring and thoughtful play, inspired by the painting of Joseph Wright of Derby, was joint recipient of the 1997 Margaret Ramsay Award.

Extremities. Play. William Mastrosimone
M1 (young) F3 (young). The living-room of an old New Jersey farmhouse. Fee code M

Helen Mirren and Kevin McNally starred at the Duchess Theatre, London, in this drama about a young woman who is attacked in her own home by a rapist. She manages to overpower the man and imprisons him. When her roommates return, they have to try to talk the victim out of her ultimate revenge. (NB. This play contains violent scenes and explicit language.) '... all the tensions of the classic thriller ... an extraordinary humanity ...' *Daily Mail*
ISBN 978 0 573 60875 9

Faith Healer. Play. Brian Friel
M2 (middle-age, 50s) F1 (middle-age). Simple settings on a bare stage. Fee code M

This is now recognized as one of the masterpieces of Ireland's greatest living playwright. In the course of four monologues the stories unfold of the travelling healer Frank who has gone all over Wales and Scotland with his wife Grace, and his manager Teddy. Brian Friel weaves their versions of the healer's performance and a terrible event into haunting, magnificent art.

The Fall of the House of Usher. Play. Steven Berkoff
M2 F1. Fee code L

Berkoff takes Edgar Allan Poe's horrific tale and explodes the text to create a new form. It is about energy twisted in upon itself and the last stages of obsessive madness.

Fallout. Play. Roy Williams
M7 (late teens (4 Black), 30s (2 Black), early 40s) F3 (late teens (2 Black), early 40s). Various simple settings. Fee code L

When a huge reward is offered in return for information about the killing of a boy, a group of close friends on the estate face the biggest test of street loyalty in their young lives. DC Joe Stephens must return to his old neighbourhood to investigate. The play premièred at the Royal Court Theatre, London in 2003.

The False Servant. Comedy. Pierre Marivaux. New translation by Martin Crimp
M4 F2. Extras. Various simple settings. Fee Code M

Lust and avarice trample on the finer feelings of love in this subversive take on sexual manners and the cruelties of courtship. The man thinks that marriage is simply a matter of money and property. But just how far should the woman go to prove him wrong? A world of darker meaning lies beneath the wit and verbal exuberance of Martin Crimp's translation of Marivaux's great comedy.

Family Circles. Play. Alan Ayckbourn
M4 (20s, 30s, 60s) F4 (20s, 30s, 50s). A living-room. Fee code M

'We all marry the wrong people,' announces Edward Gray and, looking at his three daughters and their unsuitable partners, it is difficult to disagree. Edward's marriage to mousy Emma isn't much better– otherwise why would the daughters suspect they are trying to kill each other? Just as the plot is thickening, there comes Ayckbourn's *coup de théâtre* : the younger couples change partners – and then again! – so that every possible combination is shown to the audience. ISBN 978 0 573 01764 3

The Family Dance. Play. Felicity Browne
M4 (30s, 40, 45, 50) F3 (30s, 40s). A kitchen. Fee code M

The adult members of the Musgrave family are preparing for the children's dance. Ben, head of the family, rails against his position as universal provider. His wife escapes when he comes near. Toby takes refuge from reality in drink and a romanticized past. He is still romantically attached to his wife Victoria, who is consumed with passion for the handsome Charles, whose valetudinarian brother is married to Diana, lynch-pin of the household, who attempts to instill some purpose and organization into this bickering, divided family.

Family Planning. Play. Frank Vickery
M3 (young, 21, 40s) F4 (teenage, 40s, old). Composite setting: a living-room, a bedroom, a hallway. Fee code L. ISBN 978 0 573 01685 1

Far Away. Play. Caryl Churchill
M1 F3. Various simple settings. Fee code L

A girl questions her aunt, having witnessed her uncle hitting people with an iron bar. By the play's end, years later, the world is at war – including birds and animals. The girl has returned to her aunt's and is taking refuge. She describes her journey. "There were piles of bodies and if you stopped to find out there was one killed by coffee or one killed by pins, they were killed by heroin, petrol, chainsaws … the smell of smoke was where we were burning the grass that wouldn't serve."

Far from the Madding Crowd. Play. Adapted by Matthew White from the novel by Thomas Hardy
M5 F3 or 4. Various simple settings. Fee code M (play), code A (music)

The passion, melodrama, earthy humour and strong, gripping plot of Thomas Hardy's novel *Far from the Madding Crowd* are vividly conveyed in Matthew White's fast-moving and admirably economical adaptation. Written to be performed with the simplest of settings and a relatively small cast, this is a powerfully intimate, concentrated theatrical experience. Period 1870s ISBN 978 0 573 01769 4

The Farndale Avenue Housing Estate Townswomen's Guild Dramatic Society Murder Mystery. Comedy. David McGillivray and Walter Zerlin Jnr
M1 F4 (20s-50s). A drawing-room. Fee code L

Every drama group has experienced the horrors of what can go wrong on the night and the ladies of the F.A.H.E.T.G.D.S. are no different, with the possible exception that almost everything that could happen does. The scenery collapses, cues are missed, lines forgotten, as the ladies present their ambitious evening's entertainment with the cunning whodunit *Murder at Checkmate Manor.*
ISBN 978 0 573 11141 9

The Farndale Avenue Housing Estate Townswomen's Guild Dramatic Society's Production of *A Christmas Carol.* Comedy. David McGillivray and Walter Zerlin Jnr
M1 F4 (20s, 40s, 50s). M and F voices. Various simple settings. Fee code K

In festive mood, the F.A.H.E.T.G.D.S. ladies mount yet another assault on the classics with their stage version of *A Christmas Carol.* Enthusiasm their middle name, and with the virile support of stage-manager Gordon, the cast present a dizzy array of characters from the Dickensian favourite (and a few which aren't).
ISBN 978 0 573 01680 4

The Farndale Avenue Housing Estate Townswomen's Guild Dramatic Society's Production of *Macbeth.* Comedy. David McGillivray and Walter Zerlin Jnr
M3 F7 (20s-50s), with doubling. M1 F2 voices only. Simple settings. Fee code K

This uproarious comedy introduces the ladies of F.A.H.E.T.G.D.S., their producer, Plummer, and stage manager, Henry. Their startlingly original production of Macbeth should get them to the Welwyn Garden City Finals, but, under the carefully mascara'd eye of adjudicator George Peach, events conspire against them ...
ISBN 978 0 573 11269 0

♦ **Fat Pig**. Play. Neil Labute
M2 F2. Fee Code M

'Cow'. 'Slob'. 'Pig'. How many insults can you hear before you have to stand up and defend the woman you love? Tom faces just that question when he falls for Helen, a bright, funny, sexy young woman who happens to be plus-sized – and then some. Forced to explain his new relationship to his shallow (although shockingly funny) friends, Tom finally comes to terms with his own preconceptions of the importance of conventional good looks. (Available in the British Isles only)

Fatal Attraction. Thriller. Bernard Slade
M3 (35-50s) F3 (30s, 40s). A living-room. Fee code M

Blair is a famous actress about to be divorced from her second husband Morgan who has called at Blair's hideaway Nantucket beach-house to collect some of his paintings. A second visitor is Tony Lombardi, a photo-journalist who has dogged Blair for fifteen years and whom she has sued for harassment. His obsession with Blair certainly goes beyond professional interest but what motive does he have for murdering Morgan?
ISBN 978 0 573 69009 9

Fatal Encounter. Thriller. Francis Durbridge
M5 F3. A living-room. Fee code M

Howard, a well-known publisher, is concerned for his wife, Joanna, who has become unusually distressed, nervous and mysterious. Events take a sinister turn when Howard arrives home to find Perry, a former friend, has been shot by Joanna in a struggle. She admits that Perry has been blackmailing her, and, to protect her, Howard confesses to the shooting. Perry dies before the police can question him thoroughly and, after a second attempted murder, Howard is the centre of a complex investigation where no-one is blameless.
ISBN 978 0 573 01962 3

Father's Day. Comedy. Eric Chappell
M2 (20s, 50s) F2 (16, 40s). A living-room. Fee Code M

It's a cold winter's evening and bitter divorcé Henry is enjoying another night of glorious solitude. He is soon disturbed, however, by the unwelcome appearance of his son Matthew, bringing with him his new girlfriend, the punk/Goth Christine. Sparks soon fly – but this is just the beginning and before long Henry is facing some important decisions … *Father's Day* is a warm and touching comedy based on Eric Chappell's hit TV series *Home to Roost*.
ISBN 978 0 573 11557 8

Fathers and Sons. Play. Brian Friel from the original novel by Ivan Turgenev
M10 (16, 19, 22, 40s, 60s) F5 (18, 20s, 50s, 70s). Various interior and exterior settings. Fee code M

Adapted from Turgenev's socio-political novel of rural Russia of the mid-nineteenth century, this passionate and powerful play's central topic is the confrontation of the old and the young, of liberals and radicals, romanticism and revolution.

Fawlty Towers. John Cleese and Connie Booth

All complete and unexpurgated scripts of the most celebrated TV sit-com ever are collected in this one volume. For details of the individual episodes please see the entry in Section B.

Fear and Misery of the Third Reich. Play. Bertolt Brecht
Translations: John Willett, music by Hanns Eisler
Eric Bentley
Paul Kriwaczek
About 90 characters M and F. Interior and exterior settings. Fee code M for play, code C for music

The twenty-four scenes of this play could be regarded as separate playlets covering the years from 1933 to just before Hitler's entry into Vienna. Each is preceded and linked by a short verse, forming a sort of kaleidoscope of life under the Nazi dictatorship. The whole forms a horrifying picture of darkest tyranny, but is lightened by the occasional gleams of defiance.

Female Transport. Play. Steve Gooch
M4 F6. Various simple settings. Fee code M

This is an account of six women in nineteenth century London, sentenced to be transported to a life of hard labour in Australia. During the six-month voyage, and while cramped below deck, they come to learn of the bias of a male-dominated society, represented in the play by the crew of the prison ship, that has lead to their sentence. 'A funny play, carried by racy vigour.' *Evening Standard* 'A compelling play.' *Financial Times*
ISBN 978 0 573 69185 0

A

Fen. Play. Caryl Churchill
22 characters, can be played by a cast of 6. Various simple interior and exterior settings. Fee code M

Fen tells the story of a poverty-stricken group of potato pickers working on a farm in the Fens. It traces the fortunes of one of the gang's workers, Val, and how she leaves her family for Frank, a farm labourer, against a general backdrop of greed and commercialism. '...will establish Miss Churchill without question as a playwright who expresses the complexities of the world through the lives of individual women brilliantly.' *Wall Street Journal*

A Few Good Men. Play. Aaron Sorkin
M14 (wide range of ages) F1. Extras. Various simple settings. Fee code M for play, code A for music

Two marines are on trial for their complicity in the death of a fellow marine. Their lawyer makes a valiant effort to defend his two clients and, in so doing, puts the whole US military mentality on trial because the defendants were following orders and are willing to go to jail if need be to maintain the marine honour code. Period 1986
ISBN 978 0 573 69200 0

Fewer Emergencies. Play. Martin Crimp
3 actors (including F1). A bare stage. Fee Code M

Three short pieces: the first depicts a loveless marriage, the second tells the story of a school shooting and the third piece unmasks an emergency that is occurring "right now". Crimp's surreal and cruel script intertwines ideas and shocking truths about life, death, relationships, abuse and emergencies. The play was seen at the Royal Court Theatre, London in 2005. NB. These three pieces must be performed together.

Fiddlers Three. Double bill comedy. Eric Chappell
M5 (20s, 30s, 40, 50s) F2 (20s, 30s). Two adjoining offices. Fee code M

We Don't Want to Lose You and *Cut and Dried* are self-contained one-act plays but can be performed together as *Fiddlers Three*. In the offices of Multiple Holdings, Rex, Harry and Osborne form an uncomfortable alliance against the management, as personified by the devious Fletcher. In the first, Rex, ordered to sack Osborne, offers Fletcher his own resignation in protest. To his horror, it's accepted! In *Cut and Dried* everyone's after Rex's job but Harry ingratiates himself with the bosses to better effect.
ISBN 978 0 573 01980 7

The Fifteen Streets. Play. Adapted by Rob Bettinson from the novel by Catherine Cookson
M8 F8, with doubling. 2 boys 2 girls. Various simple interior and exterior settings. Fee code M

Set in 1910, this tells the story of one family's fight for physical and moral survival in the poverty and squalor of the dockland slums of Tyneside. At the centre is the apparently impossible love affair between rugged docker John O'Brien and Mary Llewellyn, a schoolteacher. With elements of tragedy, humour, intrigue and love, this simple tale affords plenty of scope for imaginative and evocative production.
ISBN 978 0 573 01688 2

A

Fighting Chance. Play. N. J. Crisp
M4 (40s, middle-age) F4 (30s). Basic set representing several interiors. Fee code M

Based on the author's own experiences, *Fighting Chance* is set in a residential rehabilitation centre for neurological patients, and charts the progress made by five patients over the course of eight weeks. The five demonstrate the humour, frustration, anger and pity of their situation, and help each other to progress, each to a different degree, through the course of this funny and ultimately optimistic play.
ISBN 978 0 573 01629 5

Filumena. Play. Eduardo de Filippo, adapted by Keith Waterhouse and Willis Hall
M6 F5. Extras. A dining-room. Fee code M

After twenty-five years Filumena is to be thrown over for a younger woman. She pretends to be dying, inveigling Domenico into a 'deathbed' marriage. When he proves the marriage null and void she informs him she has three grown sons – one of them his. After trying in vain to discover his son's identity he marries her. Filumena keeps the secret and as the play ends they are fully reconciled, with every promise of happiness before them. Period 1946
ISBN 978 0 573 11130 3

Find Me. Play. Olwen Wymark
M3 F5 (variable). A bare stage. Fee code L

At the age of twenty Verity was charged by the police with damaging a chair by fire in the mental hospital where she was a patient. Later she was committed to Broadmoor 'from where she may not be discharged without permission of the Home Secretary'. Using a technique of multiple characterization, the play seeks to investigate in depth the personality of the young girl – to 'find her' – and at the same time studies the effects of her behaviour on those around her.
ISBN 978 0 573 11136 5

First Things First. Comedy. Derek Benfield
M3 (middle aged) F3 (young-60s). A living-room. Fee Code L

George was Pete's best man at *both* of his weddings. They are close. However, Pete is appalled when George arrives with the news that his first wife Jessica was not killed in a climbing accident as they had thought but is alive and keen to resume her life with Pete! This revelation leads to a series of hilarious situations as Pete and George try to find a way out of this desperate plight without upsetting either of Pete's wives or his second wife's powerful mother.
ISBN 978 0 573 11219 5

The Firstborn. Play. Christopher Fry
M10 F3. Pharoah's palace, Miriam's tent. Fee code M

Fish Out of Water (Revised version). Comedy. Derek Benfield
M3 (young, 40s, 50s) F4 (20, middle-age, 50s). A hotel lounge. Fee code K

The peaceful atmosphere of a hotel on the Italian Riviera is shattered by the arrival of Agatha, an outspoken widow, and her timid sister, Fiona. Agatha crushes all protests as she rounds up the guests into communal games, her unflagging spirit of togetherness invading the private lives of the other characters. All the ingredients of package holidays – late flights, double bookings, foreign food etc. – provide an evening of uproarious and innocent fun.
ISBN 978 0 573 11187 7

A

Five Finger Exercise. Play. Peter Shaffer
M3 (19, 20, 40s) F2 (14, 40). A weekend cottage. Fee code M

Walter, a sensitive young German, has been engaged as tutor to Pamela Harrington. He has fled to England from a Nazi father hoping to find a new home and nationality. His stay in the Harrington family begins propitiously, but the Harringtons are a desperately unhappy family. As Clive says, 'This isn't a family. It's a tribe of wild cannibals'. It takes a near tragedy to shock them into an awareness of their cruelty to each other. Period 1950s
ISBN 978 0 573 01132 0

The Five Wives of Maurice Pinder. Play. Matt Charman
M3 (17, 30s, 50s) F5 (20s, 30s, 40s, 50s). A living-room, garden and caravan. Fee Code M

Maurice Pinder is outwardly an ordinary South Londoner. His first wife was unable to have children, so he acquired another to bear him a son. Amazingly, as the play progresses, we see him acquire three more, the marriages taking place at home to avoid charges of bigamy. Yet they all seem to co-exist happily together, each wife having her own night with Maurice, and everything appears to be going well... until Fay brings home a one-night stand.

Flare Path. Play. Terence Rattigan
M7 F4. An hotel lounge. Fee code M

Filmed as *The Way To The Stars* and set in the 1940s, Rattigan's famous play concerns Patricia's love for a film actor, despite her marriage to Flight-Lieutenant Teddy Graham. Going to the hotel to break with Teddy, followed by Peter, Pat encounters Doris, married to a Polish Count, who is one of two pilots not to return from a bombing raid. Hearing the Count's last letter, Pat realizes how much Teddy needs her, and gives Peter his dismissal.
ISBN 978 0 573 11128 0

FlatSpin. Comedy, from *Damsels in Distress*. Alan Ayckbourn
M3 (30s, 50s) F4 (20s, 30s, 40s). An apartment. Fee code M

A night of romance in her luxurious riverside apartment with the good-looking stranger from next door. How can Joanna possibly go wrong? Except the flat isn't hers, her name isn't Joanna, it's Rosie (she's an actress), and heaven knows what the good-looking stranger is really after. Instead of romance comes considerable danger ... Rosie's only way out is to play the role to the end.
ISBN 978 0 573 11565 3

A Flea In Her Ear. Farce. Georges Feydeau, translated by John Mortimer
M9 F5. A drawing-room, the Coq d'Or. Fee code M

Raymonde suspects her husband, Victor, of infidelity and she turns to her best friend, Lucienne, to help her gain proof. They concoct a ploy – based on a perfumed letter – to trap him at the Hotel Coq d'Or. In true Feydeau fashion the plan misfires; the plot is complicated by confused identities, revolving beds, a great many doors and the fact that the foolish hotel porter, Poche, is the exact double of Victor. Period early 1900s
ISBN 978 0 573 01148 1

A

♦ **The Flint Street Nativity.** Comedy. Tim Firth
M7 F5. Various simple settings. Fee code M

A class of seven year olds is about to perform their nativity play - the children are played by adults, who later play their parents so the set changes accordingly to reflect the difference in scale. This warm, witty, funny play is an ideal alternative to the usual Christmas fare with original lyrics set to the tunes of the usual Christmas carols. It was first performed to critical acclaim at the Liverpool Playhouse. Music available separately on hire.
ISBN 978 0 573 11131 0

A Fly in the Ointment. Comedy. Derek Benfield
M3 (19, 50s) F3 (30s, 40s). A living-room. Fee code M

Why should Ron Corley MP, the Minister for the Environment, be searching the seaside bungalow of his ex-mistress Donna? And why does his virtuous wife, Louise, turn up at the same place on the same day? And what was a romantic doctor with a bunch of flowers doing in Sussex when his practice is in London? Add to these questions the presence of a frustrated policewoman and a devious pizza delivery boy ...
ISBN 978 0 573 01761 2

Flying Feathers. Comedy. Derek Benfield
M3 (40, middle-age, 60) F6 (young, 30, 50). A drawing-room. Fee code L

When Chief Constable Henry Potterton and his wife Sarah arrive at the country house of their late lamented brother Bernard, they are astonished to find several scantily-clad ladies wandering about, not knowing that Bernard's housekeeper has turned the place into a 'house of sin'. There are many hilarious comings and goings and when Bernard turns up, proving to be Henry's identical twin, the household is thrown into further confusion and chaos.
ISBN 978 0 573 01657 8

Fools. Comic fable. Neil Simon
M7 F3. A village square, a house. Fee code M

Leon Tolchinsky is ecstatic at landing a job as schoolteacher in the idyllic Ukrainian village of Kulyenchikov in 1890. But the village has been cursed with chronic stupidity for two hundred years and the desperate villagers have hired Leon hoping he can break the curse, which he must do in twenty-four hours or become stupid himself. Instead of leaving he falls in love, gets the girl and breaks the curse. (**Slightly restricted**)
ISBN 978 0 573 60877 3

A Foot in the Door. Comedy. Richard Harris
M3 (young- late 30s (1 black, 1 Polish) F3 (mid-30s- elderly). A sitting-room. Fee Code M

May an elderly widow, has invited several salespeople to her London semi. The first "guest" to arrive is Warren, (windows), soon followed by an increasing array of colourful characters (decorating, keyboard etc). Each salesperson adopts a persona they think will persuade their prospective client to put her money their way, but May's inability to wrench her eyes from her TV – and her lack of interest in any of the products – look set to wreck their hopes.
ISBN 978 0 573 11276 8

A

Forget-Me-Knot. Comedy. David Tristram
M2 (young-middle age) F2 (young-middle age). Split set. Fee code L

Robert Zeinfeld is found wandering the streets of Leicester at 4 a.m. There's no clue how he got there, just a bruised head and a suspicious policeman for company. But … Perhaps he hasn't lost his memory at all; perhaps it's all an elaborate cover-up. The deeper the policeman digs, the more confused he gets. But the truth always comes out in the end. Or does it?

The Forsyte Saga. Play. Pat and Derek Hoddinott, dramatized from the novels of John Galsworthy
M6 F5, M5 F5 with doubling. Extras 1M 1F. Various simple interior and exterior settings. Fee code M

Galsworthy's famous trilogy has been superbly adapted for the stage and achieved enormous acclaim following a national tour, starring Nyree Dawn Porter. Set between 1886 and 1920 with multiple locations cleverly contained within one set – a Victorian-style conservatory – requiring the minimum of props, the play centres on Soames and Irene and the stifling, destructive power of the Forsyte family, embodied in the cold hauteur of Soames.
ISBN 978 0 573 01766 7

Fortune's Fool. Play. Ivan Turgenev. Adapted by Mike Poulton
M7 F2. Extras. A garden room, a drawing-room. Fee code M

This is a fine, Tony Award-winning adaptation of Turgenev's *Nakhlebnik*. The homecoming of Olga Petrovna and her husband, Yeletsky, should be a happy affair for the house's resident penniless gentleman, Kuzovkin. But Tropatchov, a wealthy neighbour who enjoys humiliating all he considers his inferior, connives to get Kuzovkin drunk, revealing a family secret that will challenge its very identity. In a moving denouement Kuzovkin wins back what has been his all along but cannot reclaim his honour. Period nineteenth century
ISBN 978 0 573 01971 5

Forty Years On. Play. Alan Bennett
M5 F2. Schoolboys (minimum of 6). A public school assembly hall. Fee code M

At a public school, now past its prime, the annual school play is being prepared. The progress of the play is severely impeded by the conflicts between the Headmaster and the play's producer, Franklin, and by the behaviour of the boys. *Forty Years On* is original, witty, erudite, moving and frequently hilariously funny.

Francis. Play. Julian Mitchell
M18 F2. Extras. Various simple settings. Fee code M

Saint Francis was born in Assisi in 1181 and in his early life was the playboy son of a rich merchant. Today the whole city is a memorial to him, but even during his lifetime there was conflict in his Order as to how far simplicity and poverty were to be taken. The play pictures him as 'a man whose inspiration could never come to terms with the real world'. Period 1205-1226

Frankenstein. Tim Kelly, adapted from Mary Shelley's novel
M4 F4. 1 set. Fee code L

Perhaps the truest adaptation of Mary Shelley's novel, this play opens on Victor's, a young scientist, and Elizabeth's wedding night. Previously Victor has created a 'Creature' out of bits and pieces of the dead. The creature tracks Victor to his sanctuary to demand a bride to share its loneliness. Against his better judgement Victor agrees and soon the household is invaded by murder, despair and terror! However there is enough macabre humour to relieve the mounting tension.
ISBN 978 0 573 60917 6

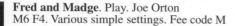

A

Fred and Madge. Play. Joe Orton
M6 F4. Various simple settings. Fee code M

The Freedom of the City. Play. Brian Friel
M16 (20s, 60s, elderly) F1 (43). Extras. A parlour in the Town Hall. Fee code M

Set in Derry in 1970, in the aftermath of of a Civil Rights meeting, this play conjures the events of Bloody Sunday. Three unarmed marchers find themselves in the mayor's parlour in the Guildhall. Reports and rumours exaggerate their 'occupation' to forty armed rebels and they are shot by British soldiers as they surrender. The play documents the victims' final hours and a subsequent tribunal of inquiry into their deaths.

French Without Tears. Comedy. Terence Rattigan
M7 (15, 20, 30, 60) F3 (20s). A living-room. Fee code H
ISBN 978 0 573 01144 3

The Front Page. Play. Ben Hecht and Charles MacArthur
M17 F5. A press room. Fee code M. ISBN 978 0 573 60912 1

Frozen. Play. Bryony Lavery
M1 (30s) F2 (30s). 1M extra. 1 male voice. Various simple settings. Fee code M

Ten-year-old Rhona goes missing. Her mother, Nancy, retreats into a state of frozen hope. Agnetha, an American academic, comes to England to research a thesis entitled "Serial Killing: A Forgivable Act?" Then there's Ralph, a loner with a bit of previous who's looking for some distraction … Drawn together by horrific circumstances, these three embark upon a long dark journey which finally curves upwards into the light. This award-winning play was first seen at Birmingham Rep and revived at the National Theatre, London.
ISBN 978 0 573 11137 2

Funeral Games. Play. Joe Orton
M4 F1. Fee code F

Pringle has called in Caulfield to investigate his wife, who is having an affair with McCorquodale, although Tessa insists she is only giving him blanket baths. According to his religion it would be best if Pringle murders Tessa, although she will in fact live with her patient, who has already killed his wife, Tessa's friend. This is true black comedy in best Orton style, with bogus religion, a severed hand, and a corpse in the cellar.

Funny About Love. Comedy. Terence Frisby
M2 (young, middle age) F2 (young, middle age). A living-room. Fee code L
ISBN 9780 573 01961 6

Funny Business. Comedy. Derek Benfield
M4 F2. A hotel foyer, two bedrooms. FEE CODE L

Ferris has agreed to look after his sister's seedy hotel but hasn't anticipated the arrival of a notorious hotel critic/journalist. Or that this will coincide with an assortment of guests who have guilty secrets they do not wish to have divulged. Ferris is caught up in a dizzy round of lies and subterfuge as he tries to protect the hotel's reputation in the eyes of the journalist, a task made more difficult by the fact that he does not know which of his guests *is* the journalist! A riotous sequel to *Bedside Manners*.
ISBN 978 0 573 01993 7

Funny Money. Comedy. Ray Cooney
M6 F2. A living-room. Fee code M

A

Good friends Betty and Vic arrive for Henry's birthday dinner and Jean is frantic because Henry is late. When he eventually arrives he wants to emigrate immediately, and with good reason: the briefcase he accidentally picked up on the Underground is stuffed with £735,000! When two police inspectors call, Henry, Vic, Betty and a bemused (and tipsy) Jean are forced into a frantic game of cat and mouse. Hilarious innuendo and cruelly funny turns of fate ensue as the two couples assume various identities in their battle to keep the money.
ISBN 978 0 573 01762 9

Fur Coat and No Knickers. Comedy. Mike Harding
M9 (20s, middle-age, elderly) F5 (20s, middle-age), with doubling. Various simple settings. Fee code M

This hilarious play concerns the wedding of Deirdre and Mark. The fun begins on the stag night when an inebriated Mark is chained to a lamppost with a blow-up rubber doll. The wedding itself is quite high spirited too with half the guests, including the priest, suffering blinding hangovers. The play ends in comic chaos when Father Molloy, paralytically drunk, stumbles into the reception clad only in his ecclesiastical underwear, brandishing the blow-up doll!
ISBN 978 0 573 11145 7

Gagarin Way Play. Gregory Burke
M4 (20s, 30s, 50s) A factory storeroom. Fee code M

In a storeroom of a multi-national electronics factory, Tom, an undergraduate security guard, has been supplementing his wage by assisting Eddie, an articulate, self-educated, psychopathic factory worker, in a computer chip scam. Tom returns to the storeroom to discover Eddie, together with anarchist revolutionary Gary, has kidnapped a management consultant with the intention of making a political statement. The consultant isn't Japanese but from Scots mining stock. Eddie declares he's only in it for the violence. Everything goes hilariously, hideously, wrong. Contains strong language.

GamePlan. Comedy, from *Damsels in Distress*. Alan Ayckbourn
M3 (30s, 40s) F4 (16, 30, 40). An apartment. Fee code M

Teenage Sorrel fights to keep herself and her abandoned mother, once a dot.com businesswoman, financially afloat by setting up as a part-time hooker, advertising for clients on the Internet and persuading her tearful school chum to act as her maid. Just when you wonder what will happen in this terrible situation the play becomes a farce about body disposal, police questioning and media intrusion.
ISBN 978 0 573 11567 7

Games. Play. James Saunders
Any number of players. Fee code F. (Published with *After Liverpool.*) Playing time one to one and a half hours according to use made of the material. ISBN 978 0 573 02501 3

Garden. Play. Alan Ayckbourn
Please see the entry under *House & Garden* in this section.

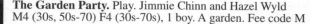

A

The Garden Party. Play. Jimmie Chinn and Hazel Wyld
M4 (30s, 50s-70) F4 (30s-70s), 1 boy. A garden. Fee code M

It's Richard's seventieth birthday. To his home come his children: Sam, unhappily married; Charlie, a discontented alcoholic; and Ben, whose generosity and sense of fun hide a mystery in his life. With Ben comes an unexpected addition to the party: Brice, the first husband of Richard's wife Jan, and the real father to her children. The scene is set for a day and a night of revelations, arguments and moments of tenderness.
ISBN 978 0 573 01879 4

Gaslight. Victorian thriller. Patrick Hamilton
M2 (45, 60s) F3 (19, 34, 50). A living-room. Fee code M

This classic Victorian thriller was first produced in 1938. Jack Manningham is slowly, deliberately driving his wife, Bella, insane. He has almost succeeded when help arrives in the form of a former detective, Rough, who believes Manningham to be a thief and murderer. Aided by Bella, Rough proves Manningham's true identity and finally Bella achieves a few moments of sweet revenge for the suffering inflicted on her.
ISBN 978 0 573 11579 0

Gasping. Comedy. Ben Elton
M3 (young, middle-age) F2 (young) with doubling, or M3 F2, 3 other roles M or F. Various simple settings. Fee code M

Lockheart Industries are making serious money, but Sir Chiffley Lockheart is looking for the buzz given by a new way to make money where no money existed before. Philip, his pushy workaholic exec., suggests selling designer air as a privatized alternative to polluted urban fug. Eventually, oxygen runs low and new supplies have to be found. The third world is plundered for its resources, the world starts gasping and only the biggest suckers survive ... Period 1990
ISBN 978 0 573 01773 5

The Gentle Hook. Play. Francis Durbridge
M6 (30s, 40s, 60) F2 (30s, 50s). A living-room. Fee code M. ISBN 978 0 573 11153 2

Gentle Island. Play. Brian Friel
M11 (10, young, 20s, 30s, middle age, 60s) F3. Composite set: a kitchen, a street. Fee code M

A morning in June. The inhabitants of Inishkeen, the Gentle Island, off the west coast of Co. Donegal, are leaving for good – all except Manus Sweeney and his family. In this parable of Ireland one of the characters remarks, 'There's ways and ways of telling every story. Every story has seven faces', and the title of Friel's brave work belies a set of violent sexual and homosexual tensions. The island's story and history unfold towards a shattering climax.

◆ **A bullet mark next to a title indicates that it is new to this edition of the Guide.**

The Geometry of Love. The Marriage of Lord Byron. Play. Peter Dunne
M8 (20s, 30s, 40s) F7 (20s, 40s), may be played by M4 F3. 1M 1F. Various settings. Fee code K

Set in Regency London, this is the story of the poet Lord Byron, his ever-increasing notoriety and his steps to appease Society by marrying Annabella Milbanke. With debtors on his heels and facing the ignominy of his sexual life being made public, Byron separates from Annabella, parts broken-hearted from the love of his life, his half-sister Augusta, and quits England. This by turns amusing, serious and moving treatment of Byron's flawed personality and the ultimate tragedy it engenders was seen at Barons Court Theatre, London, in 2004. The play contains strong language. Period 1812-16
ISBN 978 0 573 11177 8

Getting Attention. Play. Martin Crimp
M4 F3. Various simple settings. Fee Code M

It's a funny thing attention; too much of it if paid to your private business, not enough when there's a genuine cry for help. A young couple, Carol and Nick, live with her four-year-old child, Sharon. When Nick and Carol have sex, the neighbours listen in, but when the couple begin to violently abuse Sharon, no-one notices. It emerges that Sharon has been scalded and starved, but the bleakness of the story reaches its brutal climax when a social worker visits the house...

Getting On. Play. Alan Bennett
M4 (17, 19, middle-age) F3 (30s, 50s, 60). A basement flat. Fee code K

George Oliver is a middle-aged Labour MP who lives in his middle-class home with his children and his second wife, the bustling, attractive Polly. Disillusioned by the passing years and the changing world George is out of touch with his family, his friends and neighbours, with the world he has tried to improve. 'He's a socialist,' says Polly, 'but he doesn't like people' – the disenchanted reformer.
ISBN 978 0 573 01133 7

Ghetto. Play. Joshua Sobol, in a version by David Lan, with lyrics translated and music arranged by Jeremy Sams
M14 (young, 30s, 40s, 50s) F5 (20s, 30s). Extras. Various simple settings. Fee code M

Set in the Jewish ghetto of Vilna, Lithuania, in 1942, and based on diaries written during the darkest days of the holocaust, *Ghetto* tells of the unlikely flourishing of a theatre at the very time the Nazis began their policy of mass extermination. Premièred in Britain in 1989 at the Royal National Theatre.

The Ghost Train. Drama. Arnold Ridley
M8 (young, 20s, 60, elderly) F4 (20s, elderly). A station waiting-room. Fee code M

Arnold Ridley's classic drama was first produced in 1925 and filmed no less than three times. A very silly young man accidentally strands six passengers at a small Cornish wayside station. Despite the pyschic stationmaster's weird stories of a ghost train, they decide to stay the night in the waiting-room. Soon they regret this decision as ghostly and not so ghostly apparitions materialize before the young man reveals the true reason behind the night's events.
ISBN 978 0 573 01155 9

A

Ghost Writer. Comedy thriller. David Tristram
M3 (20s-30s) F3 (20s-30s). A bedsit. Fee code M

Edward is a promising young playwright and husband of the talented but tempestuous actress Ruby. Tragically, Ruby is found dead in bed: an overdose of naughty pills and booze. A year later, Edward remains deeply affected and has moved into the attic room of one of his oldest actor friends, Alex, who is gay. We join the story on the first anniversary of the death of Ruby Pinfold. May she rest in peace.

Ghosts. Play. Henrik Ibsen, in a new version by Richard Harris. From a translation by J Basil Cowlishaw
M3 F2. A garden room. Fee code M

It should be a happy day in Mrs Alving's household; the day her son returns from Paris and the eve of an orphanage opening dedicated to her late husband. However, as final preparations are being made, old family secrets unravel the perceived identities of the key players. In a rigidly structured society the consequences are disastrous. Ibsen's *Ghosts,* in Richard Harris's new accomplished version, offers a bleak view of the human condition. Period late nineteenth century
ISBN 978 0 573 01969 2

The Gift of the Gorgon. Play. Peter Shaffer
M4 (20s, middle age, elderly) F5 (20s, middle age, elderly). Extras. A living-room and other simple settings. Fee code M

Edward Damson, famous English playwright, has died violently at his remote Aegean home. His son, whom he has never acknowledged, American academic Philip Damson, has had a lifelong obsession with the father he never knew and he begs permission from his stepmother, Helen, to write Edward's biography. She agrees reluctantly on the proviso that he tells the whole story – a story, she warns, he will find painful ... Period 1975 and 1993.
ISBN 978 0 573 01774 2

The Gin Game. A tragi-comedy. D. L. Coburn
M1 F1. A sunporch. Fee code M. ISBN 978 0 573 60976 3

The Gingerbread Lady. Play. Neil Simon
M3 (20s-40s) F3 (17, 40s). A flat. Fee code M

Evy, a popular singer and an alcoholic, completes a ten-week drying-out period. Her friend, her daughter and an actor try to help her adjust to sobriety. But all have the opposite effect: the birthday party washes out, the gingerbread lady falls off the wagon and careers onward to her own tragic end. 'His characteristic wit and humor are at their brilliant best, and his serious story of lost misfits can often be genuinely and deeply touching.' *New York Post* (**Slightly restricted**)
ISBN 978 0 573 60935 0

Give Me Your Answer, Do! Play. Brian Friel
M4 (30s, 50s-60s) F5 (20s, 40s-60s). Composite set: a living-room, a lawn/garden. Fee code M

David Knight is staying in Donegal with novelist Tom Connolly and his wife, Daisy. He has been assessing Tom's papers, which he may purchase. Also visiting are novelist Garret Fitzmaurice and his wife whose marriage may break up, and Daisy's father and arthritic mother who may be soon in a wheelchair. Absent but casting a dark shadow is the Connolly daughter, institutionalized since she was a child. Everybody is waiting for an answer which may – or may not – come.

The Glass Menagerie. Play. Tennessee Williams
M2 (young) F2 (young, middle-age). A living-room. Fee code M

In a St Louis slum apartment lives Amanda Wingfield who clings frantically to another time and place when she was a southern belle with a myriad of 'gentlemen callers'. With her live her son Tom and crippled daughter Laura. Tom spends every spare moment losing himself at the movies while Laura's separation from reality increases until she is like one of her glass collection, too fragile to move from the shelf. Period 1945

Glengarry Glen Ross. Play. David Mamet
M7 (40s, 50s). A restaurant, an office. Fee code M

The scene is a real estate office in America – a fly-by-night operation selling tracts of underdeveloped land in Arizona to gullible Chicagoans. A sales contest is near its end; the winner will get a Cadillac, the second a set of knives, the bottom two get fired. This is the background to Mamet's seedy morality play filled with the spiralling obscenity and comic bluster of the salesmen. 'The dialogue becomes mesmerizing ... rich seam of humour and pathos ... ' *New Statesman*

Glorious! Comedy. Peter Quilter
M2 (30s, 60s) F4 middle age- 70s).Various interior and exterior settings. Fee Code M

Glorious! is based on the life of Florence Foster Jenkins, the legendary New York heiress and socialite who wanted to be a great operatic diva despite having one of the worst singing voices in history, and who used all her money, charm and unstoppable will-power to make it happen. Following the exploits of its attractive and formidable protagonist up until the crowning moment of a sell-out concert at Carnegie Hall, *Glorious!* is a delightful and irresistible account of an extraordinary life. Period 1940s
ISBN 978 0 573 11156 3

God Only Knows. Play. Hugh Whitemore
M3 (50s) F2 (40s, 50s). A terrace. Fee code M

God's Favorite. Comedy. Neil Simon
M5 F2. Interior. Fee code M

Neil Simon's actually made a funny play from the Book of Job – transferring the scene to a Long Island mansion where resides a tycoon, his wife, a prodigal son and a pair of zany twins. Then a messenger from God enters (wearing a big 'G' on his sweatshirt) and everything becomes a test of the tycoon's faith, including his family. 'Awesomely funny ... The work of a man of vision. It'll make you laugh out loud.' *New York Daily News* (**Slightly restricted**)
ISBN 978 0 573 60972 5

Going Dutch. Play. John Godber
M3 (52, 40) F2 (52, 47) or M2 F2 with doubling. Various simple settings. Fee code M

Mark and Sally are travelling to Amsterdam to celebrate Mark's fiftieth birthday at a Bruce Springsteen concert. Unfortunately, they tackle the journey across the channel with their old friend Gill, who arouses conflicting emotions in Mark and has brought along her new boyfriend, Karl, who knows a little too much about Amsterdam's seedier side. Godber's salty comedy about social angst and culture clash is packed with near-the-knuckle language.
ISBN 978 0 573 11189 1

Going Straight. Play. Richard Harris
M2 (mid-60s) F3 (20s, 40s, 60s). 1M Voice only (Spanish). A sitting-room in a Spanish villa.
Fee Code M

As young men, Michael and Ray were East End villains, working together on a series of lucrative crimes. Today Michael is living a comfortable life in Spain while Ray, married to sharp-tongued Brenda, is struggling to make ends meet back in Britain. After two years without any contact Michael has invited Ray and Brenda over to Spain for a visit, but Brenda is suspicious: what are Michael's true motives? NB. Contains strong language.
ISBN 978 0 573 11211 9

The Golden Pathway Annual. Play. John Harding and John Burrows
M13 F7 but can be played by as little as M3 F1. A bare stage. Fee code M

The structure of this play is a loosely connected sequence of sketches, some deliberately written for great comic effect, and others pitched in a much lower key. It is about a boy growing up in the period from the end of the Second World War to the late 1960s. '*The Golden Pathway Annual* has things to say, says them well, looks you in the eye.' *Plays and Players*
ISBN 978 0 573 01666 0

The Good and Faithful Servant. Play. Joe Orton
M3 F3. Fee code F

This is a savage study of the disintegration of an old man when he retires after fifty sterile years in the service of a factory. More badgered than solaced by the attentions of the personnel officer and the works club for retired employees, George Buchanan's belated search for happiness lurches breathtakingly from moments of hilarity to moments of extreme pathos.

The Good Doctor. Comedy. Neil Simon. Music by Peter Link
M2 F3, much doubling and trebling. Various interior and exterior settings. Fee code M. Fee for music available on application to Samuel French Ltd

This comedy, a composite of Neil Simon and Anton Chekhov, from whose short stories Simon adapted the twelve vignettes of this collection, was first seen at the Eugene O'Neill Theatre in New York in 1973 with Christopher Plummer playing a variety of leading roles. **NB: certain Musical Material must be used in all productions, a tape of which is available on hire from Samuel French Ltd.** 'As smoothly polished a piece of work as we're likely to see.' *New York Daily News* 'A great deal of warmth and humour – vaudevillian humour – in his retelling of the Chekhovian tales.' *Newhouse Newspapers* (**Slightly restricted**)
ISBN 978 0 573 60971 8

Good Grief. Play. Keith Waterhouse
M2 (35, 50s) F2 (32, middle-age). A living-room, hall and landing, a pub. Fee code M
ISBN 978 0 573 01777 3

The Good Hope. Play. Herman Heijermans in a new version by Lee Hall. Lyrics by John Tams
M13 (late teens-elderly) F6 (20s-elderly). A quay, a courtyard. Fee code M

The voyage of the *Good Hope* is a journey on which the life of an entire community depends. A storm rages, the women and children wait ashore, an unseaworthy boat forced to put to sea follows the Greenland catch ... This Dutch classic of social realist theatre has been relocated to the Yorkshire fishing community of Whitby in 1900. The choice of music is left to the director.

Good Morning, Bill. Comedy. P. G. Wodehouse, based on the Hungarian of Ladilaus Fodor
M4 F3. A hotel suite, a living-hall. Fee code L

The Good Person of Sichuan. Play. Bertolt Brecht, translated by Michael Hofmann
M14 F8. 1 child. Extras. Various interior and exterior settings. Fee code M

This translation for the National Theatre production in 1989 starring Fiona Shaw, is based
on Brecht's 'Santa Monica' version of the play first staged in 1943. Vibrant and hard-hitting,
Brecht's famous theatrical parable begins when the gods award money to the prostitute Shen
Te but greedy neighbours instantly take advantage of her good nature. 'Michael Hofmann's
translation is engagingly free ...' *Daily Telegraph* '... a beautifully natural-sounding
translation.' *Sunday Correspondent*

The Good Person of Szechwan (**The Good Woman of Setzuan**). Parable play. Bertolt Brecht
Translations: John Willett, music by Freda Dowie and Stephen Oliver
        Eric Bentley, music by Dessau
        Tony Kushner. Edited by Charlotte Ryland
M17 F9. Interior and exterior settings. Fee code M for play, code C for music

Three gods appear on a mission – to find one really 'good' person. A kindly prostitute, Shen Teh,
offers them lodging and is rewarded. To protect herself from spongers she masquerades as her
male cousin, Shui Ta. Later she falls in love with an unemployed airman, finds he also is a sponger,
reverts to the cousin impersonation, and is accused of murdering the missing Shen Teh. The gods
appear as her judges and accept her plea that everything she did was with good intentions.

The Government Inspector. Play. Nikolai Gogol. Translated and adapted by Alistair Beaton
Large mixed cast. A room, an inn room. Period 19th century. Fee Code L

One of the most famous comedies in world theatre, Gogol's masterpiece depicts a small Russian
town where corruption is rife. But when the powers that be learn they're going to be subject to
an undercover government inspection they panic. Mistaking a penniless nobody for the powerful
official they swiftly fall victims to their own stupidity and greed. In this hilarious new translation,
award-winning satirist Alistair Beaton brings to life its dazzling blend of preposterous characters
and all-too-real situations.

Grace Note. Play. Samuel Adamson
M3 (20s, 34) F3 (30s, 67). A living/dining-room. Fee code M

When Grace decides to leave her sheltered accommodation and return to her old home, her
children start to worry. Only Ellie, her daughter-in-law, seems to understand her need to dwell
on the past and her passion for the Australian soprano Joan Sutherland. The family gather
round to protect their inheritance, but behind the mask of genteel senility is cunning: Grace
has plans of her own.

The Grace of Mary Traverse. Play. Timberlake Wertenbaker
M5 F3, with doubling. Extras. Various simple interior and exterior settings. Fee code M

◆ **A bullet mark next to a title indicates that it is new to this edition of the Guide.**

The Graduate. Available in the UK only. Comedy. Terry Johnson, based on the novel by Charles Webb and screenplay by Calder Willingham and Buck Henry
M6 F5 (with doubling).Various simple settings. Fee Code M

A hit in the West End and on Broadway, *The Graduate* brings one of the most popular films of all time vividly to life on stage. A college student spends his first summer out of school in the arms of his father's best friend's wife. Meanwhile, he is falling in love with the man's daughter. Period 1965. Please note only the Broadway version of this play should be performed.
ISBN 978 0 573 62857 3

Grand Magic. Play. Eduardo de Filippo. Translated by Carlo Ardito
M11 (30-60) F8 (17, 20, 30, middle-age). A large hotel garden and two simple interiors. Fee code M

Great Expectations. Play. Hugh Leonard, adapted from the novel by Charles Dickens
M9 F5. Doubling possible. Various interior and exterior settings. Fee code M

Bringing to life all the vivid characters of the original and conveying the story with great clarity, atmosphere and theatrical flair, Hugh Leonard's adaptation of Charles Dickens's most popular novel is both exciting and haunting. Period early 19th century
ISBN 9780 573 01778 0

Greek. Play. Steven Berkoff
M2 F2 (with doubling). Fee code M

An adaptation of *Oedipus*, set in the East End of London.

Greetings! Comedy.Tom Dudzick
M3 (30s, mid 60s) F2 (29, mid 60s) A sitting-room and dining-room, with insert. Fee code M
ISBN 978 0 573 69257 4

Groping for Words. Comedy. Sue Townsend
M2 (young, 50) F2 (young, middle-age). Various simple settings. Fee code K

Joyce begins an Adult Literacy class. Her pupils are Thelma, a nanny, and George who is living in a hostel. Their classes, held in a nursery classroom, are interrupted by Kevin, the caretaker, who is illiterate himself. Act II sees the class three months later. George is making good progress and now living in the Wendy House while Thelma is concerned over her inability to read 'Janet and John'. Things come to a head on Joyce's birthday and culminate in Kevin's heartrending plea: 'Teach me to read'.

The Gut Girls. Play. Sarah Daniels
M6 F11, may be played by M2 F6. Various simple interior and exterior settings. Fee code M

Premièred at London's Albany Empire in 1988 and set in Deptford at the turn of the century this play traces the lives of the girls who work in the gutting sheds of the Cattle Market and how their lives are changed when the sheds are closed down. Although the girls are unwilling participants in a club founded by Lady Helena to find alternative employment the results are not without tragic consequences.
ISBN 978 0 573 01965 4

Gym and Tonic. Play. John Godber
M5 (13, 20, 21, 39/40, 42) F5 (23, 27, 37, 65, 72). Can be played by M3 F3 with doubling. Various simple interior and exterior settings. Fee code M

Don and Shirley Weston have come to the Scardale Hall Health Hydro to relax, pamper themselves and just possibly rescue their ailing marriage. Don's experiences with exercise and therapy are far from positive and the rifts in the marriage widen as his mid-life crisis becomes more and more evident, and moments of reconciliation do little to improve the situation.
ISBN 978 0 573 01807 7

Habeas Corpus. Play. Alan Bennett
M6 F5. A bare stage. Fee code M

Simply staged, this play introduces the Wicksteeds, a family for whom the determination to put sex and the satisfaction of the body before everything else is the ruling passion of their lives. Permissive society is taken to task in this farcical comedy in which the characters move in and out through a maze of mistaken identities and sexual encounters. As Wicksteed says, 'He whose lust lasts, lasts longest'.
ISBN 978 0 573 01325 6

Hapgood. Play. Tom Stoppard
M7 (11, 20s-40s (1 Black), 50s) F1 (38). 1 boy (11). Various simple interior and exterior settings. Fee code M

Duality is the name of the game in Tom Stoppard's intricate spy thriller, seen at the Aldwych Theatre in 1988, where double agents, duplicity, twins and quantum physics are inextricably bound together. Hapgood runs a British counter-espionage agency in Mayfair and someone is leaking information to Moscow ...
ISBN 978 0 573 01781 0

The Happiest Days of Your Life. Farce. John Dighton
M7 (12, 20-50s) F6 (14, 20-50s). A masters' common-room. Fee code M

The masters of Hilary Hall School for Boys are told that St Swithin's, a girls' school, will be billeted upon them. The staff try desperately to conceal the fact that boys and girls are housed together, but in vain, for the parents find out. They are about to remove their offspring when a message arrives: a third school is to share Hilary Hall. Against this common enemy, both staff and parents unite to barricade the gates. Period 1940s
ISBN 978 0 573 0 1169 6

Happy Birthday. Comedy. Marc Camoletti, adapted by Beverley Cross
M2 (30s) F3 (20, 36). A living-room. Fee code M

Bernard invites his mistress, Brigit, to his home on her birthday despite the fact that his wife Jacqueline is present. To lull Jacqueline's suspicions he has also invited his oldest friend, Robert, and asks him to complete the cover-up by pretending that Brigit is his own mistress. Thus are laid the foundations for a shaky edifice of frantic complications, in which identities, plots and bedrooms are changed around with ever-increasing confusion.
ISBN 978 0 573 11172 3

Happy Families. Play. John Godber
M3 (young-70s) F6 (young-70s), may be played by M3 F5. Various simple settings. Fee code M

Full of warmth, understanding and humour, this is an affectionate and appealing portrait of an ordinary family struggling with change, bereavement and the generation gap. On his graduation day in 1978, John looks back over his teenage years, from 1967-1973, recalling all the embarrassments, tensions, joys and sorrows of family life in West Yorkshire. Older and better educated, he finds himself alienated from his working-class family who cannot understand his growing intellect and theatrical aspirations.
ISBN 978 0 573 01782 7

Happy Jack. Play. John Godber
M1 F1. A bare stage. Fee code M

Hard Feelings. Play. Doug Lucie
M3 F3. A living-room/ kitchen area. Fee code M

Hard Times. Play. Stephen Jeffreys, adapted from the novel by Charles Dickens
M2 F2 (minimum). Various interior and exterior settings. Fee code M

The wide expanse of Dickens's novel on the riches and hardships of the Industrial Revolution is triumphantly brought to life in this skilful adaptation. The nineteen or so main speaking parts are portrayed by two actors and two actresses, although it can be produced on a larger scale with each role cast individually. 'The strength of this version ... is its preservation of the satiric vitality of Dickens's original, and a real feel for the superb rhetoric of his prose.' *Time Out*
ISBN 978 0 573 01659 2

Haunted. Play. Eric Chappell
M4 (30s, 40s, middle age) F2 (30s). A study. Fee code M

Nigel Burke, aspiring playwright, is neurotic and agoraphobic and hasn't written a word for three months, to the chagrin of his wife, agent and friends. He is visited by the mysterious Potter, who knows of Nigel's interest in Byron and gives him a goblet used by the poet. Drinking from the goblet brings about subtle changes in Nigel's confidence and manner – and then, out of nowhere, Byron himself appears! *Haunted* is a flippant and exciting play from the author of *Natural Causes*.
ISBN 978 0 573 01794 0

The Haunted Through Lounge and Recessed Dining Nook at Farndale Castle. Comedy.
David McGillivray and Walter Zerlin Jnr
M1(20) F5 (20-50). A through lounge, car, bedroom. Fee code K

The ladies of the Farndale Avenue Housing Estate Townswomen's Guild Dramatic Society make yet another spectacle of themselves, complete with their harassed producer and some extremely vigorous sound effects, in this sinister, spine-chilling mystery of murder and mayhem that is guaranteed to bring the house down, or at least a substantial part of the set.
ISBN 978 0 573 01615 8

◆ **A bullet mark next to a title indicates that it is new to this edition of the Guide.**

Hay Fever. Comedy. Noël Coward
M4 (young, middle-age) F5 (young, middle-age, elderly). A hall. Fee code M

A

The Bliss family are ultra-Bohemian. One Saturday, they all casually announce that they have invited guests for the weekend, and each Bliss is furious. When the guests arrive, they suffer an uncomfortable tea and then, after dinner, have to play a word game which only the family understand. The evening is capped by a histrionic display by the whole family which succeeds in sending their terrified guests scuttling away by the first train the following morning. Period 1925
ISBN 978 0 573 01174 0

Haywire. Comedy. Eric Chappell
M2 (20s, 50s) F4 (20s, 30s, 50s, 70s). A living-room. Fee code M

Alec Firth is having an affair with his assistant, Liz, and has organized his domestic life so that they can go to Spain on holiday without making Alec's wife Maggie remotely suspicious. What could possibly go wrong? The answer: plenty. On the doorstep, in dizzyingly rapid succession, are: Phoebe, Alec's mother, who has discharged herself from her old people's home; Alec's son Jamie, with a broken ankle; and his daughter Mandy, heavily pregnant and not planning to marry the child's father ...
ISBN 978 0 573 01798 8

Heatstroke. Comedy. Eric Chappell
M4 (30s, 50) F2 (20s, late 30s), 1F voice. 2M extras. A living-room/terrace. Fee code M

Assumed identities, breakneck pace and hilarious mishaps of farce mix with the tension and startling plot reversals of a thriller in this clever, amusing play which toured as *Snakes and Ladders* in 2002. The Spencers arrive for a peaceful holiday in a luxurious Spanish villa, closely followed by actor Howard Booth and his girlfriend. Unfortunately, Sam and Howard have matching holdalls which have become mixed up. Yet a third, identical holdall, full of money, brings the sinister Raynor to the villa ...
ISBN 978 0 573 01800 8

Hedda Gabler. Play. Henrik Ibsen. A new version by Christopher Hampton
M3 (29, 33) F4 (33, 45, 65). A drawing-room. Fee code M

The Ibsen classic, in a new version by Christopher Hampton, was seen at the Royal National Theatre in 1989 starring Juliet Stevenson as Hedda '... Hampton's was, above all, language made to be spoken not quoted. As such it is the key to the production's success in establishing the sense of the, at times, appallingly comic spectacle oa claustrophobic and fragile world coming apart at the seams.' *What's On*
ISBN 978 0 573 01693 6

Hedda Gabler. Play. Henrik Ibsen, adapted by John Osborne
M3 F4. Fee code M

Hedda's father seems to have been the only person Hedda loved. He left her his duelling pistols and in her hands they play an important part in the life of more than one person. Thea is loving, talented, and doomed, it seems, to be one of Hedda's victims. Yet at the end Thea saves herself through her own unselfish love of another victim of Hedda's cruelty. John Osborne's adaptation of Ibsen's drama was first seen at the Royal Court Theatre in 1972 with Jill Bennett in the role of Hedda.

Henceforward ... Play. Alan Ayckbourn
M2 (40s) F3 (teenage, 30s, 40s). Extras 1M 1 girl. A studio. Fee code M

In a fortified, steel-shuttered flat in North London, lonely composer Jerome sits surrounded by sophisticated, high-tech audio-visual equipment with only a robot nanny for company. Jerome desperately wants to get his teenage daughter back from his estranged wife, and enlists the services of Zoë, an unemployed actress, in his cunning plan. When his plan doesn't work, Jerome has to improvise and it's amazing what can be done with some new microchips and a screwdriver ...
ISBN 978 0 573 01691 2

Pirandello's **Henry IV**. In a version by Tom Stoppard
M9 F2. A throne room, a room. Fee Code M

A twenty-first-century Italian nobleman dressed as Henry IV falls from his horse during a pageant. When he comes round, he believes he is the medieval German Emperor, King Henry IV. For twenty years he lives this illusion but today a plot is being hatched to shock him out of this "madness" and into the twenty-first century.

♦ **Her Naked Skin.** Play. Rebecca Lenkiewicz
M15 (20s-60s) F10 (20s-70s). Extras. Doubling/trebling possible. Various simple settings. Fee code M. Period 1913

London 1913. Militancy in the Suffragette Movement is at its height. Thousands of women of all classes serve time in Holloway Prison in their fight to gain the vote. Amongst them is Lady Celia Cain who feels trapped by both the policies of the day and the shackles of a frustrating marriage. Inside, she meets a young seamstress, Eve Douglas, and her life spirals into an erotic but dangerous chaos. Premièred at the National Theatre, London, in 2008.

Heroes. Comedy. Gérald Sibleyras. Translated by Tom Stoppard
M3 (elderly). A terrace. Period 1959. Fee code M

It's 1959 and Philippe, Gustave and Henri, three veterans from the First World War, dream of making their escape from the soldiers' home, if not to Indochina then at least as far as the poplar trees on the hill ... This translation of Gérald Sibleyras' play, a smash hit in Paris under the title *Les Vents des Peupliers*, premiered at Wyndham's Theatre, London, to critical acclaim, starring Richard Griffiths, John Hurt and Ken Stott.

Hiawatha. Play. Michael Bogdanov
M8 F3. Extras if required. A giant tepee. Fee code M. Certain music must be used with this text. Please enquire for details. ISBN 978 0 573 01786 5

♦ **Hi-de-Hi.** Comedy. Paul Carpenter and Ian Gower, adapted from the original TV series by Jimmy Perry and David Croft
M9 F8. Various simple settings. Fee code M. Period 1950s

In this stage adaptation of the hugely popular TV series by Jimmy Perry and David Croft, Paul Carpenter and Ian Gower revisit the 1950s and Maplin's Holiday Camp with its host of colourful characters – Gladys Pugh, entertainments manager Jeffrey, Peggy the chalet-maid, comic Ted and his assistant Spike, ballroom dancers Yvonne and Barry and the rest of the yellowcoats. Hi-de-hi, campers!
ISBN 978 0 573 11168 6

Hidden Laughter. Play. Simon Gray
M5 (teenage, middle-age, elderly) F3 (teenage, 30s). Composite setting: garden, kitchen and sitting-room. Fee code M

Harry and Louise, a London couple, decide they have found the perfect weekend retreat in a Devon cottage: they can escape London's trials and traumas, their two children can grow up with nature and without television, and Harry's widowed father can relax. But the wiles of the outside world obtrude into this rural idyll and the cottage is soon for sale, leaving a trail of failure and disillusionment in its wake.
ISBN 978 0 573 01784 1

The History Boys. Play. Alan Bennett
M11 (17-18, 25, 40s, 50). F1 (middle age) Extras. A classroom. Period 1980s. Fee code M

An unruly bunch of bright, funny sixth-form boys in pursuit of sex, sport and a place at university. A maverick English teacher at odds with a shrewd supply teacher. A headmaster obsessed with results; a history teacher who thinks he's a fool. Staff room rivalry and the anarchy of adolescence provoke insistent questions about history and how you teach it; about education and its purpose. NB. A performing licence does not include permission to use the copyright music.

Hitchcock Blonde. Play. Terry Johnson
M3 (20s, 40s,) F2 (20s). Simple settings.. Fee Code M

Cleverly intertwining three stories concerning film director Alfred Hitchcock, *Hitchcock Blonde* sees Alex, a media tutor suffering from a mid-life crisis, invite one of his students to Greece to examine a long-lost film fragment that Hitchcock made in 1919. Meanwhile, in 1959, Hitch is auditioning Blonde, an actress, for the shower scene of his film *Psycho*, and finally, the lost film is recreated, arguably explaining the director's obsession with persecuted blondes. NB. The play contains nudity. Period 1999, 1959, 1919.

Hobson's Choice. Lancashire comedy. Harold Brighouse
M7 (26, 30, 50s, elderly) F5 (20s, elderly). Three interiors. Fee code M

Henry Hobson, widower and boot-shop proprietor, twits his daughter Maggie on her being past the marrying age. Maggie retaliates by marrying Hobson's best boot-hand, Will Mossup, and turning this retiring youth into a sturdy fellow whose new confidence makes him a real business rival to Hobson. Bowing to the circumstances, Hobson has no choice but to accept Will as partner in the new firm of 'Mossup and Hobson'. Period 1880
ISBN 978 0 573 01181 8

Hock and Soda Water. Play. John Mortimer
M6 F3. Extras. May be played by M5 F3. Various simple settings. Fee code M

Holiday Snap. Comedy. Michael Pertwee and John Chapman
M4 (40, 50) F3 (20, 30, 70). Extra 1F. The living-room of a villa. Fee code M

A time-share villa has been double booked unbeknown to the company rep, myopic tippler 'Chitto' Chittenden. When Mary and Henry arrive shortly after Eve and Leslie, Chitto manages to remain unaware that there is more than one couple on the scene. The confusion is compounded when each couple mistakes the other for the servants and what follows is a tale of comic predicament and mistaken identity which unfolds with real wit and style.
ISBN 978 0 573 11284 3

The Hollow. Play. Agatha Christie
M6 (38, 40, elderly) F6 (30s, 60). A sitting-room. Fee code M

Gathered at the home of Sir Henry and Lucy Angkatell are various guests amongst whom is
Dr John Cristow, his mistress Veronica, his ex-mistress and his wife. Veronica ardently desires
to marry Cristow but he refuses to divorce, and Veronica unwisely declares that if she can't
have him no-one else will. Within five minutes he is dead. Nearly everyone had a motive and
opportunity to murder Cristow, but who actually committed the deed has to be discovered by
Inspector Colquhoun and Sergeant Penny.
ISBN 978 0 573 01182 5

The Hollow Crown. Anthology devised by John Barton
M3 F1, 1 musician. Fee code L

A unique entertainment composed of the letters, speeches, poems, songs and music by and
about Kings and Queens of England. Against a background of the simplest design, four readers
and a musician can perform this work, which sparkles with the wit of several centuries and
demonstrates the vulnerable humanity of those who have worn the crown. The script in this
volume is that of the version of *The Hollow Crown* that played at the Royal Shakespeare Theatre,
Stratford-upon-Avon, in March 2005.
ISBN 978 0 573 01183 2

Holmes and the Ripper. Play. Brian Clemens. Based on the book *Jack the Ripper, the Final
Solution* by Stephen Knight
M14 F6 can be played by M8F5 or M8 F3. Various simple settings. Fee code M. Typescript
on hire

A fast-moving dramatization of one of the most plausible of Ripper theories will prove an instant
magnet for audiences as well as a satisfying play to perform. Sherlock Holmes and Dr Watson
become embroiled in the grisly murders in Whitechapel, East London in 1888.

The Holy Terror: Melon Revised. Play. Simon Gray
M7 (17, young, middle-age, elderly) F3 (young, 30s-40s), may be played by M4 F3. A platform,
the mind. Fee code M

Home. Play. David Storey
M3 (middle-age, elderly) F2 (middle-age). A terrace. Fee code J

Two elderly gentlemen stroll on to an almost bare terrace. They discuss various subjects – the past,
schooldays, climate, the sea, moustaches, the war, families, etc., etc. It is not until the following
scene when we meet two women that we realize we are actually in the grounds of a mental
hospital, and that these people are patients. Although with no plot at all in the conventional sense
and sparse dialogue, by the end of the afternoon we have been moved to compassion and respect.
ISBN 978 0 573 01220 4

Home Before Dark, or the Saga of Miss Edie Hill. Play. Jimmie Chinn
M12 (teenage-40s, 2 black) F9 (teenage-middle-age). Extras. Various simple settings. Fee code M
ISBN 978 0 573 01787 2

The Home Place. Play. Brian Friel
M8 (14-60s) F3 (20s, 30s, middle age) 1 girl(11). A garden, a breakfast room. Fee Code M

Widowed Christopher Gore, his son David and their housekeeper Margaret, the woman with whom they are both in love, live at The Lodge in Ballybeg. But in the era of unrest at the dawn of Home Rule, their seemingly serene life is threatened by the arrival of Christopher's English cousin, who unwittingly ignites deep animosity among the villagers. Period 1878.

The Homecoming. Play. Harold Pinter
M5 (30, 63, 70) F1(30). One interior. Fee code M

Teddy arrives home to pay his family a visit with his wife Ruth, who settles into the household as if into a well-known niche. Teddy's brothers and his father all take it for granted that she is anyone's for the asking – and she is. It is then suggested that they should set her up in trade, in a little flat in Soho. Calmly Ruth lists the conditions she requires before acceptig, barely batting an eyelid as Teddy returns to America.
ISBN 978 0 573 01555 7

Honeymoon Suite. Play. Richard Bean
M3 (18, 43, 67) F3 (18, 43, 67). A hotel suite. Fee code M

If Romeo and Juliet had lived, would their marriage have survived? How long? How would the union have coped with poverty, corruption, his ignorance, her aspiration, an ungrateful daughter, no sons, infidelity with an attractive bloke in a night class, God knows how many miscarriages and even murder? In a honeymoon suite in Bridlington, Eddie and Irene begin married life with great excitement, but the future may have other ideas … The play premièred at the Royal Court Theatre, London, in 2004.

Hotel Paradiso. Farce. Georges Feydeau and Maurice Desvallieres. English adaptation by Peter Glenville
M9 F8. Extras. Two interiors. Fee code M

The Hothouse. Play. Harold Pinter
M6 F1. Composite set: 2 offices, a stairway, a sitting-room, a soundproof room. Fee code M

It is Christmas Day and a mysterious death and an unexpected birth are troubling Roote, the director of a Government 'rest home'. Who the patients are and what they might be suffering from, we never discover, but as the unstable, megalomaniacal and terminally insecure Roote begins to investigate, we find that the other members of staff are, in various ways, as mad and as dangerous as the people they are supposed to be helping.

The Hound of the Baskervilles. Mystery play. Tim Kelly, from the thriller by Sir Arthur Conan Doyle
M5 (young, 40s, 50s) F5 (young, 50s). A sitting-room. Fee code L. ISBN 978 0 573 61041 7

♦ **A bullet mark next to a title indicates that it is new to this edition of the Guide.**

House & Garden. Two interlinked plays. Alan Ayckbourn
M6 (20, 30s-late 50s-early 60s) F8 (17, 30s-50s). Children (7-8). Extras. A sitting-room, a garden. Fee code M for each play

Two plays with the same characters running simultaneously in adjacent auditoria, actors leaving one stage to join the action on the other – who else but Alan Ayckbourn could have devised such a scheme? In *House*, Teddy Platt, whose marriage is spectacularly on the rocks, is visited by the creepy Gavin Ring-Mayne, who is trying to persuade him to stand for Parliament; in *Garden*, Teddy's jilted mistress threatens suicide as a garden fête is prepared.
ISBN 978 0 573 01978 4

House Guest. Thriller. Francis Durbridge
M4 (young, middle-age) F4 (young, middle-age). A living-room. Fee code M

Robert and Stella learn that their son has been kidnapped – not for ransom, but to force them to allow one of the kidnappers to remain in their house. Two other men, supposedly police officers, arrive and reveal that one of the kidnappers has been murdered. Soon, however, it is clear that these two are far from what they seem. A highly exciting thriller, first seen at the Savoy Theatre in 1982 with Gerald Harper and Susan Hampshire.
ISBN 978 0 573 11178 5

The House of Bernarda Alba. Tragedy. Federico García Lorca. Translated by Richard L. O'Connell and James Graham-Luján
F11. Extras. A living-room. Fee code J

The House of Dracula. Comedy-horror. Martin Downing
M7 F5, extra 1M; or M6 F5, extra 1M, with doubling. A castle hall. Fee code L

Hailed as 'A Monster Hit' by the Yorkshire Evening Post, this clever spin-off from *The House of Frankenstein!* sees the Baron, Baroness and their repulsive retainers, Ygor and Frau Lurker, going to stay at a macabre Transylvanian fortress. Excitement turns to terror, however, when they are greeted by more than a few of their mortal (and immortal) enemies. A wickedly funny, fast-moving horror farce.
ISBN 978 0 573 01790 2

The House of Frankenstein! Comedy-horror. Martin Downing
M6 (30s, 40s) F4 (20s-40s). A castle hall. Fee code L

Baron Von Frankenstein, bored with his attempts to give life to the lifeless, has turned his attention to curing the supposedly incurable. He plays host to various mysterious and menacing denizens of the night (invited or otherwise) who visit the Baron to beg him to rid them of their vices. But his challenge, although a welcome diversion for the headstrong young scientist, proves to be no picnic ... more of a living nightmare!
ISBN 978 0 573 11356 7

◆ **A bullet mark next to a title indicates that it is new to this edition of the Guide.**

Edith Wharton's **The House of Mirth**. Adapted by Dawn Keeler
M5 (20s, 30s, 40s, 50s) F5 (20s, 30s, 40s). Grand Central Station. Fee code M

A

Set in New York in the early part of the twentieth century the play charts the disastrous career of socialite Lily Bart. Educated to be nothing more than a highly decorative ornament, she is forced by her father's financial ruin into the invidious status of impoverished house guest of rich friends while in pursuit of a wealthy husband. But Lily's ultimate tragedy is her inability to forsake her free spirit and independence to achieve that goal.
ISBN 978 0 573 69573 5

How the Other Half Loves. Comedy. Alan Ayckbourn
M3 (30s, middle-age) F3 (30s, 40s). Two merged living-rooms. Fee code M

In this suburban trio of married couples, one couple is at the top of the social ladder. One of the other couples is attractive and upcoming, despite the fact that she is an utter slob and he is a boor; and the third pair is socially hopeless but earnest. The action takes place at two dinner parties given on consecutive nights. The single set, representing two living-rooms, is almost a character in itself.
ISBN 978 0 573 11166 2

Howard Katz. Play. Patrick Marber
M22 F10, 2 boys, may be played by M5 F2, 1 boy. Various simple settings. Fee code M

Howard Katz received its première at the National Theatre in 2001 and, with *Dealer's Choice* and *Closer*, completes a loose trilogy set in contemporary London. Howard Katz, foul-mouthed, aggressive Jewish showbiz agent of C-list celebrities, has hit fifty and a major mid-life crisis. Told in flashback, we witness his life falling apart until his final life-affirming plea: "Tell me how to live." "Patrick Marber's desperately moving, often bleakly funny new play ..." *What's On*

Humble Boy. Comedy. Charlotte Jones
M3 (35, 60s) F3 (30s, late 50s). A garden. Fee code M

All is not well in the Humble hive. Felix Humble is a Cambridge astro-physicist in search of a unified field theory. Following the sudden death of his bee-keeping father, Felix returns home to his difficult and demanding mother, where he soon realizes that his search for unity must include his own chaotic home life. Parallels are drawn with the plot of *Hamlet* as this wry, witty and very funny portrait of middle-class England is revealed.

Hysteria. Play. Terry Johnson
M3 (60s, old) F1 (20s-30s). A room. Fee code M

♦ **I Am Of Ireland: An Entertainment of W.B. Yeats**. Edward Callan
M1. One simple setting. Period 1890-1937. Fee code L

An elderly Yeats prepares to write his will and reminisces on his life as a poet, playwright and political figure in Ireland. Yeats talks about his literary influences and inspiration, his nationalist activity, his affair with Maud Gonne, friendships with Oscar Wilde, Lady Augusta Gregory and John Synge, his later exploration of automatic writing with his wife Georgie, and being awarded the Nobel prize for literature. This challenging two-act monologue is an evocative tribute to Yeats and his Ireland.

I Dreamt I Dwelt in Marble Halls. Play. Ade Morris,based on a short story by Bryan Gallagher M3 (20s, 30s, 70s) F2 (20s to older), or M2 F1 with doubling. A croft, a hoolie room, a barracks.. Fee Code L

At a dilapidated smallholding near Enniskillen, Northern Ireland, two men are the only mourners at the funeral of "Mad" Maddy Ingram. Ade Morris's play skilfully weaves the narrative backwards and forwards through a span of 50 years as the men share their memories of this remarkable woman, resulting in a richly emotive, lyrical drama of enduring love. Period 1930s – 1980s
ISBN 978 0 573 11570 7

I Have Been Here Before. Play. J. B. Priestley
M4 (28, 40s, 60s) F2 (28, 35). An inn sitting-room. Fee code H

Dr Görtler believes that a future dimension of time can be entered in dreams, and is drawn to a Yorkshire inn in search of proof. He had dreamed of an unhappy couple coming to this inn, the wife meeting a lover, and the discovery driving her husband to suicide. To his horror, Dr Görtler sees the dream in danger of becoming reality. He warns them of the potential unhappiness and fortunately, they heed him. Written in 1938
ISBN 978 0 573 01194 8

I Remember Mama. Play. John van Druten
M11 (teenage, young, 40s, 50s, elderly) F15 (young, 20s, 40s, 50s) 2 boys. Three interiors and insets. Fee code M. Period 1910
ISBN 978 0 573 01197 9

Icecream. Play. Caryl Churchill
M7 F6, may be played by M3 F3. Various simple settings. Fee code H

Produced to acclaim at the Royal Court Theatre, this eighty-minute play was subsequently produced in New York as a double bill with *Hot Fudge*. A middle-class American couple travel to England on a genealogical search and find third cousins who are decidely low-life and whom they aid following a violent event. Who is the worse: the doer of evil deeds or he who enables him to continue? 'Highly comic ... works like a short, sharp shock: an acidly entertaining statement about mutual cultural incomprehension.' *Guardian*

♦ **If I Were You.** Play. Alan Ayckbourn
M3 (40s,20s,15) F2 (40s,20s). Composite set. Fee Code M

The Rodales seem like an ordinary family, but beneath the surface things are beginning to crack. Jill and Mal have lost the spark in their marriage and Sam and Chrissie, their children, have their own problems. Waking up one morning, Mal and Jill see things from a dramatically different perspective – Mal is in Jill's body and Jill in Mal's. Will seeing things from the other side make matters worse, or is this just what they need in order to save their family?
ISBN 978 0 573 11195 2

♦ **A bullet mark next to a title indicates that it is new to this edition of the Guide.**

If We Are Women. Play. Joanna McClelland Glass
F4 (18, 40s, 60s). A beach-house veranda, a kitchen and dining area. Fee code M

Jessica, a writer approaching middle-age, her mother Ruth (who is unable to read or write) and her Jewish mother-in-law, Rachel, find themselves emotionally stranded in Jessica's Connecticut beach home. Weighing the choices each have made as women, as daughters, as mothers, their recollections of guilt and regret are punctuated by wry observations on sex, history, ideas and their relationships with the men in their lives.
ISBN 978 0 573 13009 0

I'll Be Back Before Midnight! Thriller. Peter Colley
M2 (30s, 50s) F2 (20s). A farmhouse living-room. Fee code M

Following a nervous breakdown, Jan is brought to an isolated farmhouse by her husband Greg, ostensibly to complete her recovery. But unsettling things start to happen as soon as they arrive. First, Greg's sister Laura, with whom he seems to have an unnaturally close relationship, arrives. There is also George, the slightly demented old farmer who lives nearby. A nightmare of frightening occurrences results in a thrilling and heart-stopping ending!
ISBN 978 0 573 01652 3

I'll Get My Man. Farce. Philip King
M4 (20s, 40s, 60s) F5 (20s, 40s). A lounge-hall. Fee code L

Peter, a famous television series hero, seeks refuge at a country rectory with his mild Uncle Humphrey from all the females who continually chase after him. Humphrey, horrified by the dismissal of his housekeeper by his formidable sister, advertises for a wife, but absent-mindedly omits the important word 'marriage'. Answers to the advertisement arrive by the sack-load and the arrival of the dignified Bishop of Lax adds to the hectic confusion.
ISBN 978 0 573 01533 5

I'll Leave it to You. Comedy. Noël Coward
M4 (20s, 40s) F6 (young, middle-age). 1 girl. A hall. Fee code M. ISBN 978 0 573 61060 8

I'm Not Rappaport. Comedy. Herb Gardner
M5 (16, 35, 40s, 80 (one Black)) F2 (25, 40s). Central Park. Fee code M

This warm comedy concerns two octogenarians determined to fight off all attempts to put them out to pasture. Nat is a lifelong radical determined to fight injustice (real or imagined) and has a delightful repertoire of eccentric personas, which makes the role an actor's dream. The other half of this unlikely partnership is Midge, a black apartment janitor who spends his time hiding out from tenants who want him to retire.

The Imaginary Invalid. Play. Molière. Adapted by Miles Malleson
M8 (25, middle-age, 50s-70s) F4 (15, 20s, 30s). A sitting-room. Fee code H
ISBN 978 0 573 01200 6

Imaginary Lines. Comedy. Reggie Oliver
M2 (30s, 60s) F3 (20s, 30s, 60s). A flat and a bookshop. Fee code L. ISBN 978 0 573 11241 6

The Importance of Being Earnest. Comedy. Oscar Wilde
M5 (young, middle-age) F4 (young, middle-age). Two morning-rooms, one garden. No fee

The Importance of Being Earnest. Oscar Wilde. Four-act version reconstructed by Vyvyan Holland
M7 (young, middle-age) F4 (young, middle-age). Two morning rooms, one garden. Fee code J

Wilde originally wrote this play in four acts, but it was thought too long and he was asked to reduce it to three. In 1954 the BBC broadcast the 'lost scene' with Mr Gribsby, an amusing character with a short scene in the second act. Dramatic critic James Agate commented, 'The fun in the scene Wilde deleted is better than any living playwright can do.'
ISBN 978 0 573 11198 3

Improbable Fiction. Comedy. Alan Ayckbourn
M3 (30s, 40s, 60s) F4 (18, 30s, 40s). Scene The hall of a large house. Fee Code M

Six aspiring authors meet on a winter's evening to discuss their work. The chairman, Arnold, attempts to persuade the group to collaborate on a piece of writing, an idea that is quickly dismissed. However, as Arnold is clearing up after the meeting there is a clap of thunder, a black-out – and then the story that would have resulted from the collaboration takes place before his very eyes. Sharp comedy and affectionate satire characterize this zany, imaginative play.
ISBN 978 0 573 11322 2

In at the Deep End. Comedy. Derek Benfield
M3 (young, middle age) F3 (young, middle age). Composite set: various parts of a health farm. Fee code L

The highly moral Mr Potter presides over a health farm and prides himself on his high standards. But when Gerald Corby arrives in search of peace and tranquillity – only to be followed by a trio of ladies in his life and an apparently sex-mad window-cleaner – the resulting misunderstandings and mix-ups prove more than a headache for the hapless Mr Potter as he strives to keep the moral fabric of the health farm intact. The play is based on the author's earlier *A Toe in the Water*.
ISBN 978 0 573 01982 1

In Flame. Play. Charlotte Jones
M2 (30s) F4 (young, 20s, 30s, 60s), with doubling. Various simple settings. Fee code M

Premièred at the Bush Theatre in 1999 and revived at the London's Ambassadors Theatre, Charlotte Jones's award-winning play compares and contrasts the lives of two women, one in London in the present, the other in Yorkshire in 1908. "A play about life and death, love and lust, guilt and hope and dreams ... It has some of the best writing I have come across recently: vigorous, poetic and lethally funny, probing hearts with warmth, compassion and irony." *Sunday Times*. Period 1908/today

In for the Kill. Thriller. Derek Benfield
M3 (25, 40s) F2 (19, 30s). A living-room. Fee code L. ISBN 978 0 573 11180 8

In Praise of Love. Play. Terence Rattigan
M3 (young, 40s, 50s) F1 (50s). A living-room, hall and kitchen. Fee code J

Lydia has an incurable disease, a fact she conceals from her husband Sebastian, a man apparently totally bound up in himself. They are visited by Mark, who discovers that in reality Sebastian has known about Lydia's illness but thinks she does not know of it herself, and puts on a false front to protect her. Mark contrives that Lydia should discover the truth, knowledge which she decides to keep to herself.
ISBN 978 0 573 11170 9

In the Bar of a Tokyo Hotel. Play. Tennessee Williams
M3 (young, middle-age) F2 (middle-age, Hawaiian). An hotel bar. Fee code M

An artist, Mark, is worn to a nervous ruin by a breakthrough in his painting technique and is abandoned and destroyed by his witch of a wife. The intensity of the work, the unremitting challenges and demands it makes of him leave so little of him after the working hours that simple comfortable *being* is impossible for him ...

In the Jungle of the Cities (In the Cities' Jungle). Play. Bertolt Brecht
Translations: Gerhard Nellhaus
Ronald Hayman
Anselm Hollo
Eric Bentley
M12 F5. Extras. Interior and exterior settings. Fee code M

In Two Minds. Thriller. Richard Harris
M2 (30s, 70s) F2 (20s, 30s). A sitting-room and hallway, a kitchen/breakfast room. Fee code M
ISBN 978 0 573 01968 5

The Increased Difficulty of Concentration. Comedy. Václav Havel. Translated by Vera Blackwell.
M4 F4. A living-room and hall. Fee code MISBN 978 0 573 61082 0

Indian Ink. Play. Tom Stoppard
M11 (20s, 30s, (2 Indian) middle-age (1 Indian)) F4 (young, 30s, elderly) Male extras. Various simple settings. Fee code M

Flora Crewe, a liberated English poet, travels to India for health reasons in 1930 and meets Nirad Das, an Indian artist. Their developing friendship mirrors the shifting relationship between the Indians and English in the latter stages of the Raj. Five and a half decades later her sister Eleanor helps an earnest American academic, Eldon Pike, research Flora's life. As he travels to India, Nirad's son, Anish arrives in Shepperton ... Period 1930 and 1985
ISBN 978 0 573 01796 4

◆ **A bullet mark next to a title indicates that it is new to this edition of the Guide.**

A

Inside Job. Thriller. Brian Clemens
M2 (30s, 40s) F1 (30s). A living-room. Fee code M

Spain is a well-known haven for criminals who skip abroad. On the Costa del Sol, professional safe-cracker Larry has struck it lucky. Gorgeous Suzy asks him to steal the diamonds from her husband Alex's safe and run away with her to Rio. At the same time Alex also employs Larry to murder Suzy for her £100,000 life insurance policy. Larry decides to tell Suzy about her husband's plans, and they together plot to steal the diamonds, murder Alex, and make off with the dividend from Alex's similar insurance policy. Several twists add to the suspense in this exciting thriller.
ISBN 978 0 573 01792 6

Inside Trading. Comedy. Malcolm Bradbury. Heavily adapted from the play *Jugend Voran or Ho-Ruck* by Paul Vulpius
M12 F2, M10 F2 with doubling. An executive suite. Fee code M

Insignificance. Play. Terry Johnson
M3 (40s, middle-age, 70) F1 (30s). An hotel room. Fee code M

It is New York, 1953. High above the city, in a luxury hotel bedroom, on a hot summer's night, four of America's most famous legends – a beautiful film star, a Nobel Prize-winning scientist, a renowned baseball player and an infamous senator – meet for an extraordinary confrontation. '... a young writer of peculiar promise ... Mr Johnson is that rare creature; a moralist with wit. He writes with responsible gaiety.' *Guardian* '... tremendously powerful and moving ...' *Time Out*

Inspecting Carol. Comedy. Daniel Sullivan and The Seattle Repertory Co.
M7 (African-American 30, 40s, 60s) F4 (40s, 60s). 1 boy (11). A bare stage. Fee code M
ISBN 978 0 573 69368 7

An Inspector Calls. Play. J. B. Priestley
M4 (25, 30, 50s) F3 (20s, 50). A dining-room. Fee code M

Priestley's classic play of the believable middle-class Yorkshire family called to account for its moral crimes by the enigmatic Inspector Goole stands as a metaphor for our own failure to accept our responsibility to others. Stunningly revived by the Royal National Theatre in 1992, the production transferred to the West End the following year. Period 1912
ISBN 978 0 573 01205 1

Inspector Drake and the Black Widow. Comedy. David Tristram
M2 F1 (multiple roles). A room. Fee code K

Inspector Drake and his sidekick Sergeant Plod return in their most perplexing case yet. A maid discovers the corpse of wealthy oil tycoon John Johnson with a sword sticking out of his back. An ordinary case of murder? If so, then why is Johnson dressed as a woman, appearing to have swallowed a tortoise? Inspector Drake attempts to solve the murder whilst also avoiding his own, as Plod has had a premonition that Drake has only a matter of hours to live!

◆ **A bullet mark next to a title indicates that it is new to this edition of the Guide.**

Inspector Drake and the Perfekt Crime. Comedy. David Tristram
M3 F2. A living-room. Fee code K

When a genius commits a murder, the plan is perfect. But is it foolproof? Inspector Drake is back to face his greatest-ever challenge. Who is the mysterious Doctor Short, and why did he marry a warthog? Has he murdered his fourth wife – or did she murder him first? These are just some of the questions facing the indomitable Drake in this hilarious sequel to *Inspector Drake and the Time Machine*.

Inspector Drake and the Time Machine. Comedy whodunit. David Tristram
Nine characters, may be played by a cast of five with doubling. Interior of an old house, a spaceship. Fee code K

The professor's dead body is found floating weightlessly in the study, his daughter has vanished, and everything points to the mysterious Time Machine. Can the intrepid Inspector Drake, ably hampered by Sergeant Plod, solve the crime of the century? – the thirtieth century that is. Fasten your seat belts for a comedy that's way ahead of its time!

Inspector Drake's Last Case. Comedy. David Tristram
M7 F4 or 5. A room. Fee code K

No-one could have foreseen the strange events that took place one dark evening at the home of Mrs Gagarin. We see her taking a stroll. Next she screams, 'Who is it?' Oh, it's you!' Next a gunshot! It's up to the world's greatest detective to solve the crime. But, in the words of Sergeant Plod, 'don't believe everything you see ...' After all, is it safe to say that Mrs Gagarin is actually dead?

Interpreters. Play. Ronald Harwood
M4 (40s, 50s) F2 (40s, 93). A small conference room, a living-room. Fee code M

This ingenious ironical comedy of betrayed love was produced at the Queen's Theatre, London, in 1985-86. Nadia is an interpreter at the Foreign Office in London involved in negotiations with a Russian delegation. Her Russian counterpart turns out to be Victor, with whom she had a tempestuous affair some ten years previously. Moving and comic complications ensue in this tale of love across the Iron Curtain.

Intimate Exchanges. A related series of plays. Alan Ayckbourn
M1 F1 (minimum). A garden. Any one of several places. A churchyard. Fee code M for each play

Intimate Exchanges is a related series of plays totalling eight scripts which can be performed by just two actors, although more could be used if desired. As each scene ends, a character faces a decision, the result of which determines the course of the rest of the play.

VOLUME I: **Affairs in a Tent, Events on a Garden Terrace, A Garden Fête, A Pageant**
ISBN 978 0 573 01612 7

VOLUME II: **A Cricket Match, A Game of Golf, A One Man Protest, Love in the Mist**
ISBN 978 0 573 01613 4

The Invention of Love. Play. Tom Stoppard
M12 (18, 20s-77) F1 (19, 35) with doubling. Various simple settings. Fee code M

'From the bare bones of the dry life of A. E. Housman ... Tom Stoppard has been inspired to write the most emotionally powerful and enthralling play of his career. Never before has he written with such exciting eloquence ... It's a tremendous, scaring vision of a sacrificed life.' *Evening Standard*. Period 1877-1936.

The Invisible Man. Play. Ken Hill, from the novel by H. G. Wells
M17+ F5+. A stage. Fee code M (play) Fee code A (music). Optional illusions available under licence

Ken Hill has turned H.G. Wells's gripping novel into a music-hall romp, combining tongue-in-cheek humour with tragedy and magic. The sinister Griffin arrives in the village of Iping with a bandaged face and an unsociable manner. Was it really an accident that destroyed his face, or is he a criminal on the run? He takes off his gloves to reveal no hands and his bandages to reveal no head! Then the pranks – comic and malevolent – truly begin ...
ISBN 978 0 573 01793 3

The Invisible River. Play. Gautam Raja
M2 (30s) F3 (late 20s, 50s) 2 boys, played by M2 F2 1 boy. Simple settings. Fee code K

Uma, a young scientist, arrives in Allahabad to investigate bacteriophages in the Ganga as the starting point of a new era of disease eradication, setting off a ripple effect. Dr Ajay, a government doctor, supports cleaning the river and represents the conventional wisdom of the medical profession entangled with his demons – a religious mother, dying slum children and a government that doesn't care. Everything is interconnected, and nothing is as simple as it seems.

Ion. Play. Euripides, in a new version by David Lan
M6 F2, or M5 F3. F chorus. The Temple of Apollo. Fee code M

It Can Damage Your Health. Comedy. Eric Chappell
M5 (1 Indian) (20s, 30s, 40, 50s) F1 (20s). A hospital ward. Fee code M

Based on Eric Chappell's hit TV series *Only When I Laugh*, this traces the fortunes of a disparate trio who share a Men's Surgical ward: the cynical, defensive Higgins; the young, nervous Gary; and the weary hypochondriac Palmer. Together, they form an uneasy alliance against the confusions and insecurities of hospital life.
ISBN 978 0 573 01795 7

It Could Be Any One of Us. Comedy. Alan Ayckbourn
M3 (early 40s, mid 50s) F3 (16, late 40s, mid 50s). A living-room. Fee code M

A thunderstorm. A windswept country house. A family of failures – a detective who has never solved a case; a writer, an artist and a composer whose work has never been aired publicly; a dysfunctional teenager – wrangling over a bequest ... All the prime ingredients for a murder-mystery thriller in the traditional mould. But this thriller is by Alan Ayckbourn and has within it a number of surprises.
ISBN 978 0 573 01797 1

It Runs in the Family. Comedy. Ray Cooney
M7 (20s, middle-age, 50s, old) F5 (18, 40s, old). A doctors' common room. Fee code M

A

Dr David Mortimore is about to address a neurologists' convention, which will probably earn him a knighthood. While putting the final touches to his speech an old flame arrives and announces that their liaison years ago resulted in a son who is downstairs desperate to meet his dad. Frantic to hide this catastrophic news from his wife and the hospital authorities, David is forced to invent not one but two non-existent husbands!
ISBN 978 0 573 01799 5

It Started with a Kiss. Play. John Godber
M2 (young) F4 (young). Various simple settings. Fee code M

In the late Seventies, five students on a drama teaching course at a northern college discover sex, drugs and rock 'n' roll. Stan, a mature student, and Rich, the local boy-made-good, share a room, as do the girls – upper-crust Charlotte, feisty Helen and religious Tina. Babs, their tutor, does her best for them, supporting them through the travails of teaching practice with unruly kids, but the student parties, romantic intrigues and class conflict take their toll.
ISBN 978 0 573 01859 6

It Was a Dark and Stormy Night. Mystery-comedy spoof. Tim Kelly
M6 F8, or M5 F9. An isolated house. Fee code L

A shameless spoof that's loaded with laughs and thrills. The creepy, haunted *Ye Olde Wayside Inn* oozes New England Gothic atmosphere and never has guests. Ebenezer, one of the residents, is dangerous when there's a storm – and there's a storm! Several intruders from the outside world are forced to seek shelter, but who's the skeleton in the wheelchair and why is it wearing a bridal veil? When the wind howls and the lights flicker the chilling time begins!

It's Ralph. Play. Hugh Whitemore
M3 (young, 40s, 50s) F1 (40s). The ground floor of a converted farmhouse. Fee code M

Andrew and his wearily frustrated wife Clare are spending the weekend in their Gloucestershire cottage, which, like their marriage, is well in need of repair. Ralph, an old friend of Andrew's, visits and remembers their shared radical youth. Ralph brings Andrew face to face with his own spiritual bankruptcy and the latter finally unburdens himself to his visitor. Clare leaves, the house decays rapidly and Ralph helps Andrew to regain his integrity, but at a price ... NB. Contains explicit language

Ivanov. Play. Anton Chekhov, adapted by David Hare
M7 (wide range of ages) F5 (wide range of ages). Extras. Various interior and exterior settings. Fee code M

Perhaps the least performed of Chekhov's plays, *Ivanov* is the fierce and funny portrait of a man whose life is plummeting fast into domestic and philosophical chaos. Ivanov is an impoverished, anti-Semitic landowner who has rejected his Jewish wife who is dying of tuberculosis, and is now infatuated with the daughter of a rich neighbour. Period nineteenth century

---

◆ **A bullet mark next to a title indicates that it is new to this edition of the Guide.**

Jack the Lad. A musical celebration. Book and lyrics by David Wood and Dave and Toni Arthur. Music by Dave and Toni Arthur
M6 (20s, 50s, 80) F4 (20s-40s). 3 children, 1 dog. A gypsy encampment. Fee code M

In a gypsy encampment, a series of Jack tales and songs (from Little Jack Horner, through Jack and the Beanstalk to Spring Heeled Jack) is performed by the gypsies, with singing and dancing, a mumming play, a shadow-mime and puppetry, to celebrate the eightieth birthday of their senior member, Jack the Lad. Vocal score sold separately.
ISBN 978 0 573 01801 5

Jack the Ripper. Musical reconstruction. Ron Pember and Denis de Marne
M8 (young, middle-age) F8 (young). Extras. Equally suitable for small drama societies as well as musical societies. Composite standing set: a music hall, a pub, London streets. Fee by arrangement

The play is a musical reconstruction of the East End murders which took place in 1888, an atmospheric commentary rather than an historical re-enactment, shifting between reality and artificiality, with characters representing 'real' people as well as members of the music hall audience and players. Period late Victorian
ISBN 978 0 573 08042 5

Jane Eyre. Play. Willis Hall, adapted from the novel by Charlotte Brontë
M4 F8, with doubling. Various simple settings. Fee code M for play, code A for music

Whilst retaining all the familiar passionate qualities of Charlotte Brontë's novel, Willis Hall successfully transposes the nineteenth-century world of *Jane Eyre* to the stage with simply staged short interconnected scenes and intimate locations. With the passages of direct narration broken up and shared out amongst the Company, a fictional tale of a penniless, plain girl becomes a work of great emotional force in the most complete stage adaptation of the classic novel.
ISBN 978 0 573 01802 2

Jane Eyre. Play. Charlotte Brontë. Adapted by Charles Vance
M4 (30s) F6 (young, 18, 20s, middle age, elderly) (F5 with doubling), 1 child. A library and passageway. Fee code M

Focusing on the love story between Jane and Rochester, the play begins as Jane arrives in 1846 to take up the post of governess to Rochester's ward, Adèle, at Thornfield Hall. Jane and Rochester fall in love but their happiness is jeopardized by the discovery of the terrible secret from Rochester's past, resolved by the dramatic fire which maims Rochester. The action, contained in a single setting with one small inset scene, makes for exciting theatre.
ISBN 978 0 573 01803 3

Jeffrey Bernard Is Unwell. Play by Keith Waterhouse, based on the life and writings of Jeffrey Bernard
M1. M2 F2 playing at least 22 parts. A pub. Fee code M

Gambler, journalist, fervent alcoholic and four-times married Jeffrey Bernard writes the weekly 'Low Life' column for the *Spectator* magazine, chronicling Soho life as well as offering a very personal philosophy on vodka, women and race-courses. From this, Keith Waterhouse has brilliantly constructed a play which is set in the saloon bar of Bernard's favourite Soho pub, the *Coach and Horses*.
ISBN 978 0 573 01804 6

A

Joking Apart. Play. Alan Ayckbourn
M4 (20s, 30) F4 (20s). A garden. Fee code M

Charming, naturally successful in everything, Anthea and Richard almost unconsciously but ruthlessly dominate the lives of those with whom they are associated. Over twelve years Sven, Richard's partner, is virtually nudged out of the firm. Brian, who works for Richard, is ineffectual; Hugh, the local vicar, whose wife is on drugs, falls hopelessly in love with Anthea. The play ends ith Anthea's daughter awaiting her eighteenth birthday; perhaps a new reign may be beginning ...
ISBN 978 0 573 11204 1

Joseph Andrews. Comedy. P. M. Clepper, from the novel by Henry Fielding
M7 (20s, 50, middle-age) F10 (18, 20, 45, middle-age). Extras. Various simple settings. Fee code K. ISBN 978 0 573 11209 6

Journey's End. Drama. R. C. Sherriff
M11 (young, 40s, middle-age). A dug-out. Fee code M

Second Lieutenant Raleigh, the new officer assigned to C Company, is welcomed by everyone except, apparently, Captain Stanhope, who reveals, later, that Raleigh was at school with him and hero-worshipped him. What neither of them knows is that if 'Stanhope went up those steps into the front line without being doped with whisky, he'd go mad with fright.' The drama of the personal relationships between the men is played out against the larger tragedy raging around them. Period 1918
ISBN 978 0 573 04003 0

Jumpers. Play. Tom Stoppard
M12-17 (40-50s, old) F2 (young). Multiple interior set. Fee code M

The hero is a professor of moral philosophy, and the play is a serious attempt to debate the existence of a moral absolute, of metaphysical reality, of God. Unfortunately, George's trained hare disappears and an Inspector Bones arrives to investigate the rumour that one of George's team of gymnasts has been shot dead while performing in his sitting-room. Intelligent, surreal and zany, this is Stoppard at his best.

Juno and the Paycock. Play. Sean O'Casey
M12 (young, 20s, 50s, 60, elderly) F6 (22, 45, very old). A tenement room. Fee code M

A stark, uncompromising tragedy which unsparingly shows that Irish gaiety and song are the despairing camouflage for a dirge. It is the waste that is tragic – Juno's staunchness has to suffer a shiftless strutting husband, 'Captain' Jack Boyle, the 'Paycock' of the title. True, there are moments of raucous comedy, but they are satire, O'Casey's revelations by antithesis. Period 1922
ISBN 978 0 573 01214 3

Just Between Ourselves. Play. Alan Ayckbourn
M2 (30s, 40s) F3 (30s, 40s, 60s). A garage, pathway and yard. Fee code M

Dennis spends his spare time messing about in his untidy garage, indifferent to the fact that his wife is being driven to distraction by his possessive and jealous mother who is slowly undermining her, both physically and mentally. Each scene occurs on the birthday of one of the characters, but the comedy becomes increasingly sharp and ironic as the action proceeds and darkens.
ISBN 978 0 573 11212 6

Just the Three of Us. Play. Simon Gray
M1 (50s) F2 (20s, 50s). A studio. Fee code M

Whenever Enid writes one of her best-selling novels, she adopts a domestic pet as a companion, sends her husband away and retreats to her converted lighthouse. This time there is a difference – her adopted "pet" is Terri, her husband's PA. Chained up, but with plenty of home comforts, Terri is desperate to escape initally.Then she settles into the odd ménage consisting of herself, Enid and the eccentric vicar, Ronnie. Dependence, obsession, redemption and retribution are all themes of this unusual and observant comedy.

Kafka's Dick. Comedy. Alan Bennett
M5 F1. A living-room, heaven. Fee code M

It is 1919 and the tubercular Kafka adjures Max to burn his writings after his death. Max doesn't and goes on to publish all Kafka's work. Moving to the 1980s, in an English suburban living-room sit Sydney, a Kafka-besotted insurance agent, his frustrated wife and his elderly father. Into their midst descends the dead but lively Max, closely followed by a cadaverous Kafka and Kafka's larger-than-life father. It seems everyone wants to get in on the act ... This text is the revised 1992 edition.
ISBN 978 0 573 01663 9

Katherine Howard. Play. William Nicholson
M7 (50s-60s) F4 (18, 20s, 40s). Extras. Various simple settings. Fee code M

Opening on the wedding night of Henry VIII and his fourth wife, Anne of Cleves, and closing with the execution of his fifth wife, Katherine Howard, found guilty of adultery, Nicholson's play takes a slice of Tudor history and turns it into pure theatrical magic. A touching May-to-September romance; political intrigue, plots and betrayals; a pointed and sometimes comic portrayal of women's lives in Tudor times: all these, and more, are elements of this entertaining, thoughtful, intelligent play from the author of *Shadowlands.* Period 1540-1542
ISBN 978 0 573 01811 4

Keep an Eye on Amélie. Farce. Georges Feydeau. Translated and adapted by Robert Cogo-Fawcett and Braham Murray
M13 F5. Extras. A salon, the Town Hall, two bedrooms. Fee code M

Feydeau's hilarious farce *Occupe-toi d'Amélie* is here translated in a lively new version – seen at the Royal Exchange, Manchester, under the title *She's in Your Hands!* Marcel will inherit one million francs – on his wedding day. Unwilling to relinquish his bachelorhood, but in dire need of cash, he persuades Amélie, a cocotte, to act as his fiancée for benefit of his godfather. But events don't go according to plan!
ISBN 978 0 573 01813 8

Keeping Down with the Joneses. Comedy. John Chapman and Jeremy Lloyd
M5 (1 Asian-Indian) F4. An underground atomic shelter. Fee code M. ISBN 978 0 573 61115 5

♦ **A bullet mark next to a title indicates that it is new to this edition of the Guide.**

A

Kennedy's Children. Play. Robert Patrick
M2 (young) F3 (young). Extra 1M. A bar. Fee code L

'The theme of the play is the death of the ideas of heroes as guides for our lives. I think the sad thing about Kennedy's children is that they have so very much to offer one another and are held away from one another by fear and despair ... the play stands as my tribute to their valour and suffering.' Robert Patrick.
ISBN 978 0 573 61126 1

The Kerry Dance. Play. Tony Rushforth
M3 F6. A parish hall. Fee code L

Yorkshire, 1961. Jamie wants to study drama at RADA, something he knows would not be approved of by his Catholic Irish mother, Maureen. Jamie begins to take lessons for his audition in secret with Margaret, a relief teacher. Their relationship sparks jealousy from Jamie's girlfriend Sarah, then indignation from Maureen, who forbids the lessons to continue. Jamie's fate seems sealed; he has a powerful ally in his Auntie Bridget, however, whose own profound secret proves the turning point. Period 1961, recalled in 1971
ISBN 978 0 573 01814 5

Key for Two. Comedy. John Chapman and Dave Freeman
M3 (30-50) F4 (30-middle-age). Composite setting. Fee code M

In this wickedly amusing play Harriet solves her financial problems by entertaining two married gentlemen on different days of the week. The scheme faces collapse when her friend, Anne, arrives, hotly pursued by her husband; one of Harriet's lovers is confined to bed with a sprained ankle and the second lover turns up unexpectedly, closely followed by two irate wives in search of their itinerant husbands! The long-running London production starred Moira Lister, Patrick Cargill, Barbara Murray and Glyn Houston.
ISBN 978 0 573 11258 4

Killers. Play. Adam Pernak
M6 (20s-elderly) F4 (20s, middle-age). Simple interior and exterior settings. Fee code M

Winner of the Royal Court Young Writers' Festival this brilliant début play shows two brothers and their working-class parents. Jonathan, the high-flier, causes the death of his errant girlfriend's older lover, whilst David, a fighter pilot, is sent to the Gulf War. Both are killers, but one is revered as a patriotic hero whilst the other is imprisoned for his *crime passionel*. '... a beautifully simple play that wafts over the audience with the warmth of reality.' *City Limits*
ISBN 978 0 573 01815 2

The Killing of Sister George. Comedy. Frank Marcus
F4. A living-room. Fee code M

Sister George is a fictional character in a popular radio serial about English village life. To boost ratings, this character is to be killed off and Mrs Mercy of the BBC comforts June Buckridge who has played the part for some 2000 performances. June has a lesbian relationship with 'Childie' McNaught, a babyish 'girl-woman' who shares her home, and the impending catastrophe of June's lost job tips the insecure relationship over. Beryl Reid triumphed in both the stage and screen versions of this comedy.
ISBN 978 0 573 03017 8

Killing Time. Play. Richard Stockwell
M1 (30s) F1 (30s). A living-room/kitchen area. Fee code M. ISBN 978 0 573 01818 3

Kindly Keep It Covered. Farce. Dave Freeman
M3 (early middle-age) F4 (20s, middle-age). A reception area. Fee code M

Roland Dickerby runs a health farm with his wife Julia, bought with the proceeds of a hefty insurance payout on the demise of Julia's first husband, Sidney. Life isn't easy for Roland and today Fate has something extra special in store for him: Sidney has decided to resurrect himself and turns up at the farm, just as Vanessa, the wife of Roland's ex-boss from the Kindly Mutual, checks in for a health-giving visit. A fast, furious and frantic farce.
ISBN 978 0 573 01817 6

Kindly Leave the Stage. Comedy. John Chapman
M3 (40s, old) F5 (young, 30s-60s). A sitting-room. Fee code M

To the embarrassment of their dinner guests Rupert and Sarah announce that they are to divorce. Moments later, the actor playing Rupert stumbles on a line and we realize that the previous action is a play within a play. As the prompter tries to get the show moving again the cast begin to argue, out of character, and the result is complete chaos. Laughs abound in this fast-paced comedy of theatrical disasters.

King Cromwell. Play. Oliver Ford Davies
M6 (30s, 40s, 58) F2 (28, 35). A bedchamber. Fee code L

The year is 1657 and an infirm Oliver Cromwell, Lord Protector of England, Scotland and Ireland, is nearing the end of his life. But who will succeed him? Parliament want him to be king which will unite the people but is against Cromwell's republican principles and will mean his ill-suited son, Richard, succeeds him. But the alternative is a military dictatorship under Cromwell's second-in-command, John Lambert. This elegant, witty play presents a very human portrait of Cromwell.
ISBN 978 0 573 11213 3

Kingdom of Earth. Play. Tennessee Williams
M2 (one black) F1. Composite setting. Fee code M

Lot, a seriously ill young man, still unhealthily weighed down by the memory of his dead mother, has married – on a TV show – a young woman, Myrtle. Goodheartedly she hopes to nurse him back to health. Lot takes her back to the family home, inhabited by his half-brother, Chicken, and Myrtle discovers that Lot intends she should steal the deeds of the place from Chicken to whom he has weakly given them. But Chicken has other ideas for Myrtle as he waits for Lot to die. Period 1960

The Kingfisher. Comedy. William Douglas Home
M2 (70, old) F1 (60). A garden. Fee code M

Cedric is a best-selling novelist living comfortably with his butler, Hawkins, who has served him for fifty years. There have been many women in Cedric's richly disordered life but now he is contemplating marriage to the only one he has loved. The object of his proposal, Evelyn, has just been to her husband's funeral whom she married on the rebound from Cedric. Now she is confronted by Cedric's charming and candid proposal and must make a decision.
ISBN 978 0 573 61130 8

Kiss Me Like You Mean It. Play. Chris Chibnall
M2 (20s, late 60s-early 70s) F2 (20s, late 60s-early 70s). A garden, a flat and rooftop. Fee code K

A

On a midsummer's night in Manchester, Tony and Ruth meet at a party in a shabby terrace house. On the floor above, Don and Edie, married fifty years, are having a party of their own: only gradually does its purpose become apparent. As the night progresses, love is in the air: the start for Tony and Ruth, the end for Edie and terminally ill Don who will take death, as they have life, together.

Kiss of Death. Play. Simon Williams
M3 F1. A refurbished lecture room, a dilapidated flat. Fee code L

Actress Zoë Lang attends an unusual improvisation workshop and finds herself auditioning to be the bait for a real-life serial killer. Taking on the role of a runaway, Zoë meets with the sinister and manipulative John Smith. Layer upon layer of twisted unreality are stripped away as Zoë and the police home in on their target... A hard-hitting, tightly-structured story, *Kiss of Death* is a very modern thriller with plenty of dark, sardonic humour to punctuate its mood of prevailing menace.
ISBN 978 0 573 01984 5

A Kiss on the Bottom. Comedy. Frank Vickery
F7 (20s, middle-age, 60s). May be played by F5. 2F extras. A hospital ward. Fee code L

Three women are in East Glamorgan hospital for cancer treatment. Each woman must cope not only with the uncertainties of her health, but with the inevitable secrets and half-truths which are maintained by relations and nursing staff. It's up to Marlene, the strongest and most outspoken of them all, to keep the atmosphere in the ward cheery. Her activities make her bedfellows' time in hospital somewhat more interesting than it would otherwise have been!
ISBN 978 0 573 13004 5

The Knack. Comedy. Ann Jellicoe
M3 (young) F1 (17). A room. Fee code M

Jellicoe's best play, written in 1961 and later filmed with Rita Tushingham, is an exuberant, liberating youthful comedy. Three young men share a flat. Into their midst wanders Nancy, a gawky seventeen-year-old Northerner looking for the YWCA, who will give the tough Tolen a chance to demonstrate his knack with women. The staccato dialogue skims along in this study of the shifting relationships and power balances among the four young people. An undercurrent is Tolen's Nazi characteristics and whether negotiation is possible with such people.

Kvetch. An American Play About Anxiety. Steven Berkoff
M3 F2. Fee code M

"Kvetch" is the dialogue of anxiety that is forever foiling our endeavours. But what if we listened more closely to that voice in the back of our head – might it be speaking more sense than the one at the front ...? The *Guardian* described *Kvetch* as "a work of genius, pure and simple."

♦ **A bullet mark next to a title indicates that it is new to this edition of the Guide.**

Ladies Who Lunch. Comedy. Tudor Gates
M3 (middle-age, 50s) F7 (21, 30s, 40s, middle-age), with doubling. 1 male voice. A drawing-room, a duplex apartment, an apartment. Fee code M

In *Ladies Who Lunch,* commissioned for the BT Biennial 1998, Amelia, Rachel and Joane, wives of three of the world's richest men, meet regularly to do charity work. In order to increase the charity's turnover Amelia thinks up a scheme to play the stock market, exploiting the information gained secretly from their spouses' business dealings. When the husbands find out, the resulting showdown is not the walk-over they think it will be ...
ISBN 978 0 573 01853 4

Lady Audley's Secret, or **Death in Lime Tree Walk**. Melodrama. Brian J. Burton, based on the novel by Mary Braddon
M4 (20s, 60s) F4 (20s) Various settings. Fee code L

The Lady in the Van. Play. Alan Bennett
M10 F4 (doubling possible). Residential street and house interior. Fee code M

Adapted for the stage by the author from his autobiographical memoir, *The Lady In The Van* tells the story of Miss Shepherd, whom Alan Bennett first came across when she was living in the street near his home in Camden Town. Taking refuge with her van in his garden originally for three months, she ended up staying fifteen years. Funny, touching and unexpectedly spectacular. "… a wonderfully bittersweet comic diary …" *Spectator*.
ISBN 978 0 573 11266 5

The Lady's Not for Burning. Play. Christopher Fry
M8 F3. A room. Fee code M

♦ **Landscape With Weapon**. Play. Joe Penhall
M3 F1. Fee Code M

To his family's horrow, Ned reveals he's the brains behind a new military technology so sophisticated, so extraordinary, it will revolutionise the nature of warfare. When the Ministry of Defence demands intellectual ownership Ned begins to question himself. A wry account of private anguish, public responsibility and a problem with no solution. The play premiered at the National Theatre in 2007.

Largo Desolato. Play. Václav Havel. English version by Tom Stoppard
M9 (middle-age) F3 or M7 F3. A living-room. Fee code M

Professor Nettles lives in constant fear because of his refusal to denounce his work. The play's sense of the sinister gives a chilling edge to this account of life in a totalitarian state by the once-banned writer and president of Czechoslovakia. Stoppard's English version was premièred at the Bristol Old Vic in 1986 and seen subsequently at the Orange Tree, Richmond, in 1989. 'It is unlikely that we shall see a better play this year. Inconceivable that we shall see one more important.' *Daily Telegraph*

♦ **A bullet mark next to a title indicates that it is new to this edition of the Guide.**

The Lark. Play. Jean Anouilh. Translated by Christopher Fry
M16 F5. A permanent setting. Fee code M

A

To the great lords of her time as well as the politicians of the Church expediency was God. So the Maid had to die. So to Warwick and Cauchon, her life has the somewhat artificial, and certainly impersonal, quality of a play. Short scenes from it are played out during the trial as they struggle to turn her simplicity into heresy. But it is the glory of her life rather than the tragedy that is the triumphant climax of the play. Period 1429-31
ISBN 978 0 573 01225 9

Lark Rise. Play. Keith Dewhurst, from the book by Flora Thompson
M12 F7, with doubling. An open stage. Fee code M. (In a volume with *Candleford*)

A literary sampler of English village life in late Victorian Oxfordshire, *Lark Rise* re-enacts the first day of harvest. The play is written to be peformed as a promenade production with no distinction between stage and auditorium. The interest lies in the lively picture of typical country life of the period, with music and songs, with a brief flash forward to the 1914-18 war. Period 1880s
ISBN 978 0 573 10011 6

Last of the Red Hot Lovers. Comedy. Neil Simon
M1 (46) F3 (20, 30s). An apartment. Fee code M

Barney, who has been married to an irreproachable wife for twenty-three years, feels the urge to join the sexual revolution before it is too late. Taking advantage of the fact that his mother's flat is unoccupied two days a week he invites three women to his lair in succession. With no experience of adultery he fails on each occasion. As the play ends he is telephoning his wife – to meet him that afternoon in his mother's apartment. (**Slightly restricted**)
ISBN 978 0 573 61143 8

Last Tango in Whitby. Play. Mike Harding
15 speaking, 6+ non-speaking can be played by M4 (middle-age) F8 (young, middle-age), with doubling. Extras M and F. Various simple settings. Fee code M

For Pat, recently widowed, this year's charabanc trip to Whitby is tinged with sadness, but she is determined to enjoy herself. Phil and Edna provide entertainment with old-time dancing. Phil, too, is trying to enjoy himself, despite being trapped in a dead marriage, and during their first dance together he and Pat feel the unexpected spark of mutual attraction. Despite disapproval from others, they decide to seize this second chance and start a new life together.
ISBN 978 0 573 01822 0

The Late Edwina Black. Play. William Dinner and William Morum
M2 (40s) F2 (30s, elderly). A lounge. Fee code M

The Late Mrs Early. Comedy. Norman Robbins
M4 (14, 40, 60) F4 (17, 40s). A living-room. Fee code K

Terry Early's announcement that he and Susan intend to marry rouses the fury of his overbearing mother Alice. Alice's sudden demise, following her handling of a faulty electric kettle, promises a peaceful solution. But Alice as a vengeful ghost is even more formidable than as a live wife and mother. Much drama ensues in which both families are involved before Alice's ashes can be persuaded to lie quiet in her urn.
ISBN 978 0 573 01586 1

A Laughing Matter. Play. April De Angelis
M9 F8 (doubling and trebling possible). Various simple settings. Fee code M

It's 1773 at the Theatre Royal, Drury Lane, London. The crowd is getting restless. The leading man's unconscious but the show must go on. This irreverent version of real-life events tells the story of David Garrick, Dr Johnson, Oliver Goldsmith and a new play called *She Stoops to Conquer*. Caught between financial pressures and artistic ambition, Garrick must decide if he can risk staging a play which could make or break his career. Garrick failed to snap up *She Stoops* and it premièred at the rival venue of Covent Garden.

Laughing Wild. Comedy. Christopher Durang
M1 F1. A supermarket. Fee code M

Laughter in the Dark. Comedy. Victor Lucas
M6 (20s, 50s) F5 (20s, 50, 70s). Extras. A manorial hall. Fee code K. ISBN 978 0 573 11218 2

Laying the Ghost. Play. Simon Williams
M2 (young, 71) F5 (young, middle age, elderly, 70). 2 extras. A sitting area in a retirement home. Fee code L

Margot Buchanan is a witty ex-actress in a retirement home. She is visited by a young actress who is having an affair with Leo, Margot's ex-husband – and by Leo's current wife Judy. Leo arrives but suffers a fatal heart attack. Thus the scene is set for chaotic hilarity as Leo's ghost appears, anxious to sort out matters between his three women, and visible only to Margot's psychic friend Freda!
ISBN 978 0 573 01854 1

Leaves. Play. Lucy Caldwell
M1 (late 40s) F3 (40, 19, 15) 1 girl (11). Various simple settings. Fee code L

Lori is returning to her Belfast home from her first term at university where she attempted to commit suicide. It's only been a few weeks but things have gone badly wrong. None of the rest of the family knows, or understands, what really happened. In this fiercely observed family drama, three teenage girls struggle to define who they are where they might be going. Leaves won the George Devine Award 2006, for emerging playwrights in the UK and Ireland.

Leave it to Psmith. Comedy. Ian Hay and P. G. Wodehouse
M10 F8. 3 interiors, 1 exterior. Fee code L

Freddie Bosham, son of the short-sighted Earl of Middlewick, owner of Blandings Castle, is anxious to marry Phyllis Jackson, whose family manufacture jam. To win Phyllis he must either work in the jam factory or put £5,000 into the business and he prefers the latter. To this end he conspires with Psmith, an obliging advertiser ready to do anything – crime included, to get his hands on his lion-hunting stepmother's diamond necklace. But he's not the only one after the necklace ...

◆ **A bullet mark next to a title indicates that it is new to this edition of the Guide.**

Lend Me A Tenor. Comedy. Ken Ludwig
M4 (young, 30s, 50s) F4 (20s, 30s, 50s). An hotel suite. Fee code M for play, fee code A for music

A concert in Ohio in 1934 is jeopardized when the lead Italian tenor falls into a drunken stupor. So the impresario's diminutive assistant blacks up and goes on as Otello. The tenor awakens, dons his costume, and thence follows an hilarious comedy involving two Otellos, a volatile Italian wife, an outrageous bellhop and a cynical impresario. 'A furiously paced comedy with more than a touch of the Marx brothers ... wonderful farcical moments and funny lines ...' *Time Out*
ISBN 978 0 573 01640 0

Lent. Play. Michael Wilcox
M2 F2, 1 boy. Various simple interior and exterior settings. Fee code L

Lenz. Play. Mike Stott, loosely based on the story by George Büchner
M4 (20s-30s) F2 (20s-30s). Various simple interiors. Fee code M

Léocadia. Play. Jean Anouilh, translated by Timberlake Wertenbaker
M8 F3. Extras. The drawing-room, the Château grounds. Fee code M

This is a new translation, broadcast on BBC Radio, of the Anouilh play which first appeared in 1939. Léocadia was an opera singer who died after three blissful days of love with Prince Albert who has mourned her ever since. His aunt, the Duchess, does everything she can to help him and finds Amanda, who bears a striking resemblance to Léocadia, and encourages her to lay Léocadia's ghost which she does with honesty and gentle perseverance.

♦ **Less Than Kind.** Play. Terence Rattigan
M4 F5. A house; a flat. Fee Code M

Let It Be Me. Play. Carey Jane Hardy
M2 (30s, 50s) F4 (30s, 50s, 60s) A living-room. Fee code K

Amy cares for her Aunt Sylvia who has Alzheimer's. Sylvia doesn't recognize the adult Amy but instead waits for the child she remembers to come back from school. Amy is loyally devoted to her aunt so finds herself seriously tested when she meets and falls in love with Gregory. With her friends for support, and with Gregory's understanding and tact, Amy begins to see that a happier, different life is possible for her. Period 1999
ISBN 978 0 573 01986 9

A Letter of Resignation. Play. Hugh Whitemore
M3 (35, middle-age, 60s) F2 (50s, 60s). A castle library. Fee code M

1963 was an amazing year and life was changing. Britain was becoming a different place and to many people, Harold Macmillan, the Prime Minister, seemed outdated and irrelevant – an Edwardian grandee lingering uncomfortably in the world of E-type Jaguars, Carnaby Street and Beatlemania. But few were aware that his life was scarred by domestic unhappiness and sexual betrayal. Hugh Whitemore explores the events that lay hidden behind the headlines and examines a complex web of personal and political morality.

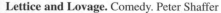

Lettice and Lovage. Comedy. Peter Shaffer
M2 (middle-age) F3 (middle-age). Extras. A grand hall, an office, a basement flat. Fee code M

Daughter of an actress who toured with an all-female company playing Shakespeare's plays, Lettice has inherited both theatricality and eccentricity. Now employed as a tourist guide in a shabby stately home, she enlivens its dull history with her own over-imaginative fantasies, until she is caught in the act and promptly sacked. She is later visited by the starchy Preservation Trust official who fired her, and an unlikely friendship develops between the two.
ISBN 978 0 573 01823 7

Les Liaisons Dangereuses. Play. Christopher Hampton
M3 (20s, 30) F6 (15, 20s, late 30s, elderly). Extras. Various interior and exterior settings. Fee code M

Le Vicomte de Valmont begins the play as an unworthy, cynical pleasure-seeker, proud of his reputation as a seducer. He is encouraged in his enterprises by his former mistress, La Marquise de Merteuil, who would seem to share his cynicism, but who has an ulterior motive. Set in France among aristocrats before the Revolution, this is nevertheless a play for all time about sexual manners and manipulation, ending in tragedy.
ISBN 978 0 573 01639 4

The Lieutenant of Inishmore. Play. Martin McDonagh
M7 (17, young, middle age) F1 (16) Various simple settings. Fee code M

"Come on in ahead of yourselves. I'm just in the middle of shooting me Dad." Who knocked Mad Padraic's beloved cat over on a lonely road on the island of Inishmore – and was it an accident? He'll want to know when he gets back from a stint of torture and chip-shop bombing in Northern Ireland: he loves his cat more than life itself. Presented by the Royal Shakespeare Company at Stratford, The Pit and later The Garrick, London in 2001/2002. Period 1993

A Life. Play. Hugh Leonard
M4 (20s, 60s) F4 (20s, 60s). Triple set: a kitchen, living-room, bandstand. Fee code M
ISBN 978 0 573 61199 5

Life After George. Play. Hannie Rayson
M2 (50s) F4 (28, 32, 52, 60) Various interior and exterior settings. Fee code M

Peter George, charismatic academic, idealist, lover of life, is dead. His three wives and his daughter come together to arrange his funeral. So begins a fascinating retrospective on George's life. *Life After George* offers a moving and perceptive insight into social change across three decades, from the student barricades of the late 1960s to the new Millennium. "This is a play of tremendous insight, warmth and humanity, leavened by humorous moments." *Birmingham Evening Mail*

Life Goes On. Comedy. Adrian Hodges
M2 (30s, 42) F3 (20s-40). 1 female voice. A living-room, a bedroom. Fee code M

A thoughtful and engaging comedy which opens in the hours following the funeral of George Marlowe who left this life unexpectedly. George's younger brother, Michael, attempts to seduce Debbie, youngest sister of his partner Helen and of George's widow, Joyce. During the evening Michael leaps from one sisterly assignation to another until the arrival of George's ghost, back to tie up the loose ends of his life, including Michael's philandering ways. The play ends with the right balance having been struck for all concerned.
ISBN 978 0 573 01809 1

A Life in the Theatre. Play. David Mamet
M2. Various spots around a theatre. Fee code L

In twenty-six scenes the play presents 'two actors – a seasoned professional and a novice – backstage and onstage, going through a cycle of roles and an entire wardrobe of costumes'. In some scenes they are seen portraying characters in various plays from the repertory theatre in which they work. Though there are many scenes – some very brief – staging is simple.
ISBN 978 0 573 64024 7

Life is a Dream. Pedro Calderón de la Barca. Translated by Gwynne Edwards
M4 F3. Extras. Various simple settings. Fee code M

The Life of Galileo. Play. Bertolt Brecht
Translations: Charles Laughton, music by Hanns Eisler
　　　　　　　Desmond Vesey
　　　　　　　Howard Brenton
　　　　　　　John Willett
　　　　　　　Ralph Manheim and Wolfgang Sauerlander
　　　　　　　David Hare

M35 F11, with doubling possible. Extras, children. Interior and exterior settings. Fee code M for play, code C for music

Life X 3. Play. Yasmina Reza. Translated by Christopher Hampton
M2 F2. A child's voice. A living-room. Fee code M

Henri and Sonia are putting their son to bed when Hubert and Inés arrive for dinner, a day earlier than expected ... As the evening degenerates, Yasmina Reza's play – elegantly translated by Christopher Hampton – blends cruel observations with high comedy in an hilarious and poignant examination of our most personal intimacies and private longings. We see three versions of the same socially hapless evening in which the characters change subtly each time, providing a dramatically different outcome for each.

Light Shining in Buckinghamshire. Play. Caryl Churchill
M21 F4 originally played by M4 F2. Various simple settings. Fee code M

First staged in 1976 by the Joint Stock Company at the Royal Court Theatre Upstairs. Set in England in the Civil War, twenty short scenes depict the life of a struggling nation: the Putney Debates, the war in Ireland, poverty, preaching and hypocrisy. The Millennium approaches and with it the Parousia; how do the beggar, the butcher, and the soldier approach this belief? Period 1640s

The Lightning Play. Play. Charlotte Jones
M4 (young, 40s,) F4 (young, 25, 30s). Front room; various interior and exterior settings. Fee Code M

Celebrity ghost-writer Max Villiers and his shop-a-holic wife Harriet, are hosting a party at Hallow'een. Their guests include a failed monk,; his date, who dabbles in New Age ideas; the heavily-pregnant Imogen, a friend of the Villiers' daughter and her strait-laced husband. Max's new plasma screen TV dominates the set but only he can see the images from the past that appear on it, revealing the tragedy that the Villiers have long tried to bury but must now face.

A

Like A Virgin. Play. Gordon Steel
M2 (24, 30s) F3 (16, 30s). Various simple settings. Fee code L

A romp through the bubble-gum years of teenage life. Angela and Maxine, besotted with Madonna, play truant from school, form a band, attempt to write songs and, with hairbrushes in hand, live out their adolescent dreams of becoming famous. Meanwhile Angela's mother, Viv, struggles to come to terms with her marriage break-up and her daughter's explosive lifestyle, as the play rollercoasters through hope, sex, ambition, despair and, most of all, love.

♦ **Lingua Franca.** Play. Peter Nichols
M3 F4. A classroom. Fee code M. Period mid 1950s

Based around a leading character in Peter Nichols' acclaimed *Privates on Parade*, and inspired by his own experiences, this is a fast-paced, sexually-charged story that plays with notions of xenophobia and cultural stereotypes to comic effect. It's the mid-1950s and "innocent abroad" Steven is in Florence to teach English in a chaotic language school. As Steven tries to make sense of his own life and a Europe at peace after so many years of war, fellow Brit Peggy's unrequited obsession leads to highly dramatic consequences.
ISBN 978 0 573 11228 7

The Lion in Winter. Play. James Goldman
M5 (teenage, 20s, 50) F2 (young, middle-age). Henry's castle at Chinon. Fee code M

Although the outcome of the relationships depicted in this play is historical fact, the quality and content of these relationships are here imagined to be as vitriolic, lacerating, witty, disillusioned and self-destructive as anything created by Strindberg or Albee. Henry II and his Queen, Eleanor, whose mutual passion has long since been destroyed by their obsession with intrigue and power, barter, cajole and threaten to win for their favourite sons the Aquitaine, Alais Capet, or the throne of England. Period 1183
ISBN 978 0 573 01234 1

A Little Hotel on the Side. Translation by John Mortimer of *L'Hôtel du Libre Échange* by Georges Feydeau and Maurice Desvallieres
M9 F4. 4 girls. Extras. An apartment, an hotel. Fee code M

Seen at the Royal National Theatre in 1984, this witty, stylish translation remains true to the Feydeau spirit of backfiring and naughty wordplay, containing all the classic ingredients: thwarted lust, spiralling panic and a seedy hotel where the corridors see more action than the beds. 'Mr Mortimer's translation never sounds like one. Can one pay a higher compliment.' *Daily Telegraph*
ISBN 978 0 573 01616 5

Little Women. Play. Peter Clapham, adapted from the novel by Louisa M. Alcott
M4 (young, 40s, elderly) F7 (20, 40, 70). A parlour. Fee code L

This revised version of Clapham's earlier play is now shorter in running time and has one fewer male character. It still faithfully keeps to the novel, interweaving the lives of the March girls and the boy next door as they grow happily together, yet the action is contained neatly in one set. A full introduction and helpful production notes complete the text.
ISBN 978 0 573 11232 4

Little Women. Play. Louisa May Alcott, adapted by Emma Reeves
M5 F10. Minimal set. Fee code L (play), code A (music)

A

Little Women tells the classic story of the four spirited March sisters growing up in genteel poverty against the backdrop of the American Civil war that looms in the background. Conjoined with her later classic *Good Wives*, Reeves' charming adaptation sensitively illustrates the sisters' path to maturity encompassing the many reversals of fortune in their lives. The romantic, tragic and comic elements are flawlessly captured, successfully creating an emotional journey that tugs at the heartstrings. Period 1860s

Living Quarters. Play. Brian Friel
M5 (24, 30s, middle age, 50s, 64) F4 (18, 20s). Composite set: a living-room, a garden. Fee code M

Living Quarters reconstructs a day in the life of the Butler family in the village of Ballybeg. Frank Butler, who has served all his life in the Irish army, returns from United Nations service a hero, to learn of his young wife's affair with his son from a previous marriage. Parallels with Greek tragedy are marked in Friel's absorbing study of family relationships and the absence of a refuge from destiny.

Living Together. Play. Alan Ayckbourn
M3 F3. A sitting-room. Fee code L. See the entry under *The Norman Conquests*
ISB 978 0 573 01574 8

♦ **Lizzy, Darcy and Jane.** Play. Joanna Norland
M5 (teenage, 20s), F7 (20s, 30s, 40s, 50s) or M2 F4 with doubling. Various simple settings. Fee code L

Heady with her first taste of love for dashing Tom Lefroy, Jane Austen, 20, creates intrepid heroine Elizabeth, with Mr Darcy taking on the role of her arch enemy and reluctant admirer. But when Jane's romance sours, she sentences Elizabeth to marry the odious Mr Collins, and herself to an equally disastrous marriage. The fates of the author, the novel and its heroine are at stake. Elizabeth Bennet must take action. Period 1796-1802
ISBN 978 0 573 11233 1

Local Affairs. Play. Richard Harris
M4 (20, 40s) F5 (20-40, 60). A living-room, a bedroom, a kitchen. Fee code M

An earlier version of *Party Piece*, this play ingeniously uses the same set to represent three different homes. We see Charles, preoccupied with finding a fancy dress costume, and Norma, obsessed with her garden and kitchen; Hilary, returned from a health farm to find her mother-in-law in residence; and Susan and Keith, unable to enjoy a weekend without their children. Add a suicidal Katy and an incorrect party date and we are set for a confusing evening!
ISBN 978 0 573 11236 2

The Local Authority. Play. Eduardo de Filippo. Translated by Carlo Ardito
M15 (20, 60, middle-age, 75) F5 (20, 45, middle-age, 65). A living-room and a dining-room. Fee code M

Antonio Barancano acts as the arbitrator in local disputes, but interference in a certain quarrel is resented and he is fatally wounded. His last hours are spent covering up the cause of his death so that his sons will not seek to avenge him. However, his assisant, Dr Fabio, feels that for once he must tell the truth, even if a blood-feud which will last for generations is the result.

London Suite. Comedy. Neil Simon
M3 (50s) F3 (30s, 50s). A hotel suite. Fee code M

America's premier comic playwright crosses the Atlantic for a suite of hilarious comedies set in a deluxe, discreet London hotel. In *Settling Accounts*, an inebriated Welsh writer holds his business manager at gunpoint. In *Going Home* an American widow and her daughter take over the suite. The hotel guests in *The Man on the Floor* are a married couple from New York who are about to lose their suite. The evening ends on a bittersweet note with *Diana and Sidney*, another chapter in the lives of two characters from *California Suite*. (**Slightly restricted**)
ISBN 978 0 573 69509 4

The Lonesome West. Play. Martin McDonagh
M3 (20s-40s) F1 (17). A kitchen/living-room. Fee code M

Two eccentric bachelor brothers, Coleman and Valene Connor, live at war with one another. Coleman has murdered their father and passed it off as an accident. But Valene knows the truth and has blackmailed Coleman out of his inheritance. The priest, Father Welsh, a drinker, intervenes in a violent quarrel between the two brothers, and then commits suicide, leaving a letter in which he pleads with them to make peace. Coleman and Valene try ... but the indications are not good.

The Long and the Short and the Tall. Play. Willis Hall
M8 (young, 30s). A store hut. Fee code M

Set in the Malayan jungle, this critically acclaimed play is tough, realistic and full of comedy. Its characters are British soldiers who look upon their duty in the jungle with a marked lack of enthusiasm until they discover that soldiering is something more than the game they thought it was at first. Before the play comes to its unexpected climax, the men have faced up to unforeseen issues of loyalty and danger. Period 1942
ISBN 978 0 573 04016 0

Look Back in Anger. Play. John Osborne
M3 (25, 60) F2 (25). A one-room flat. Fee code M

Jimmy Porter, frustrated and bitter in his drab flat, lives with middle-class wife Alison. Also sharing the flat is Cliff who keeps things tenuously together. Alison's friend Helen arrives and persuades her to leave Jimmy only to fall for him herself. When Alison becomes pregnant Helen leaves them together. This play originally opened at the Royal Court Theatre in 1956 and has since proved to be a milestone in the history of theatre.
ISBN 978 0 573 11255 3

Look, No Hans! Comedy. John Chapman and Michael Pertwee
M2 (30s, middle-age) F4 (20, 30). Extras 1M (voice only) 1M (optional). An office/living-room. Fee code M

This play enjoyed a successful run at the Strand Theatre starring David Jason as the hapless Fisher, manager of the West Berlin office of a British car company. When his wife Monica returns from the airport because her flight has been delayed, what follows is a fast-paced fun-filled farce by the masters of the genre involving Heidi, Fisher's mistress, Mitzi, a voluptuous singing telegram girl and Cadwallader, from British Security of Industry, amongst others.
ISBN 978 0 573 01606 6

Look Who's Talking! Comedy. Derek Benfield
M2 (40, 50) F3 (26, 40). A drawing-room. Fee code L

A

When two unexpected guests, Jane and Brian, drop in on Sheila and Andrew, a devoted middle-age couple, what ensues is a complicated and hilarious series of misunderstandings and mistaken identities as Sheila and Andrew begin to weave an elaborate web of lies and half-truths to hide their own possible infidelities.
ISBN 978 0 573 11250 8

Loot. Play. Joe Orton
M5 (middle-age, young) F1 (young). A living-room. Fee code M

When Hal robs a bank and hides the money in Mrs McLeavy, his late mother's, coffin, Fay, who is trying to marry Mr McLeavy for his money, becomes suspicious and demands a share. From then on, outrageous development follows outrageous development. Truscott the police inspector accuses Fay, rightly, of having poisoned Mrs McLeavy, but the evidence is destroyed. Finally McLeavy finds himself arrested for the robbery and Truscott shares in the proceeds.

Lord Arthur Savile's Crime. Improbable Comedy. Constance Cox. Based on the short story by Oscar Wilde
M5 (20, 40, 50, elderly) F5 (20, 40, middle-age, 60). A drawing-room. Fee code L

After Lord Arthur has had his palm read by Podgers who tells him he will commit a murder, he feels duty bound to get it over with before his marriage to Sybil. But, aided by the anarchist Winkelkopf, his attempts prove futile. It emerges Podgers is a charlatan and so Lord Arthur is free but on the way to the wedding rehearsal he finds the carriage contains Winkelkopf's newest bomb. Period 1890
ISBN 978 0 573 01245 7

Terry Pratchett's **Lords and Ladies**. Adapted by Irana Brown
M18 F9. Extras. Composite setting. Fee code M

The Lancre witches, Granny Weatherwax and Nanny Ogg, are the Discworld's only hope of rescue when elves threaten to take control with their hypnotic "glamour". Standing stones; wizards; Morris men and Rude Mechanicals; country lore and ancient magic: all these are elements of this hilarious, fast-moving and exciting adaptation of Terry Pratchett's well-loved novel.
ISBN 978 0 573 01888 6

Lost in Yonkers. Comic drama. Neil Simon
M2 (30s, 40s) F3 (30s, 70s).2 boys. An apartment. Fee code M

New York, 1942. When Eddie Kurnitz's wife dies he deposits his two teenage sons with their formidable Grandma Kurnitz who runs a candy store in Yonkers. But Grandma Kurnitz is not all the boys have to contend with. There is also Bella, and Louie her brother, who may have mob connections. Gradually the mood deepens and darkens, as we become aware that this is a family full of emotionally crippled people. (**Slightly restricted**)

◆ **A bullet mark next to a title indicates that it is new to this edition of the Guide.**

◆ **Love and Understanding**. Play. Joe Penhall
M2 F1. Fee Code M

Live-in lovers Neal and Rachel are overworked doctors. Their relationship suffers as they rarely see each other. Enter Neal's good-for-nothing friend, Richie, straight from South America or somewhere, looking for a place to stay. Neal is too weak to say no and Rachel doesn't want him either, but Richie manipulates her, creating a sexual tension between them. Richie stirs up trouble between the couple insinuating that Neal is boring and Rachel needs a good time with a black sheep like himself.

Love from a Stranger. Play. Frank Vosper. Based on a story by Agatha Christie
M4 (30s, middle age, 60) F4 (30, middle age). 2 sitting-rooms. Fee code M

Cecily wins a small fortune in a sweepstake and takes a European tour. She meets charming American Bruce Lovell and, after a whirlwind marriage, he takes her to their isolated country cottage. But Lovell is a homicidal maniac now determined on Cecily's murder. When Cecily realizes, it is too late to find help. Desperately she plays for time while Lovell grows more inhuman every minute. Finally, she succeeds in tricking him.
ISBN 978 0 573 01248 8

◆ **Love in Idleness.** Play. Terence Rattigan
M3 F6. A house; a flat. Fee Code M

Love in the Title. Play. Hugh Leonard
F3 (20, 30, 37). A meadow. Fee code M

This gentle and lyrical play portrays the lives of three generations of women. When Katie arrives in Corcamore in Ireland to paint a watercolour of the legendary stone of Clough-a-Regan, she is accompanied by the youthful versions of her mother, Triona, and her grandmother, Cat. Katie exists in the present but Triona and Cat are in their own time. Their conversation reveals their family history and its intricate relation with the wider history of their culture.
ISBN 978 0 573 01889 3

Love of the Nightingale. Play. Timberlake Wertenbaker
M12 F8, with doubling. A bare stage. Fee code M

In this treatment of the Philomele myth, war hero Tereus takes his Athenian wife Procne to live in Thrace. She becomes lonely and begs him to fetch her younger sister, Philomele, from Athens to be her companion. During the arduous return journey Tereus rapes Philomele and then cuts out her tongue. Despite Tereus's claim that Philomele died at sea, the two sisters are finally reunited, whereby, through a disturbing puppet show, Philomele reveals her horrific ordeal. The sisters wreak their revenge in true tragic style.

Lovers. Double-bill. Brian Friel
M3 or 2 (17, 50) F5 or 4 (17, 40, 60). Adaptable setting. Fee code L

The first play, *Winners*, tells the story of Mag and Joe. Young and in love, they spend a glorious summer's day laughing and talking together and planning their future. But for Mag and Joe there is to be no future. The second play, *Losers*, tells of Hanna and Andy, a couple to whom love has come late, and for whom courting is made almost impossible by the upstairs presence of Hanna's demanding invalid mother. They do eventually get married, but gradually Andy realizes that Hanna is bidding fair to becoming a replica of her mother.

The Loves of Cass McGuire. Play. Brian Friel
M4 (17, 60s, elderly, 70) F6 (18, 50, 70s, 89). A spacious room. Fee code M

Low Level Panic. Play. Clare McIntyre
F3 (20s). Fee code H

Presented by the Women's Playhouse Trust at the Royal Court Theatre Upstairs in 1988 and the Lyric Studio, Hammersmith in 1989, this is a careful examination of the role of pornography in our society and the way it affects three young women in particular, using short scenes to show how popular images of women influence the way they are seen by others and the way they see themselves.

Lucky Sods. Play. John Godber
M4 (30s, 40s) F4 (30s, 40s, 70s) can be played by M2 F2. Various simple interiors and exteriors. Fee code M

When Morris and Jean win the National Lottery – to the tune of two million pounds – they can't believe their luck. But the cracks in their marriage widen, their past catches up with them and their relatives become increasingly resentful. Jean keeps winning and Morris takes off to Amsterdam with an old flame, but will his prophecy that bad luck always follows good turn out to be true?
ISBN 978 0 573 01825 1

The Lying Kind. Farcical comedy. Anthony Neilson
M4 F3. Simple settings. Fee code L

Police constables Gobbel and Blunt have the task of informing a woman's parents that she has died in a car crash on her way home for Christmas. Garson, her mother, is understandably distraught, but her father, Balthasar, is strangely unaffected by the news. It quickly becomes clear that there has been a serious misunderstanding. Enormous, butch Gronya, meanwhile, is out to expose Balthasar as a paedophile. 'Neilson's play gleefully and skilfully heaps an ever more precarious load of farcical indignities upon his hapless cast.' *Time Out*

♦ **Lysistrata – The Sex Strike.** Play. Germaine Greer, after Aristophanes,
adapted for performance with additional dialogue by Phil Willmott
M8 F11. A bathhouse steam room. Fee code L. Period Ancient Greek

The ancient world is gripped by a long and futile war. While the men of Athens fight in a foreign land, the Athens women can take no more. In secret, they meet with the enemy women and form a pact. The battle moves into the bedroom. No sex for the men – unless the women get peace.
"Fast, broad, silly and profound." *Independent on Sunday*
"Wonderfully fragrant, upper crust Lysistrata" *Guardian*
ISBN 978 0953675 708

Mad Forest. Play from Romania. Caryl Churchill
40 characters, may be played by a cast of 11. Various interior and exterior settings. Fee code M

Focussing on two families, life before the 1989 Romanian revolution is portrayed. The play, with a large cast, was performed by eleven actors and was seen at the Royal Court Theatre in 1990. 'The work is speedy, poetic, urgent and electrifying ... The trial and execution of the Ceausescus is done as a sickening revue sketch, an indicator of the double-edged, sceptical tone throughout. A triumph! The future of our theatre, if not that of Romania, is secure.' *Observer*

Madame Melville. Play. Richard Nelson
M2 (15, 40s)F2 (30s) An apartment living-room. Fee code M

Set in 1966 in a soon-to-be-exploding Paris, *Madame Melville* is the intimate story of Carl, a fifteen-year-old American, and his teacher, the beautiful Claudie Melville. Over a night and day, Carl discovers an unimagined world where beauty, loneliness, love, sex and art are one. *Madame Melville* premièred at the Vaudeville Theatre, London in October 2000 with Macaulay Culkin and Irene Jacob as Carl and Claudie. Period 1966 " ... you become suddenly aware that you are in the presence of something rare and special." *Daily Telegraph*

Made in Bangkok. Play. Anthony Minghella
M7 (20s, 30s, 50s) F5 (30s), with doubling. Various interior settings. Fee code M

The setting is Bangkok – market place of the world where everything is for sale; the message is a bleak indictment of commercial sex and the condemnation of human exploitation. The main characters are a bunch of British tourists who arrive in Thailand armed with good intentions but are soon unzipping their sexual frustrations of a lifetime. 'Minghella handles his powerful, complex theme with great accomplishment, building to a scarifying climax.' *Time Out*

A Madhouse in Goa. A double bill by Martin Sherman
M4 (Part One: 18, 20s, 30s; Part Two: 19, 20s, 40s) F2 (Part One: 60s; Part Two: 20s, 40s). Two verandas. Fee code M

Part One, *A Table for A King*, chronicles the experiences of a young writer, David, who takes part in a plan to blackmail another guest into giving up her favourite table for the King of Greece. Part Two, *Keeps Rainin' All the Time*, moves to the volcanic island of Santorini, where the existence of several disparate expatriates is ruptured by nuclear rain, terrorism and the impending eruption of the volcano.

The Madness of George III. Play. Alan Bennett
M22 F5, with doubling. Various simple interior and exterior settings. Fee code M

What, what? Is the King mad? The Whigs think so, and begin campaigning for the Bill of Regency to allow the power-hungry Prince of Wales to ascend the throne. Meanwhile the King endures humiliating, torturous treatment at the hands of incapable doctors. Bennett's clever, funny and ultimately compassionate play sheds new light on a monarch often dismissed as inconsequential. It was first performed to great acclaim by the Royal National Theatre with Nigel Hawthorne in the title role.

Mahler's Conversion. Play. Ronald Harwood
M3 (37, 50s) F3 (22, 24, 39). Various simple settings. Fee code M

Gustav Mahler, a composer and conductor of passion and genius, was born in Bohemia and faced a lifetime of prejudice. But in 1897, obsessed with power and fame, Mahler rejected his Jewish background and his friends with devastating consequence: to be granted the prestigious position of Director of The Vienna Court Opera, he decided to convert to Catholicism. In time, however, as his world collapsed, he came to believe he was being made to pay a dreadful price for his ruthless ambition. Period 1897-1911

A

The Maiden Stone. Play. Rona Munro
M2 (30s-50s) F4 (14, 16, 30s, 40s). A boy. Children. Various simple settings. Fee code M

Set in the North-east of Scotland in the early nineteenth century, this tells a story of women struggling against their circumstances, desires and ambitions in the persons of Harriet, an educated English actress leading her touring troupe in search of work, and Bidie, the Scottish traveller she engages as a wet nurse.

Mail Order Bride. Play. James Robson
M2 (30, 50) F3 (26, 35, 55). 2M 4F, voices only. A large kitchen. Fee code M

Martin, a craggy, hard-working Yorkshire landowner and bachelor, lives with his punctilious spinster sister Ivy on the farm they inherited from their parents. Desperate for companionship, Martin pays for a Filipino woman, Maria – whom he has discovered through a video-dating agency – to come and live with them. But Ivy resents the intrusion, and, on the day of Maria and Martin's wedding, she digs up information about Maria's past, with shocking consequences for them all.
ISBN 978 0 573 01847 3

Make and Break. Play. Michael Frayn
M11 (20s-50s) F2 (young, 40). An exhibition stand in an hotel bedroom. Fee code M

John Garrard is a compulsive businessman, and his self-absorption is complete. During one climactic night amid the hectic activities of a trade fair in Germany, it looks as if the shell of his self-concern might at least be pierced; an unexpected relationship with an attractive secretary, a lesson in Buddhism, a sudden apparent heart attack and confrontation with death. But death when it comes strikes unexpectedly elsewhere – and Garrard's character seems unchanged, unless for the worse ...
ISBN 978 0 573 11257 7

Make Way for Lucia. Comedy. John van Druten from the novels of E. F. Benson
M5 (38-45, 45, 50, old) F6 (35, 40s, 50, old). A drawing-room. Fee code M

E. F. Benson's hilarious novels, written in the 1920s and 30s, of the war for social supremacy between Lucia and Miss Mapp in Tilling are brought to the stage with all the wit, irony and humour of the originals. Hitherto, Tilling's doyenne has been Miss Mapp; Lucia is the supreme poseuse who peppers her speech with Italian phrases she doesn't understand. When Lucia rents Miss Mapp's house for the summer the battle lines are drawn ...
ISBN 978 0 573 01820 6

Making History. Play. Brian Friel
M4 (20s, 40s) F2 (20s). A living-room, a thicket, a palace apartment. Fee code M

♦ **Making Money**. Play. Adapted for the stage by Stephen Briggs from Terry Pratchett's novel.
M19 F10 Extras. Various simple settings. Fee Code M

Lord Vetinari wants to overhaul the banks of Ankh-Morpork so he appoints former con-man Albert Spangler, *aka* Moist von Lipwig, to the position of Master of the Royal Mint. Mrs Lavish, the bank manager, dies, leaving her dog, Mr Fusspot – who happens to be the majority shareholder – to Moist. Suddenly he finds himself in charge and his talent for a swindle soon has customers queuing up . . . but making money is not always easy.
ISBN 978 0 573 11264 5

Making Waves. Play. Stephen Clark
M3 (20s, 54) F3 (19, 22, 49) A kitchen, a workshop, a beach. Fee code L

Mike, father of the Tanner family, is the coxswain of the Teesmouth Lifeboat. The demands of his job take priority over the needs of his family. But he's a hero. What can they do? Lyricist and playwright Stephen Clark has constructed a tense family drama from the brave men who go to sea to save others but whose families must bear the consequences.

Mammals. Play. Amelia Bullmore
M2 (30s) F4 (4 (played by an adult),6 (played by an adult), late 20s, 30s). A kitchen. Fee Code L

Amelia Bullmore's first stage play (she is an accomplished television dramatist) makes uncomfortable viewing for anyone married with children. Jane and Kev have two girls, aged four and six, who are played by large grown-ups. Their unmarried, childless friends, Phil and Lorna, lead what seems very desirable lives, unencumbered by children, and when they arrive for a weekend visit it is a time for half-hearted adulteries and catastrophic confessions.
ISBN 978 0 413 77522 1

Man and Boy. Drama. Terence Rattigan
M5 (young, 30s, 50s) F2 (young). A basement apartment. Fee code M

A tense drama of the business world which requires a comparatively simple set. Gregor, a tycoon of Hungarian origin, arrives at the apartment of his illegitimate son, Basil, for a business meeting to discuss a highly-profitable merger. After achieving apparent success he finds everything collapsing aound him and learns from Basil that a warrant is out for his arrest. Basil offers help, but Gregor acquires a conscience for the first time in his life and determines his own way out.
ISBN 978 0 573 11267 6

A Man for All Seasons. Play. Robert Bolt
M11 (30s, 40s, 60s) F3 (24, 47, 55). Composite setting. Fee code M

Paul Schofield starred in both play and film as Sir Thomas More, the sixteenth-century Chancellor unwillingly in conflict with Henry VIII. More loves God, but he loves the world also. He has a subtle intellect, a scrupulous conscience and a very human fear of death, nowing full well the penalty of even silently opposing the king. All the while the chorus figure of the Common Man evades all personal responsibility for orders carried out, even to being More's executioner.
ISBN 978 0 573 01260 0

Man Is Man. (Man Equals Man) Play. Bertolt Brecht
Translations: Steve Gooch
              Carl Mueller, music by Dessau
              Gerhard Nellhaus, music by Dessau
M8 F2. Soldiers. Various interior and exterior settings. Fee code M for play, code C for music

---

◆ **A bullet mark next to a title indicates that it is new to this edition of the Guide.**

Man of the Moment. Play. Alan Ayckbourn
M6 (30s-50s) F4 (19-50s). Extras 3M 3F, 1 child (7). Male voices. A patio/pool area of a Mediterranean villa. Fee code M

This joint winner of the *Evening Standard* Best Comedy Award starred Peter Bowles as the ex-robber turned successful media personality and Michael Gambon as the timid clerk who once heroically foiled his bank raid. ' ... one of the best things he has ever done ... It is, in fact, a masterpiece ... Ayckbourn at the peak of his powers using comedy to say harsh, true things about our society ...' *Guardian*
ISBN 978 0 573 01833 6

Mansfield Park. Play. Adapted by Willis Hall from the novel by Jane Austen
M11 (young-elderly) F9 (young-elderly). Various interior and exterior settings. Fee code M
ISBN 978 0 573 01839 8

Map of the Heart. Play. William Nicholson
M4 (20s-40s) F4 (17, 30s, 40s). Extras. Various interior and exterior settings. Fee code M
ISBN 978 0 573 01832 9

Mappa Mundi. Play. Shelagh Stephenson
M4 (30s Black, 45, 50s, elderly) F2 (41, 60s West Indian) Dancers (1 Black, 1 Asian). A garden. Fee code M

While Anna prepares for her wedding to a Black lawyer, her father Jack, a passionate map collector, is forced to confront the limits of his life. Although research into his ancestry proves the family is related to an eighteenth-century cartographer and plantation owner, Anna is interested by the discovery that they may also be descended from a slave. *Mappa Mundi* premièred at the National Theatre, London, in October 2002.

♦ **Martha, Josie and the Chinese Elvis.** Play. Charlotte Jones
M2 (young, 50) F4 (20s, 40s). A front room. Fee code M

January 6th – the feast of the Epiphany. It's also Josie's birthday but she's in no mood to celebrate her fortieth and has decided to hang up the tools of her dominatrix profession for the last time. But then Lionel, her most loyal customer arrives and insists she has a party. A knock at the door sets an extraordinary chain of events in motion – it's now or never for all her guests. A perfectly-crafted, bittersweet comedy from an award-winning playwright.

Mary Stuart. Friedrich Schiller, in a version by Peter Oswald
M12 F3, may be played by M8 F3. Various simple settings. Fee Code M

Schiller's play pits Mary, Queen of Scots against her rival Queen Elizabeth I. The meeting never happened but, as Goethe said, "It will be good to see those two whores alongside each other". Schiller's Mary redeems her youthful crimes through an ordeal that lifts her into realms of spiritual serenity, while Elizabeth descends deeper into rage, revenge and deception. Oswald has written this striking new version in a mixture of prose and poetry. Period sixteenth century.

A

Terry Pratchett's **Maskerade**. Play. Adapted by Stephen Briggs
M16 F9. Extras. Various simple interior and exterior settings. Fee code M

All is not well in the Ankh-Morpork Opera House. A ghost stalks the dark corridors, leaving strange letters for the management and ... killing people. Granny Weatherwax and Nanny Ogg, two Lancre witches, investigate, and are soon involved in all kinds of skulduggery, mayhem and ear-splittingly loud singing. Quirky and original characters, a labyrinthine plot and numerous witty one-liners make this a treat for Discworld fans and 'uninitiated' theatregoers alike. ISBN 978 0 573 01829 9

Massage. Play. Michael Wilcox
M2 F1. A living-room. Fee code L

The Matchmaker. Farce. Thornton Wilder
M8 F7. Four interiors. Fee code M

An rich old merchant in Yonkers decides to take a wife and employs a matchmaker. She subsequently becomes involved with two of his menial clerks, assorted young, lovely ladies, and the headwaiter at an expensive restaurant where this swift farce runs headlong into a hilarious climax of complication. After everyone gets straightened out romantically, and everyone has his heart's desire, the merchant of Yonkers finds himself affianced to the astute matchmaker herself. Period 1880s. 'Loud, slapdash and uproarious ... Something extraordinarily original and funny.' *New York Times*.

The Maths Tutor. Play. Clare McIntyre
M4 (teens, 30s, middle age) F2 (teens, middle age). A kitchen, various other simple settings. Fee code M

Tom and J.J. are best mates, sharing hobbies and the same Maths tutor. Tom's parents seem to have the perfect marriage – yet nobody knows the secret deal that has kept the family together for years. But when J.J.'s mother starts a relationship with a younger man and J.J. fabricates a terrible lie in revenge, everyone is forced to confront the hidden parts of their lives. Clare McIntyre's wryly comic play lays bare the trip wires running through the relationships between the generations.

Me and Mamie O'Rourke. Play. Mary Agnes Donoghue
M2 (20s, 30s) F2 (30s). A converted basement. Fee code M. ISBN 978 0 573 01844 2

Me and My Friend. Play. Gillian Plowman
M2 (30s-40s) F2 (20s-30s). Two flats. Fee code M

(Please note that the first two acts of this play may be presented as one-act plays, but that the third act may not.)

A black comedy, the play explores the relationships between two 'odd' couples thrown prematurely out of hospital care. Firstly, we see two men conduct fantasy interviews for jobs they will never get, then two women trying to 'make plans' as urged to do by the hospital. They all meet when Oz throws a disastrous party with the four desperately attempting the niceties of social intercourse.
ISBN 978 0 573 01831 2

The Memory of Water. Play. Shelagh Stephenson
M2 (30s, any age) F4 (30s-40s). A bedroom. Fee code M

In *The Memory of Water* (winner of the 2000 Laurence Olivier Award for Best Comedy), three sisters meet on the eve of their mother's funeral. As the conflicts of the past converge, everyday lies and tensions reveal the particular patterns and strains of family relationships. "... the dialogue sparkles ... this cracking new work." David Nathan, *Jewish Chronicle* " ... a deeply felt, richly funny study of the pervasive power of the past." Michael Billington, *Guardian*

Men of the World. Play. John Godber
M2 F1 play 18 characters. Various simple settings. Fee code M

Preparing for a mystery trip to Scarborough three northern coach drivers pass the time remembering more exciting trips, such as the one down the Rhine Valley. Stick hates his passengers and wishes he was doing the Spanish run, Larry is a seasoned traveller and Mario Lanza fan and Frank is their female counterpart. The three actors take turns playing an assortment of passengers, from dotty old complainers to retired miners seeking excitement on too little money. A touching, often hilarious, bitter-sweet play.
ISBN 978 0 573 01997 5

Men Should Weep. Play. Ena Lamont Stewart
M4 F9. 1 girl (11), 1 boy (8), babies (voices only). A kitchen. Fee code M

Written for Glasgow Unity in 1947, this extraordinarily moving play of women surviving in the east end of Glasgow of the 1930s was revived by 7:84 Company to tremendous critical acclaim. It finds in the lives of Maggie, her family and her neighbours not only all the tragedy that appalling housing, massive unemployment and grinding poverty can produce, but also a rich vein of comedy – the sense of the ridiculous, the need for a good laugh.
ISBN 978 0 573 01838 1

The Mercy Seat. Play. Neil LaBute
M1 (30s) F1 (40s). A spacious loft apartment. Fee code M

The world has changed overnight. On September 12, 2001, Ben Harcourt finds himself in the New York downtown apartment of his lover and boss, Abby Prescott. His endlessly ringing mobile phone haunts their conversation as Ben and Abby explore the choices now available to them in an existence different from the one they knew just the day before. Will Ben let his family know he's alive, or will he and Abby take this chance to create a new life for themselves?

Messiah. Play. Steven Berkoff
Large mixed cast. Fee code M

Messiah deals with the way that traces of Christ's Jewish origins have been removed as he has been embraced by Christianity. It begins with the image of Christ on the cross and pits his humanity and transcendent goodness against the evil of those who would kill him and all he stands for. (*Please specify author when ordering.*)

◆ **A bullet mark next to a title indicates that it is new to this edition of the Guide.**

Messiah. Play. Martin Sherman
M2 (24, 50s) F4 (28, late 40s, middle-age). Extras. Musicians. Various simple interior and exterior settings. Fee code M

Messiah is set in Poland in 1665 following the Cossack uprising in which over a third of the once thriving Jewish community has been slaughtered, the rest impoverished. Now everyone is obsessed with the certainty that the Messiah will come. So, with the news that the Mesiah is preaching in the Middle East, Rachel and her family journey to Gallipoli with tragic results. ' ... handles the Jewish dilemma with humanity and humour.' *Standard. (Please specify author when ordering.)*

Metamorphosis. Steven Berkoff, adapted from Franz Kafka
M3 F2 plus 3 or 1. Fee code M

Gregor Samsa wakes one morning to find he has turned into a giant insect. On a set resembling an insect, Gregor's sad, comic, frightening story is played in a hugely theatrical style which makes all of the characters insect-like in different ways.

♦ **Micky Salberg's Crystal Ballroom Dance Band.** Play with music. Ade Morris. Original music by Paul Kissaun (available on hire)
M2 (18, middle age) F1 (24). A farmyard and farmhouse. Fee code L for play, A for music. Period 1950s

Struggling to make a living, Jewish Polish immigrant Micky Salberg revives his old band with daughter Sam and guitarist Tommy, in an attempt to raise money. Soon the trio is touring the dance halls of Stoke, but when Tommy is called up, the future of the Crystal Ballroom Dance Band looks doubtful. A very funny, emotive play about love, loss and rock 'n' roll.
ISBN 978 0 573 11291 1

The Milk Train Doesn't Stop Here Any More. Play. Tennessee Williams
M5 (young, 17) F4 (young, elderly). Composite setting. Fee code M

A stranger arrives at Mrs Goforth's Italian villa, a young poet known as the Angel of Death because he has been present at the decease of a number of elderly ladies. She thinks that he will afford her a final fling before she dies, but it turns out that he is there as a spiritual rather than fleshly guide and merely wishes to comfort her during her declining years. The author describes his play as 'a comedy about death'.

Mindgame. Play. Anthony Horowitz
M2 (50) F1 (40s). An office. Fee code M

Mark Styler, a writer of "true crime" paperbacks, tries to get an interview with Easterman, a notorious serial killer. First he has to get past Dr Farquhar, the quixotic head of Fairfields, the asylum where Easterman is kept. But soon he discovers that very little is quite what it seems. Worse still, even the things that are what they seem, are slowly changing. Who is the mysterious Benson? Where did he get the meat in the fridge? And why isn't the skeleton in the closet?

♦ **A bullet mark next to a title indicates that it is new to this edition of the Guide.**

The Miracle Worker. Play. William Gibson
M6 (9 (Black), 20s, 40s, 60s, elderly) F7 (6, 8 (Black), 17, 20s, 35 (Black), middle-age).
Composite setting. Fee code M

A

Helen Keller is world-famous for her work with those born blind, deaf and dumb. The play tells the story of Annie Sullivan's efforts to teach Helen to communicate, fighting against the thoughtless indulgence of Helen's family and her doting possessive mother until, at last, Annie achieves the miracle of teaching Helen language. Here, Helen's life can truly be said to have begun. Period 1880
ISBN 978 0 573 61238 1

The Misanthrope. Comedy. Martin Crimp after Moliere
M6 F3. Luxury hotel, other various simple settings. Fee Code M

Martin Crimp's version of Molière's 1666 French classic updates the play by bringing it into a contemporary London world of theatre and media moguls, giving it a sublime, carefully balanced blank verse language that is enjoyably savage. The misanthropic, ruthless Alceste is in love with Jennifer, an American film star, but he is thwarted by various male callers. Alceste mocks critic-turned-playwright Covington, but then extends his scathing satiric attack to anti-smokers, celebrity journalists and the whole media circus that encircles him. Divine retribution comes with Jennifer's final rejection of him.

The Miser. Comedy. Molière. Adapted by Miles Malleson
M11 (20s, middle-age, elderly) F3 (young, 20s, middle-age). A room in Paris. Fee code H
ISBN 978 0 573 01279 2

Les Misérables. Play. Jonathan Holloway, adapted from the novel by Victor Hugo
M9 (range of ages) F3 (range of ages), or M4 F3 with doubling. Various interior and exterior settings. Fee code M

Hugo's passionate, epic tale of social injustice, class conflict, love and revolt is brought to exciting theatrical life in this intense adaptation. Using conventions of "Poor Theatre" – small cast; simple, flexible settings; clear, uncluttered storytelling; strong political sensibility – the play follows its many vividly-drawn characters through a story spanning several years with pace and economy. Period early 19th century.
ISBN 978 0 573 01880 0

Miss Roach's War. Play. Richard Kane. Adapted from *The Slaves of Solitude* by Patrick Hamilton
M3 (35, 59, 70s) F5 (20, 39, 60s) or M3 F4 with doubling. Five acting areas. Fee code M

1943. The Rosamund Tea Rooms houses several women and elderly men, all of them single and lonely, who nurse resentments and wage minor wars with each other. Enid Roach makes two unfortunate friendships which heighten the tension to breaking point: one with Pike, an American lieutenant, the other with Vicki Kugelmann, a German who steals Pike from Enid and then sets about humiliating her former friend.
ISBN 978 0 573 01919 7

Mistero Buffo. Farce. Dario Fo. Translated by Ed Emery
Flexible casting. A bare stage. Fee code M

A series of short pieces, either for one actor portraying multiple roles or for numerous players. Divided into sections of eight Comic Mysteries and four Passion Plays, Fo's satirical and controversial interpretations of the Gospels have been performed by him worldwide to critical acclaim as a one-man show. 'Fo is the determined enemy of pomp, ceremony and the material aspects of religion but what shines out of this exhilarating show is his love of humanity and truth.' *Guardian*

Mixed Doubles. An entertainment on marriage by George Melly, Alan Ayckbourn, James Saunders, Harold Pinter, Alun Owen, Fay Weldon, David Campton, Lyndon Brook and John Bowen. M1 F1 for each sketch. M1 for linking scenes. Fee code M

If individual scenes are presented separately fee codes vary. Please enquire for further details to Samuel French Ltd.
ISBN 978 0 573 01584 7

Mixed Feelings. Comedy. Donald Churchill
M4 (young, middle-age) F2 (middle-age). A basement flat. Fee code M

Moment of Weakness. Comedy. Donald Churchill
M1 (40s) F2 (18, 40s). A cottage living-room. Fee code M. ISBN 978 0 573 69280 2

A Month in the Country. Play. Brian Friel, after Turgenev
M7 (21, 30s, 40s, 57) F5 (17, 20s, 37, 58). A drawing-room, a garden. Fee code M

A Month in the Country. Comedy. Ivan Turgenev. Adapted into English by Emlyn Williams
For cast and settings see above. Fee code M

A Month of Sundays. Play. Bob Larbey
M3 (40s, 60s) F3 (24, 40s). A room in a rest home for the elderly. Fee code M

Set in a rest home, this play revolves around two residents: Cooper, who has voluntarily left his family to avoid the indignity of depending on them, and his friend Aylott, both on the verge of some geriatric embarrassment. To the painful ritual of family visits and empty condescension the two inmates reply with humour and wit, aware that life can only be endured if treated as a comedy.
ISBN 978 0 573 01956 2

Moonlight. Play. Harold Pinter
M4 (20s, 50s) F3 (16, 50s). Simple settings depicting 2 bedrooms and an undefined space. Fee code M

Andy is a civil servant who lies dying in his bed. Desperate for consolation from his family, he spends his time railing against his long-suffering wife Bel. They remember their past, in particular their friendship with Maria, with whom they both had affairs. Alongside them, Andy's unemployed sons act out a series of fiercely high-powered mind-games, while daughter Bridget hovers over the action, subtly suggesting that she was the victim of some terrible childhood wrong.

Moonlight and Magnolias. Play. Ron Hutchinson
M3 Fl. An office. Fee code M

A

Legendary producer David O. Sleznik has just suspended filming of the most eagerly-anticipated movie of all time, *Gone With The Wind*, scrapping the script and sacking its director in the process. He drafts in script doctor Ben Hecht to rewrite it, but Hecht happens to be the only man in the country who has not read the novel. Along with director Victor Fleming, whom they have poached from the set of *The Wizard of Oz*, they have five days to rescue the film. Period 1939.

The Mother. Play. Bertolt Brecht. Translated by Steve Gooch, music by Hanns Eisler
M15 F3. Extras. Various simple exterior and interior settings. Fee code M for play, code C for music

Pelagea Vlassova is drawn by her son Pavel into the revolutionary movement. Though hostile to it at first, she refuses to let him distribute leaflets, preferring to run the risk herself. She takes part in a peaceful demonstration, where Pavel is arrested; she learns to read, helps striking peasants, and works an illegal press. Pavel escapes from Siberia, but is caught and shot. Pelagea is beaten up for protesting against the 1914 war and finishes by carrying the red flag in a huge anti-war demonstration in the winter of 1916.

Mother Courage and her Children. Chronicle play. Bertolt Brecht
Translations: John Willett
            Eric Bentley, music by Dessau; Milhaud
            Ralph Manheim
            Hanif Kureishi
            David Hare
            Lee Hall, music by Dominic Muldowney
            Michael Hofman, songs trans. John Willett
M19 F6. Extras. Twelve simple exterior settings. Fee code M for play, code C for music

For years through the terrible Thirty Years War Mother Courage has followed the Swedish armies with her mobile canteen, and her three children (each by a different man). Life during war is reduced simply to a series of business transactions: soldiers rob peasants and steal from their own stores, peasants sell their last cherished possessions. Mother Courage's business and motherly instincts constantly betray her. Finally, alone, she hitches herself to her wagon and continues to follow the army. Period 1624-1636

Mr Puntila and his Man Matti. Play. Bertolt Brecht
Translations: John Willett, music by Dessau
            Paul Kriwaczek
            Gerhard Nellhaus
            Lee Hall, music by Chris Larner (for details of the music please apply to
            Samuel French Ltd)
M14 F7 (children). Extras. Interior and exterior settings. Fee code M for play, code C for music

Mr Puntila suffers from a dual personality. When drunk he is human and humane; when sober he is surly and self-centred. In the former condition he proposes to Eva to marry his own loyal and sardonic friend, his chauffeur Matti. When he sobers up he throws Eva out and abuses Matti. However, after putting Eva's suitability to the test, and having had enough of Puntila's instability, Matti leaves him, saying 'water and oil can never blend.'

Mr Quigley's Revenge. Play. Simon Brett
M14 F20 (speaking parts). A village hall. Fee code M

Frinsley Village Hall is the hub of community life, lovingly tended by the amiable Mr Quigley, whose little blue book ensures the aerobics class never clashes with the wedding bookings. But plans are afoot to change this cosy existence ... the invidious Keith has plans to sell the site. Feeling sure of success, Keith launches his attack on Mr Quigley – a big mistake, for Mr Quigley is wilier than he looks. Offers acting opportunities for all and great fun for the audience!
ISBN 978 0 573 01845 9

Mr Whatnot. Comedy. Alan Ayckbourn
M7 F4, doubling possible. Various settings. Fee code M

Mr Whatnot is Mint, a piano tuner, summoned to the stately home of Lord and Lady Slingsby-Craddock. Once there he falls in love with their daughter, Amanda, elopes with her, fails to save her from marriage to Cecil but wins through in the end. With plenty of mime and sound effects *Mr Whatnot* offers great opportunities to an imaginative director for a highly entertaining and unusual production.
ISBN 0 573 11287 4

Mr Wonderful. Play. James Robson
M3 (50s, middle age) F2 (45, 65). 2M extras. Various interior and exterior settings. Fee code L
ISBN 0 573 01857 2

♦ **Mrs Affleck.** Play. Samuel Adamson, from Henrik Ibsen's *Little Eyolf*
M3 (teenage, 39) F4 (30s), 2 boys (aged 9). Extras. A kitchen, a tea-house, a beach. Fee code M

Ibsen's haunting psychodrama of guilt, sexual frustration and self-deceit, re-located to 1950s England. Rita Affleck, a sensual woman consumed by jealous love, welcomes home her troubled ex-serviceman husband Alfred. But Alfred vows to devote himself to their disabled son Olly, and tragedy ensues. Presented at the National Theatre in 2009, directed by Marianne Elliott and starring Claire Skinner. Period 1955
"Laden with fine writing (and) a keen dramatic intelligence ..." *The Independent*
ISBN 978 0 573 11289 8

Mrs Klein. Play. Nicholas Wright
F3 (30s, 52). A living-room. Fee code M

Seen in London at the National and Globe theatres in 1988 starring Gillian Barge, Francesca Annis and Zoë Wanamaker, this powerful drama centres on an episode in the life of controversial child-psychoanalyst Melanie Klein. Because of the death of her son, Hans, Melanie is confronted with the irony of being a successful child analyst but a failed mother. She attacks her own daughter Melitta who leaves for good and whose role as daughter is replaced by Melitta's friend, Paula. Period 1934

♦ **A bullet mark next to a title indicates that it is new to this edition of the Guide.**

Murder at Rutherford House. An audience participation play by Tom Chiodo and Peter DePietro. Original music by James Followell. (A Murder à la Carte Mystery Play) M5 (20s-60s) F6 (20s-70s). A room. Fee code M. Production manual on hire

A complete production manual describes in detail the format for producing an audience-participation murder mystery utilizing the entire theatre. Actors stage scripted and improvised scenes throughout the theatre. Every audience member can become his or her favourite detective, complete with clue pads provided by the theatre; at the peak of the evening, after several murders, the audience must determine whodunit and why.
ISBN 978 0 573 69195 9

Murder by Misadventure. Play. Edward Taylor
M3 (30s-40s) F1 (30s). A penthouse flat. Fee code M. ISBN 978 0 573 01835 0

The Murder Game. Play. Constance Cox
M2 (28, 40) F2 (26, 35). A living-room. Fee code L. ISBN 978 0 573 01222 8

A Murder Has Been Arranged. Ghost Story. Emlyn Williams
M4 (young, 40s) F6 (young, 20s, middle-age, 45). A stage. Fee code H

There is a legend concerning a murder once committed at the St James' Theatre, that a dumb woman will appear on stage to reveal the murderer. Sir Charles Jasper holds a dinner-party in the theatre. Tonight he will come into a vast fortune. Should he die before eleven, his nephew Maurice will inherit it. Maurice arrives and engineers his uncle's murder. Then the dumb woman of the legend appears ...
ISBN 978 0 573 01294 5

Murder in Company. Play. Philip King and John Boland
M4 (21, 40s) F4 (20s-40). An empty stage. Fee code L

A dramatic society is assembling on the stage of a church hall to rehearse a production of a mystery-thriller. The rehearsal proceeds under difficulties until the mysterious death of the caretaker brings the situation of the whodunit even more closely into real life. It transpires that almost everyone might, and could have, murdered the dead man – eventually the identity of both killer and prowler is revealed.
ISBN 978 0 573 01289 1

Murder in Play. Play. Simon Brett
M3 (30s, 40s, 60s) F5 (20s, middle-age). A living-room box set. Fee code M

Boris Smolensky's budget repertory production of 'Murder at Priorswell Manor' is looking decidedly shaky. The cast are more interested in their egos than the play and life imitates art when Boris's wife, Renee, is murdered on stage. Simon Brett's hilarious text, a worthy companion to his Charles Paris theatrical thriller novels, ruthlessly satirizes the politics of the inept company and the numerous red herrings keep the audience guessing until the final moments of the play.
ISBN 978 0 573 01840 4

A Murder is Announced. Play. Agatha Christie. Adapted by Leslie Darbon
M5 (young, 20s, 50s) F7 (20s, middle-age, 50s, elderly). A drawing-room. Fee code M

The 'announcement' is in the local paper, stating time and place of a murder to occur in Miss Blacklock's early Victorian house. However, the victim is not one of several occupants, temporary and permanent, but an unexpected and unknown visitor. What follows is a classic Christie puzzle, with Miss Marple on hand to provide the final solution in a dramatic confrontation scene just before the final curtain.
ISBN 978 0 573 11295 9

The Murder of Maria Marten or The Red Barn. Melodrama. Brian J. Burton
M5 F8. Various simple interior and exterior settings. Fee code L

Murder on the Nile. Play. Agatha Christie
M8 (young, 28, middle-age) F5 (young, 24, 60). A ship's saloon. Fee code M

Simon and Kay Mostyn are honeymooning aboard a Nile steamer. With them, apparently by accident, are Canon Pennefather, Kay's guardian and Jacqueline, Simon's ex-girlfriend. During the course of the voyage Jacqueline works herself into a state of hysteria and shoots at Simon, but only wounds him in the knee. A few minutes later Kay is found shot. Canon Pennefather lays bare an audacious conspiracy and ensures that the criminals shall not go free.
ISBN 978 0 573 01298 3

The Murder Room. Mystery Farce. Jack Sharkey
M3 (young, 40s, 50s) F3 (young, 30s, 60s). A living-room. Fee code M. ISBN 978 0 573 61283 1

Murder Weekend. Comedy thriller. Bettine Manktelow
M3 (40s, 50s) F6 (18, 40s, 50s). A country hotel reception area. Fee code L

Livia, a romantic short story writer, and her husband Stan, arrive at a country hotel for a "Murder Mystery" weekend. They are joined by Patsy and her husband Ashley, and Vi and Dorothy. Each receives an anonymous "Murder Mystery" game envelope. Someone has left extra notes for Patsy and Stan exposing Livia's and Ashley's illicit affair. Next, Shelley, the chambermaid, mysteriously disappears, and intrigue and suspicion deepen when one last uninvited guest arrives …
ISBN 0 573 02000 1

Murder with Love. Play. Francis Durbridge
M6 (28, 40s) F3 (young, 30s, middle-age). Split set: two living-rooms. Fee code M

Many people dislike Larry Campbell but none feel more embittered than David Ryder. Ryder pursues his vendetta by nefariously obtaining a key to Campbell's flat to kill him. Deceit, suspicion, blackmail and incrimination are woven into the web of crime which is completed by a second killing and a tantalizing twist at the climax.
ISBN 978 0 573 11302 4

Murderer. Play. Anthony Shaffer
M2 (35, 40s) F2 (25, 30s). A living-room, bathroom and sauna. Fee code M
ISBN 978 0 573 01590 8

A

Murmuring Judges. Play. David Hare
M19 F6. Extras. Various simple interior and exterior settings. Fee code M

When Irina Platt embarks on her first case as a lawyer, she finds that all sections of the criminal justice system – police, courts and prisons – are running far from smoothly. With its large multicultural cast and contemporary settings ranging from prison interiors to the Inns of Court, *Murmuring Judges* presents a broad yet finely detailed picture not only of the judicial system but of British society in the 1990s.

My Brilliant Divorce. Play. Geraldine Aron
F1 (middle age). (M3 (30, 40, 54) F2 (50, 75) optional extra actors). Simple set. Fee code M

In this brilliantly observed one-woman play, middle-aged Angela attempts to find a new life when husband Max leaves for a younger woman. Using a wonderful mixture of comedy and pathos, she recounts her journey back to happiness. " … great jokes … but there are also shafts of piercing emotional truth … the sequence when Angela goes to a sex-shop to buy a vibrator is a small masterpiece of comic embarrassment." Charles Spencer, *Daily Telegraph*
ISBN 978 0 573 03021 5

My Cousin Rachel. Play. Diana Morgan. From the novel by Daphne du Maurier
M5 (young, 40s, 50s, elderly) F2 (18, 30s). A hall. Fee code L

Philip Ashley travels to Italy to find his cousin Ambrose has died suddenly and Rachel, Ambrose's wife, has gone. Philip returns to England convinced Rachel was responsible for Ambrose's death, oping to inherit his possessions. When Rachel arrives in England Philip falls in love with her. One small event after another causes a kind of see-saw of belief and disbelief. Is Rachel a scheming murderess or a grossly maligned woman? Period mid-1800s
ISBN 978 0 573 11305 5

My Fat Friend. Comedy. Charles Laurence
M3 (18, 30s, 40s) F1 (29). A flat in Hampstead. Fee code K

Vicky, a Hampstead bookseller, is a heavyweight. When a handsome customer seems attracted to her she resolves that while he is abroad she will slim. Aided by the two male "characters" who share the flat above her shop, hard exercise, diet and a graph, she manages to reduce to a streamlined version of her former self – only to find that it was her rotundity that attracted the book buyer in the first place.

My Friend Miss Flint. Comedy. Donald Churchill and Peter Yeldham
M3 (20s, 50s, middle-age) F3 (30s, 40s). A studio/apartment. Fee code L
ISBN 978 0 573 11271 3

My Heart's a Suitcase. Play. Clare McIntyre
M2 (18, early 50s) F4 (early 20s, 30, indeterminate age). A room. Fee code M

Chris is an impoverished waitress, paranoid and angry at her lot in life. Hannah, a ceramics teacher with the beginnings of multiple sclerosis, is calm and genuinely unmaterialistic. Their weekend in Brighton is interrupted by visits from Tunis, shopaholic wife of the flat-owner, and Elliott, a drunken down-and-out. Chris also has spectral visits in the shape of Pest, a bad memory, and Luggage, the Patron Saint of Heavy Burdens. It seems Chris can never escape her lot.

A

My Mother Said I Never Should. Play. Charlotte Keatley
F4. Various simple interior and exterior settings. Fee code M

Charlotte Keatley's first play was premièred at the Contact Theatre, Manchester in 1987 and produced at the Royal Court, London. 'Totally engrossing, warm, funny, human look at four generations of women, Ms Keatley refuses to preach about a woman's nature and her place in the world, letting action and characters speak for themselves.' *Manchester Evening News*
ISBN 978 0 573 01700 1

My Own Show. Play. Lesley Bruce
M1 (30s) F4 (45-55). A living-room. Fee Code L

Fay, a TV chat show host, is worried that her career is on the wane – and her private life isn't up to much either. She is mortified to be reunited, on the set of *This Is Your Life*, with old school friend Caroline Pollard, but Caroline's bereavement gives her an idea that could rescue her ratings. The fickle nature of fame, the difficulties faced by older women in the media and the vagaries of friendship are dissected hilariously in this sly and witty comedy.
ISBN 978 0 573 11263 0

♦ **My Romantic History**. Play. D.C. Jackson (Slightly restricted)
M1-9 F2-12. Various simple settings. Fee Code K

One moment you're colleagues, and then Friday-night drinks, a quick grope, and you're an item. But all too soon the ghosts of relationships past begin to interfere with the here and now. A comedy about love, loss and laminating machines, *My Romantic History* premiered at the Traverse Theatre, Edinburgh in 2010. " . . . this is 90 minutes with which you should certainly make a date." *Guardian*
ISBN 978 0 571 26957 0

My Sister in this House. Play. Wendy Kesselman
F4. 3 male voices. Composite setting. Fee code M

Set in Le Mans in the early 1930s, this extraordinary, award-winning drama is based on a celebrated historical murder case in which two maids, sisters, were convicted of murdering their employer and her daughter. Wendy Kesselman's very cinematically structured work explores the motivations which led the two emotionally repressed sisters to commit the most gruesome of murders. The play was presented by Monstrous Regiment at the Hampstead Theatre Club in 1987.
ISBN 978 0 573 61872 7

My Three Angels. Comedy. Sam and Bella Spewack. From the French play *Cuisine des Anges* by Albert Husson
M7 (20s, 40s, middle-age) F3 (20s, middle-age). A living-room. Fee code M
ISBN 978 0 573 01304 1

♦ **My Wonderful Day**. Play. Alan Ayckbourn
M2 (40s) F3 (20s, 20s/30s, 30s) 1 girl (9). Downstairs in a town house. Fee Code M

Laverne, second-generation Afro-Caribbean, is cleaning Kevin Tate's house but dreaming of a return to Martinique. She is accompanied by her daughter, Winnie, who is not well enough for school. Insisting Winnie speaks French on Tuesdays, like today, in preparation for Martinique, Winnie settles to write about My Wonderful Day. She amasses plenty of material from the variety of adults who parade before her in the minor TV celebrity's house. A hilarious and bitter-sweet classic which transferred to New York.
ISBN 978 0 573 11304 8

My Zinc Bed. Play by David Hare
M2 (30s, early 50s) F1 (early 30s). Simple settings. Fee code M

David Hare's play continues the run of work in which he has sought to describe the atmosphere of contemporary Britain. A successful entrepreneur, Victor Quinn, employs young journalist and poet, recovered alcoholic Paul Peplow, to write advertising copy for his fast-growing Internet business. However Paul is now addicted to Alcoholics Anonymous and with Victor's sexy young wife, who has also conquered alcohol and cocaine only to deny Victor the children he craves, the three together make for a compelling ménage of romance and addiction.

The Mysteries. Trilogy of plays. Tony Harrison
M17 F3. A bare stage. Fee code M for each play

The Mysterious Mr Love. Play. Karoline Leach
M1 (early middle-age) F1 (39). Various simple settings. Fee code M. ISBN 978 0 573 01830 5

The Mystery of Irma Vep. A penny dreadful. Charles Ludlam
M2 playing various male and female roles. A library drawing-room, various simple sets. Fee code M

The definitive Gothic melodrama written to be performed as a quick-change act in which two actors perform all the roles. A sympathetic werewolf, a vampire and an Egyptian princess brought to life when they open her tomb make this the play that has everything. This American award-winning romp was cited by *Time* magazine and the *New York Times* as one of the best plays of its year. ISBN 978 0 573 64046 9

Nabokov's Gloves. Play. Peter Moffat
M3 F3. Various locations on an open stage. Fee code L

Nick, a successful barrister and devotee of football and pop trivia, is emotionally estranged from his wife while recklessly embroiled with a young, female client – a small-time drug dealer, who may or may not be more than she appears. The plot hinges on whether or not Nick will compromise his career and marriage by having an affair. Moffat investigates the emotional hypocrisy of the legal profession, women in a man's world and in particular the childishness of male bonding. Contains strong language.

Napoli Milionaria. Play. Eduardo de Filippo. Adapted by Peter Tinniswood
M14 F11. A large room. Fee code M

Life is hard in Naples during World War II but Donna Amalia does her best to keep the family afloat by dealing on the black market. Amalia prospers while Gennaro, her law-abiding husband, goes missing and is presumed dead. He returns unexpectedly to find his wife unfaithful, his son a car thief, his daughter pregnant and his other daughter critically ill. Shocked by the effects of corruption on his family, Gennaro prepares to resume his role as head of the household. Tinniswood's adaptation for the National Theatre moves the play to Liverpool.

◆ **A bullet mark next to a title indicates that it is new to this edition of the Guide.**

The National Health or Nurse Norton's Affair. Play. Peter Nichols
M12 (18, 30s-60s, 82, very old) F8 (young West Indian, young, 30, old). A hospital ward (with insets). Fee code M

The scene is a men's hospital ward. Against a beautifully detailed documentary background the author juxtaposes scenes of rich satire, in which the hosital staff become the highly romanticized characters of a television hospital series. The author's comments on the joys and pains of living and his observations on society are juggled with breath-taking dexterity.

Natural Causes. Comedy thriller. Eric Chappell
M3 (40s), F2 (20s, 40s). A study/library. Fee code M

Vincent is a professional suicide merchant. Contracted by Walter Bryce, he arrives at his country house and mistakenly assumes that the potion was intended for Walter's consumption. It then becomes clear that Walter's wife Celia is the client – or is she? Why are her suicide letters all typed and unsigned? After several thwarted attempts to poison various characters (resulting in multiple poisonings of a rubber plant), will anyone actually manage to drink the potion? This is black comedy at its blackest and best.
ISBN 978 0 573 01841 1

Never Land. Play. Phyllis Nagy
M4 (30s-40s, middle age) F3 (30s, middle age). Various simple settings. Fee code M

Set in a small village in the South of France, in a world of colour, light and sensuality, *Never Land* is a moving and heartbreaking exploration of the final days of a singular French family whose one dream is to settle in England. Phyllis Nagy's family drama is full of cutting twists and turns and farcical humour, showing in high relief a "never land" that is the habitation of disillusionment, failed love and cultural dispossession.

Never the Sinner. Play. John Logan
M6 (late teens, 20s, middle-age, 67) F1. Various interior and exterior settings on an open stage. Fee code M. ISBN 978 0 573 62671 5

Neville's Island. Comedy. Tim Firth
M4 (40s) The shore of a wooded island. Fee code M

Four out-of-condition, middle-aged businessmen sent off on a team-building exercise in the Lake District succeed in being the first people ever to get shipwrecked on an island on Derwentwater. Bound in by fog, menaced by the wildlife and cut off from the world, this perfunctory middle-class exercise turns into a carnival of recrimination, French cricket and sausages.What should have been a bonding process for Gordon, Angus, Roy and Neville turns into a muddy, bloody fight for survival.
ISBN 978 0 573 14005 1

New Anatomies. Play. Timberlake Wertenbaker
F5, 1 musician, play 15 characters. Various interior and exterior settings. Fee code H

Timberlake Wertenbaker's second play for the Women's Theatre Group, first seen at the Edinburgh Festival, considers women trapped in the 'golden cage' of normality. It portrays the eccentric Isabelle Eberhardt, an explorer who lived from 1877 to 1904, who travels through Algeria dressed as an Arab boy before going to Paris, where she encounters other women adopting male dress as a basis for greater freedom. ' ... an ambitious drama. Ms Wertenbaker's writing shows remarkable range ... ' *Time Out*

New England. Play. Richard Nelson
M4 (may be played by M3 with doubling) (30, 40s, 60s) F4 (30s, 41, 54). A study, part of a
kitchen. Fee code M

Next Time I'll Sing to You. Play. James Saunders
M4 F1. A bare stage with platform. Fee code M

Night and Day. Play. Tom Stoppard
M7 (8, 20s (Black), 40s, 50s (Black)) F1 (30s). A living-room, hall and stairs. Fee code M

The action takes place in the imaginary African state of Kambawe, which is undergoing a civil
war against a dictatorial President. The main subject of the play, however, is British journalism
– the relationships and competitiveness between rival journalists. Underlying both themes is that
of the freedom of the press and, more widely, freedom itself. Presented at the Royal National
Theatre starring Diana Rigg.
ISBN 978 0 573 11308 6

Night Must Fall. Play. Emlyn Williams
M4 (young, 50s, old) F5 (28, 35, 50s). Interior setting. Fee code M. ISBN 978 0 573 01843 5

The Night of the Iguana. Play. Tennessee Williams
M8 (1 Black) F6. A roofed veranda. Fee code M

Shannon, a minister defrocked for blasphemy and seduction, is now a travel guide in Mexico.
Coping with a group of Baptist women furious because he has taken them off the advertised
route and slept with a girl in the party, he arrives at a ramshackle inn run by a brash and
'rapaciously lusty' proprietress. The confrontations among these ill-assorted characters lead to
Shannon's final degradation, and to a general acceptance that personal fates must be accepted,
and life endured. Period 1940

A Night on the Tiles. Play. Frank Vickery
M4 (20s, middle-age, old) F3 (20s, middle-age). A backyard. Fee code L

A perceptive, entertaining and highly comical play from the author of *One O'Clock from the
House*. Gareth and Shirley's wedding day does not get off to an auspicious start. Gareth, egged
on by his cocky, good-looking brother Kenneth, has a post-stag-night hangover so bad that he
can barely speak, the bride is three months' pregnant and Grandad, confused after getting stuck
in the outside loo, is unsure whether Shirley is marrying Gareth or Kenneth!
ISBN 978 0 573 11350 5

The Night Season. Play. Rebecca Lenkiewicz
M3 (30s, 50s) F4 (20s, 30s, 70s). Simple settings. Fee code L

A funny modern, intoxicated tale of love and loss which premièred at the National Theatre in
2004. Late at night, shoeless in the rain, a film actor playing the poet Yeats turns up drunk at
his appointed Sligo digs. He is met by the grandmother and they dance together. In the morning
they are discovered, sharing a blanket, by Patrick and his three daughters. Patrick craves tobacco,
whiskey and a date with the local barmaid; the sisters yearn for sensation and escape.

Night Watch. A play of suspense. Lucille Fletcher
M5 F4. Interior set. Fee code L

Nightmare. Play. Norman Robbins
M3 (20, 35, 40) F4 (24, 36, 71). A living-room. Fee code L

Marion Bishop, an elderly writer, is dying. Katherine looks after her in a most caring way, while coping with her mentally retarded brother. When Katherine takes some leave, Laura, an experienced nurse, comes to take care of Marion. A series of mysterious phone calls and the appearance of Raymond, Marion's rapacious nephew, set off a nightmare situation. Deceit, suspicion, blackmail and incriminations are subtly woven into a web of crime which is completed by a dramatic confrontation scene with an ingenious twist.
ISBN 978 0 573 11306 2

Nightmare: the Fright of Your Life. Horror thriller. Roger S. Moss
M2 (20s, 50s-elderly) F2 (20s, 40s-elderly). A converted chapel. Fee code L

Frank and Jenny Gilman think they have found their dream house: a converted chapel in a quiet country village. The dream soon turns into a nightmare, however, as they are attacked by intruders who seem, for some reason, to be interested only in the contents of the deep freeze. Frank and Jenny investigate and the true horror of their situation soon emerges in this taut and exciting, yet often blackly hilarious, horror thriller.
ISBN 978 0 573 01842 8

Nil By Mouth. Comedy. John Chapman
M6 (1 young West Indian, under 40, 2 elderly) F6 (1 West Indian, 1 elderly) (1F old, non-speaking) Mixed hospital ward. Fee code L

By the successful author of *Kindly Leave the Stage* and *Shut Your Eyes and Think of England,* comes this very funny take on the National Health Service. Chaos erupts as patients, agency nurses, doctors and sisters battle it out at the start of another busy weekend on the under-funded and under-staffed mixed ward of St Christopher's Hospital. A catalogue of disastrous mistaken identities leads to wrongful diagnosis, visitors becoming patients, and all manner of medical mishaps.
ISBN 978 0 573 01983 8

No Dinner for Sinners. Comedy. Edward Taylor
M2 (20s, 50s) F4 (20s, 40s, middle age). A living-room. Fee code L

Stockbroker Jim has to entertain Bill and Nancy, the visiting international director and his wife, at his London flat. As they strongly disapprove of unmarried couples co-habiting, Jim asks his current girlfriend to pose as his wife but when she walks out and ex-girlfriends won't help he turns to Edna, his eccentric cleaning lady. Hilarious disaster reigns supreme as Jim tries to save his job by trading lies and wives almost as quickly as Bill is trading shares.
ISBN 978 0 573 11309 3

♦ **A bullet mark next to a title indicates that it is new to this edition of the Guide.**

No Man's Land. Play. Harold Pinter
M4 (30s, 40s, 60s). A living-room. Fee Code M

Hirst, a successful writer, meets Spooner, a failed poet, and together they return to Hirst's flat to indulge in a night of heavy drinking and witty banter. Hirst is experiencing writers' block, his servants have more control than he does and poor old Spooner ends up locked in a room overnight. The next morning Hirst greets Spooner with a different name and refers to their days at Oxford. Spooner may be able to manipulate this confusion for his own good, that is, if Hirst stays sober long enough.

No Sex Please – We're British! Comedy. Anthony Marriott and Alistair Foot
M6 (young, 30s, 50s) F4 (young, 50). A living-room and kitchen. Fee code M

This riotous comic farce notched up a staggeringly successful sixteen-year run in the West End! Peter and Frances could reasonably expect to look forward to a calm, happy start to thir married life together. Owing to an unfortunate mistake, however, they find themselves inundated with pornographic material from the 'Scandinavian Import Company'. Senior bank officials, Peter's snobbish mother, and a prim, respectable bank cashier become inextricably entangled in the rumbustious events that follow.
ISBN 978 0 573 01309 6

Nobody's Fool. Comedy. Simon Williams
M2 (middle aged, 60s) F3 (20s, middle aged). A basement study, a living room. Fee Code L

As anyone familiar with Simon Williams' play *Nobody's Perfect* will know, the popular romantic novelist Myrtle Banbury is none other than divorced, male, statistician Lenny. In this sequel Lenny finds himself with the problem of how to conduct a TV interview without having to appear to the nation in drag! Just as the situation appears to be under control, an additional complication arrives in the form of Fran, Lenny's ex wife.
ISBN 978 0 573 11518 9

Nobody's Perfect. Comedy. Simon Williams
M2 (middle age, old) F2 (teenage, middle age). 1 M extra. A flat, an office. Fee code L

Shy Leonard is anxious to break into print and sends book after book to Love Is All Around, a feminist publisher dedicated to writing "for women by women". Editor Harriet rejects his efforts until Leonard submits a novel, based on his experiences as a single parent, under the pseudonym Myrtle Banbury. Eventually Myrtle must appear and Leonard has no choice but to assume her identity. Then he falls in love with Harriet …
ISBN 978 0 573 01819 0

Noises Off. Comedy. Michael Frayn
M6 F4. A living-room stage set, backstage behind the set. Fee code M

This clever, smash-hit farce won numerous awards. 'The play opens with a touring company dress-rehearsing *Nothing On*, a conventional farce. Mixing mockery and homage, Frayn heaps into this play-within-a-play a hilarious mêlée of stock characters and situations. Caricatures – cheeky char, outraged wife and squeaky blonde – stampede in and out of doors. Voices rise and trousers fall … a farce that makes you think as well as laugh.' *Times Literary Supplement*
ISBN 978 0 573 11312 3

The Normal Heart. Play. Larry Kramer
M14 (or M10) F1. Various interior settings. Fee code M

Set in New York in the early 1980s, this powerful, passionate and controversial play was the
first to treat seriously the poignant and awesome subject of AIDS, following a writer's struggle
to break through indifference and hypocrisy surrounding the killer disease and his attempt to
draw attention to the plight of the gay community in contemporary America. After a successful
New York run, the play was acclaimed in London at the Royal Court Theatre with Martin Sheen
in the central role.

The Norman Conquests. Three plays. Alan Ayckbourn

> **Table Manners**. M3 F3. A dining-room. Fee code M
> ISBN 978 0 573 01573 1
> **Living Together**. M3 F3. A sitting-room. Fee code L
> ISBN 978 0 573 01574 8
> **Round and Round the Garden**. M3 F3. A garden. Fee code M
> ISBN 978 0 573 01575 3

These three plays form a trilogy. They are not consecutive, ut all occur during a single weekend,
and each takes place in the same house, with the same cast of characters, set individually in
two of the rooms and the garden. Thus we are watching, at times, but not all the time, events
which are taking place simultaneously with those we have seen (or about to see) in another set.
Each play is complete in itself and can be played as a separate entity. However each benefits
if all can be produced as one threefold whole.
ISBN 978 0 573 01576 2 (complete volume)

Jane Austen's **Northanger Abbey**. Play. Adapted by Matthew Francis
M9 (wide range of ages) F7 (wide range of ages). Extras. Children. Can be played by M5 F4.
Various interior and exterior settings. Fee code M. ISBN 978 0 573 01849 7

Not About Heroes. Play. Stephen MacDonald
M2 (24, 30s). Several simple sets on an open stage. Fee code M

The play 'shows the strangely fruitful encounter between Siegfried Sassoon, war hero and
aristocrat, now obsessed with exposing every sham ideal used to justify war, and Wilfred Owen,
recovering from the effects of neurasthenia attributable to shell-shock, looking desperately for
a hero who was not immune to the pity of war.' *Times Literary Supplement.* Period 1917-18

Not About Nightingales. Play. Tennessee Williams
M14 F3. Male extras. A prison. Fee code M

Written in 1938 and based on fact, the play follows the events of a prison scandal which
shocked America when convicts leading a hunger strike were locked in a steam-heated cell
and roasted to death. Its sympathetic treatment of a black character and of a transvestite may
have kept the play suppressed and unproduced during its own time. But its flashes of lyricism
and compelling dialogue presage the great later plays of Williams and shows young Williams
as a political writer, passionate about social injustice.

◆ **A bullet mark next to a title indicates that it is new to this edition of the Guide.**

Not Quite Jerusalem. Play. Paul Kember
M4 F2 (20s). Four settings. Fee code M. ISBN 978 0 573 11311 6

A

Not with a Bang. Play. Mike Harding
M3 F4. A living-room; outside an army barracks. Fee code M

When their wives join the Women's Peace Movement, Nobby, Tommy and Ken, pals in the Territorial Army, treat it as a joke. But as the women become more involved in demonstrations the men become the laughing stock of their TA battalion. Finally, the women, attempting to make their husbands give up the army, go on sexual strike with the slogan 'No Nooky Against the Nukes'. A wry, amusing look at the nuclear disarmament issue set in the author's North of England.
ISBN 978 0 573 11299 7

Now You Know. Play. Adapted from his novel by Michael Frayn
M4 (19 (Black), 30s, 50s) F4 (20s (Asian), 30-40s). A small office. Fee code M

Terry runs an organization campaigning for freedom of information which is funded by his girlfriend who also organizes the close-knit staff. When Hilary, a civil servant, arrives with a highly-confidential file detailing a cover-up Terry is given a not-to-be-missed opportunity. But his increasingly intimate involvement with Hilary presents him with a personal and professional dilemma, exposing the ultimate irony that everyone has something to hide.
ISBN 978 0 573 01848 0

Nude with Violin. Light comedy. Noël Coward
M8 (1 West Indian) F6. A Paris studio. Fee code M. ISBN 978 0 573 61318 0

A Number. Play. Caryl Churchill
M2 (35, early 60s). Simple setting. Fee code F

The play seen at the Royal Court Theatre, London, in 2002 to critical acclaim, is a series of encounters between a man and his sons, duplicated by cloning. "Caryl Churchill's magnificent new play only lasts an hour but contains more drama, and more ideas, than most writers manage in a dozen full-length works. Part psychological thriller, part topical scientific speculation, and part analysis of the relationship between fathers and their sons, it combines elegant structural simplicity with an astonishing intellectual emotional depth." Charles Spencer, *Daily Telegraph*

Observe the Sons of Ulster Marching Towards the Somme. Play. Frank McGuinness
M9 (20s, 30s, old). Various simple interior and exterior settings. Fee code M

Eight men volunteer to serve in the 36th Ulster Division at the outbreak of the First World War. Seven are from working-class backgrounds, fervent Protestants united in hatred against the Fenian. The eighth is from a wealthy family, a widely-travelled sculptor who has lost faith and enlists in the sole hope of dying. 'A play of extraordinary depth of feeling and understanding.' *Sunday Telegraph*

◆ **A bullet mark next to a title indicates that it is new to this edition of the Guide.**

The Odd Couple. Comedy. Neil Simon
M6 F2. A living-room. Fee code M

Divorced from his wife, Oscar lives in the cheerful chaos his carefree nature thrives on. Into the midst of his smoke-laden, beer-sodden weekly poker session, comes Felix, newly separated from his wife and, so he says, suicidal. At Oscar's invitation Felix moves in, and is soon finding comfort in performing, with the same thoroughness which lost him his wife, the cooking, cleaning, polishing and laundry until Oscar is almost reduced, by continuous nagging, to a nervous wreck. (**Slightly restricted**)
ISBN 978 0 573 61331 9

The Odd Couple (Female Version). Comedy. Neil Simon
M2 F6. An apartment. Fee code M

In this hilarious female version of *The Odd Couple*, Olive Madison, like her original male counterpart, is divorced and living in cheerful chaos in her New York apartment. At Olive's invitation, the suicidal Florence Ungar, newly separated from her hunband, moves in and is soon finding comfort in cooking, cleaning, and fussing until Olive is almost reduced to a nervous wreck. It becomes clear that the patterns of their disastrous marriages are already re-occurring. **NB. Please state Female Version when ordering. (Slightly restricted)**
ISBN 978 0 573 61828 4

Oedipus. Play. Steven Berkoff
M8 F1. Chorus. Fee code L

A sharp and accessible adaptation of Sophocles's landmark tragedy, seeking to relate parts of it to images of today. Berkoff says: " ... its shadow lies across the years and its arguments are mankind's into perpetuity."

Office Suite. Double-bill. Alan Bennett

Green Forms
M2 (1 Black) F3 (30s, 40s). An office. Fee code F

Doris and Doreen are comfortably installed in an obscure department of a large organization. It is a cushy number: on a normal day work is nowhere. However, this is not a normal day. A shadow falls across their tranquil lives. Is it redundancy?
ISBN 978 0 573 12087 9

A Visit from Miss Prothero
M1 (60s) F1 (middle-age). A living-room. Fee code E

Retired and sitting at home, Mr Dodsworth contemplates his life and achievements with quiet satisfaction when there is sharp ring at the door: his former secretary has come to ruin it all.
ISBN 978 0 573 12286 6

♦ **A bullet mark next to a title indicates that it is new to this edition of the Guide.**

The Old Country. Play. Alan Bennett
M3 (20s, 50s, 60s) F3 (30s, middle-age, 60s). A veranda. Fee code M

Hilary and Bron await the arrival of Hilary's sister and brother-in-law in a very English setting: Bron potters about the garden and Hilary sits asleep on the veranda, Elgar's music drifts from the house. The visitors arrive, bringing an assortment of particularly English things, and as the conversation proceeds, it becomes apparent they are not in England. In fact Hilary fled into exile some years previously after betraying his country, but now it seems he must return.
ISBN 978 0 573 11317 8

The Old Masters. Play. Simon Gray
M3 (middle age) F2(30s/ 40s, late 40s). A garden, a library. Fee Code M

Set in the Villa of I Tatti outside Florence in 1937, under the menacing shadow of Mussolini, *The Old Masters* explores the turbulent relationship between the famous art historian Bernard Berenson and the notorious art dealer Joseph Duveen, as they edge towards an explosive final encounter. Period : 1937

Old Times. Play. Harold Pinter
M1 (40s) F2 (40s). A sitting-room, a bedroom. Fee code M

Kate and Deeley are married and live in a large country house. Into their calm, composed world comes Anna, Kate's best friend – her only friend – whom she has not seen for twenty years. '*Old Times* is a tone poem – an ironic elegy to lost youth and hopes, set at the crossroads where memory meets fantasy and cut through with the searing recognition of the power games people play.' *City Limits*

Oliver Twist. Play. Jeremy Brock. Adapted from the novel by Charles Dickens
34 characters. Extras. May be played by a cast of eleven. Various interior and exterior settings. Fee code M

Jeremy Brock's splendidly theatrical stage version of *Oliver Twist* combines all the richness of Dickens's story – the sinister antics of Fagin, the comic pomposity of Mr Bumble the Beadle, and the horror of Nancy's murder at the hands of Sykes. Originally devised for eleven actors playing multiple roles, the play is easy to stage, makes good use of sound effects for atmosphere and makes more than a nod to the contemporary world.
ISBN 978 0 573 01851 0

On Approval. Comedy. Frederick Lonsdale
M2 (middle-age) F2 (young, middle-age). A drawing-room, a living-room. Fee code M
ISBN 978 0 573 01855 8

On Monday Next. Comedy. Philip King
M9 F5. A stage. Fee code M. ISBN 978 0 573 01318 8

◆ **A bullet mark next to a title indicates that it is new to this edition of the Guide.**

A

On the Razzle. Farce. Tom Stoppard. Adapted from *Einen Jux Will Er Sich Machen* by Johann Nestroy
M13 F9. 1 boy. Extras. Six settings. Fee code M

Deciding to wine and dine his intended in town, Zangler, a prosperous merchant grocer, leaves his shop in the charge of two assistants who decide they, too, will have a day out. As they pursue wine, women and song through 1850s Vienna the precise intricate machinery of plot and sub-plot is soon whirring at full speed to deploy all the elements of classic farce. 'A dazzle of verbal wit.' *Daily Telegraph*

♦ **On the Rocks.** Play. Amy Rosenthal
M2 F2. Interior and exterior settings. Period 1916. Fee code L

DH Lawrence and his wife Frieda have found a new life for themselves in a remote Cornish village. Rejuvenated by the wild beauty around them, they persuade close friends Katherine Mansfield and John Middleton Murry to join them in their idyll. But long-simmering tensions bubble to the surface, and Lawrence's dream of communal living starts unravelling before his eyes. An uplifting and passionate comedy about four friends, two marriages struggling for survival and a group of writers striving for creativity in the midst of war.

On the Shore of the Wide World. Play. Simon Stephens
M6 (teens, 36, middle age, elderly) F4 (young, 35, middle age, elderly).Composite set. Fee Code M

Simon Stephens' play takes us through nine months in the lives of three generations of the Holmes family in Stockport. At 15 and 18, Alex and Christopher are growing fast whilst their parents have descended into middle-age and the one set of grandparents we see is old and unreliable. An unexpected tragedy turns the family upside down whilst the waves of the wide world crash ominously on to the shore.

Once a Catholic. Comedy. Mary O'Malley
M4 F10. Various interior and exterior settings. Fee code M

In choosing the title, the author would seem to imply 'always a Catholic', but this extremely funny, irreverent comedy based on her own school days in a London convent certainly belies the Church's claim, as far as the author is concerned. For what emerges rather is the resilience of children to survive – in spite of, not because of, their upbringing and indoctrination. Period 1956-57

Once in a Lifetime. Play. Moss Hart and George S. Kaufman
M24 F14, much doubling possible. A living-room, an hotel room, a reception room, a film set, a Pullman car. Fee code M. ISBN 978 0 573 61388 3

One Fine Day. Play. Dennis Lumborg
M1. A kitchen, a bedsit, a prison holding cell. Fee code M

Eddie, a young metal worker, lives contentedly on a suburban housing estate with his wife, Jeanie, and two adored small children, Katie and Billy. He and Jeanie have always believed in being frank with their children about matters of sex, but when his little daughter stumbles into their bedroom during her parents' lovemaking and then cheerfully recounts the details next day at school, Eddie finds himself investigated by social services, suspected of child abuse. This is his story. ISBN 978 0 573 04021 4

One Flew Over the Cuckoo's Nest. Play. Dale Wasserman. From the novel by Ken Kesey
M17 F5. A ward in a mental hospital. Fee code M

A

The story of the devil-may-care rogue who has committed himself temporarily to a mental home rather than work in a prison. He transforms the home, charming everyone, except the fierce martinet of a hed nurse, and works wonders with a presumed deaf-and-dumb Indian. However, he is condemned by the nurse to a frontal lobotomy, which will leave him a vegetable, and to save him his fellow inmates smother him.
ISBN 978 0 573 61343 2

One for the Road. Comedy. Willy Russell
M2 (35) F2 (30s). A lounge. Fee code M

This wickedly observant comedy by the author of *Educating Rita* finds Dennis on the eve of his thirty-fifth birthday, making a last-ditch attempt to break away from the confines of his middle-class, housing-estate existence. Reaching breaking point at his birthday party he packs a rucksack to make his escape but everyone wants to accompany him and he sinks down in front of the television, defeated. But there's always next year ... and the year after ...
ISBN 978 0 573 11320 8

One Last Card Trick. Comedy. Stewart Permutt
F4 (47, 70s) Club room in a West End synagogue. Fee Code L

In a West End synagogue three septuagenarians, Sophie, Hetty and Magda meet every Tuesday to play cards. Loretta, a youthful forty-seven year-old, keeps the score. But all this is about to change as their synagogue is to be sold to a strip club owner. These intrepid ladies decide to take direct action and barricade themselves in their fated synagogue. Can they succeed or will their constant bickering put paid to their plan?
ISBN 978 0 573 03024 6

One O'Clock from the House. Comedy. Frank Vickery
M5 (30s-50s) F8 (30s-40s). 1 boy (9). Extras. A living-room. Fee code L. ISBN 978 0 573 01628 8

One Way Pendulum. A farce in a new dimension. N. F. Simpson
M10 (20s-50) F4 (18, 45, 50). A living-room (containing a court room in Act II). Fee code M

Each of the Groomkirbys has an *idée fixe*. Kirby is teaching his speak-your-weight machines the 'Hallelujah Chorus'; his mother pays the neighbour to eat their left-overs; his aunt in her wheelchair is convinced she's touring the Hebrides; his father is building the Old Bailey in the living-room. When this is complete the judge and jury move in with some bizarre results ...
ISBN 978 0 573 01321 8

The Opposite Sex. Comedy. David Tristram
M2 F2. A living-room. Fee code L

David Tristram, author of *What's for Pudding?*, turns his attention to marital infidelity and its warring consequences in this adult-humoured comedy. Mark and Vicky and Judith and Eric have something in common and a chance meeting could have made for a pleasant social evening. Unfortunately, as they all come face to face, the common denominator turns out to be that they each had an affair with their opposite partner and it isn't long before the air is thick with insults, black eyes and broken china!

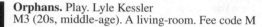

Orphans. Play. Lyle Kessler
M3 (20s, middle-age). A living-room. Fee code M

Two adult but somehow childlike brothers live in an old row house in North Philadelphia. Treat, the elder brother, supports himself and his slightly retarded younger brother by petty thievery. He brings home a rich man, Harold, intending to get him drunk and swindle him. Harold moves in and establishes the house as a hideout and base of operations and, in a strange, hilarious, moving, tender way, becomes the father figure the boys have never had and always longed for. ISBN 978 0 573 61978 6

Orpheus Descending. Play. Tennessee Williams
M10 F9. Extras. Split set: a dry goods store, a confectionery. Fee code M

A vague reworking of the Orpheus and Eurydice legend in modern America, with a Southern township presumably representing Hell. Thirty-year-old Val Xavier arrives in the gossipy, prejudice-ridden township with his guitar, and meets 'Lady' Torrence, whose elderly husband is dying of cancer. His attempts to bring some happiness into her sex-starved life, together with other developments, lead to tragedy for both of them. Period 1940

Other Hands. Play. Laura Wade
M2 (30s, 4os) F2 (30s). Various simple settings. Fee Code L

Steve is a computer technician who suffers from RSI, as does Hayley, his long term girlfriend, a Human Performance Analyst who leads an equally automated life. Each has the urge to experience something more in life, and so each goes about uncovering their own platonic relationship that challenges the effects of emotional and physical monotony. In this poignant, clever play, Laura Wade has paralleled the increasing efficiencies of technology with emotional vulnerability in a way that both amuses and appeals.

Other People's Money. Play. Jerry Sterner
M3 (40s, 68) F2 (35, 60s). Composite setting: three offices. Fee code M

This award-winning off-Broadway play was seen at London's Lyric Theatre starring Martin Shaw and Maria Aitken. Doughnut connoisseur and Wall Street takeover artist Lawrence Garfinkle goes after a vulnerable company. Set against the charmingly rapacious financier are genial company chairman Jorgensen, and his chief executive. They bring in Kate who specializes in fending off takeovers ... 'It is something to find a modern American comedy that openly criticizes the moral bankruptcy of our times.' *Guardian*
ISBN 978 0 573 69101 0

Otherwise Engaged. Play. Simon Gray
M5 (young, 39, middle-age) F2 (young). A living-room. Fee code M

Simon lives surrounded by all the comforts of the day and strives to keep himself 'otherwise engaged' from the demands of friends, relatives and associates. However, the world keeps intruding: his attempts to play his new *Parsifal* recording are continually thwarted; his answerphone recounts the tragic results of a casual, thoughtless liaison with a girl; and there is a final shock from his wife. Eventually he finds himself listening to *Parsifal*, but perhaps with a little less than his usual self-absorption.
ISBN 978 0 573 01261 7

Our Boys. Play. Jonathan Lewis
M6 (20s). A hospital ward. Fee code M

1984. Five soldiers, among them veterans of the Falklands War and the Hyde Park bombing, are convalescing in a military hospital, with pornography, bragging one-upmanship and cynical humour as their only means of mental escape. Tensions arise when an officer is billeted with them, and a bitter, savage war of words, only just disguised as humour, is waged against him. After an hilarious birthday party, the six find themselves facing charges of misconduct – and then the fighting really starts.
ISBN 978 0 573 14009 9

Our Country's Good. Play. Timberlake Wertenbaker. Based on the novel *The Playmaker* by Thomas Keneally
M17 F5 or M7 F4. Various interior and exterior settings. Fee code M

This adaptation was performed at The Royal Court Theatre in 1988 and 1989 to critical acclaim. Set in Botany Bay in 1789 it tells of the rehearsals for the first play to be performed in Australia. Surrounded by forbidding conditions Lieutenant Clark attempts, under the authority of the first Governor General, to bring culture to the penal colony through a production of Farquhar's *The Recruiting Officer,* with a motley bunch of villains, murderers and prostitutes.

♦ **Our House.** Play. John Godber
M5 (20s, 20-70s, 18-40s, 50s) F5 (20-70s, 18-40s, 20s) A living-room. Fee code M

May's husband Ted, a retired miner, has died, so May is moving to Spain. Through a series of flashbacks, we share May's memories of the past fifty years - marriage, parenthood, the miners' strikes and neighbour problems. Son Jack, now highly successful and absent, returns to help with the move and finally shows some loyalty by finding a house buyer who will give the neighbours from hell their comeuppance.
"Its portrait of a comfortable, disputatious marriage is so subtle ..." *Observer*

Our Song. Play. Keith Waterhouse, adapted from his own novel
M4 (middle-age, 50s) F3 (late 20s, middle-age). Various simple settings. Fee code M
ISBN 978 0 573 01856 5

Our Town. Play. Thornton Wilder
M17 F7. Extras. A bare stage. Fee code M

With compelling simplicity Wilder depicts New Hampshire village life through the story of two families. George and Emily grow up together as children, they fall in love and marry. All too soon Emily dies and goes into the village cemetery where the former inhabitants of Grover's Corner welcome her to the peace that can never be understood by the living. When first produced, *Our Town* was considered a remarkable theatrical innovation and it still has a universality that does not date. Period 1901-11
ISBN 978 0 573 61349 4

♦ **A bullet mark next to a title indicates that it is new to this edition of the Guide.**

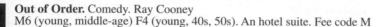

A

Out of Order. Comedy. Ray Cooney
M6 (young, middle-age) F4 (young, 40s, 50s). An hotel suite. Fee code M

When Richard Willey, a Government Junior Minister, plans to spend the evening with Jane Worthington, one of the Opposition's typists, things go disastrously wrong, and he sends for his PPS, George Pigden who, through Richard's lies, sinks further and further into trouble and ends up going through an identity crisis! A hugely successful sequel to Ray Cooney's *Two Into One*, *Out of Order* received the 1990 Olivier Award for Comedy of the Year.
ISBN 978 0 573 01858 9

Out of Sight ... Out of Murder. Mystery comedy. Fred Carmichael
M4 (young, 30s, middle-age, 60s) F5 (young, 40s, middle-age, 60). A living-room. Fee code L
ISBN 978 0 573 61360 9

Outside Edge. Play. Richard Harris
M5 (20s-40s) F4 (19, 28, 30s). A cricket pavilion. Fee code M

Roger has enough trouble assembling his cricket team to play against the British Railways Maintenance Division Reading East, but these complications pall before those occurring among their various wives and girlfriends. As a final catastrophe, rain starts to fall. The play, from the author of *Stepping Out*, was first seen at the Queen's Theatre, London, starring Julia McKenzie and Maureen Lipman.
ISBN 978 0 573 11314 7

Over My Dead Body. Comedy. Derek Benfield
M2 (40s, 69) F4 (30s, 40s, 60s). A drawing-room. Fee code L

Following his wife's death Gerald hopes to spend the rest of his days alone with his memories. But he reckons without his late wife's "forward planning", which results in a series of unexpected events occurring that Gerald had not anticipated. With the help of his daughter and son-in-law, Gerald strives to maintain his independence and keep unexpected visitors at bay. But recalling memories revives events from the past that are both funny and sad. A delightfully amusing comedy from the author of *Bedside Manners*.
ISBN 978 0 573 11599 8

Over the Moon. Comedy. Ken Ludwig
M4 (20s-50s) F4 (young, middle age, elderly). A stage, backstage. Fee code M. (Typescript on hire)

The Owl and the Pussycat. Comedy. Bill Manhoff
M1 (35) F1 (26). An apartment in San Francisco. Fee code M

Doris storms into the apartment of F. Sherman, would-be writer, and states that because his report to the landlord got her evicted for taking paying gentlemen callers, she is now going to camp in his apartment. She says she is a prostitute but not promiscuous, and is hurt when Sherman questions her respectability. He is a self-advertising intellectual whose counterfeit emotions are reflected in his unsuccessful writing. Their exchanges are turbulent and very funny.
ISBN 978 0 573 61354 8

Pack of Lies. Play. Hugh Whitemore
M3 (40s, 50s) F5 (16, 20s-40s). A living-room, kitchen, hall. Fee code M

A

Based on the true story of the Krogers, convicted in 1961 of spying for the Russians, Whitemore has written a fictional account of the quiet, totally unsuspecting Jackson family who live opposite the Krogers and consider them their closest friends. When an MI5 official arrives suddenly to use the Jacksons' house as a surveillance post their decent, happy life is shattered as they are plunged into a sordid, alien world of deceit and intrigue.
ISBN 978 0 573 11343 7

Paddywack. Drama. Daniel Magee
M4 (20s, 30s, 50s) F2 (20s, 60s). A living-room. Fee code M. ISBN 978 0 573 69578 0

♦ **Painting by Numbers.** Comedy. Simon Mawdsley
M4 play 7 characters. A large utility room in a modern prison. Fee code L

Four prison inmates try to teach themselves how to paint, taking them on a collision course with the prison authorities, and with each other. When a public visit becomes a public relations disaster, their newly discovered creative freedoms are brought to an abrupt end. The play, partly based on Simon Mawdsley's experience of working with a prison drama group, was seen at The Old Red Lion Theatre, London, in 2008. NB. The play contains explicit language.

Painting Churches. Play. Tina Howe
M1 (70s) F2 (30s, 60s). A living-room. Fee code M

Gardner Church, once a famous poet, slips in and out of senility as his wife Fanny valiantly tries to keep them both afloat. Their daughter Mags, an artistic celebrity, comes home hoping to finally paint their portrait and, in this way, to come to terms with them – and they with her. Mags triumphs in the end as Fanny and Gardner actually step through the frame and become a work of art, ineffable and timeless.
ISBN 978 0 573 61939 7

♦ **Pale Horse**. Play. Joe Penhall
M7 F5. Fee Code L

Charles, who, disillusioned by the sudden death of his wife, propels himself into a world of urban alienation and self-destruction in an attempt to assuage the private demons that haunt him. Along the way he encounters the capricious Lucy and is forced to examine the nature of his own mortality, identity and beliefs.

Panic Stations. Farce. Derek Benfield
M4 (35, middle-age, 60s) F5 (20s-60). A cottage interior. Fee code L
ISBN 978 0 573 11352 9

The Parasol. Play. Anton Chekhov. Adapted from the novel *Three Years* by Frank Dunai
M8 (20s, 30s, 50s, 60, 80) F2 (21, 30). 2 drawing-rooms, an office. Fee code M

Pardon Me, Prime Minister. Farce. Edward Taylor and John Graham
M4 (30s, 50s) F5 (20s-40s). A study. Fee code L. ISBN 978 0 573 11334 5

Party Piece. Comedy. Richard Harris, suggested by the author's earlier play, *Local Affairs*
M3 F4. The gardens of a pair of Victorian terraced houses. Fee code M

This is a fast-paced and very funny play set in the back gardens of feuding neighbours. It is the night of Michael's and Roma's fancy dress house-warming party. The evenig looks set to be a lively one until a string of hilarious disasters strike, including a distinct lack of guests, a burning garden shed, a marauding Zimmer frame and the prospect of an irate husband on the prowl. ISBN 978 0 573 01862 6

A Party to Murder. Play. Marcia Kash and Douglas E. Hughes
M3 (40s, 50s) F3 (late 20s, 40s). A living-room. Fee code M

Writer Charles Prince has invited six people to play a murder mystery game at a rustic cottage on an island somewhere in North America. They appear set for a fun weekend until past ghosts begin to haunt the proceedings and all is not as it seems. The game takes on a sinister dimension when guests begin to die and the remaining players realize that they are playing for their lives.

A Passage to India. E. M. Forster. Play. Martin Sherman
M14 F4, may be played by M8 F3. Extras. Various settings. Fee code L

Adela Quested wants to discover the "real India" for herself. Newly arrived from England, she agrees to see the Marabar Caves with the charming Dr Aziz. After the visit, the fragile structure of Anglo-Indian relations collapses as Aziz is brought to trial for assault. E. M. Forster's prize-winning novel about colonial British India is here adapted for the stage by Martin Sherman, the acclaimed author of *Bent* and *Rose*. Period early 20th century

The Passing-Out Parade. Play. Anne Valery
F9-12 (18-early 20s, late 30s, 40). A barrack-room and adjoining places. Fee code M

The play charts the fortunes of a group of ATS girls from their arrival as a raw, awkward, ill-assortment of individuals to their passing-out parade as a "perfectly drilled unit of faceless soldiers", following the shifts and tensions of their personal relationships, the comedy, drama and – in one case – eventual tragedy that occur during their period of training together. The action centres on the girls' barrack room, with small insets in adjacent places. ISBN 978 0 573 13003 8

Passion Killers. Play. John Godber
M4 (20s, 30s) F5 (20s, 30s). Can be played by M4 F3. Composite set. Fee code M
ISBN 978 0 573 01868 8

♦ **Passion Play.** Play. Peter Nichols
M2 F4. Extras. Various interiors. Fee code M

James Croxley is a successful picture-restorer. His wife Eleanor sings in a choir which is to perform Bach's St Matthew Passion at the Albert Hall. Together, they have shared twenty-five happily married years, faithful, fulfilled – and boring. James easily falls prey to a banal affair. There follows a searing examination of the disruption and hurt caused by marital infidelity with alter-egos for James and Eleanor – Jim and Nell – acting as the couple's conscience, commenting on their actions and the pretences they must now adopt as a survival tactic.

A Passionate Woman. Play. Kay Mellor
M3 (early 30s, 50s) F1 (50s). F1 extra, offstage voices. A loft and rooftop. Fee code M

Betty, a passionate, doting mum from Leeds finds it hard to accept that her son, Mark, is leaving the fold to get married. On the wedding morning she retreats to the loft where she re-lives her long-lost youth and the affair with the man she might have married, and gradually reconciles herself to the imminent departure of Mark. A heartfelt, provocative, masterful play.
ISBN 978 0 573 01866 4

Peer Gynt. Play. Henrik Ibsen. Translated by Christopher Fry and Johan Fillinger
Large cast. Various interior and exterior settings. Fee code M

Peggy for You. Play. Alan Plater
M3 (20-40s) F2 (20s, 50s). Two office rooms. Fee code M

Showing a day in the life of Peggy Ramsay, the most celebrated play agent of her time, this is a gloriously witty, wry and unsentimental account of an extraordinary woman as she takes on principalities, powers, producers and, above all, playwrights. Eccentric, intimidating, contradictory and inspiring, she ruled an anarchic roost, including dramatists as famous and diverse as Joe Orton, Christopher Hampton, Stephen Poliakoff, Alan Ayckbourn, Edward Bond and, for thirty years, Plater himself. Period 1960s-1980s.

The Perfect Murder. Play. Hugh Janes adapted from a story by Jeffrey Archer
M9-12 F3-6. Can be played by M7 F2 with doubling. A living-room, an office, Number Four Court at the Old Bailey. Fee code M

Carla Moorland has been murdered, and accountant John Hoskins, who has been having an affair with her, is certain he knows who did it – himself. John's wife Elizabeth, rather than calling the police, is determined to keep John out of prison, even if it means that an innocent man will be punished for the crime …
ISBN 978 0 573 01954 8

The Perfect Party. Comedy. A. R. Gurney
M2 (middle-age) F3 (middle-age). A study. Fee code M

Perfect Pitch. Play. John Godber
M2 (30s, middle age) F2 (mid 20s, middle age). A caravan site. Fee code M

Ron, a prematurely retired headteacher, and his wife, Yvonne, a would-be marathoner, are on their first caravan holiday. Pitched on a cliff in Yorkshire, the slightly dull, slightly snobby couple grapple with this strange holiday. That evening an elderly caravan appears next to theirs and sounds of noisy love-making cause Ron and Yvonne to blush. Steph and Grant, a younger, more working-class pair of seasoned caravanners have arrived and Ron's and Yvonne's lives will never be the same.
ISBN 978 0 573 01966 1

◆ **A bullet mark next to a title indicates that it is new to this edition of the Guide.**

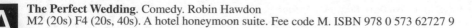

A

The Perfect Wedding. Comedy. Robin Hawdon
M2 (20s) F4 (20s, 40s). A hotel honeymoon suite. Fee code M. ISBN 978 0 573 62727 9

Period of Adjustment. Comedy. Tennessee Williams
M4 (30s, middle-age) F4 (young (Black), middle-age). A living-room, with dining alcove and bedroom visible. Fee code M

Ralph Bates and his wife are on the verge of breaking up after five years together, partly through trouble with in-laws. George Haverstock, a wartime friend of Bates is a newly-wed concealing beneath his ebullient exterior a secret fear, which seems to be that he may be impotent. By the end of the day, however, all ends well – with each pair correctly together.

The Petition. Play. Brian Clark
M1 (80) F1 (72). A living-room. Fee code M

Philadelphia, Here I Come! Play. Brian Friel
M10 (young, 40s, 60s) F3 (young, 50s, 60s). Composite setting. Fee code M

Gar O'Donnell has accepted his aunt's invitation to come to Philadelphia, as he is fed up with the dreary round of life in Ballybeg with his uncommunicative father, his humiliating job, his frustrated love for Kathy Doogan, and the total absence of prospect and opportunity in his life at home. Now, on the eve of his departure, he is not very happy to be leaving Ballybeg, despite his fantasies of success, wealth and endless love that he will attain in America.

The Philanthropist. Comedy. Christopher Hampton
M4 (young, middle-age) F3 (young). A living-room. Fee code J. ISBN 978 0 573 01336 2

The Physicists. Play. Friedrich Dürrenmatt. Translated by James Kirkup
M16 (teenage, 40s, middle-age) F4 (30s-50s). A drawing-room. Fee code M

Because in a mad world the only defence of the sane is to assume madness, the genius who has invented a nuclear weapon of world-consuming force decides he can only protect the world from destructive ambition by pretending to be mad. He is pursued by two agents of the super-powers who also pretend to be madmen. In the end, all three find themselves totally in the power of a truly mad megalomaniac.
ISBN 978 0 573 01340 9

Piano/Forte. Play. Terry Johnson
M3 (mid 50s, late 40s, late 20s) F4 (mid 20s) Extras. A reception room. Fee code M

From the author of *Hitchocock Blonde*, *Hysteria* and *Insignificance* comes an unpredictable, funny and disturbing new play about a Tory MP and his alarmingly difficult offspring. There's a wedding at the weekend, *Hello!'s* gazumped *OK!*, the piano's locked and the starlings are overdue ...The play premièred at the Royal Court Theatre, London, in 2006. NB the play contains nudity. "... is a pitch-black comedy of dysfunctional family manners ..." Mark Shenton, *Sunday Express.*

◆ **A bullet mark next to a title indicates that it is new to this edition of the Guide.**

A

Picasso at the Lapin Agile. Comedy. Steve Martin
M7 (20s, older) F2 (19, older). A Parisian bar. Fee code M

This long-running Off-Broadway absurdist comedy places Albert Einstein and Pablo Picasso in a Parisian café in 1904, just before the renowned scientist transformed physics with his theory of relativity and the celebrated painter set the art world afire with Cubism. Bystanders, including Picasso's agent, the bartender and his mistress, Picasso's date, an elderly philosopher, Charles Dabernow Schmendimen, and an idiot inventor introduce additional flourishes of humour. Period 1904
ISBN 978 0 573 69564 3

The Picture of Dorian Gray. Moral entertainment. John Osborne. Adapted from the novel by Oscar Wilde
M11 F4. Extras. A studio. Fee code M

Pictures of Clay. Play. Sharif Samad
M2 (30s, 40s) F4 (teens, 40s, 50s). Various simple settings. Fee Code K

Pendle Hill, Lancashire 1610. England is at the height of the Protestant Reformation but in this barren, poverty-stricken spot Catholicism is still being practised and old superstitions abound. *Pictures of Clay* tells the story of three women accused of witchcraft, who testify against each other to try to save their own lives. Grave-robbing, ritual and the struggle to crush Catholicism provide a richly-textured background to this dark tale of fear, suspicion, hatred and betrayal. Period 1610.
ISBN 978 0 573 11581 3

The Pied Piper. Play with music. Based on Robert Browning's poem. Book and lyrics by Peter Terson. Music by Jeff Parton
M12 F3, doubling possible. Extras. Various settings on an open stage. Fee code M for play, fee code D for music. ISBN 978 0 573 05060 2

The Pillowman. Play. Martin McDonagh
M4 F1, 1 boy, 1 girl. Various simple settings. Fee code M

A viciously funny, seriously disturbing tale about a writer in a totalitarian state who is interrogated about the gruesome content of his short stories and their similarities to a number of child murders that are happening in his town. Martin McDonagh's searingly brilliant play premiéred at the National Theatre, London, with Jim Broadbent. Please note the play contains scenes and language that may offend. "Stomach-churning and wildly comic ... Martin McDonagh's most disturbing work to date ..." Susannah Clapp, *Observer*

Pillars of the Community. Henrik Ibsen, in a new version by Samuel Adamson
M11 F9. Extras. A living-room and terrace. Fee Code M

Samuel Adamson's highly-acclaimed new version of this Ibsen classic portrays shipbuilder Karsten Bernick, a respected, highly successful businessman in a small Norwegian coastal town. Bernick's wealth has been founded on a long-buried deceit which is now being threatened with exposure. As the wily, unscrupulous Bernick struggles to preserve his standing in the community, he sets in motion a chain of events that threatens to destroy all he holds most dear. Period 1870s
ISBN 978 0 573 11336 9

Pinocchio. Family Entertainment. John Morley
9 to 14 principals, adult and/or juvenile chorus. One permanent set with three or four frontcloths. Fee code L

This delightful dramatization of Collodi's story of Pinocchio has all the charm of the original. The story is simple to stage with many music and production suggestions, and the cast is flexible for both large and small companies.
ISBN 978 0 573 11345 1

Pizzazz. Three plays. Hugh Leonard
Fee code M (for trilogy). ISBN 978 0 573 01641 7

These three plays, intended solely as entertainment, share the common theme of travelling – near Dublin, in Rome and on the Shannon river.

A View from the Obelisk.
M2 F1. A hilltop. Fee code D

Convalescing fom heart surgery, Owen returns to his native Ireland with Rosemary and insists on showing her the view from a hilltop near Dublin. But the climb takes rather a lot out of him and Rosemary goes off to summon a car. While she is gone, a young man appears, sketching the view. Owen strikes up a conversation with him, talking as though he'd known him for years. The boy goes, and it is only when Rosemary returns that Owen realizes why the boy seemed so familiar to him ...

Roman Fever. From the story by Edith Wharton
M1 F2. A terrace. Fee code E

On a restaurant terrace in Rome, Mrs Slade and Mrs Ansley are reminiscing about a Roman holiday they had together many years before. Mrs Slade, envious of Mrs Ansley's daughter's engagement to a young and rich *marchese* cannot resist a spiteful jibe at Mrs Ansley, thereby destroying a cherished memory. But in the end it is Mrs Slade herself whose illusions are shattered. Period 1930

Pizzazz.
M2 F3. A reception area. Fee code F

Whilst waiting to hire out cabin cruisers on the River Shannon, two apparent strangers play an elaborate game, which involves re-enacting a marriage on the rocks, with the other people in the reception area as supporting cast. But this is a Chinese Box of a play, and all is not what it seems ...

Play it Again, Sam. Comedy. Woody Allen
M3 (young, 28) F8 (young). A living-room with platform area. Fee code M

Allan has this thing about Humphrey Bogart. His wife has left him and his friends have been trying to fix him up with beautiful dates, but he is so gauche they always end abysmally. His day-dreams of Bogart and the beautiful people are always rudely shattered by real life. And when he falls for his best friend's wife things really seem black. But the homely hero is saved and is left to dream of being greater things.
ISBN 978 0 573 61404 0

♦ **A bullet mark next to a title indicates that it is new to this edition of the Guide.**

Play On! Comedy. Rick Abbot
M3 (20, 25) F7 (17, 22, 35, 42, middle-age); or M6 F4 if preferred. A stage in a community theatre. Fee code M

A theatre group try desperately to put on a play, amid all kinds of maddening interference from its authoress, Phyllis, who keeps revising the script until almost opening night and during the actual performance anything that can go wrong does. At the curtain call Phyllis decides to give a speech on the state of the modern theatre and what befalls her is the madcap climax to this hilarious romp.
ISBN 978 0 573 61361 6

Play with Repeats. Play. Martin Crimp
M3 F3. A pub, a laundrette, a bus stop. Fee Code M

"Yes, we accumulate wisdom, but what use is it to us? Because the events when the wisdom would've been useful, they're over and gone". This is the mantra of earnest, inadequate protagonist Tony Steadman. Tony sits in a pub on the eve of his fortieth birthday with Nick, a man who seemingly has no regrets. The play follows Tony's clumsy attempts to make something of himself, leading nowhere but back to the pub, where his second encounter with Nick becomes increasingly sinister.

♦ **Plague Over England.** Play. Nicholas de Jongh
M14 (20s, 30s, 40s) F2 (40s), doubling possible. Various simple settings. Fee code M

In 1953, actor Sir John Gielgud was arrested in a public lavatory, and pleaded guilty to persistently importuning male persons for immoral purposes. In prim, homophobic 1950s Britain, Gielgud's offence attracted vicious criticism and threatened to terminate his career. A few weeks later, however, when Gielgud opened in a new play, something extraordinary happened. This play relates Gielgud's emergency to the country's political mood, depicting a nation in the grip of a gay witch-hunt.
ISBN 978 0 573 11339 0

Playhouse Creatures. Play. April De Angelis
F5 (16, 20s, 50, 60). Simple settings. Fee code M

Of vital importance to the development of English drama was the entrance of the first actresses upon the English stage. April De Angelis has taken five actresses – Nell Gwyn, Elizabeth Farley, Rebecca Marshall, Doll Common and Mary Betterton – and given us a fascinating look at the precarious lot of actresses in the Restoration period. A moving and often comic account of a true story, with some earthy language! Period 1669
ISBN 978 0 573 13007 6

Playing the Wife. Play. Ronald Hayman
M2 (20s, 52) F2 (20s, 40s). A stage. Fee code M
ISBN 978 0 573 01867 1

♦ **A bullet mark next to a title indicates that it is new to this edition of the Guide.**

Plaza Suite. Comedy. Neil Simon
M3/2/2 F1/2. An hotel suite. Fee code M

The comedy consists of three separate plays all occurring in the same hotel suite, and all parts can be played by separate artists. In the first play, *Visitor from Mamaroneck*, a middle-aged couple re-visit the hotel room of their honeymoon – but the arrangement does not end as romantically as might have been expected. *Visitor from Hollywood* recounts the meeting of two old flames and what can happen under the influence of repeating magic Hollywood names. The last play, *Visitor from Forest Hills*, tells of a mother and father and their daughter who has locked herself in the bathrooom and refuses to come out for her wedding. (**Slightly restricted**)
ISBN 978 0 573 61407 1

The Plough and the Stars. Tragedy. Sean O' Casey
M9 (25, 40, middle-age) F6 (15, 20, 23, 40). Three interiors. One exterior. Fee code M

To the Irish Citizen Army 'The Plough and the Stars' symbolizes their futile patriotism. To all the slum dwellers the Easter rebellion brings the realization that there is no help against the strength of the English forces. This tragic satire ends amid a scene of final desolation where two Irishmen sit playing cards until they are rounded up by the King's soldiers. Period 1915-16
ISBN 978 0 573 01344 7

Popcorn. Play. Ben Elton
M4 (young, late 30s, middle-age) F5 (teenage, young, late 30s). A lounge-room. Fee code M

Set in the Beverly Hills home of Tarantino-style, Oscar-winning, movie director Bruce Delamitri, *Popcorn* is a satirical comedy thriller that took the West End by storm. Notorious killers Wayne and Scout interrupt Bruce and Brooke Daniels (nude model and actress) intending to use Bruce's 'art' as justification for murder. Events are disrupted with the arrival of Karl (Bruce's producer) and Farrah Delamitri (Bruce's soon-to-be-ex-wife) with spoilt daughter, Velvet. But Wayne means to succeed – whatever the cost.
ISBN 978 0 573 01869 5

The Pope and the Witch. Play. Dario Fo. Edited by Franca Rame. Translated by Ed Emery
M8 F3. Doubling. Extras. A corridor and room in the Vatican, a room. Fee code M

The Vatican is the target of this fast and furious satire. The Pope is to give his first world televized press conference but is suffering from acute paranoia and nervous paralysis. Enter Elisa, the 'witch' of the title, who alone seems to have the power to cure the Pope. Visiting her drug clinic he is so impressed that he issues a papal encyclical with startling global results.

Portrait of Fear. Play. Edward Taylor
M3 (young, 20s) F2 (20s). A room in a tower. Fee code M. ISBN 978 0 573 11583 7

♦ **Posh.** Play. Laura Wade
M11 F2. A gentleman's club; a pub private dining-room. Fee code M

In an oak-panelled room in Oxford, ten young bloods with cut-glass vowels and deep pockets are meeting, intent on restoring their right to rule. Members of an elite student dining society, the boys are bunkering down for a wild night of debauchery, decadence and bloody good wine. But this isn't the last huzzah: they're planning a takeover. Welcome to the Riot Club.
"... a satirical, humorous and finally chilling view of the upper classes – and a really fine metaphor for our times." – *The Stage*

The Positive Hour. Play. April De Angelis
M2 (30s-40s, 51) F4 (30s, 46), 1 girl. Various simple settings. Fee code M

Miranda is a social worker, with no shortage of problems herself. Her best friend, Emma, is a failed artist having a mid-life crisis; her partner, Roger, is a frustrated academic, desperately trying to finish his book on Hegel. Personal problems are exacerbated by work and, especially, Miranda's relationship with Paula, an unemployed single mother who takes up prostitution to survive. Funny and disturbing, *The Positive Hour* brings issues of gender and sexuality into a new, modern context.

The Power of the Dog. Play. Ellen Dryden
M2 (young, 30s) F4 (17, 40s, 60s, 70s) A cottage interior, an office. Fee code M

Vivien, an English teacher, is about to become headmistress of another school, thus leaving Lisa, her difficult but bright protégée, stranded without her inspiration. When Lisa takes violent action to express her unhappiness, Vivien is shocked out of her usual detached emotional state into an understanding of the consequences of her actions, which have affected all her relationships, including that with her crippled mother.

Pratt of the *Argus*. Play. Michael Birch. Adapted from the novel by David Nobbs
M35 F15 can be played by M4 F2. Various simple settings. Fee code L. ISBN 978 0 573 01967 8

♦ **Prepare to Meet Thy Tomb.** Comedy-thriller. Norman Robbins
M4 (20s, 30s,60s) F6 (19, 30s, 40s, 50s, 60s). A garden room. Fee code L

This completes the trilogy about the murderous Tomb family. As night and fog descend on Monument House Hotel, Hecuba Tomb and her niece Drusilla receive a series of unexpected visitors, who are soon snooping around the secret passages and asking too many questions. Gradually, they fall victim to violent deaths by devious techniques. This irresistible combination of spoof and murder mystery, over-the-top characters and shocking plot twists will thrill and delight in equal measure.
ISBN 978 0 573 11359 8

Prescription for Murder. Thriller. Norman Robbins
M3 (40s, 50s, 60s) F4 (30s, 45, 60s). A living-room. Fee code L

There is never a dull moment for busy Dr Richard Forth. He has an awkward yet close friendship with his ex-girlfriend while his wife, Barbara, is chronically and mysteriously ill. Richard believes her symptoms are psychological but when a stranger, claims to have known Richard's second fiancée – a woman Richard says does not exist – Barbara's health worsens and it becomes apparent somebody is out to kill her and anyone else who gets in their way. This thriller is sure to keep you guessing until the final twist.
ISBN 978 0 573 11338 3

Present Laughter. Light comedy. Noël Coward
M5 (30-40) F6 (23-40). A studio. Fee code M

Popular actor Garry Essendine revels in being a temperamental prima donna. Now separated from wife Liz he still remains under her control. When he becomes more deeply involved with Joanna, his manager's wife, and it becomes clear that it will be difficult to extricate himself, Liz returns and takes him once again under her control.
ISBN 978 0 573 01354 6

The Prime of Miss Jean Brodie. Play. Jay Presson Allen
M4 (young, middle-age) F8 (young, middle-age). 4 girls non-speaking (11-12); 7 girls non-speaking (8-11). Fee code M

Jean Brodie, teacher at the Marcia Blaine Academy, incurs the disapproval of her colleagues by her unconventional teaching methods, her favouritism among her pupils, and also by her admiration for Mussolini and Italy. Scandals increase, chiefly involving the art teacher and the music teacher. One member of her group of favourites is killed while running off to fight for Franco. Her chief protégée, Sandy, denounces her as a murderer. Period 1930s
ISBN 978 0 573 61427 9

The Prisoner of Second Avenue. Comedy. Neil Simon
M2 (40s, 50s) F4 (40s, 50s). A 14th floor apartment. Fee code M

When Mel is made redundant he starts to fight a battle with the environs of New York: the pollution, the paper-thin walls of the high rise apartment. When his apartment is burgled and his psychiatrist dies with $23,000 of his money Mel has a nervous breakdown. It is on recovery that we come to esteem him all the more. For Mel and his wife and people like them have the resilience, the grit to survive. (**Slightly restricted**)
ISBN 978 0 573 61429 3

The Prisoner of Zenda. Play. Matthew Francis, adapted from the novel by Anthony Hope
M17 (can be played by M9) F2, 1 child. Various interior and exterior settings. Fee code M
ISBN 978 0 573 01865 7

Private Fears in Public Places. Play. Alan Ayckbourn
M3 F3, 1 male voice. Various simple settings. Fee Code M

This piece is unusually structured in 54 short scenes. The central theme of the play is that our lives are linked more closely than we realize and the actions of individuals will often create ripples which turn into waves. In this mosaic of short scenes between two or sometimes three people the six characters all connect with each other in some way.

Private Lives. Intimate comedy. Noël Coward
M2 (30) F3 (young, 30). A balcony, a living-room. Fee code M

Sybil and Elyot arrive at a hotel in France for their honeymoon. Amanda, Elyot's first wife, happens to take the adjoining suite with her new husband Victor. When Amanda and Elyot meet they elope but together they veer between happiness and bickering which turns into physical fighting. Victor and Sybil discover them rolling on the floor and a four-handed quarrel begins during which Elyot and Amanda steal away. Period 1930
ISBN 978 0 573 01357 7

Privates on Parade. Play with songs. Peter Nichols. Music by Denis King
M10 (20s, 35, 45, 50s) F1 (28). Several simple settings on an open stage. Fee code M

Designed in the form of a variety show, the production of an Army Concert Party show in Malaya is intermingled with the story of their adventures, comic and tragic, as they tour the jungle-type countryside, menaced by Communist guerrillas. Among the varied company are an aggressive, dishonest Sergeant-Major, a raw newcomer, an earnestly religious major, and a colourful homosexual. Finally, bruised, battered but still ebullient, the survivors board ship for England and home. Period 1948
ISBN 978 0 573 11347 5

Progress. Play. Doug Lucie
M6 (21-30s) F2 (20, 33). A living-room. Fee code M

A

Progress exposes the hard underbelly of a slightly older generation of trendy lefties and sexual liberationists living appalling lives in London NW6, where Will, a Channel 4 researcher, and his wife Ronee, breakfast to the accompaniment of the taped sob-outs from his men's therapy group, plus the occasional phone call from Ronee's German girlfriend. '... brutally satiric eye for modern manners and speech ...' *Guardian*. '... vicious satirical comedy ... appallingly funny ...' *The Times*

The Promise. Play. Alexei Arbuzov. Translated by Ariadne Nicolaeff
M2 (17) F1(15). A living-room. Fee code M

During the siege of Leningrad in 1942, three young people – a girl and two boys – find shelter in a semi-derelict house. The play follows the intricacies of their triangular relationship over the next seventeen years, as their hopes and feelings for themselves and each other rise and fall, and offers a moving and fascinating glimpse of life in the Soviet Union after the Second World War. *The Promise* was originally performed at the Oxford Playhouse in 1966, in a production starring Judi Dench, Ian McKellen and Ian McShane.

Proof. Play. David Auburn
M2 (28, 50s) F2 (20s). The back porch of a house in Chicago. Fee code M

Catherine has spent years caring for her brilliant but unstable father, Robert. When he dies she has more than grief to deal with: there's her estranged sister, Claire, and Hal, a former student of her father's who hopes to find valuable work in the 103 notebooks that Robert left behind. And a further problem: how much of her father's madness – or genius – will Catherine inherit? Gwyneth Paltrow starred in this Pulitzer Prize-winning play which opened at the Donmar Warehouse in 2001.

Proscenophobia (Stage Fright). Play. Bettine Manktelow
M2 (50-ish) F4 (20s, 40s, middle age). A theatre dressing-room. Fee code L

The action of this clever whodunit takes place in the dressing-room of a provincial theatre during a performance of a thriller. The star, Addie, is attempting a comeback and is understudied by Millie, her best friend for many years. Suspense builds when Addie feels unwell and Millie must take over. In the dramatic and violent last act of the play, in a startling twist, the violence becomes real – Millie is dead. With everyone suspect, the tension doesn't let up until the final revelation. ISBN 978 0 573 01973 9

Pull the Other One. Farce. Norman Robbins
M4 (35, 65, elderly) F3 (18, 35, 60). A living-room. Fee code L

When Albert's mother-in-law Boadicea discovers a letter written to Albert from his friend Hilary she refuses to believe it is perfectly innocent or that Hilary is a man. Along comes Hilary in blonde wig and evening dress straight from his drag act at the local pub. Further disasters ensue as Hilary attempts to make amends for the trouble he has caused and tries to help Albert. ISBN 978 0 573 11358 1

♦ **A bullet mark next to a title indicates that it is new to this edition of the Guide.**

♦ Punk Rock. Play. Simon Stephens
M5 (teens;middle-aged) F4 (teens). School Library. Hospital room. Fee Code M

William Carlisle has the world at his feet but its weight on his shoulders. In the library of a fee-paying grammar school, William and his fellow sixth-formers are preparing for their mock A-levels while navigating the pressures of teenage life. They are educated and aspirational young people, but step-by-step, the dislocation, disjunction and latent aggression is revealed. Premiered at the Lyric, Hammersmith in 2009. "powerful and compelling ... evokes the twilight world of the teenager with scary vividness. . . " *Independent*
ISBN 978 1 408 12636 3

Pullin' the Wool. Comedy. Frank Vickery
M3 (30-40s) F3 (30s-40s), with doubling. Composite set: two living-rooms. Fee code M
ISBN 978 0 573 01959 3

♦ Purgatorio. Play. Ariel Dorfman
M1 F1. A white room. Fee code L

From the author of *Death and the Maiden*. A man and a woman sit in a stark white room under video camera surveillance, both wishing to escape purgatorial afterlife, and hiding a secret. They have the chance to interrogate each other in turn and as the woman gradually confronts her past actions there emerges a timeless version of the myth of Jason and Medea. Dorfman takes up many of his previous themes of forgiveness, retribution and redemption. "Fascinating, brilliant, elegant, funny and ... revolting ... " *Seattle Post-Intelligencer*

Pyrenees. Play. David Greig
M2 (middle age) F2 (young, middle age). The terrace of a mountain hotel. Fee Code L

A man, Keith, has been found unconscious in the mountains with only the clothes on his back and a scallop shell – the age-old symbol of the pilgrimage to Santiago del Compostela which passes that way. He has no memory of who he is or how he came to be there. As Keith confronts the void that is his past, tension swells to near-breaking point in this intelligent, haunting and mysterious play.

Quartermaine's Terms. Play. Simon Gray
M5 F2. A staffroom. Fee code M. ISBN 978 0 573 11364 2

Quartet. Play. Ronald Harwood
M2 (70s) F2 (70s). A music room and terrace. Fee code M

Cecily, Reggie and Wilfred are in a home for retired opera singers in Kent. Each year, on 10th October, there is a concert to celebrate Verdi's birthday. Jean, who used to be married to Reggie, arrives at the home and disrupts their equilibrium. She still acts like a diva and refuses to sing. But the show must go on ... By turns funny and poignant, *Quartet* premièred in September 1999 at the Albery Theatre, London.

Racing Demon. Play. David Hare
M8 (20s, 40s-60s). F3 (20s, 30, 50s). Extras. Various simple interior and exterior settings. Fee code M. ISBN 978 0 573 11369 7

The Ramayana. Play of the Hindu epic. Peter Oswald
20 speaking parts. Extras. Simple settings. Fee code L

The ancient Hindu epic poem *The Ramayana* tells of the journey of Rama, an incarnation of God, to set free his wife Sita from the ten-headed demon Ravana, with the aid of an army of monkeys. This divine story, here set forth in dramatic form, encapsulates the rise of humanity from animal to God. Peter Oswald's colloquial verse dramatization, with its blend of the spiritual and the secular, was premièred in Birmingham in 2000 and seen at the Royal National Theatre in 2001.

Real Estate. Play. Louise Page
M2 (30s, 50s) F2 (38, 60). Various simple interior and exterior settings. Fee code M

First performed at the Tricycle Theatre, London, in 1984, this is a touching, sensitive play which stirs deep emotions. Jenny, single and pregnant, returns to visit her mother after twenty years, hoping to find some kind of assistance and support, and possibly a home in which to raise her child. As the play unfolds, the characters are visibly fighting to penetrate each other's defences and ultimately Jenny realizes that her mother is not prepared to give up her happiness for her daughter's sake.

The Real Story of Puss in Boots. Play. David Foxton
M6 F3, or M7 F4. Various interior and exterior settings. Fee code K

The story of *Puss in Boots* is ingeniously combined with that of *Cinderella* in this hilarious new show. Puss in Boots transforms humble Colin Miller into Prince Charming. Cinderella's Fairy Godmother helps her to become Princess Priscilla, despite the meddlings of her stepsisters. Prince Charming and Princess Priscilla marry, thus providing happy endings for both their stories. This hugely likeable show, which can be performed by a small cast without songs, is suitable for any scale of production.
ISBN 978 0 573 06497 5

The Real Thing. Play. Tom Stoppard
M4 (20s, 40s) F3 (17, 30s). Various interior settings. Fee code M

Tom Stoppard's brilliant, award-winning play of surprise and deftly witty comparison was premièred at London's Strand Theatre in 1982 starring Roger Rees and Felicity Kendal and revived in 1999. Henry is a successful playwright married to Charlotte who has the lead role in his latest play about adultery. Her co-star, Max, is married to another actress, Annie, and Annie and Henry are madly in love but is it any more real than the subjects of Henry's play?
ISBN 978 0 573 01637 0

Rebecca. Play. Daphne du Maurier
M8 (young, 30s, middle-age) F3 (young, middle-age). Extras. A lounge-hall. Fee code M.
Period 1940
ISBN 978 0 573 01373 7

◆ **A bullet mark next to a title indicates that it is new to this edition of the Guide.**

A

Rebecca. Play. Daphne du Maurier. Adapted by Clifford Williams
M8 (young, 30s, middle-age) F3 (young, middle-age). Extras. A lounge-hall. Fee code M

Max de Winter brings his shy young bride to Manderley, his great house in Cornwall. Everywhere, she senses the overpowering presence of Rebecca, Max's drowned wife. Mrs Danvers, the grim housekeeper, will not allow her to forget her shortcomings. She doubts Max's love until Rebecca's body is found. Max confesses that he murdered Rebecca, hating her depravity. The husband and wife now face the exciting fight to save Max from the gallows. Period 1940
ISBN 978 0 573 11365 9

Recipe for Murder. Play. J.D. Robins
M2 (40s) F2 (30s, 40s). A sitting-room. Fee code K

David Lawson, a research scientist, is not a well man. His sister Beatie thinks his wife Claire doesn't take proper care of him and visiting journalist Kit Kelly begins to suspect that Claire may be guilty of more than just negligence … Claire's grandmother and first husband died in mysterious circumstances leaving her generous legacies: is it possible that David is the next victim on her list? Suspicions deepen as this tightly-plotted, fast-moving and often funny thriller moves to its surprising conclusion.
ISBN 978 0 573 01985 2

Red in the Morning. Thriller. Glyn Jones
M4 (23, 40s) F3 (30s, 70s). Extras. A conservatory and part of the hall. Fee code L
ISBN 978 0 573 69094 5

Redevelopment. Play. Václav Havel. English version by James Saunders. From a literal translation by Marie Winn
M7 F3, with doubling. A spacious hall in a medieval castle. Fee code M

The Rehearsal, or Love Punished. Play. Jean Anouilh. Translated by Jeremy Sams
M5 F3. An elegant room, an attic room. Fee code M

A hedonistic Count and his friends rehearse Marivaux's *The Double Inconstancy* in the rural splendour of a provincial castle. Most of the 'actors' keep to the amorous rules and restrict their dalliances to their own class. Yet when the Count himself threatens to step beyond theatrical boundaries by falling in love with a young governess, stage romance suddenly becomes the drama of life. This sparkling translation was presented in the West End to critical acclaim.

Relative Values. Light comedy. Noël Coward
M5 (30-middle-age, 60) F5 (18, 35-50s). A library living-room. Fee code M

Moxie is maid to Felicity, Countess of Marshwood. When Felicity's son Nigel announces his engagement to Miranda Frayle, the film star, Moxie is distressed as Miranda is really her sister, who ignored her family after becoming famous. Miranda starts describing the home from which she ran away, saying her sister drank and she had to care for her mother. Outraged, Moxie blurts out the truth – and the engagement becomes rather strained.
ISBN 978 0 573 01375 1

Relatively Speaking. Comedy. Alan Ayckbourn
M2 (young, middle-age) F2 (young, middle-age). A bedsitting-room, a garden patio. Fee code M

Greg and Ginny are living together, but Greg is becoming somewhat suspicious that he is not the only man in her life. He wonders about Ginny's plan 'to visit her parents' and decides to follow her. Ginny is really going to see a considerably older lover, but only in order to break with him. Greg mistakes the ex-lover and his wife for Ginny's parents. Ginny's arrival further compounds an already wildly hilarious situation.
ISBN 978 0 573 11355 0

Remembrance. Play. Graham Reid
M2 (30s-40s, 68) F4 (30s-40s, 63). A cemetery, two living-rooms, a garden. Fee code M

Bert and Theresa, both mourning sons, meet in the cemetery and fall in love. Their blossoming relationship is complicated by the fact that he is a Protestant and she a Catholic ... and this is Belfast. Bert's son, who believes his father would rather have lost him than his adored brother, and Theresa's daughters, one of whom is married to an imprisoned IRA gunman, oppose the romance from the start, but Bert's daughter-in-law, herself trapped in an unhappy marriage, supports the elderly lovers.
ISBN 978 0 573 69321 2

Rents. Play. Michael Wilcox
M10 (can be played by M5). Various simple interior and exterior settings. Fee code L

The Resistible Rise of Arturo Ui. Play. Bertolt Brecht
Translations: Ralph Manheim
        George Tabori
        Ranjit Bolt, music by Dominic Muldowney
M28 F2. Extras. Numerous simple interior and exterior settings. Fee code M for play, code C for music

The Restless Evil. Play. Charlotte Hastings
M3 (24, 38) F7 (20s West Indian, 40s, 50s, 60, 70s). A café. Fee code L
ISBN 978 0 573 11370 3

Retreat from Moscow. Play. Don Taylor
M2 (50s) F2 (16, 22). A living-room. Fee code M

Cocooned in their suburban home are Tom, idealistic socialist and unemployed classics lecturer, and Phillipa, his disillusioned daughter. Into their lives unexpectedly comes Boris, a bellowing bear-like Muscovite who only wants to enjoy the fruits of the capitalist good life. But beneath Boris's laughing exuberance lies a bitter, dreadful secret past which, when revealed, shakes the beliefs Tom holds firm. The play was presented at the New End Theatre, Hampstead, in 1993 in a production directed by the author.

◆ **A bullet mark next to a title indicates that it is new to this edition of the Guide.**

The Revengers' Comedies. Play in two parts by Alan Ayckbourn
M11 F10, M1 F1 voices only, some doubling possible. Various interior and exterior settings. Fee code M for each part

Hapless Henry Bell, depressed at being ousted from his firm, is distracted from committing suicide by another would-be suicide. He rescues her, and after hearing her tale of abandonment by her married lover, agrees that revenge is sweeter than suicide. Karen persuades Henry that they should swap revenges – she will see to the man who took Henry's job, while he will take care of her ex-lover's wife, Imogen.
ISBN 978 0 573 01881 7

Ring Round the Moon. Play. Jean Anouilh. Adapted by Christopher Fry
M8 (young, middle-age, old) F6 (young, 30, middle-age, elderly). A winter garden. Fee code M

Christopher Fry calls this play 'A Charade with Music'. The same actor plays the twins Hugo and Frederic. Hugo, fascinating and heartless, sets the charade in motion. He has invited Isabelle, a ballet dancer, to the ball that evening, intending that she should make diffident Frederic love her and leave the beautiful Diana. The would-be puppetmaster is overruled by his aunt, who arranges for the four young people to be happy.
ISBN 978 0 573 11380 2

The Ring Sisters. Comedy. Charles Laurence
M4 (30-50s) F3 (50s, 70s). A living-room. Fee code M

Silva Ring is a world-famous singer with a severe hangup about her age so when an interviewer reveals it she resorts to increasingly desperate measures to prove him wrong. Aided by her housekeeper she pretends to be her own sister Iris, who is tough. Lola Wales, an old singer, is brought in to be her aunt and Fred, a petty forger, is persuaded to attempt to destroy her files at the Family Record Centre. But Silva wins through and emerges stronger than ever.
ISBN 978 0 573 62677 7

The Rise and Fall of Little Voice. Play. Jim Cartwright
M3 (young, 40s, 50s) or 4 F3 (young, 40s). A living-room and club. Fee code M

Little Voice (LV) lives alone with her mother Mari whose sole purpose is to find another man. Mari's imposing presence drives the shy LV into spending her time in her bedroom listening to her beloved father's records. When small-time impresario Ray Say hears LV's faultless impersonation of famous singers, he recognizes the gold in her voice and determines to exploit it, but the whirlwind rush for success breaks LV. Later, however, she learns to sing in her own voice ...
ISBN 978 0 573 01883 1

A Rise in the Market. Comedy. Edward Taylor
M4 (40s, elderly) F3 (20s, late 30s). A lounge area. Fee code L

Sir Clive Partridge hopes to be president of the European Community, but he needs the support of puritanical elder statesman Jacques Berri. So it's bad news for Partridge when Berri calls on a day that he is trapped in a luxurious Paris flat where he is beset by glamorous young women he can't account for, plus an angry wife and an exploding boiler. Wild mishaps and comic confusion abound right up to the hilarious climax in this sharp satire.

Rising Damp. Comedy. Eric Chappell
M3 (20s (1 black), 40s) F1 (late 20s). An attic room. Fee code K. Typescript on hire

The part of the mean, highly-bigoted, seedy landlord Rigsby, so successfully created by
Leonard Rossiter in the TV version, is now brought to the stage, along with other inmates
in the dilapidated house: Alan, a naïve medical student; Philip, a black student and Ruth, an
admin. worker at the college who's having an affair with Philip but is hotly pursued by the
besotted Rigsby.

Ritual in Blood. Play. Steven Berkoff
Large mixed cast. Fee code L

Set in thirteenth-century England, *Ritual in Blood* looks at the persecution of the Jews and, by
implication, the persecution of all peoples. One small incident frighteningly escalates and mob
hatred is fomented by the cool cynicism of the moneyed classes.

Road. Play. Jim Cartwright
M17 F13, can be played by M4 F3 with doubling. In and around a road in a small Lancashire
town. Fee code M

Under the guidance of the rum-soaked wideboy Scullery, we are taken on an evening's tour of a
scruffy, depressed road in a small Lancashire town. Moving from street corner to living-room,
from bedroom to kitchen, we meet the inhabitants, glimpsing their socially and emotionally
wretched lives in this sharp, sad, funny and angry play. ' ... the most significant and original
new English play to appear in London for a long time ...' *Observer*
ISBN 978 0 573 01664 6

The Road to the Sea. Play. Don Taylor
M2 (28, 70s) F2 (29, 38) Various simple settings. Fee code L

Jay paces his squalid London flat ruminating on mankind in the twentieth century. Jo, the
daughter he abandoned along with her mother twenty-five years before, has turned up,
determined to know her father. His stepdaughter, Harriet, is protective of him and suspects Jo's
motives. But who is Jay? The charismatic political agitator? Or a hypocrite who abandoned his
radical principles to make a fortune? Or the loving stepfather and devoted husband who gave
away a fortune to charity – a paragon amongst men?

Robin Hood. Comedy drama. Larry Blamire
M14 F7, doubling possible. Extras. Various simple settings. Fee code M

Larry Blamire has accomplished the enviable task of synthesizing the conflicting legends and
ballads about the outlaw folk hero into a sometimes hysterical, sprawling action-packed drama.
Besides ably retelling the legend, he indulges in and makes fun of the stilted dialogue found in
tiresome historical novels and adventure films. He has created roles that challenge and reinvent
the myth, including a wise-cracking Maid Marion who is arguably a better swords*person* than
any of Robin's merry men.

◆ **A bullet mark next to a title indicates that it is new to this edition of the Guide.**

A

Robin Hood. Musical celebration. David Wood and Dave and Toni Arthur
M14 or F14 (minimum). An open space. Fee code M

This is a series of playlets which tell the various well-known tales of Robin Hood. The possiblities for presenting the play are numerous – open stage, promenade, open air as well as on a proscenium stage. There is a basic cast of fourteen, but the authors envisage productions 'in which large numbers of local people take part', emphasizing the basic concept of the play which is that of a musical celebration by a whole community.
ISBN 978 0 573 05063 3

◆ **Rock 'N' Roll.** Play. Tom Stoppard
M11 (20s, 30s, 50s) F9 (16, 20s, 40s), all ageing 22 years. May be played by M6 F5.
Various interior and exterior settings. Fee code M

Spans the years from 1968 to 1990 from the double perspective of Prague, where a rock 'n' roll band comes to symbolize resistance to the Communist regime, and of Cambridge where the verities of love and death are shaping the lives of three generations in the family of a Marxist philosopher.
"Leaves you cheered by its wit, buoyancy and belief in the human spirit." *The Guardian*

RolePlay. Comedy, from *Damsels in Distress*. Alan Ayckbourn
M3(30, 40, 50s) F4 (20s, 45, 50s). An apartment. Fee code M

Justin and Julie-Ann, hopelessly mismatched in love, are about to introduce their respective parents to each other over dinner – Justin's upper-crust alcoholic mother from Surrey and Julie-Ann's bigoted Yorkshire father and prim mother. Into this doomed scenario drops, literally, via the balcony upstairs and the river, Paige Petite, a former lap-dancer with suicidal tendencies and her thick, gun-toting minder who is employed by her violent boyfriend …
ISBN 978 0 573 11569 1

Romantic Comedy. Comedy. Bernard Slade
M2 (30s) F4 (young, 20s, 30s, 54). A study. Fee code M

Jason Carmichael, successful co-author of Broadway romantic comedies, is about to marry a society belle and his collaborator is retiring from the fray. Enter Phoebe Craddock, a mousy Vermont schoolteacher and budding playwright and Jason acquires a talented, adoring collaborator. Fame and success are theirs for ten years and then Jason's world falls apart – his wife divorces him and Phoebe marries a journalist and moves to Paris. Jason goes into decline but re-enter a chic, successful Phoebe – and guess the ending!
ISBN 978 0 573 61504 7

La Ronde. Ten Dialogues. Arthur Schnitzler. English version by Eric Bentley
M5 F5. Simple settings. Fee code M

This is Schnitzler's popular roundelay of love, as practised in Old Vienna, and as told in ten interlocking scenes. Each scene is made for two persons, and each person plays two consecutive scenes, serving alternately as the link between them. Thus the soldier of the first scene leaves his lady of the evening to appear in the next scene with a parlour maid. An amusing *tour de force*, popular throughout the world.
ISBN 978 0 573 61192 6

Rookery Nook. Farce. Ben Travers
M5 F6. A lounge-hall. Fee code M. ISBN 978 0 573 01389 8

Roots. Play. Arnold Wesker
M5 (young, 50s, 65) F4 (young, 50). Three cottage living-rooms. Fee code M
ISBN 978 0 573 11377 2

Roots and Wings. Play. Frank Vickery
M3 (20s, 40s, 50s) F3 (youngish, 40s, 50s). A hospital corridor and room. Fee code M
ISBN 978 0 573 01885 5

Rope. Drama. Patrick Hamilton
M6 (young, 20s, old) F2 (young, 50). A study. Fee code M

Brandon wants excitement at any price. He persuades his weak-minded friend, Granillo, to assist him in the murder of a fellow undergraduate, Ronald Raglan. They place the body in a wooden chest and invite some acquaintances, including the dead man's father, to a party, the chest and its gruesome contents serving as a supper table. The horror and tension are worked up gradually and we see the reactions of the two murderers, closely watched by the suspecting Rupert Cadell, until finally they break.
ISBN 978 0 573 01989 0

Rose. Play. Martin Sherman
F1 (80). A wooden bench on a bare stage. Fee code L

Rose is a survivor. Her remarkable life began in a tiny Russian village, took her to Warsaw's ghettoes and a ship called *The Exodus*, and finally to the boardwalks of Atlantic City, the Arizona canyons and salsa-flavoured nights in Miami Beach. The play is a sharply drawn portrait of a feisty Jewish woman and a moving reminder of some of the events that shaped the century. *Rose* premièred at the Royal National Theatre in 1999 starring Olympia Dukakis.

The Rose Tattoo. Play. Tennessee Williams
M7 (25, middle-age) F13 (young-old). 1 small girl, 2 small boys. Exterior of a cottage, living-room interior. Fee code M

The Rose Tattoo, says the author, is 'the Dionysian element in human life, its mystery, its beauty, its significance'. Serafina boasts of her husband's prowess as a lover and nephew of a Baron. On hearing he had not been at all what she supposed she takes up life again with a flourish. In addition she now gives consent to her daughter's marriage to a young sailor.

Rosencrantz and Guildenstern Are Dead. Comedy. Tom Stoppard
M14 F2, flexible casting. Unit setting. Fee code M

Rosencrantz and Guildenstern sit in the Court of Elsinore endlessly spinning a coin, waiting for their stage entry – which may never come. Unsure who they are and why they are there they even have difficulty remembering which goes by which name. Against the action of *Hamlet* they seek their identities and their purpose and reflect the feelings of all those who question existence. While this play deals with themes already familiar from Beckett, its style is that of brilliant, literate comedy.
ISBN 978 0 573 01338 6

The Roses of Eyam. Play. Don Taylor
Large flexible cast including children (young-80). A village: open stage. Fee code L

A remarkable and true story of a village stricken with plague through the arrival from London of a box of clothing; of the villagers' determination, under the persuasions of the present and former Rectors, to prevent its spread by remaining within the village and containing the disease at the certain risk of their own lives; of the human tragedies and even comedies that ensued; of the idealism and the courage required to live with that idealism. Period 1666
ISBN 978 0 573 11386 4

Rough Crossing. Comedy. Tom Stoppard, from an original play by Ferenc Molnar
M5 (25, middle-age) F1 (35-40). Extras. A pre-war, ocean liner. Fee code M

This hilarious play, freely adapted from Molnar's classic farce *Játék a Kastélyban*, was seen at the National Theatre in 1984 starring Michael Kitchen, John Standing and Sheila Gish. Two playwrights and collaborators, the composer and most of the cast of a musical comedy destined for Broadway are trying to finish and rehearse the play while crossing from Southampton via Cherbourg, to New York. With music by Andre Previn, Tom Stoppard wittily parodies thirties' musicals.

Round and Round the Garden. Play. Alan Ayckbourn
M3 F3. A garden. Fee code M. See the entry for *The Norman Conquests*
ISBN 978 0 573 01575 3

Round Heads and Pointed Heads or **Money Calls to Money**. Play. Bertolt Brecht. Translated by Tom Kuhn. Songs by Tom Kuhn, Ralph Manheim and John Willett
M12 F6. Extras. Various settings. Fee code M for play, code C for music

See synopsis for *Roundheads and Peakheads*.

Roundheads and Peakheads (**Rich and Rich**). Play. Bertolt Brecht.
Translations: N. Goold-Verschoyle, music by Hanns Eisler
Alan Brown and Kyra Dietz
M12 F6. Children. Extras. Interior and exterior sttings. Fee code M for play, code C for music

This play is described by the author as a 'horror tale' in blank verse. Though the basic plot loosely follows that of Shakespeare's *Measure for Measure*, the play in fact is an allegory of the rise of Hitler (Angelo Iberin), a Roundhead who is appointed temporary ruler when the Regent leaves the country. Towards the end of the play the Regent returns and tells Angelo to prepare for war against a threatening distant country; the people are subdued and the revolutionaries executed. Period 1930s

The Royal Baccarat Scandal. Play. Royce Ryton
M9 (20s-elderly) F4 (20s-50). Extras. Composite setting. Fee code M. ISBN 978 0 573 11374 1

◆ **A bullet mark next to a title indicates that it is new to this edition of the Guide.**

The Royal Hunt of the Sun. Play. Peter Shaffer
M21 F2. Fee code M

A

This is the story of the conquest of Peru, the defeat by 167 men of a highly organized, communistic empire of over ten million people. It is also the story of two men, Francisco Pizarro, the embittered, defiant commander of the invading Spanish forces, and Atahuallpa, the young king, Sun god-upon-earth, ruler of a vast empire. Between the two, both illegitimate usurpers, there grows a deep and understanding friendship.
ISBN 978 0 573 01388 1

The Ruffian on the Stair. Play. Joe Orton
M2 (young) F1 (young). A kitchen/living-room. Fee code F

One day a strange man appears asking for a room. He begins taunting the woman and comes close to viciousness. The next day he returns, but this time Mike is there too. We can now piece things together – Mike has killed the homosexual lover and brother of Wilson. So Wilson pretends to ravish Joyce and forces Mike to shoot him – 'The heart is situated just below this badge on my pullover. Don't miss, will you?'

Rumours (The British Version). Farce. Neil Simon
M4 (40, 50) F5 (30s, 40s). A living-room. Fee code M

Ken and Chris have found their host Charley, a prominent Government official, in his bedroom, too dazed to speak, with a bullet wound in his ear lobe! Len and Claire arrive, themselves injured in a car crash, and are soon joined by Ernest and Cookie, Glenn and Cassie, each with their own problems. A second, accidental, gunshot leaves Ken temporarily deaf, the police arrive and Len has to pretend he is Charley, concocting a touching and fantastic explanation ... **(Slightly restricted)**
ISBN 978 0 573 01884 8

Rumpelstiltzkin. Play. Norman Robbins
M9 or 10 F2 or 3. Extras. Various simple settings. Fee code L

In this adaptation of the Grimms' story some children are discovered playing 'Ladder-words', a word game to change one word to another. Grettle says she can change 'flax' into 'gold'. The King hears this, mistakes it for an actual boast and orders Grettle to work the change. The gnome, Rumpelstilzkin, offers to help her – at a price. The play then follows the story of the gnome's defeat by the guessing of his secret name.
ISBN 978 0 573 06459 3

Run for Your Wife. Comedy. Ray Cooney
M6 (young, middle-age) F2 (20s). Composite setting: two living-rooms. Fee code M

John Smith is a London cabbie with his own taxi, a wife in Streatham, a wife in Wimbledon – and a knife-edge schedule! He has been a successful, if tired, bigamist for three years, but one day he is taken to hospital with mild concussion. In the ensuing complications, aided by an unwilling Stanley, John tries bravely to cope with a succession of well-meaning but prying policemen, two increasingly irate wives, and others, until he manfully confesses the truth.
ISBN 978 0 573 11383 3

A

A Russian in the Woods. Play. Peter Whelan
M7 F1. Various simple settings. Fee code M

Berlin, 1949. In the unsettling atmosphere of post-war liberation, a young English sergeant is given charge of an army outpost haunted by the graves of dead soldiers in the garden. Seeking company for the night, he innocently invites in an American GI – and ends up embroiled in a cold war drama with his conscience on trial. *A Russian in the Woods* premièred at the RSC's The Other Place, Stratford-upon-Avon, in March 2001.

Rutherford and Son. Play. Githa Sowerby
M4 (20s, 40s, 60) F4 (26, 36, middle age, 60). A living-room. Fee code M

Written in 1912 during the upsurge of the British feminist movement, this powerful play deals with the oppressive patriarchal system of the industrial North at that time. Rutherford is the hard tyrannical master of both his glassworks and his family who attacks, degrades and rejects each of his children in turn. To his daughter Janet, her banishment is a release, and she forcefully condemns her father and his values.

Sad Hotel. Play. David Foley
M3 (40s, 50s) F3 (40s). A kitchen and sitting-area. Fee code M

Set in a house on the Florida coast in the early sixties, *Sad Hotel* is a fictionalized account of a famous playwright's relationship with his male lover. The play traces the dissolution of a fifteen-year relationship under pressures of fame, failure and addiction. Trapped between a choice of love or loneliness, and the extremes of desire and betrayal, the characters in *Sad Hotel* test the limitations of human contact. Yet in the face of final loss, they struggle towards reconciliation, forgiveness and a kind of peace. Period 1961-1963

The Safari Party. Comedy. Tim Firth
M3 (20s, 50) F3 (20s, 50, early 60s). Various simple settings. Fee code M

Three households have agreed to hold a "safari party" – a dinner party, with each course served in a different house. The hors d'oeuvres are served by Daniel and Adam, young brothers whose abusive father was recently shot dead, the entrées by Lol and Esther, upwardly-mobile and vulgar, and the desserts by Inga, a seemingly benign antiques dealer. However: there's the question of the table … Seen at the Stephen Joseph Theatre, Scarborough in 2002, it opened the new Hampstead Theatre, London, in 2003.
ISBN 978 0 573 01981 4

Sailor Beware! Comedy. Philip King and Falkland Cary
M4 (20s, 40s, 50s) F5 (20s, 40s). A living-room. Fee code M. ISBN 978 0 573 01395 9

Salt of the Earth. Play. John Godber
M5 F6 or M3 F3. Various simple settings. Fee code M

Hull Truck Company's production of this richly humorous, affectionate and touching portrait of life in the West Yorkshire coalfields won a Fringe First at the Edinburgh Festival and was presented in London at the Donmar Warehouse Theatre. Spanning three generations, from 1947 to the present, this compelling saga vividly captures the dreams, ambitions, joys, fears, heartaches and disappointments of the Parker sisters, Annie and May, whose hopes centre on May's son, Paul, and his academic success.
ISBN 978 0 573 01689 9

Salvage (from *The Coast of Utopia*). Play. Tom Stoppard
M29 F11. Various interior and exterior settings. Period 1853-1865. Fee code M

Now widowed, Russian émigré Herzen, a nobleman's son and self-proclaimed socialist, comes to London and dedicates himself to his journal The Bell in the third part of Tom Stoppard's trilogy. But newer, young radicals are leading the way in Russia and in the twelve years the play spans, Herzen's influence begins to wane.

Same Old Moon. Play. Geraldine Aron
M10 F11, may be played by M3 F5 (minimum). Various simple settings. Fee code M

Chosen to reopen the Oxford Playhouse in 1991, and then seen in London's West End, *Same Old Moon* shows us scenes in the life of Brenda Barnes, the aspiring writer. We follow her from age nine to fortyish, and see through her eyes her eccentric and sometimes fiery Irish family: her wilful and self-destructive Dad, her put-upon, sometimes hot-tempered Mum and many others. A charming, but not uncritical, look at family life with some wonderful acting roles.
ISBN 978 0 573 01892 3

Same Time, Next Year. Comedy. Bernard Slade
M1 F1. A bedsitting-room. Fee code M

This long-running Broadway hit is about an adulterous love affair taking place only once a year – and also a reflection of twenty-five years of American attitudes. George picks up Doris in a California inn in 1951 and they agree to meet there once a year. Before each scene, tapes portray America of the time in speeches, sports and news broadcasts. *The New York Times* described it as the 'funniest comedy about love and adultery to come Broadway's way in years'.
ISBN 978 0 573 61604 4

The Samson Riddle. Play. Wolf Mankowitz
M17 F6 + Extras. or M5 F2 with doubling. Various simple settings. Fee Code L

Wolf Mankowitz re-tells the Samson and Delilah story with wit and insight in this simply-staged modern version. Samson's death and destiny are inevitable; Delilah betrays him because he robs her of her own identity by using her to slake his lust, for, as the author puts it in his accompanying essay "to be used, even as a vehicle of worship, is to be made into an object, and all human beings, one way or another, revolt against such abuse."

Sand Castles. Play by Bob Larbey. Based on an idea by Trish Larbey
M4 (30s, 40s, 60s) F10 (20s-old) 2 children. A beach. Fee code M

Stan and Bernice Billet and William and Margaret Patterson have been taking their holidays in the same resort for years. They don't exactly rule the waves but they have turned the area around their beach huts into a cosy little fiefdom. And then along comes Doug, with his nubile nieces. They don't care about beach hut protocol – they just want to have fun!

Sarcophagus. Play. Vladimir Gubaryev. Translated by Michael Glenny
M12 (20s, 50s) F6 (20s, 40s, 70s). Extras. A clinic ward. Fee code M. ISBN 978 0 573 01893 0

Saturday, Sunday, Monday. Play. Eduardo de Filippo, adapted by Keith Waterhouse and Willis Hall
M11 F6. An apartment in Naples. Fee code M

At first sight a typical picture of Italian family life with characteristic displays of Mediterranean temper, the play concerns the essence of any relationship between a man and a woman after years of married life. A monumental family row begins to brew on Saturday night while the Sunday *ragu* is being prepared in the kitchen. The row breaks on Sunday, the traditional day for family quarrels, and is finally and touchingly resolved on Monday.

Savages. Play. Christopher Hampton
M10 (3 Brazilian Indians) F1. Extras M. Multiple set. Fee code M

In a passionately angry, bitterly cynical and yet wholly workable play which veers from the soapbox to high comedy we are shown the contrasting publicity surrounding the murder of one diplomat and the anonymity surrounding the slaughter of a hundred Brazilian Indians. Period 1963 to 1970

Scapino! Play. Frank Dunlop and Jim Dale, a long way off from Molière
M10 F4. A café bar. Fee code K

The Scarlet Letter. Play. Phyllis Nagy, adapted from the novel by Nathaniel Hawthorne
M4 (20s, 50s) F3 (20s, 30). Various simple settings. Fee code M. ISBN 978 0 573 69529 2

The Scarlet Pimpernel. Play. Baroness Orczy adapted by Beverley Cross
M17 F3, doubling possible. Various interior and exterior settings. Fee code M

This swashbuckling tale of English aristocrats rescuing their French brethren from the jaws of Madame la Guillotine in revolution-torn, eighteenth-century France has something for everyone – humour, adventure and just a dash of romance! Beverley Cross's spectacular adaptation was seen at Chichester and subsequently at the Theatre Royal, London, starring Donald Sinden. 'It is a long time since the theatre saw an adventure so joyous ... a stunning adaptation ... an evening of simple but unalloyed theatre magic.' *Daily Telegraph*
ISBN 978 0 573 01650 9

A Scent of Flowers. Play. James Saunders
M7 F2. A room. Fee code M

A girl has died in deep distress, and as the priest and the undertaker's men proceed with burial, she is present on stage. Imagine Zoe's first real brush with life, perplexed, afraid, alone. To whom should she turn? Her family, her friends, her priest? They offer the help they deem necessary, not that which her need demands. None of them realize that interest, concern, even love, are not the same as compassion and charity. Although it is a poignant story, the dialogue is unsentimental, often grimly comic.

♦ **A bullet mark next to a title indicates that it is new to this edition of the Guide.**

A

Schweyk in the Second World War. Play. Bertolt Brecht
Translations: William Rowlinson, music by Hanns Eisler
              Susan Davies
M12 F3. Numerous simple sets. Fee code M for play, code C for music

Brecht transposes Jaroslav Hasek's satirical 'hero' from World War I to the Prague of Hitler and Heydrich. Schweyk gets out of awkward situations in his farcical adventures by a combination of cheek and guile. Eventually he is sent to fight the Russians at Stalingrad, and on the way he meets an equally lost Hitler who asks him if he knows the way back. Interludes show Goering, Goebbels and others assuring Hitler of the loyalty and devotion of the Little Man.

The Scottish Play. Play. Graham Holliday
M6 F7. Various simple interiors. Fee code L

Michael has always harboured an ambition to direct *Macbeth*, so when he is offered the autumn production by the Shellsfoot Thespians he seizes his opportunity. He encounters problems, of course, from finding enough men, to telling *grande dame* Geraldine that he doesn't want her as Lady Macbeth, despite being offered a bribe that would pay production costs. The theatrical jinx surrounding the play extends to amateur productions and Michael's life, too. A witty, humorous play, totally true to life, which was first broadcast on BBC Radio.
ISBN 978 0 573 01679 0

The Sea. Comedy. Edward Bond
M7 F7. Extras M and F. Composite setting: a beach, a shop, a house, a cliff. Fee code M

The Sea is a comedy set in an East Coast village in 1907. The action centres around the drowning of a young man and the repercussions, emotional and political, it has on the tight, inward-looking village community.

The Seagull. Comedy. Anton Chekhov,
Various interior and exterior settings. Period turn of the 19th and 20th centuries

Versions: Martin Crimp M7 F4. Fee code M
             Michael Frayn. M8 F5. Fee code M
             David Iliffe. M7 F6. Fee code H. ISBN 978 0 573 01400 3
             Mike Poulton. M7 F6. Extras. Fee code M
             Tom Stoppard. M7 F5. Fee code M

♦ **Searching for Doctor Branovic.** Comedy. David Tristram
M3 or 4 (25-45, 30-55, elderly), F1 or 2 (25-45, elderly). Various simple settings. Fee code L

Emma is mourning the sudden, unexpected death of her husband, Joe. But all is not as it seems and, in a nearby hospital morgue, something stirs. Enter Detective Inspector Monroe – last memorably seen in *Forget-me-Knot*. The grumpy, beleaguered detective soon finds himself right in the middle of another mystery which threatens to unhinge his sanity. Throughout this highly unusual romp, the audience often know far more than the characters. But can they possibly see what's coming?

Season's Greetings. Play. Alan Ayckbourn
M5 (20, 30, 40, 60) F4 (30s). Composite setting: a hall, a dining-room, a sitting-room. Fee code M

Half a dozen relatives and friends are celebrating Christmas with Neville and Belinda. Petty, and not so petty, squabbles break out. Christmas presents are rifled, mechanical toys are set off. Hilarious highlights include a chaotically incompetent puppet show and a midnight love scene that goes wrong. A final climax leads to what momentarily appears to be a tragedy as Clive, mistaken for a looter, is shot by the trigger-happy Harvey.
ISBN 978 0 573 11401 4

Second from Last in the Sack Race. Play. Michael Birch, from the novel by David Nobbs
M20 F12, 2M or F. Can be played by M3 F2. Various simple interior and exterior settings. Fee code M

This play traces the ups and downs in the life of Henry Pratt. Born in 1935, Henry's childhood is disrupted first by war, then by the death of his mother and father. Henry is packed off to prep school and then public school and then lives with grown-up cousin Hilda. The play ends in 1953, as he begins his National Service. David Nobbs is well known as a TV writer of quality and this play was screened under the title *Life and Times of Henry Pratt*.
ISBN 978 0 573 01900 5

Second Time Around. Comedy. Derek Benfield
M1 or 2 (late 20s, mid 50s) F1 or 3 (late 20s, mid 50s). A flat. Fee code L

Bernard and Marion meet by chance twenty-two years after they were lovers. And so begins a journey of memory – their first meeting, their love for each other, their marriages, their children – and why after so long they are strangers. This a romantic comedy with moments of sadness as well as wild farce. We meet not only the younger Bernard and Marion but three other people in their lives. All the parts may be played by M1 F1 or a larger cast of M2 F3 can be accommodated.
ISBN 978 0 573 01887 9

The Secret Diary of Adrian Mole Aged 13¾. Play with music. Sue Townsend. Songs by Ken Howard and Alan Blaikley
M7 F6, doubling possible. 1 boy 2 girls. Extras. Various interior settings. Fee code M

Adapted by Sue Townsend from her bestseller, this satirical comedy of adolescent manners follows the efforts of a spotty teenager to make sense of the erratic behaviour of the adults around him. The disintegration of his parents' marriage, threats from the local bully, first love pains and spots are a series of minor tragedies he must cope with in the transition from puberty to manhood.

The Secret Lives of Henry and Alice. Comedy. David Tristram
M1 (30s-50s). F1 (30s-50s). Simple settings. Fee code L

For Henry Smith – actor, comedian, raconteur, sporting hero, business tycoon, secret agent, Casanova and acting President of the United States – life was rarely dull. For Alice Smith – housewife – life was rarely anything else. Enter Michel – tall, dark, and available. Exactly what happened next no-one's quite sure and only their pet goldfish Orca and you, will ever know the truth. This is a virtuoso piece for two versatile performers who play numerous characters as they act out their fantasies.

The Secret Love Life of Ophelia. Play. Steven Berkoff
M1 F1. Fee code L

Hamlet and Ophelia express the infinite variety of their passion in a work which takes the form of an epistolary play in verse.

The Secret Rapture. Play. David Hare
M2 (30s, 40s) F4 (20s, 30s). Various simple settings. Fee code M

In David Hare's 'greatest play' (*City Limits*) two sisters, Isobel, a serene and good person, and Marion, an ambitious Tory Junior Minister, gather at the home of their late father for his funeral. Katherine, the sisters' young, alcoholic, stepmother announces her intention of joining Isobel's design company. Reluctantly Isobel agrees and this act paves the way for tragedy and disaster involving Isobel's lover Irwin, and Marion's evangelical, earnest husband Tom.
ISBN 978 0 573 11408 3

See How They Run! Farce. Philip King
M6 (20-40, middle-age) F3 (18, 20, 30). A lounge-hall. Fee code M

The Rev. Lionel Toop's wife, Penelope, is an ex-actress. While Lionel is away Clive, an actor, calls. He invites Penelope to dine in town which is out of bounds to servicemen. He dresses in Lionel's blacks. Miss Skillon, a parishioner, sees the couple repeating one of their theatrical scenes and draws the wrong conclusion. Matters become highly complicated when Lionel arrives, followed by the Bishop of Lax and a German POW disguised as a vicar! Period 1947
ISBN 978 0 573 01403 1

Semi-Monde. Play. Noël Coward
M16 (range of ages) F12 (range of ages). A hotel lounge, a hotel bar. Fee code M

Written in 1926, *Semi-Monde* was considered too daring and was never professionally staged in Coward's lifetime; it received its London première at the Lyric Theatre in 2001. Set in a Paris hotel in the 1920s, it presents a portrait of decadence among the idle rich where a glittering array of characters, gay, straight or lesbian, indulge in illicit affairs. " … an amazing, magical evening … exquisite and daringly unexpected" Michael Coveney, *Daily Mail*. Period 1924-26

Sense and Sensibility. Play. Roger Parsley and Andy Graham, based on the novel by Jane Austen
M3 F4, may be played by M2 F3 with doubling. (Young, middle age). Various simple settings.
Fee code M. ISBN 978 0 573 01926 5

Separate Tables. Two plays. Terence Rattigan
M3 F8. A dining-room, a lounge. Fee code M. Each play fee code F when performed separately

The typical South Coast Hotel Beauregarde is peopled by the old, the lonely and the indigent. The manageress, Miss Cooper, is unable to remain aloof from their troubles. In *Table No. 1* she attempts to help John Malcolm and his ex-wife Ann, who have ruined each other, find salvation together. In *Table No. 2* Major Pollock and Miss Railton-Bell are misfits and their despair draws them together. Miss Cooper gives them the courage to face life.
ISBN 978 0 573 01404 8

Separation. Play. Tom Kempinski
M1(40) F1 (20). Split set. Fee code M. ISBN 978 0 573 01677 6

September in the Rain. Play. John Godber
M1 F1. A bare stage. Fee code M

This play, together with its companion, *Happy Jack*, is described by the author as 'autobiographical, but not in the strict sense. Both plays are about my grandparents and chronicle their lives. All the incidents are based on fact – they were the myths of my childhood.' Their marriage is explored with great pathos and humour and '... transmitted with a directness that touches the heart ...' *Guardian*

September Tide. Play. Daphne du Maurier. Revised version by Mark Rayment
M3 (20s, middle-age) F3 (20s, middle-age). A living-room. Fee code M. ISBN 978 0 573 01905 0

Serious Money. City comedy. Caryl Churchill. Songs by Ian Dury, Micky Gallacher and Chas Jankel
M14 F6, may be played by M5 F3. Extras. Various simple interior and exterior settings. Fee code M for play, code B for music

Set post-Big Bang 1980s in the Square Mile, the action centres on a takeover bid led by the ruthless Billy Corman. When cartel member Jake Todd dies amidst the amassing of a fortune, his sister, Scilla, investigates his murder, initially from curiosity but later from greed. Churchill's witty dialogue is complemented by two songs with bawdily-satiric lyrics by Ian Dury. NB. This play contains explicit language.
ISBN 978 0 573 01711 7

The Servant of Two Masters. Comedy. Adapted by David Turner and Paul Lapworth from the original by Carlo Goldoni
M8 F3. Extras. A room. Fee code M. ISBN 978 0 573 11412 0

A Servant to Two Masters. Play. Carlo Goldoni. A new adaptation by Lee Hall. From a literal translation by Gwenda Pandolfi
M6 F3. 4M extras. Various simple settings. Fee code M

This is a lively and intelligent new adaptation by Lee Hall, with a modern free text complete with extra bawdy and juicy jokes, that loses nothing of the pathos from the original. In this eighteenth-century *commedia dell'arte* Truffaldino hits on the scam of doubling his income by serving two masters without them knowing. A co-production by the RSC and the Young Vic Theatre Company, this adaptation was first performed in 1999.

◆ **A bullet mark next to a title indicates that it is new to this edition of the Guide.**

A

sex, drugs & rick 'n' noel. Play/musical. David Tristram
M3 F2. Various simple settings. Fee code L

Richard Branson isn't *the* multi–millionaire Virgin boss, but a redundant factory worker from the Black Country whose wife has just left him for another woman. He applies to do a history course at Birmingham University and meets Noel, another "mature" student with a whole different outlook on life. Together they learn about life and women but not much about history. Can be performed as a comedy, or, with the addition of a student chorus, as a musical. The music is not available from Samuel French Ltd

Shadowlands. Play. William Nicholson
M11 F2, may be played by M7 F2. 1 boy. Various simple settings. Fee code M

Nicholson's stage adaptation of his award-winning TV play relates the story of shy Oxford don and children's author C. S. Lewis and poet Joy Davidman in academic Oxford in the 1950s. Their relationship starts as an exchange of literary correspondence. When Joy arrives in Oxford her intellectual assertiveness delights Lewis but appalls his condescending fellow academics, who are further shocked when Lewis goes through a marriage of convenience with her for immigration purposes.
ISBN 978 0 573 01894 7

♦ **Shady Business**. Comedy. Robin Hawdon
M5 (20s – 40s), F2 (young). A living-room. Fee code M

Mandy and Tania are sexy but struggling nightclub dancers living in the heart of London's Soho nightlife, and they face a crisis. Will possessive club owner Big Mack find out about Mandy's affair with Gerry and set his sidekicks on them? Will anyone figure out what is going on, and will they all survive until the curtain comes down? The action doesn't slow down from beginning to end in this madcap comedy by the author of *Don't Dress for Dinner* and *Perfect Wedding*.
ISBN 978 0 573 62257 1

The Shape of Things. Play. Neil LaBute
M2 F2. Various simple settings. Fee code M

How far would you go for love? For art? What would you be willing to change? Which price might you pay? Such are the painful questions explored by Neil LaBute in this play which received its world première at the Almeida Theatre, London, in 2001. A young student drifts into an ever-changing relationship with an art major while his best friends' engagement crumbles: so unleashing a drama that peels back the skin of two modern-day relationships, exposing the raw meat and gristle that lie beneath.

The Shell Seekers. Play adapted by Terence Brady and Charlotte Bingham, from the novel by Rosamunde Pilcher
M6 F6, or M5 F5 with doubling. Various simple settings. Fee Code M

This is the story of Penelope Keeling and her family and the passion and heartbreak that have held them together for three generations. The location of the play moves between time and place beginning with Penelope's return to her Cotswold home from hospital in the present day. The story continues through the advent of three children and Penelope's desertion by her husband, with the pull of Cornwall ever present. Period: 1940s to present day
ISBN 978 0 573 11416 8

Shipwreck (from *The Coast of Utopia*). Play. Tom Stoppard
M 1 9 F7, Extras. Varioius interior and exterior settings. Period 1 8461852. Fee code M

In the second part of Tom Stoppard's trilogy the action moves from Moscow to Germany, Paris and Nice between the 1840s and 1850s
where Alexander Herzen, the civilized revolutionary for whom the word intelligentsia was formed, becomes the main character. After years of internal exile, Herzen escapes to Paris where other Russian emigres have settled but he becomes disillusioned in the wake of the Paris revolution of 1848.

Shirley Valentine. Play. Willy Russell
F1. A kitchen, a beach. Fee code M

Underneath Mrs Joe Bradshaw – 42-year-old mother of two grown-up children – there is the former Shirley Valentine longing to get out. Her feminist friend offers her a free holiday in Greece and she seizes the opportunity. Shirley, breaking out of the mould cast for her by society, is brilliantly shown with humour, warm sympathy and human insight. 'In this play [Mr Russell] touches English audiences directly in a way that no other playwright has done since the early John Osborne ... brilliantly funny ...' *The Times*.
ISBN 978 0 573 03102 1

Shock! Thriller. Brian Clemens
M4 (20s-40s) F3 (young, 30s). A converted windmill. Fee code L

Maggie lives in a converted windmill, to which her lover, Terry, and Maggie's friend Ann are coming to celebrate her birthday. Maggie has some peculiar tastes, including tape-recording the most private intimacies between herself and her lovers. This indulgence soon causes consternation among the visitors, culminating in the death of Ann's fiancé. A second horror is the discovery that Maggie has been murdered. A final twist proves the relevance of the play's title.
ISBN 978 0 573 11410 6

Shut Your Eyes and Think of England. Comedy. John Chapman and Anthony Marriott
M6 (40s-50s) F3 (young, early middle-age). A penthouse apartment. Fee code M

This hilarious, smash-hit West End comedy starred Frank Thornton and Donald Sinden. When Mr Pullen comes into the office on Saturday to finish the books for the audit he is astonished to find his employer, Sir Justin Holbrook, in the penthouse flat with a call-girl. As the day progresses and new arrivals include Lady Holbrook, Mrs Pullen and a very influential Arab sheik events lead to an impenetrable maze of confused identities.
ISBN 978 0 573 11411 3

Silas Marner. Play. Adapted by Geoffrey Beevers from the novel by George Eliot
M14 F6. Extras. May be played by M4 F3. Various simple settings. Fee code M
ISBN 978 0 573 01912 8

Silhouette. Play. Simon Brett
M5 (30, 35, middle-age) F3 (young, middle-age) or M4 F2. A sitting-room and study. Fee code M

In Act I of this ingeniously-structured thriller, Detective Inspector Bruton questions actress Celia Wallis about the murder of her husband Martin. Celia is quite obviously in the clear, but Neville Smallwood, the drunken journalist sleeping in her bed, argued with Martin shortly before the murder, and the solution to the initial puzzle seems simple. Act II takes place *before* the murder, and all our expectations, of the characters as well as of the plot, are turned on their heads.
ISBN 978 0 573 01877 6

Silly Cow. Play. Ben Elton
M3 (21, middle-age, old) F2 (young, 40s). A living-room. Fee code M

Doris Wallis, tough tabloid columnist, has just won a libel case brought by an actress she insulted. Just as she starts celebrating, things begin to go wrong. Her TV treatment is missing, her pal Sidney is out to get her for her double-crossing him, her accountant is about to grass on her ... To her shock and horror, Doris discovers that the actors she had defamed in her column can indeed act. NB. This play contains explicit language.
ISBN 978 0 573 01875 6

Sing On! Comedy musical. Rick Abbot
M4 F7. A stage. Fee code M

Here is the long-awaited sequel to Rick Abbot's hilarious *Play On!* in which the same disaster-prone theatre group find themselves in dire straits and need to do yet another show by the redoubtable Phyllis (with songs by her hobbyist-songwriter nephew Monte) to win a theatre-saving $10,000 endowment. The musical numbers have been designed so that your cast need *not* be able to sing, just carry a tune. The music for this show is available separately.
ISBN 978 0 573 69271 0

Sing Yer Heart Out for the Lads. Play. Roy Williams
M12 (early teens (2 black), early 20s (1black), late 20s, early 30s (1 black), mid 30s, late 40s, mid 50s) F2 (early 30s (1 black)). A pub. Fee code L

Saturday 7th October 2000. England v. Germany, The King George V v. The Duke of York. Keegan resigns and Barry plays a blinder. Tensions erupt in a South London pub as England lose again. A controversial play which premièred at the National Theatre, London in 2002. The play contains explicit language.

Single Spies. Double bill (**An Englishman Abroad** and **A Question of Attribution**). Alan Bennett
Fee code M as a double bill

An Englishman Abroad (originally a television play), is based on a true incident in the life of the actress Coral Browne and tells the witty and touching story of her meeting with Guy Burgess in Moscow in 1958. In *A Question of Attribution*, 'an inquiry in which the circumstances are imaginary but the pictures are real', Anthony Blunt, Surveyor of the Queen's Pictures, tries to solve the riddle of an enigmatic painting and is himself the subject of a more official investigation.
ISBN 978 0 573 01891 6

An Englishman Abroad.
M4 (20s, 40s, 50s) F1 (40s). A flat. Fee code F if performed separately

A Question of Attribution.
M5 (20s, 40s, 50s) F1 (40s). An office, a corridor. Fee code G if performed eparately

Sink the Belgrano! Play. Steven Berkoff
Large cast. Fee code L

Berkoff's play of the controversial order by the British Government to sink the Argentinian warship in the Falklands War. "A skilled and audacious piece of theatre." *Evening Standard*

Sister Mary Ignatius Explains It All For You and **The Actor's Nightmare.**

A double-bill by Christopher Durang. Fee code M as a double bill. For separate fee codes see below

Sister Mary Ignatius Explains It All For You.
M2 (30s) F3 (30s, 50s). 1 boy (8). A lecture platform. Fee code J

The play opens with a long lecture on Roman Catholicism by Sister Mary, starting conventionally but growing in morbidity and even horror as it proceeds. The lecture is interrupted by four of her ex-students, who present a religious 'pageant', then reveal how far they have strayed from her teaching. A climax is reached in an emotional statement of the truth from Diane, leading to the violence of two deaths by shooting. Playing time approximately 75 minutes

The Actor's Nightmare.
M2 (20s, 30s) F3 (20s, 30s). An empty stage. Fee code E

George wanders on stage and is met by stage manager Meg, who says he is to fill in for an actor who has had an accident. George is confused as Ellen Terry, Sarah Siddons and Henry Irving arrive, all apparently about to perform. But what in? *Private Lives? Hamlet?* Or something by Beckett? As each starts playing his or her respective part George tries valiantly to follow them, but is apparently facing the Exectioner as Thomas More in *A Man for All Seasons*.

The Sisterhood. Play. Molière, translated and adapted by R. R. Bolt
M5 (young, middle-age) F5 (young, middle-age), doubling possible. A salon in Paris. Fee code L
ISBN 978 0 573 01681 3

Sisterly Feelings. A related comedy. Alan Ayckbourn
M8 (20s, 30s, 50s, 60s, 70s) F4 (20s, 40s). A small hill. Fee code M

There are four possible versions of this play, each version a complete play in itself. Sisters Dorcas and Abigail are faced with a dilemma and decide to toss for it. The result is that one of them goes with Simon. Later Dorcas has a deliberate choice. One decision leads to a night under the canvas for Abigail, the other to a day at the races for Dorcas. The inevitable end of either choice is a wedding. ISBN 978 0 573 11420 5

The Sisters Rosensweig. Play. Wendy Wasserstein
M4 (17,40, 58) F4 (17, 40s, 50s). A sitting-room. Fee code M. ISBN 978 0 573 01908 1

Sitting Pretty. Play. Amy Rosenthal
M4 (18, 40s, 50s) F6 (20, 38, 40s, 50s, 60s). A living-room, a studio, National Gallery café. Fee code L

Unmarried sisters, in their fifties, share a London flat: Nina is brisk, dynamic and employed; Nancy is plump, self-conscious and redundant. Nancy unwittingly stumbles into modelling for a life-drawing class. Initially horrified to discover that life-models pose naked, Nancy is unexpectedly liberated by the experience. But her new confidence unsettles Nina's self-possession. The sisters move towards an inevitable confrontation as Nina faces her unhappy past and Nancy glimpses at a possible future. Period 1999. The play starred Maureen Lipman in a subsequent production. ISBN 978 0 573 01921 0

A

Situation Comedy. Comedy. Johnnie Mortimer and Brian Cooke
M3 (30s, middle-age) F3 (40s, middle-age). Composite setting: two living-rooms. Fee code M

Charles Summerskill and Arthur Grey are two sit-com writers with writer's block and a looming deadline for a new TV series. When the Summerskills invite the Greys round one evening, Arthur goes armed with his home-made pea wine and as the repellent vino flows, tempers rise and by next morning they have swapped wives. This provides an idea for a sit-com series, or at least it would if they could agree on an ending. Their frantic efforts to find one are moments of hysterical farce.

Ski Whizz. Comedy. Richard Ingham
M3 (20s, 30s) F3 (20s, 30s, middle-age). The hall of an Austrian pension. Fee code L
ISBN 978 0 573 01895 4

The Skin of Our Teeth. Play. Thornton Wilder
M5 (young,middle-age) F5 (young, middle-age). Small parts and extras. A living-room, one exterior. Fee code M

Down through the ages the Antrobus family have survived. They are indestructible. Antrobus invented the alphabet, the multiplication table, the lever and the wheel, and Mrs Antrobus invented the apron. Their beginnings are to be found in the Garden of Eden, although they speak in the accents of New Jersey. They are humanity, and whatever happens, they survive all catastrophes – by the skin of their teeth.
ISBN 978 0 573 61548 1

Skirmishes. Play. Catherine Hayes
F3 (30s, old). A bedroom. Fee code L

An old lady is dying. At her bedside sits her eldest daughter, Jean, who has nursed her throughout. When the younger sister, Rita, arrives the daughters angrily bicker and bait each other, gradually revealing the miserable unhappiness of their own lives. Jean gives vent to her feelings with biting, black humour and sarcasm, berating Rita, who has remained deaf to entreaties for help nursing the mother. The ultimate schism comes with the mother's final outburst, denouncing Jean and telling Rita all will be left to her.

A Skull in Connemara. Play. Martin McDonagh
M3 (teens-20s, 30s, 50s) F1 (70s). A cottage room. Fee code M

Mick and Mairton are gravediggers whose job is to disinter the bones of seven-year-old corpses and smash them to dust to make room for the new arrivals. Gossip has it that Mick murdered his wife, so Mick arranges that Tom, Mairton's policeman brother, should be at her disinterment. But the bones are missing. Mairton gives the game away by mentioning a locket which was buried with his wife – but Tom, desperate for promotion, turns a blind eye.

Skylight. Play. David Hare
M2 (18, 50) F1 (30). A living-room/kitchen area. Fee code M

Kyra Hollis is a dedicated teacher in a run-down east London school. Tom Sergeant is a successful businessman. When young, Kyra worked for Tom and his wife Alice, became part of the family, and then Tom's lover for six passionate years, finally severing all connections with the family when Alice discovered the affair. Now, a year after Alice's death, Tom's son Edward unexpectedly arrives at Kyra's flat seeking help for his father who cannot cope. Tom also visits Kyra but what is it he seeks?
ISBN 978 0 573 01876 3

Slapstick Tragedy. Tennessee Williams

The Gnädiges Fräulein. Tragicomedy

M3 (old) F3 (middle-age). Porch and exterior of a frame cottage. Fee code M if performed as *Slapstick Tragedy* or G if performed alone

The Fräulein earns her keep in the bunkhouse for 'transient residents' by trying to catch the fish thrown up by hurricanes, but is frustrated by the jealousy of the Cocaloony, a bird of prey rather like a giant pelican. This and other aspects of the interplay between the strange and odd-looking characters form a nightmarish fantasy open to many different forms of interpretation veering between the comic and the tragic.

The Mutilated. Play

M9 (middle-age) F4 (50s). Extras. A bedroom, with several other skeletal sets. Fee code M if performed as *Slapstick Tragedy* or G if performed alone

Together with *The Gnädiges Fräulein* (q.v.) this forms a double-bill known as *Slapstick Tragedy*. It is Christmas Eve and the carollers are singing. In and around a seedy New Orleans hotel two whores, one a shoplifter, the other morbidly sensitive about having had a breast removed, quarrel and make up in their wretched companionship. The implication is that all of us suffer in one way or another.

Sleuth. Play. Anthony Shaffer
M2 (30s, 50s). A living-room. Fee code M

Your programme for this play will list five names for five roles, but the actual cast will be two, for no-one is ever what he seems in this brilliant whodunit, where every event is bizarre. The scene is set in a beautiful English country house owned by a famous mystery writer. A young guest arrives and they begin a convivial round of scotch and dialogue. Suddenly the host says 'I understand you want to marry my wife' and from that moment the two are locked in mortal combat.

A Slight Hangover. Comedy. Ian Ogilvy
M4 (early 30s, middle age, 70s) F2 (26, 50s). A terrace. Fee code M. ISBN 978 0 573 01964 7

A Small Family Business. Play. Alan Ayckbourn
M7 (20s-40s, 70s) F6 (16, 20s-50s). Composite setting. Fee code M

When Jack, honest and upright, takes over as managing director of the family furniture business, he finds that his managerial skills are no match for the wholesale fraud, deceit and theft which he uncovers both in the business and amongst his family. He succumbs almost at once to blackmail because of his daughter, but this is only the first in a series of moral compromises he is forced to make.
ISBN 978 0 573 01669 1

◆ **A bullet mark next to a title indicates that it is new to this edition of the Guide.**

The Small Hours. Play. Francis Durbridge
M5 (young, 30s-50s) F3 (30s). An aircraft, a living-room. Fee code M

What do a Koala bear, a devious chef, and an emerald necklace have in common? Carl Houston, Sussex hotelier, nearly loses his life finding out in this thriller of international intrigue which bears all the Durbridge hallmarks of suspense, mystery and murder and which enjoyed a successful national tour in 1991 starring Patrick Mower. '... well-crafted with a proper sense of dramatic climaxes and some very good scenes ... It all adds up to a very good evening's theatre ...' *Birmingham Post*
ISBN 978 0 573 01897 8

Smelling a Rat. Play. Mike Leigh
M3 (young, 30, middle-age) F2 (young, 30s). A bedrom. Fee code M

Loathsome *nouveau-riche* tycoon Rex Weasel returns unexpectedly from holiday. When he hears his underling, the garrulous Vic and his wife, coming in to check on the flat as arranged, Rex hides in a cupboard to eavesdrop on the pair, who later also hide in another cupboard as Rex's near-catatonic son and lisping girlfriend arrive in search of sex (which is never realized). Various home truths spill out whilst these 'skeletons' are hiding.

Snake in the Grass. Play. Alan Ayckbourn
F3. A garden. Fee code M

Miriam has cared for her father with the help of a creepily polite nurse, Alice. On Father's death, Miriam's older sister, Annabel, comes home after over thirty years in Tasmania to find Daddy has left the bulk of his fortune to her. Alice complains to Annabel that Miriam has sacked her and is intent upon blackmail, having evidence, she says, that Miriam did away with the old man. Scatty Miriam and tough Annabel join forces against Alice and the blackmailer's body is soon hurtling down the well ...
ISBN 978 0 573 03022 2

The Sneeze. Plays and stories by Anton Chekov, translated and adapted by Michael Frayn
M4 F3, minimum cast. Extras 2M. Various simple settings. Fee code M. (Please apply to Samuel French Ltd for details of the fee codes for individual items)

This is a marvellous collection of four one-act comic 'vaudevilles' together with four adapted short stories, with Michael Frayn's fresh, idiomatic and playable translations staying close to the spirit of the original. 'Frayn's well chosen and smoothly translated *melange* comes from recognizing in some of these characters similarities with characters one encounters in the later masterpieces.' *Daily Telegraph*

So Long Life. Play. Peter Nichols
M2 (30, 55) F4 (late 20s, 40, 60, 85). A living-room. Fee code M

Bristol, 1995. It is Alice's eighty-fifth birthday – an occasion for celebration. But like many family gatherings, it is also an occasion for parading long-held resentments, as her children attempt to persuade her to relinquish her independence and move to a home. But Alice has other plans ... As the battles rage over her head, Alice's consciousness drifts, time shifts, and the past and present merge. The result is a skilful distillation of a family Sunday, comic and ghastly, strange and yet familiar.

So What Do We Do about Henry? Play. Charlotte Hastings
M3 (30s, 60) F5 (25, 30, 50, 60). A cottage living-room. Fee code L
ISBN 978 0 573 11407 6

The Soft September Air. Play. Charlotte Hastings
M4 (21, middle-age) F6 (young, late 20s, 30, 58, 60). A living-room, a bar, a casualty department.
Fee code L. ISBN 978 0 573 11423 6

♦ **Sold.** Play. John Godber
M4 F8 or M2 F4. Various simple settings. Fee code M

Ray and Jack are journalists investigating "the new slave trade": people trafficking. Ray pays Moldovan prostitute Anja to tell her story, and is soon attracted to her, planning to rescue her from the London brothel and bring her back to Hull. His wife and daughter struggle to accept her into their lives. Written as part of Hull's Wilberforce celebrations, *Sold* serves as a stark reminder that slavery remains a critical issue in 21st century Britain.
"A testament to Godber's determination to break new ground." *Guardian*

♦ **Some Girls**. Play. Neil Labute
M2 F3. Fee Code M

Your career as a writer is blossoming; your beautiful, young, fiancée is waiting to get married and rush off to Cancun by your side, so what is your natural reaction? Well, if you're a man, it's probably to get nervous and start calling up old girlfriends. So begins a single man's odyssey through four hotel bedrooms as he flies across the United States in search of the perfect woman (whom he has already broken up with). (Available in the British Isles only)

Some Sunny Day. Play. Martin Sherman
M4 (20s, 30s, 50s) F2 (40s). A sitting-room and hallway. Fee code M

Cairo, 1942. As war rages in the desert, cultures collide in the city and six individuals struggle to come to terms with love, lust and fate in an alien country. In a *melange* of Mozart, Carmen Miranda, Vera Lynn, Dixieland and cries from the minarets as the muezzins call the men to prayer, this witty and audacious play inhabits a world where everyone has something to hide and anyone may be a spy.

♦ **Some Voices**. Play. Joe Penhall
M1. Fee Code M

Some Voices focuses on Ray, a young schizophrenic trying to re-assimilate after a spell in a mental hospital. He is sent to live with his overworked brother, where he is happy until he falls in love. When Ray finds himself increasingly frustrated by a maladjusted community and an illness he'll never control, events spiral towards inevitable tragedy.

Someone Waiting. Play. Emlyn Williams
M4 (20, 40, 50) F5 (30s, 40, 60). A drawing-room. Fee code M

Someone Who'll Watch Over Me. Play. Frank McGuinness
M3 (young, elderly). A bare cell. Fee code M

An Englishman, an Irishman and an American are locked up together in a cell in the Middle East. As victims of political action, powerless to initiate change, what can they do? How do they live and survive? Frank McGuinness explores the daily crises endured by hostages whose strength comes from communication, both subtle and mundane, from humour, wit and faith.

Something to Remember You By. Play. Jimmie Chinn
M2 (30s, 40s) F3 (30s, 40s, 50s). Various simple settings. Fee code M. ISBN 978 0 573 01872 5

Something's Burning. Comedy. Eric Chappell
M2 (late 30s-early 40s, 50s) F3 (late 20s, late 30s, early 40s). A drawing-room and terrace garden. Fee code M. ISBN 978 0 573 01890 9

Son of Man. Play. Dennis Potter
M15 F2. Extras. Various simple settings on an open stage. Fee code L

Here Jesus is portrayed as a man agonized by the feeling of divinity within him, and with all a man's capacity for suffering and pain. The play also examines the historical and political situation in which the events occurred. Very simple to stage and suitable for production on stage or in church. Period New Testament
ISBN 978 0 573 16004 2

Sorry, I Love You ... Play. John Goodrum
M2 (30s) F1 (30s). Various simple interior and exterior settings. Fee code L
ISBN 978 0 573 01987 6

Speed-the-Plow. Play. David Mamet
M2 (40s) F1 (20). Gould's office, Gould's home. Fee code M

Produced at the National Theatre in 1989 after a successful run in New York, this play is a satirical and sparklingly funny vision of Hollywood back-stabbing. It centres around Charlie Fox, a producer, and Bobby Gould, studio head of production, and a major film deal involving a well-known actor. It is through the language that Mamet depicts the self-doubts and vulnerabilty that lies behind the self-congratulatory back-slapping. Fast-paced, full of witty one-liners and guaranteed to keep the audience mesmerized.

Spider's Web. Play. Agatha Christie
M8(30-50, 60) F2 (30). 1 girl (12). A drawing-room. Fee code M

When a murder occurs in Clarissa's drawing-room she suspects young step-daughter Pippa. Things are not helped by the imminent arrival of husband Henry with a VIP in tow who might take a dim view of bodies in the drawing-room. However, by the time Henry gets home, the murderer has been unmasked and all is normal, so normal that Henry is utterly unable to believe Clarissa when she explains exactly why there are no refreshments ready for their honoured guest.
ISBN 978 0 573 01427 7

Spokesong. Play with music. Stewart Parker. Music by Jimmy Kennedy
M4 (young, elderly) F2 (young). Composite interior. Fee code M

Set in and around a bicycle shop in Belfast, Northern Ireland, Frank believes that all the world's transportation problems can be solved if people simply switch to the bicycle. Songs are used to comment upon the action. The bicycle and the shop become a metaphor about the problems in Northern Ireland and, indirectly, about the problems of modern civilization. Period 1970s and the eighty years preceding.

Spoonface Steinberg. Play. Lee Hall
F1. A bare stage. Fee code H

Lee Hall's extraordinary, award-winning play about faith, love and the meaning of life was first broadcast on Radio 4 in 1997 to unprecedented acclaim. A monologue by an autistic eight-year-old girl who is dying of cancer, it is at turns funny, intensely moving and profound. "... from the first, it plunges us into the puzzle of the autistic mind and makes us experience it as if it were our own." *Financial Times* "A hard, sad, beautiful play." *Sunday Times*

Spring and Port Wine. Comedy. Bill Naughton
M4 (18, 23, 30, 50) F4 (19, 25, middle-age, 47). Composite setting. Fee code M

Rafe Crompton is not a stern man but has such unswerving integrity that his family is forced to hide slight peccadilloes from him. His daughter Hilda particularly resents this and her refusal to eat a herring which is placed before her at dinner makes the situation explosive. The family is almost broken up before Rafe is made to see the dangers in his attitudes, and they are reunited in an atmosphere more progressive and tolerant.
ISBN 978 0 573 01550 2

◆ **Spygame.** Comedy-thriller. Bettine Manktelow
M3 (middle age) F4 (youngish, middle age). A lounge. Fee code L

An intense web of deceit, intrigue and secrets from the author of *Curtain Up On Murder* and *Murder Weekend*. Prospective contestants for a TV reality show gather in a country house, aiming to win a large cash prize, but only if they survive the rigours of the ultimate Spygame. This excellent play offers seven good acting roles and will grip your audience until the totally unexpected ending.
ISBN 978 0 573 11424 3

St Joan of the Stockyards. Play. Bertolt Brecht. Translated by Frank Jones, music by Dessau
M11 F3. Extras. Chorus. Numerous simple interior and exterior settings. Fee code M for play, code C for music

In the stockyards and commercial exchanges of modern Chicago, Salvation Army girl Johanna Dark imagines that the meat-packer king Pierpont Mauler is going to save the falling market and prevent unemployment. She helps the workers to organize a general strike, and Mauler is persuaded to lead the meat ring out of its troubles. Johanna, desperately ill, is canonized by Mauler for her work among the poor, and she vainly denounces the class system as she dies.

◆ **A bullet mark next to a title indicates that it is new to this edition of the Guide.**

A

Stage Struck. Play. Simon Gray
M3 (20, 30, middle-age) F1 (30). A living-room. Fee code M

Robert's conniving wife concocts a plot to obtain grounds necessary for divorce involving the use of a private detective. Robert, recalling his days as a stage manager, works out a bizarre method of teaching them a lesson and the final moments give several grim twists to events as the 'little game' becomes stark reality.
ISBN 978 0 573 11414 1

Stages. Play. David Storey
M1 (57) F4 (20s, 30, 56). A bare stage. Fee code M

Stags and Hens (the Re-Mix). Comedy. Willy Russell
M6 (one non-speaking) F5. The ladies' and gents' toilets in a dance hall. Fee code M

Set in the ladies' and gents' toilets of a tacky Liverpool club where Dave and Linda are holdig their respective stag and hen parties. Dave gets legless while Linda meets up with ex-lover Peter whose worldly wisdom leaves Linda uncertain whether to pursue an unsuitable marriage. An exuberantly cynical play which is also a perceptive study of working-class misogyny.
ISBN 978 0 573 01609 7

Staircase. Play. Charles Dyer
M2 (middle-age), 1M voice. A barber's shop. Fee code M. ISBN 978 0 573 04011 5

Star Quality. Play. Noël Coward. Adapted by Christopher Luscombe
M5 (late 20s, 30s, 50s) F4 (50s, any age). Various simple settings. Fee code M

In his wickedly funny final play, Noël Coward takes us behind the scenes of a new West End production. Conjuring up an authentic backstage world of talent and treachery, Coward creates a gallery of unforgettable characters: temperamental leading lady, ruthless director, jaded old troupers and, caught somewhere between them all, innocent young playwright. What emerges from the mayhem is a startling evocation of that most elusive gift of all – star quality.

The Star-Spangled Girl. Comedy. Neil Simon
M2 (20s) F1 (young). A duplex studio apartment. Fee code M

This fast-moving, hilarious comedy deals with two earnest, fiercely dedicated young men who endure near-starvation to put out a 'protest' magazine in San Francisco, and the all-American girl, Sophie, who moves in next door. She is convinced they are editing a dangerously subversive magazine, and finds that the wrong man is pressing his attentions on her. Happily this situation is reversed in time, as love and politics blend delightfully in a bubbling series of funny happenings. **(Slightly restricted)**

Steaming. Play. Nell Dunn
M1 F6. The Turkish rest-room of a public baths. Fee code M

A

Steel Magnolias. Play. Robert Harling
F6 (19, 25, 40s-60s). Beauty parlour. Fee code M

Hilarious and touching, this play for six women is set in a beauty parlour in Louisiana. Through four scenes spanning three years the staff and customers engage in small-town gossip but we see a deep strength and purposefulness emerge when Shelby – a diabetic – dies following a kidney transplant operation. '...warm-hearted and sentimental ... ' *Guardian*
ISBN 978 0 573 13010 6

Stepping Out. Comedy. Richard Harris
M1(40s) F9 (1 Black or Asian) (19, 35-50s). Optional extras. A church hall. Fee code M

Stepping Out, which enjoyed a hugely successful West End run and won *Evening Standard* Best Comedy Award for 1984, is a warm and very funny play about the lives of a group of women (and one man) attending a weekly tap-dance class in a dingy North London church hall. As the play progresses, the class's dancing improves to such an extent that by the climax, a grand charity show performance, they have been transformed into triumphant tappers, worthy of any chorus line.
ISBN 978 0 573 11415 1

Stevie. Play. Hugh Whitemore, from the works of Stevie Smith
M1(youngish) F2 (middle-age to elderly). A sitting-room. Fee code M

The play follows the life and career of the poetess, Stevie Smith. Stevie's tragicomic life is portrayed by means of 'naturalistic' dialogue scenes, by her own reminiscences and comments, and by numerous examples of her poems, spoken mainly by herself but sometimes by the Man who also plays several parts. The passage of time extends from the 1950s to the 1960s, up to her death at the age of sixty-nine, time changes in the simple set being indicated by lighting cues.
ISBN 978 0 573 11418 2

The Steward of Christendom. Play. Sebastian Barry
M5 (13, 18, 20s-30s, 50, 70s) F4 (17, 20-32, 50s) A bare room. Fee code M

Set in Baltinglass, Co. Dublin, in about 1932, *The Steward of Christendom* sees Lear-like Thomas Dunne, ex-Chief Superintendent of the Dublin Metropolitan Police, trying to break free of history and himself. The play took London by storm when it premièred at the Royal Court Theatre Upstairs in March 1995. Since then it has won Sebastian Barry numerous awards. 'An authentic masterpiece ... I venture to suggest that not even O'Casey or Synge wrote better than this.' *Guardian*. Period c. 1932

Straight and Narrow. Comedy. Jimmie Chinn
M4 F3. 1 female voice. A living-room. Fee code M

Nicholas Lyndhurst and Carmel McSharry starred in the smash-hit West End production of this sharply-observed comedy of family life. The cosy domesticity of lovers Bob and Jeff is threatened. Can Bob's family – Lois and Bill, Nona and Arthur and matriarch Vera – rescue the situation? And will Bob be able to tell seemingly ignorant Vera that the straight and narrow is not for her favourite little boy ... ?
ISBN 978 0 573 01902 9

The Straits. Play. Gregory Burke
M3 (15, 16) F1 (16). Various simple settings. Fee code L

A

Rosia Bay, Gibraltar, 1982. Doink, Jock and Darren have the longest, hottest summer ahead; yomping, watching pirate copies of *Rambo* and fighting the local lads over a lucrative fleet of octopus that have just hit the Rock. With Darren's fit older sister Tracy to sell the bounty, their dominance of Rosia Bay seems assured. But for the sons and daughters of the British Forces, another war beginning in the South Atlantic will soon bring a dark heart to their world ...

The Strange Case of Dr Jekyll and Mr Hyde. Play. David Edgar, based on the story by Robert Louis Stevenson
M8 F3, or M7 F3 with doubling. 6 children. Interior and exterior settings. Fee code M

The famous tale of Dr Jekyll, the outwardly respectable and virtuous man whose darker side is given terrifying life in the form of murderous Mr Hyde, has been vividly and thrillingly adapted for the stage. Jekyll and Hyde are played by two actors; as a result, the divisions in Jekyll's character are presented in a compelling and truly theatrical style.

Strangers on a Train. Play. Craig Warner, based on the novel by Patricia Highsmith
M5 (20s, middle age) F2 (20, middle age). Composite set. Fee code L

1950s America. Two strangers meet on a train: Guy Haines, an architect, and Charles Bruno, a charming but mother-fixated playboy. Because they're strangers they "can say anything they like". Bruno proposes the perfect murder: he will murder Guy's unfaithful wife, and Guy will murder Bruno's much-hated father. Amused, Guy leaves never imagining that Bruno was serious. But Bruno was serious and when he kills Guy's wife, he expects Guy to fulfil his part of the proposition. ISBN 978 0 573 01972 2

A Streetcar Named Desire. Play. Tennessee Williams
M6 (28, 30, 35) F6 (25, 30, 1 Black, 1 Mexican). Composite setting. Fee code M

Blanche DuBois comes to live in the slums of Elysian Fields, New Orleans, with her sister Stella and Stella's husband Stanley Kowalski. Blanche enrages Stanley by her airs and affectations, her perpetual reminiscences about her genteel past and her open distaste for his coarse vitality. When he discovers that all her refinement is a mere façade, he has no compunction in destroying Blanche's only hope of salvation, which is to marry his friend Mitch.

Strictly Murder. Play. Brian Clemens
M3 (30 to middle age) F2 (young, 40s). A rustic cottage in Provence. Fee Code M

An English couple, Peter and Suzy, are living in idyllic isolation, far, it seems, from the rumblings of the coming war. However, their peace is shattered when Suzy discovers she has been betrayed: Peter is not the man he claims to be. Her life is thrown into turmoil as the possibility arises that Peter may in fact be a ruthless killer on the run. ...Lies, subterfuge and murder make this fast-moving thriller a dark and disturbing rollercoaster. Period 1939.
ISBN 978 0 573 11429 8

♦ **A bullet mark next to a title indicates that it is new to this edition of the Guide.**

Suburb of Babylon. Three inter-linked plays. Hugh Leonard
Cast as below. Composite setting: a hall and a living-room. (The basic set remains the same in each play with perhaps a few modifications in the third.) Fee code M (for complete play)

A Time of Wolves and Tigers
M1(40s). M1 or F1 voice only

Nothing Personal
M2 (30s, 40) F1 (30s)

The Last of the Last of the Mohicans
M3 (40, middle-age) F2 (30s, middle-age). M1 or F1 voice only
ISBN 978 0 573 11426 7

Suddenly at Home. Play. Francis Durbridge
M4 (30s-50s) F4 (20s, 30s). A living-room. Fee code M

When Glenn Howard decided to get rid of his wealthy wife he worked out a complicated but seemingly foolproof plan which would not only keep him in the clear but involve his wife's former lover, detective-story writer Sam Blaine. The plan, however, depends on the co-operation of another person, Sheila Wallis, and with the unexpected arrival on the scene of the formidable Remick, things begin to fall apart.
ISBN 978 0 573 01452 9

Sugar Daddies. Play. Alan Ayckbourn
M2 (late 70s) F3 (early 20s, early 30s, mid 60s). An upstairs flat. Fee code M

After a hit and run accident, naïve country girl Sasha comes to the aid of ex-villain Val who is using a bogus identity as an ex-policeman. Sasha befriends Val and welcomes him into her home; overcome by her generosity and childlike innocence, he showers Sasha with lavish gifts whilst his rival Ashley, knowing of Val's sordid past, seeks to protect Sasha from this potential danger. "… provokes a surprising deal of thought and a great measure of laughter *en route.*" *Daily Telegraph*

The Sugar Syndrome. Play. Lucy Prebble
M2 (22, 38) F2 (17, 45). Non-naturalistic simple settings. Fee code L

"I like the internet. I like that way of talking to people. It's honest. It's a place where people are free to say anything they like. And most of what they say is sex." Dani's on a mission. She's seventeen, skives college, hates her parents and prefers life on-line. What she's looking for is someone who is honest and direct. Instead she finds a man twice her age, who thinks she is an eleven-year-old boy. The play premièred at the Royal Court Theatre, London, in 2003.

The Suicide. Satirical comedy. Nikolai Erdman, translated by Peter Tegel
M11 F5. Extras. Various interior and exterior settings. Fee code M

Summer. Play. Hugh Leonard
M4 (18-24, middle-age) F4 (17-23, middle-age). A hillside. Fee code M. ISBN 978 0 573 11431 5

Summer and Smoke. Play. Tennessee Williams
M8 (young, 30, middle-age) F7 (young, 20s, middle-age). 1 girl 1 boy. A park with fountain, a rectory parlour, an office, an arbour. All sets are skeletal on an open stage. Fee code M

Alma, a nervous, ardent spinster, falls in love with John, a dissolute medical student. Though they attempt mutually to bridge the gap in their different natures this proves impossible, even though each in a sense converts the other. John marries a different, more earthy, girl; in the final scene Alma returns to the fountain and picks up a travelling salesman.

Summer End. Play. Eric Chappell
M1 F4. A bedsitting-room in a retirement home. Fee code M. ISBN 978 0 573 01995 1

Summit Conference. Play. Robert David MacDonald
M1 (19) F2. A room. Fee code M

Theatrical invention brings together the mistresses of Hitler and Mussolini in 1941 and, in daringly controversial repartee, they assume the roles of their dictator lovers. An intense atmosphere of political and sexual oppression parallels seemingly innocent worship of movie stars, but reveals the evils of twentieth century idolatry, charting the perverse, cold logic of the Nazi party. Glenda Jackson and Georgina Hale starred in the London production. '... wonderful political comedy ... develops the blueprint to say serious and pertinent things about power, lust and nationalistic endeavour.' *Financial Times*

The Sunshine Boys. Comedy. Neil Simon
M5 (30s, 70s) F2. A flat, an office, an hotel room. Fee code M

An ex-vaudeville team, Al Lewis and Willie Clark, in spite of playing together for forty-three years, have a natural antipathy to one another. CBS-TV wants to make a 'History of Comedy' series which will of course include their act. Will has been doing TV commercials and Al has been happily retired, but they get back together for the series, only for Al to start picking on Willie again. (**Slightly restricted**)
ISBN 978 0 573 61596 2

The Surgeon of Honour. Play. Pedro Calderón de la Barca. Translated by Gwynne Edwards
M13 F4. Various simple settings. Fee code M

Gutierre is obsessed with the need to preserve his honour and reputation. He marries Doña Mencia, unaware at first that she had been courted by the King's brother. Gutierre is convinced that Mencia is unfaithful and engages a bloodletter to bleed her to death; the King, suspecting his guilt, forces him to marry a previously-abandoned sweetheart. Gutierre warns that he has already been the "surgeon" of his honour and could be again ... Period 17th century

Sweeney Todd. Melodrama. C. G. Bond
M8 (young, middle-age, elderly) F3 (middle-age, elderly). Extras. Standing set. Fee code M

In this version of the old melodrama Todd has some grounds for his nefarious activities in that his wife was raped by the Judge, and his daughter abandoned, while he himself was deported on a false charge. He returns to avenge his family, accompanied by a sea captain, Anthony, whose life he has saved. Todd sets up with Mrs Lovett and provides her with fillings for her pies. He proceeds with his vengeful plans, but the outcome is bitterly ironic. Period early nineteenth century
ISBN 978 0 573 01547 2

Sweeney Todd the Barber. Melodrama. Brian J. Burton, from George Dibdin Pitt's Victorian version of the legendary drama
M10 F6. Extras. Composite setting. Fee code L. ISBN 978 0 573 11405 2

Sweeney Todd, the Demon Barber of Fleet Street. Victorian Melodrama. Austin Rosser, based upon the original by George Dibdin Pitt
M6 (10, young, 50s, 60) F3 (young, 20s, 40s). 4 small parts: M3, 1 boy. Composite setting: two rooms and an alley. (Can be performed in separate settings.) Fee code H. ISBN 978 0 573 01516 8

Sweet Bird of Youth. Play. Tennessee Williams
M15 (young, 20s, 30s, middle-age) F7 (young, old). A bedroom, a terrace, a cocktail lounge and palm garden. Fee code M

Chance Wayne, an ambitious hustler, has taken up with a fading movie star hoping this might help his own career in films. She accompanies him to his home town to see a girl with whom he had had an affair, and still loves. Unknown to him, he had infected the girl with venereal disease. Learning of his arrival, the girl's malevolent father, Boss, plans to have the young man castrated.

Sweet Panic. Play. Stephen Poliakoff
M3 (19, 30s, 40) F3 (22, late 30s). A room, other simple settings. Fee code M

A child psychologist's understanding of contemporary life is brought into question when she finds herself stalked by the mother of one of her young clients. Casting an acute eye over the changing face of urban life, Stephen Poliakoff's vibrant and compelling play pits the two women against each other in a battle for the soul of the city.

Sweet Revenge. Play. Francis Durbridge
M6 (30s-middle-age) F3 (30s-40s). A living-room. Fee code M. ISBN 978 0 573 01904 3

Sword Against the Sea. Arthur Feinsod, adapted from W.B. Yeats' *Cuculain* plays.
M5 F5. Simple settings. Fee Code L

Sylvia's Wedding. Play. Jimmie Chinn
M3 (32, 50s-60s) F4 (30s, 50s-60s). Three rooms in a terraced house. Fee code M

Table Manners. Play. Alan Ayckbourn
M3 F3. A dining-room. Fee code M. See the entry under *The Norman Conquests*
ISBN 978 0 573 01573 1

Take Away the Lady. Play. Jimmie Chinn
M3 (40s, elderly) F4 (30s, 40). A drawing-room. Fee code L

◆ **A bullet mark next to a title indicates that it is new to this edition of the Guide.**

Taking Care of Baby. Play. Dennis Kelly
M7 (30s, 50s) F6 (30s, 40s, 50s) 1 voice. Various simple settings. Fee code L

This tale of a mother accused and convicted of the deaths of her two young babies is a horrific yet powerful. By adopting a form commonly associated with verbatim theatre, the subject is imbued with a clarity that is at once both unrelenting and utterly engaging, as it slowly emerges that these events are not truth at all, but Kelly masquerading theatrical illusion as truth. What unfolds is a bleak yet tender exploration of grief, exploitation, and the innate hypocrisies of reportage.

Taking Sides. Play. Ronald Harwood
M4 (24, 35-50s, 60) F2 (20s, 32). An office. Fee code M

Wilhelm Furtwängler (1886-1954) was one of the great conductors of this century. It was his misfortune to have been at the height of his career when the National Socialists came to power. While many of his fellow artists were either forced to leave Germany or emigrated as an act of protest, Furtwängler remained. After the war he was accused of having served the Nazi regime. Period 1946

Taking Steps. Farce. Alan Ayckbourn
M4 (25-40s) F2 (20s, 30s). A lounge, bedroom, attic, hall and stairs. Fee code M

Roland is considering buying an old Victorian House. In the house are his solicitor and the vendor; Roland's wife, who is considering leaving him; her brother; and later the brother's fiancée. In the course of one hectic night and morning, with continual running up and down stairs, these characters try to sort themselves out. All this takes place in a highly ingenious and original setting, in which all the rooms, passages and stairs are on a single level.
ISBN 978 0 573 11425 0

A Tale of Two Cities. A theatrical adaptation of Charles Dickens' novel by Mark Fitzgibbons
M16 F10. The courtyard of an English inn. Fee code M

A Tale of Two Cities. Play. Matthew Francis, adapted from the novel by Charles Dickens
Large mixed cast. Various simple interior and exterior settings. Fee code M

This moving and exciting adaptation of the story of Sydney Carton and Charles Darnay, the English lawyer and French aristocrat caught up inextricably in the violence and bloodshed of the French Revolution, is played on a simple set, with numerous lighting changes and sound effects, minimal props and vivid stage images, making this an atmospheric, fast-moving and satisfyingly theatrical experience which is always true to the original. Period 1780s
ISBN 978 0 573 01942 5

The Talented Mr Ripley. Play. Phyllis Nagy, adapted from the novel by Patricia Highsmith
M5 (teenager, 25, middle-age) F2 (young, middle-age). Various simple settings. Fee code M

When Tom Ripley is sent to Italy to track down Richard Greenleaf, the errant son of a wealthy American couple, his mission takes on a sinister twist as their lives become inextricably entwined. Phyllis Nagy's stage adaptation of Patricia Highsmith's novel explores the mind of one of crime fiction's great anti-heroes; an intelligent, suave and charming psychopath whose amorality is at the centre of a plot about duplicity and murder. Period early 1950s

Tales from Hollywood. Play. Christopher Hampton
M14 F6. Extras. Various interior and exterior settings. Fee code M

Evening Standard Best Comedy Award winner, this evokes the vagaries of Tinseltown from the late thirties to 1950 McCarthyism, which welcomed the multi-talents of German émigré writers fleeing Nazism and employed them as screenwriters for the major film companies. Mixing fact and fantasy, Hampton presents comical, witty and often moving vignettes of life through the eyes of Austro-Hungarian playwright Ödön von Horvàth whom he sends to America with the Mann and Marx brothers, Garbo, Weismuller, Brecht and many others.
ISBN 978 0 573 11433 5

Tales of King Arthur. Play. John Chambers
M24 F14. Various medieval settings. Fee code M

Tracing Arthur's life from his boyhood, through his magical accession to the throne by means of the sword in the stone, his romance with Guinevere and his search for the Holy Grail, to his death at the hands of the wicked Mordred, *Tales of King Arthur* tells its story clearly and economically, provides good acting opportunities for a large cast and can be staged as simply or as lavishly as circumstances allow.
ISBN 978 0 573 05110 4

The Talking Cure. Play. Christopher Hampton
M4 (29, 30, 50) F3 (18, 20s) 2 girls. Extras.Various settings. Fee code M

This play deals with the early years of C.G. Jung and his decision to experiment, using Freud's controversial new method of psychoanalysis, with a young Russian patient, Sabina Spielrein. The success of the experiment and the blossoming of his relationship with Sabina inaugurates, haunts and ultimately poisons Jung's friendship with Freud; and the ideas and conflicts which engulf the three of them embody the destructive forces which are to overwhelm the disastrous century ahead. Period 1904 -1913

Tartuffe. Comedy. Molière. Translated by Christopher Hampton
M8 (young, middle-age) F5 (young, 30, elderly). Interiors. Fee code M

This translation of Molière's classic depiction of hypocrisy in action into colloquial, English blank verse, was commissioned by the Royal Shakespeare Company and was first presented at The Pit, London in 1983, with Antony Sher as Tartuffe, Alison Steadman as Elmire, and Nigel Hawthorne as Orgon.

Tartuffe. Comedy. Molière. Adapted by Miles Malleson
M8 F4. Interiors. Fee code H. ISBN 978 0 573 01437 6

A Taste of Honey. Play. Shelagh Delaney
M3 (20s, 1 Black, 30) F2 (17, 40). Composite setting. Fee code M

Jo, the teenage heroine who lives in a filthy tenement bedsitter, is deserted by her nagging peroxided mother, who is unaware that her daughter is pregnant by a black sailor. Jo's greatest fear is that her illegitimate baby might be mentally deficient like her own father. To soothe, clean and cook for her is Geof, an effeminate art student, with whom she makes a temporary home. Bruised by insensitivity and rejection, the boy and girl find a very real comfort in each other. Period 1958

A

Teechers. Classroom comedy. John Godber
M1 F2, playing 21 characters. A bare stage. Fee code M

Fast-moving, inventive and highly entertaining, *Teechers* vigorously evokes life at a modern Comprehensive, using the format of an end-of-term play to sketch a drama teacher's progress through two terms of recalcitrant classes, cynical colleagues and obstructive caretakers until he departs for the safer waters of a private school. The play runs the gamut of emotions, climaxing with the final scene which gives a poignant edge to the comedy. '... the style is loud, cheerful, butch and pointedly political.' *Time Out*
ISBN 978 0 573 01678 3

Temptation. Play. Václav Havel. Translated by George Theiner
M9 F6 or M6 F3, with doubling. Various interior and exterior settings. Fee code M

No longer satisfied with science, Dr Foustka experiments with necromancy, resulting in the appearance of Fistula, a repugnant tramp who offers Foustka three choices. The game of bluff and double bluff which ensues due to his inability to resist and the final ironic revelation of Fistula's identity provide a powerful and witty satire of human pride and give a perspective on life in Eastern Europe as only Havel could.

Ten Times Table. Play. Alan Ayckbourn
M6 (young, 40s, 50s) F4 (young, 30s, 40s, old). A ballroom. Fee code M

The leading lights of the village have decided to hold a pageant of local history based on a somewhat vague event. On the committee is a young left-wing schoolteacher who decides to turn the project into a rally for proletarian revolution. Committee meetings become symbolic battlefields for conflicting views and the event itself turns into a violent confrontation between the two extremes with cataclysmic results. The original production starred Paul Eddington and Julia McKenzie.
ISBN 978 0 573 01531 1

Ten Tiny Fingers, Nine Tiny Toes. Play. Sue Townsend
M5 (30s) F6 (30s), doubling possible. Various simple settings. Fee code M

In the futuristic world of 2001 babies are chosen, bought and paid for before conception. Lucinda and her husband have carefully chosen a blonde-haired, blue-eyed government baby girl. Towards the end of the pregnancy they discover that she has a defect – she has only nine toes – and will be taken at birth for government research. Lucinda joins forces with Dot, who is a lower-class citizen and therefore forbidden to breed, to defeat both State and husbands.

Tess of the d'Urbervilles. Play. Michael Fry. Adapted from the novel by Thomas Hardy. Music by Anthony Feldman
M15 F19. Can be played by M3 F4 with doubling. Various simple settings. Fee code M (play) code C (music)

All the tragic majesty of Thomas Hardy's celebrated novel is captured in this arresting and theatrically exciting adaptation, narrated by a masked Chorus in the style of Greek tragedy (Hardy's favoured form of theatre) and using songs to counterpoint and underline the action. Michael Fry's adaptation provides a clear and thrilling experience and an enlightening and fascinating re-evaluation of a familiar text. Period late nineteenth century
ISBN 978 0 573 01945 6

That Face. Play. Polly Stenham
M2 F4. Various simple settings. Fee code M

Mia returns home from boarding school, facing expulsion for giving a younger girl Valium. She took it from her mother, Martha. Her brother Henry is recovering from a drinking session with Martha the night before. Their father flies back from Hong Kong and is shocked to learn that Henry has dropped out of school and is living in chaos with his mother, both of them dependent on alcohol – and each other. A highly acclaimed debut from the "Most Promising Playwright" of 2008 (Critics' Circle Award).

That Good Night. Play. N. J. Crisp
M3 (30s, middle-age, 70s) F2 (30s, 40s). A courtyard/patio. Fee code M. ISBN 978 0 573 01913 5

Theft. Play. Eric Chappell
M3 (40s, 50s) F2 (40s). A drawing-room. Fee code M

Imagine returning from a pleasant anniversary celebration to find that your house has been burgled, the burglar is still in the house and has you convinced, for a while, that he is a policeman and then, once his true identity is known, he reveals that he knows all kinds of uncomfortable truths about you. Well, that burglar is none other than Spriggs, who succeeds, in *Theft*, Eric Chappell's witty comedy-thriller, in disrupting two seemingly happy marriages and one formerly strong friendship. ISBN 978 0 573 01943 2

There Came a Gypsy Riding. Play. Frank McGuiness
M2 (young, middle age) F3 (young, middle age, elderly). A kitchen with loft above. Fee Code M

The McKenna family convenes to mark the 21st birthday of their son, Eugene (Gene) who committed suicide two years previously. The parents have thrown themselves into their work but the siblings have been cut adrift with no real purpose or desire to procreate themselves. They worry away at the scab of Gene's suicide trying to find "closure", but then eccentric cousin Bridget produces a suicide note, previously unseen.

They Call It Murder. Play. Bettine Manktelow
M3 (20s, 35, 88) F4 (18, 25, 32, middle-age). A living-room. Fee code K
ISBN 978 0 573 11449 6

They Came from Mars and Landed Outside the Farndale Church Hall in Time for the Townswomen's Guild's Coffee Morning. Comedy. David McGillivray and Walter Zerlin Jnr
M1 F4. 2 female voices. A vicarage, Mars. Fee code K

The Farndale Avenue ladies and their long-suffering stage manager Gordon attempt lift-off with their dramatic society's unique production of this sci-fi thriller that will have the hysterical audience on the edge of their seats.
ISBN 978 0 573 01665 3

♦ **A bullet mark next to a title indicates that it is new to this edition of the Guide.**

They Came to a City. Play. J. B. Priestley
M4 F5. One exterior. Fee code M

Just before dawn the play's characters – who represent every stratum of society – come to the wall overlooking a strange city whose gate is shut against them. At daybreak they are admitted and towards the end of the day some have found it to be the ideal earth has never achieved. So that everyone may know of this attainable perfection two of them make the sacrifice of leaving the city to return to their sinful world.

They're Playing Our Song. Book by Neil Simon. Music by Marvin Hamlisch. Lyrics by Carol Bayer Sager
M1 F1, chorus. Various interior and exterior settings. Fee by arrangement

America's premier funny man and the Tony-award winning composer have produced this funny, romantic, hit show about an established composer and his relationship with a zany aspiring young female lyricist that is full of laughs and delightful music. First presented in Britain at the Shaftesbury Theatre, it had a long, very successful run. Although a musical, it may be presented equally successfully by small dramatic societies as well as musical societies. (**Slightly restricted**)
ISBN 978 0 573 68105 9

Thieves' Carnival. Play. Jean Anouilh, translated by Lucienne Hill
M9 F5. Two interiors, one exterior. Fee code M. For further details of the music apply to Samuel French Ltd

Two beautiful heiresses provide bait for thieves and adventurers, but things become serious when one girl falls in love with a young thief. Being a man of honour he rejects her love, and keeps his mind firmly on burglary. She, however, outwits him and the play ends happily as love conquers all. This light-hearted play combines ironic dialogue, wise humour, entertaining music and mime.
ISBN 978 0 573 61652 5

Things We Do For Love. Play. Alan Ayckbourn
M2 (40s) F2 (late 30s, 40s). 3 flats. Fee code M for play, code A for music

Barbara contentedly occupies the pristine, ordered, male-free ground-floor flat of her Victorian terraced house. Below, lives Gilbert – postman, handyman, bore – who secretly paints a lurid, nude study of Barbara. The top flat Barbara lets to schoolfriend Nikki and her fiancé Hamish, despite the fact that Barbara and Hamish have taken an instant dislike to one another. But, ever life's victim, Nikki is destined to suffer when Hamish and Barbara embark on a night of violent, uninhibited passion.
ISBN 978 0 573 01914 2

♦ **The 39 Steps** (Restricted availability)
Adapted by Patrick Barlow, from the novel by John Buchan, from the movie of Alfred Hitchcock and an original concept by Simon Corble and Nobby Dimon
M3 F1 playing multiple characters. Various simple settings. Fee code M

A hilarious and spectacular version of this spell-binding thriller, with all the legendary scenes including the death-defying finale at the London Palladium! With four actors playing a minimum of one hundred and thirty-nine roles, it's an astonishing theatrical tour de force.
"Clever, very funny, imaginative." *Guardian*
ISBN 978 0 573 11440 3

This Happy Breed. Play. Noël Coward
M5 (18-21, 30s) F7 (18-20, 30s, 60). A dining-room. Fee code M

Demobbed in 1919, Frank settles in Clapham with his wife Ethel, their three children, Reg, Queenie and Vi, Ethel's mother, and Frank's sister. The respectable working-class home with its commonness, its sterling qualities and its humour is vividly depicted as the family encompass marriage, separation and sorrow in the seventeen year span between the end of the World War I and the looming Second World War. Period 1919-1937
ISBN 978 0 573 01443 7

Three Birds Alighting on a Field. Play. Timberlake Wertenbaker
Large mixed cast may be played by M4 F5. Various simple settings. Fee code M

Timberlake Wertenbaker's award-winning play takes a witty, perceptive look at the art world in the boom period of the late Eighties in London. ' ... this rare, rich play for today, which unites the serious and the comical in one dramatic swoop ... a contemporary satire upon the art market, the stinging dealers and wheelers. But in the course of 22 scenes you become aware there is more here than meets the lazy eye.' *Evening Standard*

Three Judgements in One. Play. Pedro Calderón de la Barca. Translated by Gwynne Edwards
M6 F4. Extras.Various simple settings. Fee code M

Mendo, the King's ambassador, is captured by a group of outlaws. Spared his life by the leader, Lope, Mendo offers to obtain Lope's pardon and effects a reconciliation between Lope and his father. A love rivalry and tensions with his father lead to Lope fleeing; Mendo, now Chief Justice to the King, arrests him. In the accumulating darkness of the final act the central characters ponder on their individual contributions to Lope's death. Period 17th century

The Three Musketeers. Play. Willis Hall, from the novel by Alexandre Dumas
M19 F7, may be played by M13 F4. Extras. Various simple interior and exterior settings. Fee code M. ISBN 978 0 573 01909 8

Three Sisters. Play. Anton Chekhov
M9 F5. A drawing-room and dining-room, a bedroom, a garden. Fee code M

Versions: Samuel Adamson. M9 F5. ISBN 978 0 573 01949 4
            Michael Frayn. M9 F5
            Brian Friel. M9 F5
            Christopher Hampton. M10 F5. Extras. ISBN 978 0 573 01998 2

Three Sisters Two. Play. Reza De Wet
M3 (30, 47, 62) F6 (18, 40, 45, 50, 97). A nursery. Period 1920. Fee code L

Three Sisters Two places the characters form Chekhov's *Three Sisters* in the Russia of 1920, with the Bolsheviks in power following the Revolution and the civil war nearing its end. It expands the themes of the original play to offer a poignant vision of dispossession at the heart of the human condition.
ISBN 978 1 84002 168 4

A

♦ **The Threefold Cord.** Play. Scott Marshall
M1 (40s) F3 (20, 40s). Composite set. Fee code K

Sir Marcus Pennington appears to have it all: a beautiful actress wife, Victoria, two loving daughters, a successful career as a respected barrister. But behind the façade he is leading a triple life, romancing two other women: Dexie, a prostitute, and Millicent, the widow of his best friend, now his PA. In a series of highly engaging monologues, Victoria, Dexie and Millicent tell Marcus's story from three very different perspectives. Excellent characterization and vivid dialogue, with three very rewarding roles for actresses.
ISBN 978 0 573 11436 6

Thyestes. Play. Seneca, translated by Caryl Churchill
M8, 2M non-speaking. Various simple settings. Fee code M

Time and the Conways. Play. J. B. Priestley
M4 (20s, 30s) F6 (17, 20s, 40s). A sitting-room. Fee code M

Mrs Conway takes life cheerfully: she and her daughters enjoy entertaining and, although in 1919 war's shadow still lingers, the Conways look forward optimistically. Act II is the same room in 1937 and all the happy homes of 1919 are more or less in ruin. The married girls are miserable, those left spinsters are disillusioned and bitter. Act III returns to 1919 where Mrs Conway and the girls cheerfully look forward to a happy future.
ISBN 978 0 573 01446 8

Time and Time Again. Comedy. Alan Ayckbourn
M3 (30s, 40s) F2 (20s, 30s). A garden and conservatory. Fee code M

When womanizer Graham meets his employee Peter's fiancée, he makes a bee-line for her as usual. However, the young lady strays instead to Graham's brother-in-law Leonard, a poetic fumbler who holds conversations with the garden gnome. When Leonard half-heartedly tries to tell Peter about the relationship, cricket, football and even draughts supersede all other considerations in Peter's sports-mad mind.
ISBN 978 0 573 01457 4

Time of My Life. Play. Alan Ayckbourn
M4 (20s, middle-age, 50s) F3 (20s, 50s). A restaurant. Fee code M

Gerry Stratton has organized a family dinner with his sons Glyn and Adam at his favourite restaurant to celebrate his wife Laura's fifty-fourth birthday. The occasion suggests a happy domestic scene, but gradually we are made aware of the family skeletons. The present opens up to have Glyn's story move forward in time and Adam's backward, while at the centre Gerry and Laura pick apart their marriage and recall first love.
ISBN 978 0 573 11444 1

♦ **A bullet mark next to a title indicates that it is new to this edition of the Guide.**

Tiptoe Through the Tombstones. Comedy-thriller. Norman Robbins
M4 (25, 30s, 70s) F6 (18, 30s-60s). A library. Fee code L

Some months have passed since the ghastly events in Monument House, well-known to those familiar with Norman Robbins' earlier *A Tomb with a View*. (Previous acquaintance with the Tombs is not required!) Now Mortimer Crayle, the lawyer, has gathered the last remaining Tomb family members (as offbeat a bunch as the original occupants) at the old house, ostensibly to inform them about their inheritance. But Crayle has designs on the inheritance which demand the death of all Tombs ...
ISBN 978 0 573 01917 3

The Titfield Thunderbolt. Play. Philip Goulding. Based on the original Ealing comedy screenplay by T .E.B. Clarke
M10 F4, or M3 F2 with doubling. Various simple settings. Period 1952 Fee code L for play, code A for music

Finding that their branch railway line will be axed, a group of villagers decide to buy the railway and run it themselves. Now they must convince the railway authorities they are competent, and compete against a planned bus service. There are several suggestions to achieve the required special effects and music for the song composed by Alan Edward Williams is contained in the acting edition.
ISBN 978 0 573 11441 0

To Meet Oscar Wilde. Play. Norman Holland
M2 (30s, 40s) F1 (30s). Offstage voices. Simple lecture platform setting. Fee code L
ISBN 978 0 573 01948 7

To the Green Fields Beyond. Play. Nick Whitby
M10 (young-middle age, 1 West Indian, 1 Sikh) F1 (50s). A wood. Fee code L

Dusk on the edge of a forest in France in 1918. An eight-man tank crew wait to go into battle – one they know for sure they won't survive – and quell their nerves with food, morphine and the pleasures of a Belgian prostitute. At dawn, Lieutenant Child gathers the crew to discuss whether they should sabotage their tank and save themselves. With delicacy, perception and clarity, Nick Whitby delineates the tangled shaping of lives and events. Period 1918

A Toe in the Water. Comedy. Derek Benfield
M3 (young, middle-age) F3 (20s, 40s). Composite setting: a poolside and bedroom. Fee code L

Seeking peace and tranquility, Gerald goes to spend a few days in a health farm, presided over by the highly moral Mr Potter. But his hopes are soon dashed by the arrival of his secretary (declaring her undying passion for him), his daughter (intent upon naughty assignations with her boyfriend), and his wife. The resulting mix-ups caused by crafty deceit and misfiring erotic adventures prove more than a headache for the hapless Mr Potter!
ISBN 978 0 573 01906 7

Tom and Viv. Play. Michael Hastings
M5 (19-51, 26-58, 30, 80, 70-82) F3 (21-40, 26-58, 54-73), 1 M or F, with doubling. Voices.
Various simple settings. Fee Code M

Oxford 1815. Tom Eliot was a shy American graduate when he met Vivienne Haigh-Wood.
Together they plunged into a disaster-strewn marriage out of which came T S Eliot's famous
poem *The Waste Land. Tom and Viv* is an epic play of emotion which starts with hasty love
and ends after 32 years in cruel betrayal. It has been described as one of the great plays of the
20th century. Period 1915-47

Tom and Clem. Play. Stephen Churchett
M3 (20s-30s, 62) F1 (mid 30s). A large room. Fee code M

Tom, Dick and Harry. Comedy. Ray and Michael Cooney
M6 (20s,40s,80) F3 (20s, 50). A flat. Fee Code M

The Kerwood brothers are not your everyday Tom, Dick and Harry. Tom and his wife Linda are
desperate to adopt a baby and nervously await the arrival of the head of the adoption agency,
the formidable Mrs Potter. Unfortunately, at the same time, Dick returns from a smuggling
trip with brandy and cigarettes – and two illegal Kosovan refugees who sneaked into his van.
Hilarious mayhem ensues, as Tom must fabricate ever wilder explanations to placate Linda,
Mrs Potter and a suspicious policeman.
ISBN 978 0 573 11438 0

Tom Jones. Comedy. Joan Macalpine. Based on the novel by Henry Fielding
M7 F7. Extras. Composite setting. Fee code M

Tom Jones is rich, ripe and rowdy. Tom, Squire Allworthy's adopted son, falls victim to the
charms of one rustic wench after another, until at last the Squire grows tired of the trouble he
causes and sends him off to cause it elsewhere. Then Tom becomes entangled with three women
at once: Jenny Waters, a lady of warm heart and generous virtue, Mrs Fitzpatrick, a society
lady seeking diversion from her oafish husband, and Sophia Western, whom Tom truly loves.
ISBN 978 0 573 11439 7

A Tomb with a View. Comedy thriller. Norman Robbins
M4 (30s-70s) F6 (20s-60s). A library. Fee code L

The action begins with the reading of the Tomb family will (invoving some millions of pounds) to
a pretty sinister family, one member of which has werewolf tendencies, another wanders around
in a toga in the style of Julius Caesar, a third is a gentle elderly lady who plants more than seeds
in her flower-beds. By the third act there are more corpses than live members left in the cast.
ISBN 978 0 573 11451 9

Tons of Money. Farce. Will Evans and Valentine
M6 (young, 30s, elderly) F4 (20s, elderly). A library. Fee code M. Period 1922
ISBN 978 0 573 01450 5

♦ **A bullet mark next to a title indicates that it is new to this edition of the Guide.**

Tons of Money. Farce. Will Evans and Valentine, revised by Alan Ayckbourn
M6 F4. For cast and settings see above. Fee code M

Alan Ayckbourn's revised version of the first of the famous Aldwych farces, originally produced in 1922 starring the great farce actor Ralph Lynn, retains the spirit whilst altering some of the original letter of the text – changes to verbal jokes, for instance, or to some of Lynn's uniquely personal gags. The basic story, however, remains the same. The National Theatre produced this version in 1986 with Michael Gambon and Simon Cadell.
ISBN 978 0 573 01671 4

Top Girls. Play. Caryl Churchill
F7, with trebling. Various simple interior and exterior settings. Fee code M

This play for sixteen women characters was seen at London's Royal Court Theatre. 'Ms Churchill's rich, ambitious play is a powerful exposition of the way in which top girls, like top men, often achieve success at the expense of their less able sisters.' *Time Out.* ' ... brilliantly conceived with considerable wit to illuminate the underlying deep human seriousness of her theme. The play is feminist, all right, but it is an entertaining, sometimes painful and often funny play and not a mere tract.' *Spectator*
ISBN 978 0 573 13013 7

Torch Song Trilogy. Three plays. Harvey Fierstein. Fees on application

A smash-hit in New York, this trilogy had its British première at the Albery Theatre, London, in 1985, with Antony Sher portraying the alternately moving and hilarious life and loves of a drag queen. '[This play] must be the funniest as well as the most perceptive, exuberant and painful for years about sexuality, inversion and the disorders of modern love.' *Daily Telegraph* '... a remarkably bitchy, waspish and acerbically funny triptych on the nature of homosexuality.' *Punch*

The International Stud
M2 (30s). A black cyclorama.

Fugue in a Nursery
M3 (18, 30s) F1 (35). One set to represent various rooms

Widows and Children First!
M3 (15, 30s, 40s). F1 (60s). A living-room/kitchenette, a park bench

Total Eclipse. Play. Christopher Hampton
M7 (17, 20s, 43). F4 (18, 31, 50, middle-age). Extras. Various interior and exterior settings. Fee code M

An intelligent treatment of the friendship between the poets Paul Verlaine and Arthur Rimbaud, one of the most extraordinary relationships in the history of literature. With considerable insight into the bourgeois and artistic societies of the nineteenth century, and with a moving understanding of homosexuality, Hampton charts the poets' mutual need for each other as they move through and away from literary life and from Verlaine's family.
ISBN 978 0 573 61692 1

Touch and Go. Comedy. Derek Benfield
M2 (40s) F3 (20s, 30s). Two living-rooms. Fee code L

Having been encouraged to take up jogging by his wife Hilary, Brian sees his girl-friend, Wendy, in his friend George's flat when he is ostensibly running around the park. However, while Brian is visiting Wendy, helpful George knows that his own affair will not be discovered as the object of his affection is Brian's wife Hilary! It is all plain sailing until George's wife Jessica returns too soon from a business trip to America ...
ISBN 978 0 573 11301 7

A Touch of Danger. Play. Francis Durbridge
M5 (30s, 40s, middle-age) F4 (20s, 30s). A living-room. Fee code M

When author Max Telligan's secretary, Liz, and his about-to-be ex-wife, Harriet, read that he has been found dead in Munich, they are stunned. When Max walks in, very much alive, they find that the murdered man was Max's friend. Thus begins a sequence of events involving the CID, CIA, security services and a terrorist organization, all of whom seem inordinately interested in Max.
ISBN 978 0 573 01692 9

The Tower, [La Tour de Nesle], or Marguerite de Bourgogne. Play. Alexandre Dumas (Père), in a new version by Charles Wood
M18 F3, may be played by M13 F2. Extras. Various simple settings. Fee code M

Translations. Play. Brian Friel
M7 (20s-middle-age, 60s) F3 (20s). A hedge-school. Fee code M

In Baile Beag, an Irish-speaking community in County Donegal, a detachment of the Royal Engineers engaged on behalf of the British Army and Government are making the first Ordnance Survey. Lieutenant Yolland falls in love with Maire, a peasant girl, and with Ireland, but when he is murdered Maire goes mad. The British soldiers pillage the countryside in revenge. Period 1833

Traps. Play. Caryl Churchill
M4 (20s, 30s) F2 (20s, 30). A room. Fee code M

Travels with my Aunt. Play. Adapted by Giles Havergal from the novel by Graham Greene
M15 F9, but very flexible casting. Various simple settings. Fee code M

Travesties. Play. Tom Stoppard
M5 (20s, middle-age, 60s) F3 (young, 40s). A library, a drawing-room. Fee code M

James Joyce, running a Swiss theatrical company, invites Henry Carr to play in Wilde's *The Importance of Being Earnest*. Carr agrees and scores a success, but later there is a dispute over Carr's claim for reimbursement of the cost of articles of clothing bought for his role. The author uses this factual framework on which to build an extravaganza of political history, literary pastiche, and Wildean parody, even song and dance, introducing Dadaist Tristan Tzara, and Lenin and his wife. Period 1918

Treasure Island. Play. Bernard Miles, Peter Coe and Josephine Wilson from the book by R.L. Stevenson
M21. Various settings on an open stage. Fee code M. ISBN 978 0 573 04017 7

Treasure Island
Freely adapted for male and female pirates by Phil Willmott, from the novel by Robert Louis Stevenson
Flexible casting, can be played by M13 F8. Extras. Various simple settings. Period 1772. Fee Code K

This is a unique adaptation of *Treasure Island* with great parts for both male and female performers. Inspired by real-life female adventurers, Phil Willmott has changed the gender of several of the central characters without compromising the spirit of Stevenson's classic novel. Simply staged, and suitable for performance by children or adults, this refreshing version can be adapted to suit both large and small companies.

The Treatment. Play. Martin Crimp
M6 (20s, 40s, 40s (black), 60s (black), 60s) F4 (20s, 40s). Various simple settings. Fee Code M

Set in New York, the play tells the story of Anne, a young woman whose husband likes to tie her up and silence her with tape while telling her of "the beauty of the world". She decides to leave him and soon meets two film producers who become interested in making a film of her story. A scriptwriter is hired, but before long her life has been twisted into a voyeuristic fantasy, bearing little resemblance to the reality.

Trelawny of the 'Wells'. Comedy. Arthur W. Pinero
M10 (young, 27, 30, 40, 70, elderly) F8 (19, 20s, 60). Four interiors. No fee
ISBN 978 0 573 01459 8

The Trial. Play. Steven Berkoff, adapted from Franz Kafka
M8 F2. Fee code L

Joseph K's nightmare journey through the complicated and crushing world of the law is staged by Berkoff with ten moveable doors and a Greek-style chorus. It is a masterpiece of imaginative physical storytelling theatre.

Trivial Pursuits. Play. Frank Vickery
M4 (30s) F6 (20s, 30s). A garden/patio area. Fee code L

A summer evening's barbecue is the setting for a meeting of the Trealaw and District Operatic Society. Next season's play is being announced but Nick, the Society's business manager, has promised a different show and the plum roles to four different people. As the evening progresses each character's foibles and talents are revealed and the complex relationships etween players emerge as moments of pure slapstick and farce alternate with ones full of real drama and pathos. ISBN 978 0 573 11469 4

◆ **A bullet mark next to a title indicates that it is new to this edition of the Guide.**

Trumpets and Drums. Play. Bertolt Brecht. Translated by Alan Brown and Kyra Dietz, music by Wagner Regeny
M21 F12. Interior and exterior settings. Fee code M for play, code C for music

Brecht takes George Farquhar's Restoration comedy *The Recruiting Officer* and transfers it to the period of the American Revolutionary War. Captain Plume, the officer in question, arrives in Shrewsbury from London to enquire how recruitment to fight the rebels is progressing. He receives a discouraging report of military and romantic complications.

Trumpets and Raspberries. Comedy. Dario Fo. Translated and adapted by R. C. McAvoy and A. M. Giugni
M7 F2, with doubling. A hospital recovery room. Fee code M

A terrorist attack and a body needing plastic surgery are the ingredients of another Fo farce. Here he pokes incisive fun at bosses, the police and the discipline of work and as always his medicine is bitter-sweet with a sardonic aftertaste. This comedy enjoyed a successful run at London's Phoenix Theatre, in 1984, starring Griff Rhys-Jones. ' ... one of the funniest scenes I have seen on any stage.' *Guardian*

Turandot. Play. Bertolt Brecht
Translations: Derek Goldby
Stefan Lasch and Evelyn Warman
M33 F9. Extras. Various simple interior and exterior settings. Fee code M for play, code C for music

The Turn of the Screw. Play. Ken Whitmore, adapted from the novel by Henry James
M1 or 2 (35) F3 (20s, 50). 1 boy (12) 1 girl (10). A sitting-room/hall. Fee code L

Shortly after Miss Grey, a governess, arrives at Bly to take charge of Flora and Miles she sees the ghosts of the former valet and governess; it is the children they want. She determines to save the children from destruction and damnation at hands of these 'devils', but her courageous efforts are not enough to save little Miles from tragedy. Period 1875
ISBN 978 0 573 11454 0

♦ **Tusk Tusk.** Play. Polly Stenham
M4 (7, 15, 40s) F3 (teen, 40s). A living-room. Fee code M

Three children are alone in a new flat, surrounded by boxes. Their mother has gone missing, again. Eliot teases and torments his sister Maggie, leaving the flat to get Chinese food and to flirt with girls. Finn dreams of boats made out of tin cans and spills paint everywhere trying to paint the walls his mother's favourite colour. Hiding from the world, needing to be found, they wait for a mobile phone to ring. Premièred at the Royal Court Theatre, London, in 2009.

The Tutor. Play. Bertolt Brecht. Translated by Pip Broughton
M10 F10. Extras. Seven interiors, two exteriors. Fee code H

This is a modernized version of the 18th-century drama by Reinhold Lenz about the miseries and humiliations suffered by a young private tutor. Treated as a servant by his employers, he is seduced by the daughter of the house and has to flee from the outraged family. Later, in a similar situation, he lands himself in the same sort of trouble. In desperation he castrates himself, and thereafter finds life easier and is accepted by society. Period 1930s Germany. **NB. Please specify translator when ordering.**

The Tutor. Play. Bertolt Brecht
Translations: Ralph Manheim
                John Willett
                Geoffrey Skelton
                Richard Grunberger
M10 F10. Interior and exterior settings. Fee code M

For synopsis, see above.

Twelve Angry Men. Play. Reginald Rose
M13. A jury room. Fee code M

A young delinquent is on trial for the murder of his aggressive father. The judge has directed the jury to find the boy guilty if there is no reasonable doubt. Eleven of the jurors declare there is no reasonable doubt, but one of them, while far from convinced of the boy's innocence, feels that some of the evidence against him has been ambiguous. At the end of a long afternoon he wins all the others round to his view. Period 1950s.
ISBN 978 0 573 04012 2

Two. Play. Jim Cartwright
M1 F1, playing 14 characters (M6 F7, 1 boy). A pub. Fee code M

Set in a Northern pub owned by a savagely bickering husband and wife, *Two* is a series of short vignettes that skilfully combines pathos and humour, with all fourteen characters played by two actors. During the course of the evening, assorted customers pass through, including a little boy left behind by his father – an event which triggers a movement towards a fragile reconciliation between the pub couple, as their own dark tragedy is revealed.

Two and Two Make Sex. Comedy. Richard Harris and Leslie Darbon
M3 (24, 45, 50) F3 (20, 40). Split set: a drawing-room, a bedsitter. Fee code M
ISBN 978 0 573 01548 9

Two and Two Together. Comedy. Derek Benfield
M4 (30s, 50s, 60s) F3 (40s, middle-age) Split set: 2 suburban reception rooms Fee code M
ISBN 978 0 573 01947 0

Two Into One. Comedy. Ray Cooney
M5 (Oriental, 20s-40s, 60s) F5 (young, 20s, 40s). Extras optional. Multiple settings. Fee code M

While staying at the Westminster Hotel, MP Richard Willey dispatches his wife Pamela to the theatre so that his assistant, George, can arrange a suite where Richard can seduce one of the PM's secretaries. Unfortunately, George bungles the arrangements and Richard finds his illicit love-nest is the suite next to his and Pamela's. From then on George piles one outrageous deceit upon another, accidentally finding himself seducing Pamela, until staff and guests are reeling in confusion!
ISBN 978 0 573 01607 3

◆ **A bullet mark next to a title indicates that it is new to this edition of the Guide.**

A

Two of a Kind. Comedy. Hugh Janes
M2 (elderly) F2 (middle-age, elderly). A room, lobby, office and optional inset scene. Fee code M

'Wally' Wallis is hardly the perfect retirement-home resident. When his room-mate, Potts, dies and is replaced with staid, dull George, war is instantly declared! Wally decides he must leave, but before his escape with Potts' ashes he reaches a level of understanding with George and shares some tender moments with May, another resident, who has a soft spot for both men.
ISBN 978 0 573 01944 9

The Two of Us. Four one-act plays for two players. Michael Frayn
M1 F1. A bedroom, a dining-room, two living-rooms. Fee code J

The four plays are not connected except by the fact that they can all be played by the same two performers. In the first *Black and Silver*, a husband and wife return to the hotel room in which they spent their honeymoon. In *The New Quixote* a young man has spent a night with a girl, to whom the encounter is so casual that he has even forgotten it when he leaves her. However, he returns to take up residence – but will they really be happy together? *Mr Foot*, the third play, concerns a couple – he is in line for a new job, she may be 'vetted' as his wife, by his employer. She creates an imaginary interview. The last play, *Chinamen*, is the longest, and in it the players share five parts. It concerns a dinner party to which friends are invited who at all costs must not be allowed to meet. They do!

Two Planks and a Passion. Play. Anthony Minghella
M12 F4. Extras. Composite setting. Fee code L

Set in York in 1392, this play tells of a performance of the Mystery Plays. For the townspeople the competition is fierce to attract the attention of the Royal Party and to impress them at all costs. But the message of Mystery cycle as performed is strong, clear and truthful. This remarkable and beautifully written play is highly original, often very funny and ultimately deeply moving. '... a play full of bustle, life, satire and at times a most moving account of simple faith.' *Daily Mail*
ISBN 978 0 573 01604 2

Two Thousand Years. Play. Mike Leigh
M5 (28, 40, 53, 78) F3 (20s, 40s, 50). A living-room. Fee Code M

Concentrating on a North-London Jewish family, Mike Leigh explores, in a gentle tragic-comic way, a wide range of issues, including politics, religion, identity and the vexed question of Israel and the Middle East. The play premièred at the National Theatre in 2005 and received huge critical acclaim.

Uncle Vanya. Play. Anton Chekhov
A garden, a dining-room, a drawing-room, a bedroom/office. Fee code M

Versions: Michael Frayn. M6 (37, 50, old) F4 (young, late 20s, old)
　　　　 Brian Friel. M6 (37, 47, old) F4 (young, 27, elderly)
　　　　 David Mamet, from a translation by Vlada Chernomirdik. M5 F4. ISBN 978 0 573 66212 6
　　　　 Mike Poulton. M6 (37, 50, old) F4 (young, late 20s, old). ISBN 978 0 573 01958 6

Under Milk Wood. Play for voices. Dylan Thomas. With music by Daniel Jones
69 characters. Extras. Doubling possible. Various settings. Fee code M (to include use of music)

A vigorous and rich narrative, sparkling dialogue, and beautifully simple songs; this play overflows with the author's fecund vision of human experience in the small Welsh seaside town of Llareggub. Although probably the most enchanting work for broadcasting ever written this play is also suitable as a stage play. 'Dylan Thomas's beautiful, bawdy, affectionate, reckless, and deeply original play was justly crowned at its first performance by a storm of cheers ...' *Sunday Times*

The Undertaking. Play. Philip Osment
M4 (young, 30s) F1 (30s). Various simple interior and exterior settings. Fee code M

Henry has died of AIDS and his lover, Howard, ex-lover Michael and old friend Sheila – along with Michael's new lover, Eamon – travel to Ireland to scatter his ashes. Conflicts and jealousies arise between the members of the group and are exacerbated by the arrival of Patrick, Michael's straight brother, but the ash-scattering ceremony unites them again. Written with insight, humour and great compassion, *The Undertaking* is a moving and very human play tackling difficult themes with enormous but unobtrusive skill.

Undiscovered Country. Play. Tom Stoppard adapted from Arthur Schnitzler
M16 F11. 2 children and extras. Various simple settings. Fee Code M

This witty and ironic version of Arthur Schnitzler's *Das weite Land* portrays upper class characters of Vienna in the 1890s and exposes the destructive nature of their relationships. It deals with suicide, love, lust, jealousy, conquest and murder in a unique and intriguing way, as intricate affairs and devastating effects are just a scratch beneath the surface. This play offers an insightful psychological analysis of human behaviour and the social values of the period. Period : late 19th century

The Unexpected Guest. Play. Agatha Christie
M7 (19, 30s, 40, middle-age) F3 (30, 50, elderly). A study. Fee code M

Michael Starkwedder stumbles in to Richard Warwick's study to find him dead and his wife Laura standing nearby with a gun. The police are puzzled by a set of fingerprints. Do they belong to MacGregor, the man whose child Warwick killed or do they belong to Julian Farrar, Laura's lover whom Laura has lied to protect? After Warwick's half-brother confesses to the murder and then kills himself the case is closed but then Mrs Christie produces one of her surprise endings. ISBN 978 0 573 01467 3

The Unexpected Man. Play. Yasmina Reza. Translated by Christopher Hampton
M1 (middle age) F1 (middle age). A train compartment. Fee code M

Unleashed. Play. John Godber
M3 (young, late 20s, early 40s, middle age) F2 (young, late 30s, middle age). Various simple settings. Fee code M. ISBN 978 0 573 01927 2

♦ **A bullet mark next to a title indicates that it is new to this edition of the Guide.**

Unoriginal Sin. Comedy. David Tristram
M4 (20s, 30s, 50s) F2 (24, 30s). A living-room. Fee code I.

Bill and Jenny are divorcing. She tries to catch him in a compromising position while he attempts to seduce the young, innocent Eve who has come to view Bill and Jenny's country cottage. Eve arrives with her fiancé and Jenny proposes to Bill a 'first to the bedpost' competition to establish the divorce settlement. Jenny wins and Bill is humbled into reassessing his profligacy. This riotous comedy is by the author of the famous Inspector Drake farces.

♦ **An Untimely Frost** (formerly *The Lost Garden*). Play. Colin and Mary Crowther
M2 (early 50s) F4 (20s, late 40s, late 50s). In and around a terraced house. Fee code K

Paradise is a walled garden. Or it was for Geoff, until illness disabled him. Now he rages at those throttling weeds and his horticulturally-incompetent wife Elisabeth who, stifled and unwanted, yearns for escape. Paradise lost, it seems. But they both reckon without the redoubtable Fran, who brings their marriage and garden back to life. Paradise regained? An international award-winning play that is tender, warm and uplifting.

Up and Coming. Comedy. Eric Chappell
M5 (30s-60s) F2 (late 20s, mid 30s). A hotel suite. Fee code M. ISBN 978 0 573 01953 1

Up and Running. Comedy. Derek Benfield
M3 (20s, 50s) F3 (20s, 40s). A living-room. Fee code M

Veteran TV talk-show host Patrick Sumner is desperate to impress his new producer Reg Godfrey, who visits Patrick's smart London flat for drinks. But Patrick reckons without the intervention of Jenny, a pretty girl who arrives on the same evening as Reg, intent upon infiltrating Patrick's private life and even passing herself off as his wife. When Patrick's *real* wife returns unexpectedly from a Paris trip, Patrick is forced into a spiralling series of lies and subterfuge. ISBN 978 0 573 01916 6

Up for Grabs. Comedy. David Williamson
M3 F4. Various simple settings. Fee code M

Who dares doesn't always win. Loren wants to be a big-time art dealer but her husband is getting tired of bankrolling her power lunches, which get her nowhere. Suddenly she has a Pollock to sell and three potential buyers. Then she discovers how the big players really work. David Williamson has crafted a dazzling, caustic comedy where the exploration of greed and need is joyously coupled with the razor-sharp wit of his dialogue. Madonna starred in the London premier in 2002.

Up 'n' Under. Comedy. John Godber
M6 F1. A bare stage. Fee code M

Dedicated to the Rugby League fans of Hull and created for the Hull Truck Theatre Company this comedy was premièred at the Edinburgh Festival in 1984 where it won a Fringe First award and subsequently the 1984 Laurence Olivier Award for Comedy of the Year after a successful run in London. Set 'somewhere in the north of England' it centres on the amateur rugby team from the *Wheatsheaf Arms* who can only muster a side of four whose pride lies in their unbroken record of defeat. ISBN 978 0 573 01915 9

A

Up 'n' Under II. Comedy. John Godber
M7 (young, middle-age). F2 (young). May be played by M5 F1 with doubling. A bare stage with basic props. Fee code M

'In Amateur Rugby League, everything is personal.' The truth of this sentiment is proved time and again in *Up 'n' Under II*, the hilarious sequel to John Godber's hit comedy about the mixed bag of players making up the *Wheatsheaf Arms* team. Will the lost honour of the *Wheatsheaf Arms* be retrieved in their match against the *Cobblers Arms*? Audiences will be on the edges of their seats before they find out!
ISBN 978 0 573 11466 3

US and Them. Comedy. Tamsin Oglesby
M4 (21, 40s) F3 (19, 40s). Various simple settings. Fee code L

The buffer zone between trust and suspicion proves fertile ground for this witty dissection of a special relationship. A chance meeting in a Manhattan restaurant for English couple Martin and Charlotte with affluent New Yorkers Ed and Lori carries the promise of a close friendship. But are they in fact speaking the same language? A transatlantic comedy of manners in which old Europe and the New World struggle to understand each other.

Valued Friends. Play. Stephen Jeffreys
M4 (30s, 40s) F2 (20s, 30s). A living-room. Fee code M. ISBN 978 0 573 01922 3

The Vanek Plays. Triple bill. Václav Havel. Translated by Vera Blackwell
Fee code M (for triple bill)

The plays in this triple bill (two of which, *Audience* and *Private View*, were presented in the BBC-TV series *Play for Today*), have a central character in Vanek, who, like his creator, is a writer and brewery worker. Although not autobiographical, together they provide a superbly ironic comment on the position of a writer who has incurred the disapproval of an autocratic government. **Please note only translations by Vera Blackwell are licensed for performance by Samuel French Ltd.**

    Audience. M2. An office. Fee code E if performed separately. ISBN 978 0 573 04226 3

    Private View. M2 F1. A living-room. Fee code E if performed separately. ISBN 978 0 573 12212 5

    Protest. M2. A study. Fee code E if performed separately

Vanity Fair. Play. Declan Donnellan, adapted from the novel by William Makepeace Thackeray
30 named parts may be played by a cast of 7. Various simple settings. Fee code M.
ISBN 978 0 573 01974 6

Verdict. Play. Agatha Christie
M6 (24, 45, middle-age, 60) F4 (23, 30, middle-age). A living-room. Fee code M

Karl and his wife Anya are refugees who return to England to rebuild their lives with the help of Lisa who runs the house. Wealthy Helen arrives to take lessons from Karl and her infatuation for him being unreturned, she doesn't stop at murder to clear the way. When Anya dies Helen commits suicide. Lisa is left to carry the blame but then she is absolved and she and Karl build a new life from the wreckage.
ISBN 978 0 573 61931 1

A

Veronica's Room. Thriller. Ira Levin
M2 F2. A bedsitting-room. Fee code M

Susan Kerner and Larry Eastwood are invited to the Brabissant mansion by the Mackeys who are struck by Susan's resemblance to Veronica Brabissant, long-dead daughter of the family for whom they work. Susan goes along with the charade to comfort Veronica's only living relative. But once dressed in Veronica's clothes, Susan finds herself locked in the role – and locked in Veronica's room. Or is she Veronica, in 1935, pretending to be an imaginary Susan?
ISBN 978 0 573 01690 0

♦ **The Vertical Hour.** Play. David Hare
M3 (20s, 30s, 50s) F2 (20, 30s). Various simple settings. Fee code M

Nadia Blye, American war reporter turned professor, finds her faith in academia eroding and memories from the Balkans and the Middle East haunting her. She travels with her boyfriend to visit his father, Oliver, who has his own past to reckon with. An intimate play, pitting personal philosophies against global politics, showing how war and its aftermath affects so many people's lives. Premièred on Broadway in 2006, and at London's Royal Court Theatre in 2008.
'A rich, intellectually gripping play.' *Guardian*

Vieux Carré. Play. Tennessee Williams
M5 F5. Composite setting: a rooming house. Fee code M

This is an autobiographical portrait of Williams as he recalls, with pain, compassion and wry humour, a sojourn in the French Quarter of New Orleans during 1938. We see a tubercular, homosexual painter, a New York fashion illustrator now suffering from leukaemia, two elderly gentlewomen starving politely, and dominating Mrs Wire, the sentimental and cruel, comically desperate landlady.

Vinegar Tom. Play. Caryl Churchill
14 characters, can be played by a cast of 9. Various simple interior and exterior settings. Fee code L for play, code B for music

Written for Monstrous Regiment in 1976 and first presented at the Humberside Theatre, Hull, this is a history play with a difference. Set loosely in the seventeenth century, it charts the persecution of women in the name of witchcraft showing how fear of female sexuality is one of the motor forces behind the witchhunts – and in its 'modern' songs challenges the audience to examine its own attitudes to women and sexuality.

The Visions of Simone Machard. Play. Bertolt Brecht
Translations: Hugh and Ellen Rank
                        Ralph Manheim
M12 F3. Extras. A courtyard. Fee code M

♦ **A bullet mark next to a title indicates that it is new to this edition of the Guide.**

The Visit. Drama. Friedrich Dürrenmatt. Adapted by Maurice Valency
M29 F8 (9 principals and 28 small parts). Extras. Composite setting. Fee code L

Claire Zachanassian, the richest woman in the world, returns to her poverty-stricken home town. The townspeople are ready to grovel for favours and select as their representative Anton Schell, for Claire and Anton had once been deeply in love. Claire arrives with a sinister ménage. She soon announces that she has come for revenge on her onetime sweetheart, offering a million marks for his life. In the nightmarish climax Schell's corrupted friends sacrifice him to their greed.
ISBN 978 0 573 61754 6

Visiting Hour. Play. Richard Harris
M2 F4 (1 black), playing a variety of roles. A hospital ward. Fee code M (for whole play)

Six interlinked plays set in a National Health hospital during visiting hour. Alternately funny and sad – with elements of tragedy and comedy in each – your audience will be reaching for the Kleenex one minute and rolling in the aisles the next! '... packed with sharp lines and cruel characterization ... It hurts to laugh but laugh we do ... for those who like their comedy black there is much to enjoy.' *Daily Telegraph*
ISBN 978 0 573 01925 8

The Visitors. Play. Joe Orton
M2 (84) F7 (22, middle age, 1 black). A hospital ward. Fee code M

Written in 1961, this is a thoroughly convincing exercise in slice-of-life realism set in a hospital where the dying Kemp is visited by his middle-aged daughter, while the nurses spend more time on in-fighting than on patient care.

Vita and Virginia. Play. Eileen Atkins, adapted from the correspondence between Virginia Woolf and Vita Sackville-West
F2 (30, 40). A bare stage. Fee code M

Virginia Woolf and Vita Sackville-West first met in 1922. Through the course of the next twenty years, until Virginia's suicide in 1941, the extraordinary relationship between them was charted in their letters to one another, providing a remarkable insight into their love affair. Eileen Atkins has made a supremely skilful dramatization of their correspondence in which they speak of everyday life, friends, literature and, above all, themselves.
ISBN 978 0 573 13012 0

Vivat! Vivat Regina! Play. Robert Bolt
M27 F4. Extras. Doubling possible. Unit setting. Fee code J

The play follows the relationship between Mary, Queen of Scots and Elizabeth I, from shortly before the former's return to Scotland, through her marriage to Darnley, Rizzio's death, the scandal over Bothwell, Mary's imprisonment, Catholic plots, until her execution, closing as Spain's Armada is in active preparation.
ISBN 978 0 573 01489 5

◆ **A bullet mark next to a title indicates that it is new to this edition of the Guide.**

Voyage (from *The Coast of Utopia*). Play. Tom Stoppard
M16 F9. Extras. Various interior and exterior settings. Period 1833-1844. Fee code M

The first play in Tom Stoppard's trilogy is set in Russia in the 1830s and 1840s on the wealthy Bakunin family's estate and in Moscow. It concerns a group of young friends that include the anarchist Michael Bakunin, the would-be author Ivan Turgenev, the brilliant young literary critic Vissarion Belinsky, and Alexander Herzen, a nobleman's son and self-proclaimed socialist. "There is much to admire ... offers delightful comedy in the Chekhovian style ..." Charles Spencer, *Daily Telegraph*.

Wait Until Dark. Play. Frederick Knott
M6 (20s, 30s) F2 (12, 30). A basement flat. Fee code M

A drug-filled doll has disappeared from a London flat and three petty crooks try to find it. They plot to compel the owners to give away its whereabouts. The owner's wife is blind; the crooks tell her a frightening story involving her husband's supposed infidelity. She, however, becomes suspicious. In a terrifying climax she makes use of the fact that in the dark the blind have an actual advantage over those who can normally see.
ISBN 978 0 573 01050 7

Waiting for Godot. Tragic comedy. Samuel Beckett
M4 1 boy. A country road. Fee code M

Two tramps, Vladimir and Estragon, are waiting for someone. To pass the time they indulge in cross talk, they argue, they play bizarre games. Lucky, more animal than human, enters, driven by Pozzo, a wealthy, blubbering creature. Another visitor is a small boy who says he works for Mr Godot and tells the tramps his master will come *tomorrow*. The following day Pozzo and Lucky visit again, as does the small boy with another message: Mr Godot will certainly be coming *tomorrow*. The tramps wait on.
ISBN 978 0 573 04008 5

Waiting in the Wings. Play. Noël Coward
M4 (30s, 40s, 70s) F14 (20s-80s). A lounge. Fee code M

'The Wings' is a charity home for retired actresses. Here these aged ladies grow older ungracefully amidst squabbles, jealousies and grandiose memories. The once-great actress Lotta Bainbridge arrives; years ago she married the ex-husband of one of the inmates, May Davenport, and her arrival sparks off a feud. It is only resolved when one deranged old lady sets fire to her room. After this tragedy, Lotta and May spend what little time is left to them in peace and harmony.
ISBN 978 0 573 01470 3

Warrior. Play. Shirley Gee
M8 F3 or M5 F3. Opportunities for many extras. Composite setting. Fee code M

This powerful, moving drama is based on a true story. In 1750 Hannah Snell, disguised as a boy, goes to sea in search of her errant husband. For seven years she lives as a man, boldly braving wounds, bloody battles and her own troubling visions. Back home, a woman again, penniless, she and two fellow marines form a successful stage act. But apocalyptic visions force her publicly to proclaim the horrors of war and the authorities imprison her in Bedlam. Rescued, she sails away to speak out for life.
ISBN 978 0 573 01931 9

A Warwickshire Testimony. Play. April De Angelis
M2 (range of ages) F6 (range of ages) (with doubling). Various simple settings. Fee code M

Past: the "big house", the servant class, the close-knit family ties of a bygone generation. Rural idyll or claustrophobic hellhole? Present: big business and incomers, no shops and no locals, where nothing stays the same for five minutes. For better or worse? April De Angelis's funny and compassionate play powerfully illustrates a rapidly changing way of life by focusing on the loves, traumas and disputes of one Midlands family throughout the twentieth century.

Way Upstream. Play. Alan Ayckbourn
M3 (30s) F4 (young, 30s, 40). A boat and surrounding river and banks. Fee code M

What could be more pleasant than a holiday on the river? Unfortunately, things do not go quite as smoothly as Keith, self-appointed skipper, has anticipated. The last straw comes when Vince, hitching a ride upstream, is elected skipper in his place. This dark comedy was presented at the National Theatre, London, in 1982, where real water, rain and a moving boat were used; these are not essential, however, and the play can be produced using simulated or imagined water.
ISBN 978 0 573 11504 2

We Found Love and an Exquisite Set of Porcelain Figurines Aboard the SS *Farndale Avenue*. Comedy. David McGillivray and Walter Zerlin Jnr
M2 (20s, any age) F3 (20s, 40s, 50s). Various simple settings. Fee code K

Flushed and following on from their previous successes (?), the stalwart veterans of the F.A.H.E.T.G. Dramatic Society are poised to conquer another dramatic idiom. In romantic vein aboard an ocean-going liner for their excursion into the world of thirties' musical comedy *à la* Noël and Gertie, the ladies prove that the age of elegance, glamour and enchantment is not dead ... well, not quite anyway.
ISBN 978 0 573 01933 3

Webster. Play. Robert David MacDonald
M10 F4. A theatre corridor. Fee code M

Premièred at the Citizens', Glasgow, and revived at the Old Red Lion in London, this Grand Guignol is based on the few known facts of the great Jacobean playwright's life and on conjecture about his lost play *The Guise*. Trapped and embittered by an appalling family, Webster seeks solace with the attractive boy actors in his company. But then he disagrees with his patron and the theatre manager ... 'This brawling, sprawling play makes a wonderfully entertaining evening ... The language is scatalogical and downright.' *Financial Times*

Wedding of the Year. Comedy. Norman Robbins
M4 (20s, 30s, 50, 70s) F6 (20s, 40s, 70s, 80s). A living-room. Fee code K.
ISBN 978 0 573 11473 1

A Wedding Story. Play. Bryony Lavery
M2 (20s,30s) F3 (20s (black), 30s, middle age). Various simple settings. Fee code L

Taking her place in church amongst the usual screaming babies and half-whispered vows, little does Sally know that she is about to find love herself. Meanwhile, at home her parents face the toughest challenge of their marriage, as the ageing process in the form of Alzheimer's takes its toll with devastating effect. The entire family is brought face to face with the meaning of true love and commitment in an age of brief encounters and one-night stands.

The Weekend. Play. Michael Palin
M4 (30s, 60s) F5 (teenage, 30s, 50s, 60s). A dog. M1 voice only. A living/dining-room. Fee code M

A

Cantankerous, misanthropic, miserable, world-weary ... think of an adjective synonymous with 'crabby' and it will apply to Stephen Febble. All he wants is to be left alone, but, to his horror, his long-suffering wife Virginia fills the house with guests for the weekend. Stephen responds in the only way he knows how – with a monstrous display of rudeness. A riot of a comedy with an ever-present dark side.

Weekend Breaks. Play. John Godber
M2 (30s, 60s) F1(60s) A voice. An empty stage. Fee code M

John Godber's striking, easily staged play explores the complex relationship between a thirty-three year old theatre studies teacher and his elderly parents. Martin Dawson has invited his parents, Joan and Len, to visit him in the Lake District. This 'enjoyable' weekend break evolves into an opportunity for the release of the pent-up frustrations of a lifetime. Godber successfully combines biting humour with serious intent in this thought-provoking comment on age, communication and life in general.
ISBN 978 0 573 01940 1

West. Play. Steven Berkoff
M7 F2. Fee code M

Subtitled "or Welcome to Dalston Junction", *West* is about the courage to live according to your spirit and not the guidelines laid down by others. "Raw, poetic energy ... a hothouse of voluptuous imagery ... for audacious originality, Berkoff is the top boy in contemporary British theatre." *Time Magazine*

Whale Music. Play. Anthony Minghella
F10 (17, 20s, 40s). Various simple settings. Fee code L

An acutely sensitive, moving portrayal of the lives of a group of women which reflects the attitudes and feelings of women today, depicted in a series of settings which flow gently into each other. Caroline, pregnant by one of her boyfriends, escapes to her seaside birthplace where she is visited by friends. The reaction of these women to each other whilst awaiting the birth is sympathetically told and we become totally involved in the heights and depths of their collective emotions and thoughts.
ISBN 978 0 573 13015 1

What the Butler Saw. Black comedy. Joe Orton
M4 (middle-age) F2 (young, middle-age). A room in a private clinic. Fee code M

Dr Prentice is a psychiatrist who believes that the best way to interview a girl for a job is to seduce her. Geraldine does her best to comply. Mrs Prentice, who has seduced a page boy, brings him home with her, just as a state inspector pays a visit. What ensues is a wild mêlée of disappearances, disguises and discoveries as husband and wife try to hide their prizes from one another and the state inspector.

◆ **A bullet mark next to a title indicates that it is new to this edition of the Guide.**

A

What the Night Is For. Play. Michael Weller
M1 (mid-late 40s) F1 (mid-late 40s). A hotel room. Fee code M

Ten years after the end of their affair in New York, two lovers meet in a hotel room far from their homes. Both are now married, both have children and both have been wondering about the road not taken. What begins as a casual meal and an evening of catching up turns into a painful, hilarious, passionate and moving voyage towards a moment that could change both their lives forever …

When Did You Last See Your Trousers? Farce. Ray Galton and John Antrobus. Based on a story by Ray Galton and Alan Simpson
M6 F3, with doubling. An apartment. Fee code M

This hilarious farce begins quietly enough with Howard and Penny asleep in bed, when a burglar enters and steals various items, including Howard's suit! Awakening, Howard announces his intention to get back to the wife; but how is he to make it to Esher without his trousers, having been left only vest and pants by the burglar? '… Brilliantly constructed farce … achingly funny …' *Guardian*
ISBN 978 0 573 01667 7

When I was a Girl, I Used to Scream and Shout … Play. Sharman Macdonald
M1 (young) F3 (30s, middle-age). Split set: a rocky beach and prom. Fee code M

'Sharman Macdonald recounts with sympathy and deliciously rude detail, the sexual misadventures and misconceptions of Fiona, growing up with her repressive mother and best friend Vari in 1950s Scotland. She shows how the girls' excitement and expectations atrophy, so that in their thirties they have become sober stereotypes of the modern woman.' *Time Out*. Sharman Macdonald won the *Evening Standard* Drama Award for the Most Promising Playwright in 1984.

When the Cat's Away. Comedy. Johnnie Mortimer and Brian Cooke
M2 (middle-age) F4 (25, middle-age). A living-room. Fee code M

Based on the popular TV sit-com *George and Mildred,* this is a riotously funny comedy. Mildred has organized a second honeymoon in France for herself and George but he is not keen on her idea. Mildred's sister, Ethel, turns up, having left her husband Humphrey. Then Humphrey arrives, so the *women* set off for France. It isn't long before Humphrey gets George into trouble involving a date with two girls and the unexpected return of their wives!
ISBN 978 0 573 69131 7

When the Reaper Calls. Comedy thriller. Peter Colley
M2 (20s, 40s) F3 (20s, 40s). Hunting lodge. Fee Code M

Victor and Harlan have been friends, rivals and inveterate pranksters since their days as students of philosophy. Now, however, Victor has taken to a life of wild hedonism, whilst Harlan leads a passionless existence of dull stoicism. On a holiday in British Columbia with their long-suffering wives a misjudged prank leaves one of the professors dead, kick-starting a highly entertaining yet chilling nightmare that will keep audiences guessing, gasping and laughing throughout.
ISBN 978 0 573 11477 9

When the Wind Blows. Play. Raymond Briggs
M1 (60s) F1 (60s). Extras. A small cottage and garden. Fee code M

A

Raymond Briggs's stage version of his famous anti-nuclear cartoon parable is passionately on the side of sanity and survival. Jim and Hilda Bloggs, a retired couple, hear on the radio that a pre-emptive strike is on the way. Armed with Government leaflets, in which he places all his faith, Jim constructs a refuge for them both, and gathers emergency rations. They emerge after the bomb to find a devastated post-holocaust world.
ISBN 978 0 573 11496 0

When We Are Married. Yorkshire farcical comedy. J. B. Priestley
M8 (young, middle-age) F7 (young, 20s, middle-age). A sitting-room. Fee code M

Twenty-five years ago, the Helliwells, the Parkers and the Soppitts were married on the same day by the same parson. They gather at the Helliwell home to celebrate their silver wedding. The new chapel organist tells them that he recently met the parson who conducted the triple wedding ceremony – he was not authorized to do so. Pandemonium breaks out when these pillars of society believe they have been living in sin for twenty-five years. Period 1900
ISBN 978 0 573 01476 5

The White Cliffs. Play. Bettine Manktelow
M2 (20-30, 50) F5 (17, 20s-50s). A bed-sitting-room. Fee code L. ISBN 978 0 573 11588 2

Who Dies Wins. Comedy-thriller. Seymour Matthews
M4 (30s, 40, mid 50s) F3 (30s). 1M or F. A living-room. Fee code L. ISBN 978 0 573 01960 9

♦ **Who Is Sylvia?** Play. Terence Rattigan
M6 F5 (with doubling). Flat. Period 1917/1929/1950. Fee Code M

Whodunnit. Comedy thriller. Anthony Shaffer
M7 F3. An eighteenth-century library. Fee code M

This witty, wickedly funny satire, a long-running success on Broadway, is firmly in Agatha Christie country of the 1930s, complete with her stock characters and situations. A group of six strangers have gathered for dinner at Orcas Champflower Manor. One of the guests, an oily Levantine, informs each of his fellow guests that he has the means to blackmail them. Not suprisingly he gets murdered – but whodunnit? In Act II the surprise is unveiled.
ISBN 978 0 573 61823 9

Who's Afraid of Virginia Woolf? Play. Edward Albee
M2 (30, 40) F2 (26, 52). A living-room. Fee code M

George, an assistant professor of history, and his wife, Martha, invite Nick and Honey to their home on the campus of a small New England college. Throughout the long liquor-drenched night, the strangers are forcibly initiated into the demonic misery of George and Martha's eternal matrimonial *corrida*. Martha exposes a secret, which George cannot forgive, and the guests slip away, leaving George and Martha, who love each other but hate themselves and therefore can only hurt each other.

Who's Under Where? Farce. Marcia Kash and Doug Hughes
M5 (20s, 40s, 50s) F2 (30s). An hotel suite. Fee code M

Jane and Sybil are on the verge of the deal of their lives. They plan to convince the world famous Italian designer Bruno Fruferelli to buy their 'Passion Fashion Wear' line of lingerie. They arrange to give him a private fashion show in a fancy hotel suite. The models are booked, the champagne is on ice, the sexy samples are on display – and then their jealous husbands arrive, inevitably jumping to the wrong conclusions!
ISBN 978 0 573 69389 2

Whose Life Is It Anyway? Play. Brian Clark
M9 F5. Multiple set. Fee code M

Ken Harrison has been so severely injured in a car crash that he is totally paralysed; only his brain functions normally. He is being kept alive by the miracles of medicine, but wishes to die. This he could achieve by discharging himself from hospital but being wholly helpless has to gain the authorities' consent. The play examines the moral and legal aspects of the situation and the reactions of the hospital staff.
ISBN 978 0 573 01587 8

Why Me? Comedy. Stanley Price
M3 (19, 30, middle-age) F3 (30, 40, 60). A living-room, a dining area. Fee code M.
ISBN 978 0 573 01622 6

Why Not Stay for Breakfast? Comedy. Gene Stone and Ray Cooney
M3 (young, 30s) F2 (17, young). A flat. Fee code L. ISBN 978 0 573 01580 9

Widows. Play. Ariel Dorfman, with Tony Kushner
Large, flexible cast, may be played by M6 F8. Various simple settings. Fee code M

In a war-torn village the men have disappeared. The women – their mothers, wives, daughters – wait by the river, hope and mourn. Their anguish is unspoken until bruised and broken bodies begin being washed up on the banks and the women defy the military in the only form of protest left to them. Ariel Dorfman's smouldering political allegory, written in collaboration with Tony Kushner, was given its European première by the Traverse Theatre in Cambridge, Oxford, Newcastle and Edinburgh.

♦ **Wife After Death**. Comedy. Eric Chappell
M2 (30s,50s) F4(30s,40s,50s) . A living-room. Fee Code M

Comedian and national treasure Dave Thursby has died and on the day of his funeral friends and colleagues gather beside his coffin to pay their last respects. Dave's glamorous widow, Laura, has arranged a funeral to remember, complete with a horse-drawn hearse. An unfamiliar woman in flamboyant mourning clothes turns out to be Dave's ex-wife and a series of revelations ends with Dave's agent throwing a drink into the coffin and the guests asking themselves if they ever knew the "real" Dave.
ISBN 978 0 573 11475 5

♦ **A bullet mark next to a title indicates that it is new to this edition of the Guide.**

Wife Begins at Forty. Comedy. Arne Sultan, Earl Barret and Ray Cooney
M4 (16, 40s, 75) F2 (30, 40). 1 dog. A living-room. Fee code M

A

This delightful comedy was premièred by Ray Cooney's Theatre of Comedy. Forty is a traumatic age for some people, especially Linda Harper who starts worrying about it three years before the date! Dissatisfied spiritually and physically with marriage to the staid George, Linda decides to leave. George moves out, giving Linda a chance to 'find herself', but returning to discuss maintenance they discover the flames of passion are not quite dead!
ISBN 978 0 573 01636 3

The Wild Duck. Play. Henrik Ibsen, translated by Christopher Hampton
M12 F3. 8M 2F extras. A study, a studio. Fee code M

Here is the greatest account ever written of the destructiveness of missonary zeal. Gregers Werle enters the house of photographer Ekdal preaching 'the demands of idealism' (a nicely ambiguous phrase in Hampton's translation) and systematically destroys a family's happiness. 'If Ibsen's play is not a masterpiece, then the word is devoid of meaning.' *Guardian*
ISBN 978 0 573 61820 8

Wild Honey. Play. Anton Chekhov, translated and adapted by Michael Frayn
M12 (young to elderly) F4 (young, middle-age). Four settings. Fee code M

A dazzling version of this dark comedy (sometimes called *Platonov*) premièred at the National Theatre in 1984 starring Ian McKellen as the complex, but hapless schoolmaster Platonov who lurches from one amorous chaos to the next, until, tormented, self-recriminating and suffering from delirium tremens he dies in the path of an oncoming train. Frayn has subtly cut and remodelled the original six-hour running time whilst staying close to Chekhov's original.

♦ **Wild Turkey**. Play. Joe Penhall
M4. Fee Code L

Stu fancies himself as an entrepreneur; he hustles on a daily basis to keep his modest new business afloat after the collapse of his last venture. He tries to remain philosophical. For him, baseball bats and hold-ups all come with the territory. *Wild Turkey* explores themes of violence and envy on the fringes of East London's murky restaurant trade.

Wildest Dreams. Play. Alan Ayckbourn
M4 (young, middle-age) F4 (young, middle-age), 1M 1F, voices only. Three acting areas. Fee code M

Four typical Ayckbourn misfits are playing a Dungeons-and-Dragons type game in a suburban living-room. The repressed Hazel and Stanley, her meek, sex-starved husband, are joined by emotionally-retarded, computer-freak schoolboy, Warren, and Rick, a taciturn lesbian. The game offers the chance for them to be beautiful, wise and heroic – qualities they will never possess in reality. The advent of Marcie, escaping from her violent husband, blows apart their foursome.
ISBN 978 0 573 01932 6

Will You Still Love Me in the Morning? Farce. Brian Clemens and Dennis Spooner
M4 (30s-50s) F3 (25-40s), or M3 F4, 1M voice only. A country cottage. Fee code M.
ISBN 978 0 573 01935 7

The Wind in the Willows. Kenneth Grahame. Adapted for the stage by Alan Bennett. Music by Jeremy Sams
24 characters. Extras. Various settings. Fee code M (play) code C (music)

The characters of Ratty, Mole, Toad and Badger have delighted generations of readers. Alan Bennett's version is true to the original and yet carries the distinctive Bennett hallmark. It was first performed at the Royal National Theatre in 1990 and subsequently at the Old Vic Theatre, London, in a shortened version adapted for proscenium staging. This is the version given here. The music by Jeremy Sams is available in a separate songbook. (Please specify author when ordering this title.)
ISBN 978 0 573 01930 2

The Wind in the Willows. Family entertainment. John Morley, adapted from the novel by Kenneth Grahame
22 characters, chorus. Doubling possible. Various interior and exterior settings. Fee code L

John Morley has taken the well-loved characters of Toad, Mole, Ratty and Badger from Kenneth Grahame's classic tale and woven their exploits into an exciting adventure story for all the family. Designed to be staged simply or elaborately, the casting is also very flexible with choice of music left up to individual producers. This delightful play will provide an evening of magic and joy for all. (Please specify author when ordering this title.)
ISBN 978 0 573 05073 2

Wings. Play. Arthur Kopit
M4 (30, elderly) F5 (elderly, 70s). Extras. A hospital recreation room and other locations. Fee code M

Emily Stilson, once an aerial acrobat, has suffered a stroke and is in hospital. The play takes us into her strange, shattered world and concerns her gradual, painful, struggle to bring together the pieces of an existence in which time, place, language and thought have become terrifyingly dislocated. A human story of the utmost compassion, and even of hope.

Winner Takes All. Farce. Reggie Oliver, adapted from *La Main Passe!* by Georges Feydeau
M10 (range of ages) F3 (range of ages). 2 salons, an apartment. Fee code M
ISBN 978 0 573 01950 0

The Winslow Boy. Play. Terence Rattigan
M7 (14, 20-40, 60) F4 (30-50, elderly). A living-room. Fee code M

Cadet Ronnie Winslow is expelled from the Royal Naval College accused of stealing. His father, refusing to believe his guilt and dissatisfied with the manner in which the investigation was conducted, demands a new inquiry. This is refused and Arthur Winslow settles down to fight for his son's honour. Following an independent inquiry the matter is taken to the House of Commons but Arthur ruins himself financially and in health in the process. But his stubbornness wins, a civil trial is allowed and Ronnie is acquitted. Period Edwardian
ISBN 978 0 573 01494 9

♦ **A bullet mark next to a title indicates that it is new to this edition of the Guide.**

The Winter Guest. Play. Sharman Macdonald
M3 (young) F5 (young, 30s, elderly). A seaside promenade and beach. Fee code M

The play is set on a seaside promenade and intermingles the lives of several sets of people found there. A grandmother still clings on to her daughter, a young photographer, who is trying to come to terms with the death of her husband, while the photographer's son pursues love. Two young truant boys are concerned with the onset of puberty. And an elderly pair of ladies discuss their favourite pastime, funeral attendance. NB. Contains explicit language.

Without Trace. Thriller. Brian Clemens
M4 (30s-50 (2 Black), 40s) F2 (20s, 40s). 1M or F extra. A hotel lodge. Fee code M

In a remote African hotel lodge five Britons are on a safari holiday. The guests comprise Sally, a young beautician, Mark, a wheeler-dealer, and his wife Clare, and Peter and his wealthy wife Anne. That night a violent storm erupts and Anne disappears. Aboo, the barman, insists on calling in the urbane Police Captain k'Maka to investigate and as the storm rages Anne's body is discovered in the river. There are twists and turns aplenty in this ingenious thriller before the stirring conclusion. Manuscript only available on hire

Witness for the Prosecution. Play. Agatha Christie
M: 9 principals, 15 extras. F: 4 principals, 2 extras. Justice's chambers. Law Courts. Fee code M

Although circumstantial evidence is damning, Leonard Vole convinces even the perceptive Sir Wilfrid that he is innocent of murder. In the mounting tension of the trial there are three amazing developments. Vole's wife takes the stand and coldly swears away her husband's alibi. A brassy young woman then sells Sir Wilfrid's letters proving Mrs Vole has committed perjury. Vole is acquitted but only then does Sir Wilfrid discover how this acquittal has been engineered by Mrs Vole. But there is still the dramatic finale ...
ISBN 978 0 573 01500 7

Wolf at the Door. Original play (*Les Corbeaux*) by Henry Becque, translated by David Walker and adapted by Alan Ayckbourn
M9, F6 plus M3 (non-speaking). A drawing-room. Fee code M. ISBN 978 0 573 01936 4

Woman in Mind. Play. Alan Ayckbourn
M5 (20, 30, 40) F3 (20, 40s). A garden. Fee code M

Seen at the Vaudeville, London, in 1986 with Julia McKenzie and Martin Jarvis, this is one of Ayckbourn's blacker comedies, dealing with the gradual mental collapse of Susan. Starved of affectionate companionship and understanding love by an appalling husband and priggish son, Susan conjures up an ideal family. But gradually she loses control over this dream and finally breaks down in a nightmarish fantasy involving her real and imaginary families.
ISBN 978 0 573 01662 2

The Woman in White. Play. Constance Cox. Adapted from the novel by Wilkie Collins
M6 (late 20s, 40, middle age, elderly) F5 (20s, middle age, elderly). A drawing-room. Fee code L

Sir Percival Glyde, who is being hounded for money by the sinister Count Fosco, marries the heiress Laura Fairlie for her fortune. As events unfold, Glyde's efforts to secure the money – and also to remove the threat to his reputation posed by the unfortunate Anne Catherick – become more desperate and cruel. Combined with this tale of disturbing intrigue are elements of romance and comedy: the resulting mix is headily entertaining. Period 1861-2
ISBN 978 0 573 11578 3

The Women. Play. Clare Booth Luce
F44: 11 principals and 33 small parts; doubling and trebling possible. Twelve interiors. Fee code J

Mary Haines's friends are cynical about her happy, successful marriage. When news reaches the friends that Stephen, Mary's husband, is enjoying a dalliance with the gold-digging Crystal Allen, Mary is soon informed. Her mother, wise and worldly, advises her to forgive him, but she feels divorce is the only solution. Eventually, having learned from her friends the laws of the female jungle, Mary sharpens her claws, and prepares to win back the man she still loves.

Women Laughing. Play. Michael Wall
M2 (30s) F2 (30s). 2 gardens. Fee code M

Colin and Tony sit in Colin's back garden, their conversation punctuated by gales of laughter from their wives in the kitchen. The wives, Steph and Maddy, reveal the laughter had been about their husbands' visits to therapy groups. Both men have been having panic attacks. As the party degenerates, Tony makes an attempt to attack his wife. The second act of this fine play finds him in a mental asylum, doped into inertia, with Colin a less aggressive, but frighteningly manic, fellow patient.

Women on the Verge of HRT. Play. Marie Jones. Music by Neil Martin
M1 (early 30s) F2 (40s). A hotel bedroom, a beach. Fee code M

Vera and Anna have made the trip to Donegal to see their singing idol Daniel O'Donnell. Vera has been abandoned by her husband and Anna is content to dream of Daniel whilst sustaining a loveless marriage. Singing waiter, Fergal, invites the women to join him at dawn. In a series of dream-like meetings the women confront their spouses and each other. Neil Martin's country-style songs enhance this easily-staged, telling look at the spirit of women.
ISBN 978 0 573 01939 5

The Wonderful World of Dissocia. Play. Anthony Neilson
Ml9 F10. Doubling possible. Various simple settings. Fee code M

Lisa's watch is running an hour slow. The watch mender, Victor, explains that in actual fact she has lost the hour from her life. The only way to correct this 'temporal disturbance' is to descend to an underworld called Dissocia and retrieve it from the Lost Property Office. Upon arrival, Lisa learns that Dissocia is under siege by the Black Dog King, and its Queen Sarah is in hiding. A series of surreal encounters follow, but will Lisa find her missing hour?

A Word from Our Sponsor. Words by Alan Ayckbourn. Music by John Pattison
M4 F5. A disused railway station. Fee by arrangement

This futuristic musical is set in a small-town railway station, sometime all too soon. Harry Wooller, a vicar, is looking for sponsorship for his group's musical Mystery play. His call is intercepted by a dubious but immensely powerful source – Valda/Valder who alternates between male and female forms. Artistry is soon compromised; this drastic interference forces the group to reveal their past deeds, and recognize the need for change.
ISBN 978 0 573 08105 7 Vocal score ISBN 978 0 573 08603 8 (Perusal material available)

♦ **A bullet mark next to a title indicates that it is new to this edition of the Guide.**

Woyzeck. Play. Georg Büchner, translated by John Mackendrick
M10 F3, with doubling. Various interior and exterior settings. Fee code M

A

This anti-romantic and starkly realistic tragedy is about a common soldier, Woyzeck, who attempts to make sense out of life in the face of the intolerance of those about him who think him stupid. Driven mad by external forces – inhuman military discipline, environment, class and religion – he slaughters his wife and then drowns himself. Büchner's portrayal is ironic and compassionate: the play was a remarkable nineteenth-century call for the need for social reform.

◆ **Wuthering Heights.** Play. April De Angelis, from the novel by Emily Brontë
M8 F7, 1 boy, may be played by M6 F4 with doubling. Extras. Various simple settings.
Fee code L

A brand new adaptation brings Emily Brontë's passionate and spellbinding tale of forbidden love and revenge to life on stage. Period early Victorian
"I was relieved to see an adaptation of this wonderful Emily Brontë novel that was true to her creation." *Birmingham Mail*
ISBN 978 0 573 11495 3

Wuthering Heights. Play. Emily Brontë, adapted for the stage by Charles Vance
M6 F4. Composite setting. Fee code M

A new version of Emily Brontë's great classic, the immortal love story set amid the bleak beauty of Haworth Moor, the landscape over which towers the wild, terrible figure of Heathcliff. The tale of his searing passion for the beautiful Catherine Earnshaw has the vividness of nightmare, the beauty and simplicity of an old ballad and the depth and intensity of ancient tragedy. Period nineteenth century
ISBN 978 0 573 11474 8

A Yard of Sun. Play. Christopher Fry
M9 (young to middle-age) F3 (young, middle-age). A courtyard. Fee code M

A 'summer comedy' set in Sienna just after World War II. Preparations are in hand for the renewal of the Palio fiesta – a horse race which has been held in the town for hundreds of years. Angelino is one of two central characters whose families are unexpectedly reunited after the war, and the play deals with the effects of the reunion both on individuals and on the group as a whole. Period 1946

◆ **Yellow Moon.** Play. David Greig
M3 F2. Simple interior and exterior settings. Fee code L

A modern Bonnie and Clyde tale following the fortune of two teenagers on the run. Silent Leila is an introverted girl with a passion for celebrity magazines. Lee is the deadest of dead-end kids in a dead-end town. They never meant to get mixed up in a murder ... but now they need a place to hide. Premiered at the Circle Studio, Citizens' Theatre, Glasgow, in 2006 and then at the Edinburgh Festival Fringe in 2007.
"Full of contemporary themes ... Engrossing and engaging." *The Times*

Yerma. Play. Federico García Lorca. Translated by Peter Luke
M3 F13. Stark set. Fee code M

The York Realist. Play. Peter Gill
M4 F3. Farm labourer's cottage. Fee code M

Young, middle-class Londoner John has come to York to direct an amateur version of the Mystery Plays and falls in love with farm lad George who is cast in the play. Has George the courage to leave his chapel-going roots and move to London with John? The play is not only a finely drawn love story but also makes us think about the depths of class allegiances, the strength of the family and the tension between country life and the cosmopolitan city. Period 1966

You Say Tomatoes. Comedy. Bernard Slade
M2 (50s, 70) F2 (20s, 50s-60s). 2 living-rooms. Fee code M

Giles, quintessentially English, doesn't take kindly to the intrusion of Americans Libby and Daisy. Libby needs to contact T. J. Walbourne, the famous mystery writer, to put together a film deal. Walbourne is, of course, Giles, and he musters all his reserve to thwart Libby. Finally, she admits defeat. But Libby has aroused passions in Giles and within days he is knocking at her door with a neat romantic compromise!
ISBN 978 0 573 69540 7

You Should See Us Now. Play. Peter Tinniswood
M2 (40s) F4 (30s, 60). Composite setting. Fee code M. ISBN 978 0 573 11512 7

Zack. Comedy. Harold Brighouse
M6 (20, 30, middle-age) F4 (18, young, 50s). A parlour/refreshment room. Fee code M
ISBN 978 0 573 01710 0

◆ **A bullet mark next to a title indicates that it is new to this edition of the Guide.**

Give the Gift of Theatre with a

Theatre Tokens are welcome at over a hundred and eighty theatres nationwide, including all of London's West End. They are available in denominations of £5, £10, £20 and £50* and have no expiry date.

* For security reasons we recommend that tokens are sent registered post. There is an additional charge for this service within the UK. Please note that if you do not wish your tokens to be despatched by registered post we cannot accept responsibility for non-delivery.

Available from:
French's Theatre Bookshop 52 Fitzroy Street
London W1T 5JR
020 7255 4300 (Bookshop)
020 7387 9373 (Enquiries) 020 7387 2161 (Fax)
email: theatre@samuelfrench-london.co.uk

SECTION B

One Act Plays and Revue Sketches

CONTENTS

Classified Index

Plays arranged according to the number of characters

ONE CHARACTER

MALE
Actor
Advice to Iraqi Women
Chip in the Sugar
Dog
Harry's Christmas
Iphegenia in Orem
Krapp's Last Tape
Lady Bracknell's Confinement
Leslie
Monologue
Small Family Murder
Starch
Time of Wolves and Tigers
Wendlebury Day

FEMALE
Advice to Iraqi Women
Bed Among the Lentils
Cream Cracker Under the Settee
Flash, Bam, Alakazam
Her Big Chance
Human Voice
Lady Bracknell's Confinement
Lady of Letters
Maureen
Medea
Medea Redux
Post Mortem
Putting the Kettle On
Same Old Story
Soldiering On
Spoonface Steinberg
Waking Up
Woman Alone
Woman of No Importance

TWO CHARACTERS

Last Call for Breakfast (*variable cast*)

COMEDIES

M1 F1
Alas Poor Fred
Extraordinary Revelations of Orca
  the Goldfish
For Starters
Joining the Club
Late Entry
Melody
Peas
Plaster
Purvis
Waiting

M2
Massage (*min. cast*)
Music for Amelia (*M or F extra*)
Victoria Station

F2
Cruise Missile
Dancers
Day Trippers
Doggies
Indian Summer
Theatrical Digs

PLAYS

M1 F1

Blind Date
Bride-to-be
Close to Croydon
Gaggle of Saints
Holiday
Just Passing
Landscape
Last Things
Lifelines
Lunch
Mister Paradise
Penalty
Pink Bedroom
Pineapple
Secretarial Skills
Seven Stages of an Affair
Talk to Me Like the Rain ...
This Property is Condemned

Visit From Miss Protheroe
Window Cleaner

M2
Acting Exercise
Audience (Havel)
Bookends
Carrot
Drunk Enough to Say I Love You
Duck Variations
Man of Letters
Me and My Friend
Palooka
Sociable Plover
Stanley Parkers

F2
Cupboard Love
Early Blight
Garden Pests
Grannies
Henna Night
Last Post
Me and My Friend
Outdoor Pleasures
Remember Me
Shoppers
Why Do You Smoke So Much, Lily?

SERIOUS PLAYS

M1 F1
Abortive
Ashes
Whence

M2
New World Order
Protest

F2
Keeping Mum

DRAMAS

M1 F1
Auto-Da-Fé
Bar and Ger
Bow of Ulysses
Forward to the Right
Galway Girl
Half-Life
Humour Helps

Moony's Kid Don't Cry
Sound of Silence

M2
Death Artist
Dock Brief
Dumb Waiter
Zoo Story

F2
Effie's Burning
Guilt Card
Late Frost
Short Changed
Something Unspoken

B

THREE CHARACTERS

Edge (*variable cast*)
Just Passing
Tryst (*variable cast*)

COMEDIES

M1 F2
Better Half
Genteel
Remembering Things
Say Something Happened

M2 F1
Albert
Bear
Boundary
How to Make Your Theatre Pay
Matchstick Dreams
Sturm und Drang
Trip of a Lifetime

PLAYS

M1 F2

Adam and Eve on a Ferry
Kind of Alaska
Lady of Larkspur Lotion
Lunch Hour
Office Song
Open Secrets
Phoenix Too Frequent
Rape of Bunny Stuntz
Resounding Tinkle
Roman Fever

Seagulls
Summer at the Lake
Swan Song
Trip's Cinch

M2 F1
Basement
Clearing the Colours
Drag Factor
Family Voices
Fat Man's Wife
From Here To The Library
Is It Something I Said?
Jabiru
Meat and Two Veg
Municipal Abattoir
Open Couple
Ordinary Day
Private Ear
Private View
Public Eye
Silence
Touch of Rose Madder
Two Wits to Woo
View from the Obelisk
Waiting for a Bus
White Liars

M3

Escape
Kind of Vesuvius

F3
Cecily
Come and Go

SERIOUS PLAYS

M1 F2
Dark Room
I Rise in Flame, Cried the Phoenix
Lesson
Long Stay Cut Short
Sins of the Father
Sunbeams
Too Hot to Handle

M2 F1
Chairs
Escapologist
Lover
Normal
Nothing Personal
Not Not Not Not Not Enough Oxygen
Old One-Two

One-Sided Triangle
Slight Ache
Twenty-Seven Wagons Full of Cotton
Wall

F3
And Go to Innisfree

M3
Last of My Solid Gold Watches
Penetrator

DRAMAS

M1 F2
Cut in the Rates (*min. cast*)
Eliza's House

M2 F1
Edge

M3
Dwarfs
Edge
Small Family Murder

F3
Donahue Sisters
Semblance of Madness!
To Have and To Hold (*1 male voice*)

FOUR CHARACTERS

FARCES

M2 F2
As You Were
Pastiche

COMEDIES

M1 F3
Don't Blame It on the Boots
Fumed Oak

M2 F2
Bang, You're Dead!
Come into the Garden Maud
Drunkard's Wife
Fat Lady Sings in Little Grimley
Figuring Things
Intruders
Jolly Sinister Jape
Last Panto in Little Grimley
Last Tango in Little Grimley

Other People
Save My Child!
Sexual Perversity in Chicago
Split Ends
Trouble Shared

M3 F1
Before Dawn
Hamlet Part II
Mayhem at the Mill
Night Before Christmas

F4
What Ho Within

PLAYS

M1 F3
Alternative Accommodation
Ghosts of Bedlam
Departure
Lord Byron's Love Letter
Pity About Kitty
Respectable Funeral

M2 F2
Case of the Crushed Petunia
Form
Four-Play
I Do Solemnly Declare
In Room Five Hundred and Four
Joggers
Knightsbridge
One Careful Owner
Perfect Partners
Plan of Action
Seascape
Voice of the Phoenix

M3 F1
Another Moon Called Earth
Light Lunch
Luck of the Draw
Strangest Kind of Romance

M4
And Tell Sad Stories ...
Palooka
Too Much the Sun

F4
Café Society
Charity Begins
Relics

SERIOUS PLAYS

M1 F3
Blue

M2 F2
In Need of Care
Ritual for Dolls
Shadows of the Evening
Train
Three More Sleepless Nights
Yesterday Man

M3 F1
Collection
Endgame
One for the Road
Receive This Light

F4
Everybody's Friend

DRAMAS

M1 F3
Crossing
Cut in the Rates
Footprints in the Sand
Missing

M2 F2
Bill & Bob
Bottles With Baskets On
Love Course
Rats
Seascape

M3 F1
Dark
Monkey's Paw

M4
In the Penal Colony
Loophole
Sleep of Prisoners

F4
Hello from Bertha
Visitor

B

FIVE CHARACTERS

FARCES

M1 F4
Music Lovers

M3 F2
After Magritte

M4 F1
Don't Walk About With Nothing On
Englishman Abroad
Put Some Clothes On, Clarisse!

F5
Allotment

COMEDIES

M1 F4
Shop for Charity

M2 F3
Babysitting Calvin
Cahoot's Macbeth

M3 F2
Breakfast for One
Carry Me, Kate
Double, Double
Getting Along
Last of the Last of the Mohicans
What's for Pudding?
Whodidit? (*min.cast*)

M4 F1
Brave Bugler
Little Lights of Kimberley

F5
Costa del Packet

PLAYS

M1 F4
Not Bobby

M2 F3
Flood Warning
Green Forms
Hot Fudge
Pizzazz

Sour Grapes and Ashes
Teeth

M3 F2
London Vertigo
Perfect Analysis Given by a Parrot
Tippers

F5
Cards Cups and Crystal Ball
Rialto Prom
Think the Beautiful Thoughts
Whose Wedding Is It Anyway?

SERIOUS PLAYS

M2 F3
American Dream
But Yesterday
Janna Years

M3 F2
Dreamjobs
Something in the Genes

M4 F1
Measures Taken
If Yer Take A Short Cut

DRAMAS

M1 F4
In by the Half
Parentcraft
Permission to Cry
Under the Twelfth Sign

M2 F3
Baby Love
Permission to Cry
Touching Tomorrow

M3 F1
Monkey's Paw

M3 F2
Sequence of Events

F5
Alas Dear Reader
Ghost of a Chance
Nasty Things Murders
Permission to Cry
Shindig

SIX CHARACTERS

Can You Hear the Music? (*variable cast*)

FARCES

M2 F4
Magic
One Month Early

M3 F3
Take Your Medicine Like a Man

M5 F1
One Was Nude and One Wore Tails

COMEDIES

M2 F4
Blue Suede Blues
Curses, Foiled Again!
Distracted Globe
Prince Lear
Separate Peace
Showbusiness (*min. cast*)

M3 F3
Brenton Versus Brenton
Gypsy Curse
One Month to Pay

M4 F2
Double Dealing
Fanny's Prayer
Fifteen Minute Hamlet
Party
Red Peppers

F6
Darlings You Were Wonderful
Knowing Constance Spry

PLAYS

M2 F4
Droitwich Discovery
Five Kinds of Silence
Going Home
Heart's Desire (*min. cast*)
Millie's Tale

M3 F3
Dog's Life
Happy Journey

M4 F2
Dog's Life
Lovesick
Ringing of Bells
We Don't Want to Lose You

F6
Calling
Mrs Meadowsweet

SERIOUS PLAYS

M3 F3
Bald Prima Donna
Till We Meet Again

M4 F2
Are You Normal, Mr Norman?
Brighton Beach Scumbags
How Much Is Your Iron?
Portrait of a Madonna
Room
Two Summers

DRAMAS

M2 F4
After Midnight – Before Dawn

M3 F3
Gnädiges Fräulein
Goodbye Iphigenia

M5 F1
Question of Attribution

M6
Fourth Prisoner

F6
Borderline
Who Calls?

B

SEVEN CHARACTERS

Dickens' Children (*variable cast*)
Stalag 69 (*variable cast*)

B

FARCES

M4 F3
Virtuous Burglar

COMEDIES

M1 F6
Orchestra
Womberang

M2 F5
Easy Stages
Happy Birthday Me
Last Bread Pudding

M3 F4
Easy Stages
Last Bread Pudding
World Première

M4 F3
Nellie's Nightlights

M6 F1
Green Eye of the Little Yellow Dog

PLAYS

M1 F6
Just the Two of Us

M2 F5
Reading Group

M3 F4
Fatal Loins
Money Makes You Happy
Too Long an Autumn

M4 F3
Cup Final
Fatal Loins
There's None So Blind

M5 F2
Cut and Dried
Fear of Heaven
Foreign Bodies
Game of Soldiers
Hole

F7
Camp Confidence
Tea Dance

SERIOUS PLAYS

M2 F5
Suddenly Last Summer

M3 F4
Beata Beatrix
Judge's Wife
Umjana Land
Victory of the Cross

M5 F2
Browning Version
Mountain Language

DRAMAS

M3 F4
Demon

M4 F3
Agamemnon

F7
Crossways

EIGHT CHARACTERS

FARCES

COMEDIES

Top Table (*variable cast*)

M4 F4
Melons at the Parsonage

M5 F3
Black Comedy
Johnny Don't Jump
Real Inspector Hound

PLAYS

M3 F5
Two Fat Men

M4 F4
Albert's Plot

M5 F3
Gizmo
These Are the Stairs ...

M6 F2
Big Game

F8
Lovesome Thing

SERIOUS PLAYS

Cagebirds (*variable cast*)
No Name in the Street (*variable cast*)

M1 F7
Blue

M5 F3
Ringing for You (*min. cast*)

DRAMAS

M2 F6
Blue Kettle

NINE CHARACTERS

Christmas Incorporated (*variable cast*)
Present Slaughter (*variable cast*)

COMEDIES

M1 F8
Cinderella (Green)

M2 F7
Sold to the Gypsies

M3 F6
Cinderella (Green)
Merry Regiment of Women
Trapped

M5 F4
Hands Across the Sea
Out for the Count
Pride at Southanger Park
Ways and Means

LIGHT PLAYS

Zartan (*variable cast*)

SERIOUS PLAYS

M5 F4
Party Time

M7 F2
Long Goodbye

DRAMAS

M5 F4
Patient

M6 F3
Señora Carrar's Rifles

TEN CHARACTERS

Streuth (*variable cast*)

COMEDIES

M4 F6
Albert Laddin

M6 F4
Way Out West

F10
Clara's on the Curtains!

PLAYS

M5 F5
Hot Fudge

M6 F4
Tea Party

B

SERIOUS PLAYS

M7 F3
One Thing More

M9 F1
Exception and the Rule

B

DRAMAS

M5 F5
LittleBro Morning and BigSis Afternoon
What Are You Doing Here?

ELEVEN CHARACTERS AND OVER

After-Dinner Joke
Afternoon at the Seaside
Albert's Bridge
Ali's Barbara
All's Well That Ends As You Like It
Audience
Baby Love
Cahoot's Macbeth
Celebration
Cherry Sisters
Collier's Tuesday Tea
Deadly Attachment
Death
Dogg's Hamlet
Ernie's Incredible Illucinations
Everyman
Everywoman
Fawlty Towers
Fish in her Kettle
Forty Winks Beauty
God
Godiva Affair
Half an Idea
Hamelin Incident
Harlequinade
Henry the Tenth
If You're Glad I'll Be Frank
Il Fornicazione
Julius and Cleopatra
Long Christmas Dinner
Maria Marten (Cox)
Moby Dick
Mum's Army

Mutilated
Night Out
No Name in the Street
Oedocles, King of Thebes
One Thing More
Oubliette
Pullman Car *Hiawatha*
Purification
Present Slaughter
Sea Side Trippers
Showbusiness
Small Affair
Spring Song Singers
Stalag 69
Still Life
Thank You Kind Spirit
Thor With Angels
Trial of Joan of Arc at Rouen, 1431
Trial of Lucullus
Us and Them
Vagabond Prince
Whodidit?

Plays arranged under specific headings

BURLESQUES/MELODRAMAS

Brave Bugler
Curses, Foiled Again!
Double Dealing
Drunkard's Wife
Fanny's Prayer
Frankenstein's Guests
Green Eye of the Little Yellow Dog
Gypsy Curse
Little Lights of Kimberley
Maria Marten (Cox)
Mayhem at the Mill
Nellie's Nightlights
One Month to Pay
Out for the Count
Save My Child!
Sold to the Gypsies
Tram-Track Tragedy
Trouble Shared
Unhand Me Squire

COSTUME PLAYS

(Dates are given in round figures as an approximate guide)

Ancient Greek
Goodbye Iphigenia
Medea
Phoenix Too Frequent

Ancient Roman
Trial of Lucullus

Biblical
No Name in the Street
Victory of the Cross

Anglo Saxon
Thor, with Angels

Medieval
Everyman (Cox)

Gothic 1200-1450
Forward to the Right
Hamelin Incident
Healer
Trial of Joan of Arc at Rouen

Elizabethan 1550-1620
Crossways
Fatal Loins
Fifteen Minute Hamlet
Hamlet Part II
Merry Regiment of Women
Prince Lear

Louis XIV 1660 onwards
After Midnight–Before Dawn

Late Georgian 1750 onwards
Before Dawn
Gideon and the Sea Witch
London Vertigo

Early Victorian 1840-1865 (Crinoline)
Dickens' Children
Lady Audley's Secret
Maria Marten

Late Victorian 1865-1900 (Bustle)
Alas, Dear Reader
As You Were (Austrian; to 1950)
Bear
Cards, Cups and Crystal Ball
Day of Reckoning
Music Lovers
Purification
Ritual for Dolls
Smile
Who Calls?

Edwardian 1900-1910
Don't Walk About With Nothing On
(French)
Night Errant (French)
One Month Early (French)
Put Some Clothes On, Clarisse! (French)
Sequence of Events
Take Your Medicine Like a Man (French)

1920s
Better Half
Jolly Sinister Jape

1930s
Crossing
Fat Man's Wife
Fumed Oak
Hands Across the Sea
How Much Is Your Iron?

B

B

Missing
Normal
Red Peppers
Roman Fever
Señora Carrar's Rifles
Still Life
Tea Dance
Two Wits to Woo
Ways and Means

1940s
Dark Room
Deadly Attachment
Godiva Affair
I Rise in Flames Cried the Phoenix
Mum's Army
Seascape

1950s
Asylum
Browning Version
Englishman Abroad

1960s
Foreign Bodies
Game of Soldiers
If You're Glad I'll Be Frank
Kind of Alaska
Rialto Prom

Modern and Period
But Yesterday
Curses, Foiled Again!
Droitwich Discovery
Ghost of a Chance
God
Hidden Meanings
In Room Five Hundred and Four
Long Christmas Dinner
Oubliette
September Revisited
Train
Two Summers
Winter of 1917

Futuristic
Gizmo
If Yer Take a Short Cut
It's All in the Game
Not Not Not Not Not Enough Oxygen
Whence

DRAMATIZED NOVELS AND STORIES

Dickens' Children
In the Penal Colony

DRAMATIZED TELEVISION SERIES

Cut and Dried (*from* Fiddlers Three)
Deadly Attachment (*from* Dad's Army)
Fawlty Towers
Godiva Affair (*from* Dad's Army)
Mum's Army (*from* Dad's Army)
We Don't Want to Lose You (*from* Fiddlers Three)

PLAYS SET IN HOSPITALS

Drag Factor
Effie's Burning
Fear of Heaven
Going Home
Keeping Mum
Kind of Alaska
Magic
Parentcraft
Philip and Rowena
Plaster
Semblance of Madness!
Separate Peace
Showbusiness
Waiting
Woman of No Importance
Womberang

PLAYS WITH A NATIONAL OR REGIONAL SETTING OR INTEREST

AMERICAN

Adam and Eve On a Ferry
American Dream
And Go To Innisfree
And Tell Sad Stories ...
Auto-Da-Fé
Big Game
Brenton Versus Brenton
Case of the Crushed Petunia
Dark Room
Death
Duck Variations
Escape
Fat Man's Wife

Happy Journey
Hello from Bertha
Last of My Solid Gold Watches
Long Goodbye
Long Stay Cut Short
Lady of Larkspur Lotion
Lord Byron's Love Letter
Mister Paradise
Moony's Kid Don't Cry
Municipal Abattoir
Mutilated
Old One-Two
Palooka
Perfect Analysis Given By A Parrot
Pink Bedroom
Portrait of a Madonna
Pullman Car *Hiawatha*
Purification
Rape of Bunny Stuntz
Sexual Perversity in Chicago
Something Unspoken
Strangest Kind Of Romance
Suddenly Last Summer
Summer at the Lake
Thank You Kind Spirit
These Are the Stairs You Got to Watch
This Property is Condemned
Trip's Cinch
Twenty-Seven Wagons Full of Cotton
Why Do You Smoke So Much, Lily?
Zoo Story

FRENCH

Dispute
Don't Walk About With Nothing On
Forward to the Right
Human Voice
Lesson
Music Lovers
Night Errant
One Month Early
Orchestra
Put Some Clothes On, Clarisse!
Sound of Silence
Take Your Medicine Like a Man
Trial of Joan of Arc at Rouen

IRISH

Comedies
Last of the Last of the Mohicans
Pizzazz

Dramas
Fallen Heroes
Galway Girl
Hebrew Lesson
London Vertigo
Nothing Personal
Time of Wolves and Tigers
View from the Obelisk

SCOTS

Bear

SOUTH AFRICAN

Crossing
Missing

WELSH
(in English)

Footprints in the Sand

PLAYS WITH AN ENVIRONMENTAL INTEREST

Not Not Not Not Not Enough Oxygen
Singing in the Wilderness
Tippers
Whence

PLAYS WITH A THEATRICAL INTEREST

Acting Exercise
Actor
Audience (Frayn)
Cahoot's Macbeth
Clara's on the Curtains!
Curses, Foiled Again
Darlings, You Were Wonderful!
Distracted Globe
Dogg's Hamlet
Don't Blame It on the Boots
Droitwich Discovery
Easy Stages
Fat Lady Sings in Little Grimley
Fifteen Minute Hamlet
Game of Soldiers

B

Half an Idea
Harlequinade
Her Big Chance
How to Make Your Theatre Pay
Humour Helps
Lady Bracknell's Confinement
Last Bread Pudding
Last Panto in Little Grimley
Last Tango in Little Grimley
Last Things
Melons at the Parsonage
Merry Regiment of Women
Night's Candles
Real Inspector Hound
Red Peppers
Small Affair
Theatrical Digs
Too Long an Autumn
Waiting for a Bus
World Première
Yes and No

MUSICAL PLAYS

Maria Marten
Orchestra
Purification
Red Peppers

MYSTERY AND SUSPENSE PLAYS

Afternoon at the Seaside
Daddy's Gone A-Hunting
Dark
Dead End
Demon
Half-Life
Jolly Sinister Jape
Monkey's Paw
Mum's the Word
Murder Play
Nasty Things, Murders
Patient
Rats
Visitor
Who Calls?
Whodidit?

PLAYS ABOUT THE SUPERNATURAL, GHOSTS AND WITCHCRAFT

After Midnight – Before Dawn
Cards, Cups and Crystal Ball
Crossing
Crossways
Cut in the Rates
Dark
Demon
Droitwich Discovery
Edge
Epitaph for A Hard Man
Footprints in the Sand
Genteel
Ghost of a Chance
Gideon and the Sea Witch
Is There Anybody There?
Last Things
Monkey's Paw
Now and Then
Olive and Hilary
Seagulls
Till We Meet Again
Tunnel Vision
Under the Twelfth Sign
View From the Obelisk

RELIGIOUS INTEREST AND MORALITY

Abortive
Effie's Burning
Everyman
Everywoman
Hamelin Incident
Happy Journey
Hole
Long Christmas Dinner
No Name in the Street
One Thing More
Public Eye
Pullman Car *Hiawatha*
Receive This Light
Sleep of Prisoners
Thor, With Angels
Victory of the Cross

ALL MALE

Acting Exercise
And Tell Sad Stories ...
Audience
Ball Boys
Blood Sports
Bookends
Chip in the Sugar
Deadly Attachment
Death Artist
Dock Brief
Do-It-Yourself Frankenstein Outfit
Duck Variations
Dumb Waiter
Dwarfs
Edge
Escape
Fourth Prisoner
Iphegenia in Orem
Kind of Vesuvius
Krapp's Last Tape
Lady Bracknell's Confinement
Last of My Solid Gold Watches
Leslie
Loophole
Man of Letters
Me and My Friend
Memento Mori
Monologue
Music for Amelia
New World Order
Out of the Flying Pan
Palooka
Penetrator
Protest
Sea Side Trippers
Sleep of Prisoners
Small Family Murder
Spring Song Singers
Stanley Parkers
Starch
Time of Wolves and Tigers
Too Much the Sun
Top Table
Victoria Station
Vigil
Wendlebury Day
Zoo Story

ALL FEMALE

Alas Dear Reader
Allotment
And Go To Innisfree
Bed Among the Lentils
Café Society
Calling
Camp Confidence
Cards, Cups and Crystal Ball
Cecily
Christmas Incorporated
Clara's on the Curtains
Come and Go
Costa del Packet!
Crossways
Cruise Missile
Cupboard Love
Dancers
Darlings, You Were Wonderful
Day of Reckoning
Day Trippers
Doggies
Donahue Sisters
Dreamjobs
Early Blight
Effie's Burning
Everyman
Ghost of a Chance
Guilt Card
Hello from Bertha
Henna Night
Her Big Chance
Human Voice
In by the Half
Indian Summer
Keeping Mum
Knowing Constance Spry
Lady Bracknell's Confinement
Lady of Letters
Last Post
Late Frost
Lovesome Thing
Maureen
Me and My Friend
Medea
Medea Redux
Mrs Meadowsweet
Nasty Things Murders
Once and for All
Permission to Cry
Post Mortem
Putting the Kettle On
Relics
Rialto Prom
Same Old Story

B

Sea Side Trippers
Semblance of Madness!
September Revisited
Shindig
Shoppers
Short Changed
Soldiering On
Something Unspoken
Spoonface Steinberg
Spring Song Singers
Tea Dance
Terrace Talk
Theatrical Digs
Think the Beautiful Thoughts
To Have and To Hold (*1 male voice*)
Top Table
Trial
Visitor
Waking Up
What Ho Within!
Who Calls?
Whose Wedding Is It Anyway?
Why Do You Smoke So Much, Lily?
Woman Alone
Woman of No Importance

DOUBLE BILL PLAYS (Long one act plays and some others that make a double bill)

Acting Exercise
Actor's Nightmare
Afternoon at the Seaside
Albert's Bridge
American Dream*
Ashes to Ashes*
Bald Prima Donna
Ball Boys
Black Comedy*
Blood Sports
Blue Kettle
Browning Version*
Cahoot's Macbeth
Chairs*
Collection*
Come into the Garden Maud*
Cut and Dried
Dark
Deadly Attachment
Dock Brief
Dogg's Hamlet
Dumb Waiter
Endgame*
Englishman Abroad
Family Voices
Foreign Bodies
Form
Fumed Oak
Gaggle of Saints
Game of Soldiers
Godiva Affair
Green Forms
Half an Idea*
Hands Across the Sea
Harlequinade*
Heart's Desire
Hole*
Hot Fudge
Humour Helps
Iphegenia in Orem
Kind of Alaska
Last Panto in Little Grimley
Last Tango in Little Grimley
Last Things
Leslie
Lesson
Lover
Lunch Hour
Maureen
Medea Redux
Monkey's Paw
Mountain Language
Mum's Army

Night Out* (Pinter)
Office Suite
On Location
One for the Road (Pinter)
Party Time
Patient
Private Ear
Public Eye
Question of Attribution
Rats
Real Inspector Hound*
Red Peppers
Resounding Tinkle
Room
Sexual Perversity in Chicago*
Shadows of the Evening*
Sister Mary Ignatius Explains It All For You*
Slight Ache
Small Affair*
Soldier and the Woman*
Still Life*
Victoria Station
Waiting for a Bus
Ways and Means
We Don't Want to Lose You
White Liars
Zoo Story

*Indicates a playing time of one hour or longer

B

B

Authors' Index

B

Entries in italics refer to novels by well-known authors which have been dramatized either under their own name or under another title which is given in parenthesis

B

Aeschylus
Agammemnon (*adapt. Berkoff*)

Albee, Edward
American Dream
Zoo Story

Aldrich, Arthur
Ghosts of Bedlam
Shindig

Allen, Woody
Death
God

Anouilh, Jean
Orchestra

Aron, Geraldine
Bar and Ger
Donahue Sisters
Galway Girl
Joggers
Stanley Parkers

Austin, Harry
Brave Bugler
Green Eye of the Little Yellow Dog
Little Lights of Kimberley
Nellie's Nightlights

Ayckbourn, Alan
Cut in the Rates
Ernie's Incredible Illucinations
Gizmo

Ayckbourn, Philip
Plan of Action

Barnes, Peter
Acting Exercise
Humour Helps
Last Things
Waiting for a Bus

Basden, Tom
Party

Bean, Rupert
Pride at Southanger Park

Beard, Paul
Meat and Two Veg

Beckett, Francis
Money Makes You Happy

Beckett, Samuel
Come and Go
Endgame
Krapp's Last Tape

Bennett, Alan
Bed Among the Lentils
Chip in the Sugar
Cream Cracker Under the Settee
Englishman Abroad
Green Forms
Her Big Chance
Lady of Letters
Question of Attribution
Say Something Happened
Soldiering On
Visit From Miss Protheroe
Woman of No Importance
(*See also* Beyond the Fringe *in the Revue section*)

Berkoff, Steven
Actor
Agamemnon
Bow of Ulysses
Brighton Beach Scumbags
Dog
Harry's Christmas
In the Penal Colony
Lunch
Massage
Sturm und Drang

Blackwell, Vera
Audience (*trans.*)
Private View (*trans.*)
Protest (*trans.*)

Booth, Anthony
Costa Del Packet!

Booth, Connie and Cleese, John
Fawlty Towers

Bower, Margaret
Tea Dance
Whose Wedding Is It Anyway?

Brecht, Bertolt
Exception and the Rule
How Much Is Your Iron?
Measures Taken
Señora Carrar's Rifles
Trial of Joan of Arc at Rouen, 1431
Trial of Lucullus

Brett, Simon
Putting the Kettle On
Small Family Murder

Brooks, Vanessa
Swan Song

Burton, Brian J.
Double Dealing
Drunkard's Wife
Fanny's Prayer
Ghost of a Chance
Gypsy Curse
Mayhem at the Mill
One Month to Pay
Save My Child
Sold to the Gypsies
Trouble Shared

Campton, David
After Midnight – Before Dawn
Cagebirds
Can You Hear the Music?
Cards, Cups and Crystal Ball
Mrs Meadowsweet
Permission to Cry
Relics
Us and Them
What Are You Doing Here?
Who Calls?

Carley, Steve
Edge

Cashmore, Bill and Powrie, Andy
Trip of a Lifetime

Chappell, Eric
Cut and Dried
We Don't Want to Lose You

Chekhov, Anton
Bear

Chinn, Jimmie
But Yesterday
From Here to the Library
In Room Five Hundred and Four
Leslie
Maureen
Pity About Kitty
Respectable Funeral
Too Long An Autumn

Christie, Agatha
Afternoon at the Seaside
Patient
Rats

Churchill, Caryl
Abortive
After-Dinner Joke
Blue Kettle
Drunk Enough to Say I Love You
Heart's Desire
Hot Fudge
Judge's Wife
Lovesick
Not Not Not Not Not Enough Oxygen
Seagulls
Three More Sleepless Nights

Clark, Brian
Post Mortem

Cleese, John and Booth, Connie
Fawlty Towers

Cocteau, Jean
Human Voice
Sound of Silence

Coles, Enid
Under the Twelfth Sign

Connolly, H
Bill & Bob
One Careful Owner

Cook, Peter
(*See* Beyond the Fringe *in the Revue section*)

Coward, Noël
Better Half
Come into the Garden Maud
Fumed Oak
Hands Across the Sea
Red Peppers
Shadows of the Evening
Still Life
Ways and Means
(*See also Revue section*)

Cox, Constance
Everyman
Maria Marten

Crimp, Martin
Advice to Iraqi Women

Creagh-Henry, M.
Victory of the Cross

Crowther, Colin
Footprints in the Sand
Tryst

B

Crowther, Colin and Mary
Calling
Just Passing
Till We Meet Again

Darby, Katy
Half-Life
Open Secrets

de Wet, Reza
Crossing
Missing

Derrett, Bridget
Light Lunch

Dickens, Charles
(*See* Dickens's Children)

Doust, Paul
Lady Bracknell's Confinement

Downing, Martin
Demon
Out for the Count

Dunmore, Heather
Blue

Durang, Christopher
Actor's Nightmare
Sister Mary Ignatius Explains It All For You

Emery, Ed (*trans.*)
One Was Nude and One Wore Tails

Exton, Clive
(*See* Stoppard and Exton)

Farquhar, Simon
I Do Solemnly Declare

Farrell, Joe (*trans.*)
Ordinary Day
Virtuous Burglar

Feydeau, Georges
Lèonie est en Avance
(*see* One Month Early)
Mais N'te Promène Donc Pas Toute Nue! (*see*
Don't Walk About with Nothing On *and* Put
Some Clothes On, Clarisse)
On Purge Bébé
(*see* Take Your Medicine Like a Man)
(*see* Meyer, Peter; Oliver, Reggie; *and* Pilch,
Michael)

Firth, Tim
Man of Letters

Fo, Dario
One Was Nude and One Wore Tails
Virtuous Burglar

Fo, Dario and Rame, Franca
Open Couple
Ordinary Day

Forrest-Turner, Lorraine
Seven Stages of an Affair
To Have and To Hold

Fosbrook, Michael
Figuring Things
Remembering Things

Foxton, David
Breakfast for One
Oubliette

Frayn, Michael
Audience
(*see also* Listen to This *in the Revue section*)

Friel, Brian
London Vertigo

Fry, Christopher
One Thing More
Phoenix Too Frequent
Ringing of Bells
Sleep of Prisoners
Thor With Angels

Green, George MacEwan
Goodbye, Iphigenia
Ritual for Dolls
Sequence of Events

Green, Lily Ann
Forward to the Right

Green, Michael
All's Well That Ends As You Like It
Cherry Sisters
Cinderella
Collier's Tuesday Tea
Fish In Her Kettle
Henry the Tenth (Part Seven)
Il Fornicazione
Julius and Cleopatra
Last Call for Breakfast
Moby Dick

Oedocles, King of Thebes
Present Slaughter
Pride at Southanger Park (ed.)
Stalag 69
Streuth
Trapped
Vagabond Prince

Grenfell, Joyce
Old Tyme Dancing
The Whizzer

Gurney, A. R.
Love Course
Old One-Two
Rape of Bunny Stuntz

Hall, Lee
Spoonface Steinberg

Hall, Nick
Pastiche

Harris, Richard
Albert
Going Home
Is It Something I Said?
Keeping Mum
Magic
Plaster
Showbusiness
Waiting

Harrison, Neil
Whodidit?

Hartwell, Bob
Albert's Plot

Havel, Václav
Audience
Private View

Hawkins, Jim
Too Hot to Handle

Holloway, Jonathan
Dark
Monkey's Paw (adapt.)

Hood, Evelyn
Curses, Foiled Again!

Hood, Stuart (trans.)
Open Couple

Horsler, P. H.
Intruders

Ionesco, Eugene
Bald Prima Donna
Chairs
Lesson

Jacobs, W.W.
Monkey's Paw

John, Miriam
Orchestra (trans.)

Johnson, Margaret
Jabiru

Jones, Graham
Dreamjobs

Kelly, John
Two Wits To Woo

Kafka, Franz
In the Penal Colony

Kinahan, Deirdre
Melody

LaBute, Neil
Gaggle of Saints
Iphegenia in Orem
Medea Redux

Larbey, Bob
Half an Idea
Small Affair

Lawrence, Bernard
Bear (adapt.)

Lee, Maureen
Visitor

Leonard, Hugh
Last of the Last of the Mohicans
Nothing Personal
Pizzazz
Roman Fever
Time of Wolves and Tigers
View From the Obelisk

Leviticus, Louis I.
Train (trans.)

B

B

Lomas, Derek
Darlings, You Were Wonderful!

Lovegrove, Arthur
Clara's on the Curtains!
Nasty Things, Murders

Macrae, Arthur
(See *Living for Pleasure* in Revue section)

Macklin, Charles
(*See* Friel, Brian)

Mamet, David
Duck Variations
Sexual Perversity in Chicago

Mander, Charles
Getting Along
Shop for Charity
World Première

Manktelow, Bettine
Charity Begins

Marcus, Fiz
Matchstick Dreams

Maskell, Valerie
Alas, Dear Reader

Mason, Rosemary
Sunbeams

Maurice, Lucy
Indian Summer

McConnell, Jean
Cruise Missile
Cupboard Love
Dancers
Day Trippers
Doggies
Early Blight
Garden Pests
Grannies
Guilt Card
Last Post
Late Frost
Lovesome Thing
Millie's Tale
Outdoor Pleasures
Remember Me
Shoppers
Short Changed
Theatrical Digs

Messik, Robert
Pineapple

Meyer, Peter
Don't Walk About With Nothing On
One Month Early
Take Your Medicine Like a Man

Miller, Jonathan
(See *Beyond the Fringe* in Revue section)

Moore, Dudley
(See *Beyond the Fringe* in Revue section)

Mortimer, John
Dock Brief
Fear of Heaven
Knightsbridge
Lunch Hour
(See also *One to Another* in Revue section)

Moruzzi, Ros
Just the Two of Us

Murch, Edward
No Name in the Street

Murray, Brendan
Eliza's House

Musgrove, Rachel
Carry Me, Kate

Nagy, Phyllis
Trip's Cinch

Neilson, Anthony
Night Before Christmas
Normal
Penetrator

Nestroy, Johann
As You Were

Newmeir, John H.
Babysitting Calvin
Semblance of Madness!

Nichols, Peter
Foreign Bodies
Game of Soldiers

O'Connor, Jim
Touch of Rose Madder

Ogden, Alan
Johnny Don't Jump

Oliver, Reggie (adapt.)
Music Lovers
Put Some Clothes On, Clarisse!

Parkinson, Carol
Voice of the Phoenix

Parry-Davis
Crossways

Perry, Jimmy and Croft, David
Deadly Attachment
Godiva Affair
Mum's Army
Floral Dance (*sketch*)

Perry, Scott
Bookends

Pierpan, Nicholas
Too Much the Sun

Pinter, Harold
Ashes to Ashes
Basement
Celebration
Collection
Dumb Waiter
Dwarfs
Family Voices
Kind of Alaska
Landscape
Lover
Monologue
Mountain Language
New World Order
Night Out
One for the Road
Party Time
Room
Silence
Slight Ache
Tea Party
Victoria Station
(*see also* One to Another *and* Three Sketches
by Pinter *in the Revue section*)

Plowman, Gillian
Allotment
Beata Beatrix
Cecily
Close To Croydon
Janna Years
Kind of Vesuvius
Me and My Friend
There's None So Blind

Tippers
Touching Tomorrow
Two Fat Men
Two Summers
Umjana Land
Window Cleaner

Pontac, Perry
Fatal Loins
Hamlet Part II
Prince Lear

Quilter, Peter
Blind Date
Bride-to-be
Holiday
Secretarial Skills

Raffle, Diana
Blue Suede Blues
Camp Confidence

Raif, Ayshe
Café Society

Rame, Franca
(*See* Fo, Dario)

Rattigan, Terence
Before Dawn
Browning Version
Harlequinade

Reakes, Paul
Bang, You're Dead!

Rensten, Mary
Knowing Constance Spry

Rhodes, Derek
Music for Amelia

Richardson, Alan
Perfect Partners

Robertson, A. S.
Luck of the Draw

Rosenthal, Amy
Henna Night
Lifelines

Rowley, David E.
In Need of Care

B

B

Rushforth, Tony
Seascape

Saunders, Geoff
Other People
Starch

Saunders, James
Alas Poor Fred

Shaffer, Peter
Black Comedy
Private Ear
Public Eye
White Liars

Shirley, Rae
Merry Regiment of Women
Think the Beautiful Thoughts
What Shall We Do with the Body?

Simpson, N. F.
Form
Hole
Resounding Tinkle
(See also *One to Another* in Revue section)

Skelton, Geoffrey
As You Were (trans.)

Slotboom, Carl
Train

Smith, Colin
Four-Play

Smith, Leo
Sins of the Father
Whence

Smith, Stephen
Departure
One-Sided Triangle
Parentcraft
Penalty

Stead, Stephen (trans.)
Missing

Stephenson, Shelagh
Five Kinds of Silence

Stoppard, Tom
After Magritte
Albert's Bridge
Another Moon Called Earth

Cahoot's Macbeth
Dogg's Hamlet
Fifteen Minute Hamlet
If You're Glad I'll be Frank
Real Inspector Hound
Separate Peace
Teeth

Stoppard, Tom and Exton, Clive
Boundary

Strange, Elliot
Jolly Sinister Jape

Stubbs, Norman
Ringing For You

Tibbetts, Mike
Bottles With Baskets On
LittleBro Morning and BigSis Afternoon

Toddie, Jean Lennox
And Go To Innisfree

Townsend, Sue
Womberang

Tristram, David
Brenton Versus Brenton
Carrot
Extraordinary Revelations of Orca the
    Goldfish
Fat Lady Sings in Little Grimley
Joining the Club
Last Panto in Little Grimley
Last Tango in Little Grimley
Late Entry
Peas
What's For Pudding?

Tydeman, Richard
Albert Laddin
Ali's Barbara
Forty Winks Beauty
Sea Side Trippers
Spring Song Singers
Way Out West
What Ho Within!

Valentine, Pam
Alternative Accommodation
Dog's Life

Vickery, Frank
Drag Factor
Split Ends

Vollmar, James
Clearing the Colours

Walker, Graham
Hamelin Incident

Warburton, N. J.
Dickens' Children (adapt.)
Distracted Globe
Don't Blame It on the Boots
Droitwich Discovery
Easy Stages
For Starters
Last Bread Pudding
Loophole
Melons at the Parsonage
Not Bobby
Office Song
Purvis
Receive This Light
Sour Grapes and Ashes
Zartan

Watson, Donald
Bald Prima Donna (trans.)
Chairs (trans.)
Lesson (trans.)

Weldon, Fay
Flood Warning
Reading Group

Wharton, Edith
(Roman Fever)

Whitnall, Tim
Sociable Plover

Wilder, Thornton
Happy Journey
Long Christmas Dinner
Pullman Car *Hiawatha*

Wilding, Sue
Flash, Bam, Alakazam

Williams, Hugh Steadman
Everywoman

Williams, Simon
Happy Birthday Me

Williams, Tennessee
Adam and Eve on a Ferry
And Tell Sad Stories
Auto-Da-Fé

Bid Game
Case of the Crushed Petunia
Dark Room
Escape
Fat Man's Wife
Gnädiges Fraulein
Hello from Bertha
I Rise In Flame Cried the Phoenix
Lady of Larkspur Lotion
Last of My Solid Gold Watches
Long Goodbye
Long Stay Cut Short
Lord Byron's Love Letter
Mister Paradise
Moony's Kid Don't Cry
Municipal Abattoir
Mutilated
Palooka
Perfect Analysis Given By a Parrot
Pink Bedroom
Portrait of a Madonna
Purification
Something Unspoken
Strangest Kind of Romance
Summer at the Lake
Suddenly Last Summer
Talk to Me Like the Rain ...
Thank You Kind Spirit
These Are the Stairs You Got to Watch
This Property Is Condemned
Twenty-Seven Wagons Full of Cotton
Why Do You Smoke So Much, Lily?

Wilson, David Henry
Are You Normal, Mr Norman?
Death Artist
Escapologist
Fourth Prisoner
How to Make Your Theatre Pay
If Yer Take A Short Cut
Wall
Wendlebury Day

Windsor, Valerie
Effie's Burning

Wood, Anthony
Human Voice (trans.)
Sound of Silence (trans.)

Wood, Margaret
Top Table

Wye, Angela
Rialto Prom

B

B

One Act Plays

B

Abortive. Play. Caryl Churchill
M1 F1. A bedroom. Fee code D

Roz and Colin lie in bed discussing the effect on them of Roz's recent abortion. The father of the child was not Colin but Billy, a pathetic under-privileged character whom they befriended for three months. Billy and Roz's sexual encounter began as rape but ended differently, and as she and Colin recall the events leading to it the gulf between the couple is revealed.

Acting Exercise. Play. Peter Barnes
M2 (20s, 40s). A rehearsal room. Fee code B

B

Rowan, an actor, is rehearsing. A distraught husband demands the actor give him back his wife. With a superlative performance, Rowan convinces the husband he is mistaken, but alone again he crows: 'I could sell electric fans to Eskimos!' May be presented as part of the full-length entertainment *Corpsing*. For details, please see the entry in Section A.
ISBN 978 0 573 10006 2

Actor. Play. Steven Berkoff
M1. Fee code C
An actor, walking on the spot, talking to friends, agents, anyone who can get him a job. The obsessive, demoralizing life of an actor between parts is displayed forcibly in this swift and savage monologue.

Actor's Nightmare. Play. Christopher Durang
M2 (20s, 30s) F3 (20s, 30s). An empty stage. Fee code E

See full synopsis in Section A under *Sister Mary Ignatius Explains It All For You*.

Adam and Eve on a Ferry. Play.Tennessee Williams.
M1 F2. A sun porch. Fee code E

A comic portrait of D.H. Lawrence as someone who functions as an analyst for repressed women. Embroidering on his porch, Lawrence is visited by Miss Peabody. Adopting a Sherlock-Holmesian intuition, Lawrence divines that spinsterish Miss Peabody was propositioned by a man aboard a ferry, but in her passionate excitement she forgot his name and where they were to meet. Lawrence helps Miss Peabody recover her memory.

Advice to Iraqi Women. Soliloquy. Martin Crimp
M1 or F1. A bare stage. Fee Code B
"The protection of children is a priority." This is the first line and the driving message throughout this short script. After all, a home is like a minefield for a child. There are so many ways injury can occur that everything from a zip to a colouring-in book can be seen as a potential war zone.

Available on hire

◆ **A bullet mark next to a title indicates that it is new to this edition of the Guide.**

The After-Dinner Joke. Play. Caryl Churchill
Large mixed cast. Various simple settings. Fee code G

A secretary decides to quit her job and become a fundraiser for an international charity. She is determined to remember that 'A charity is by definition nonpolitical. Politics is by definition uncharitable.' But everything she experiences in her new job makes this precept untenable. The play has a large cast with a wide age range and provides excellent opportunities for multiple role playing.

B

After Magritte. Farce. Tom Stoppard
M3 (40) F2 (30s, old). One interior. Fee code F

Harris and his family are eccentrics. Two police officers place them under arrest. It is not clear why: something about a parked car, a bunch of .22 calibre shells in the waste basket and a robbery of the box office of a minstrel show. From there, the plot goes haywire.

After Midnight – Before Dawn. Play. David Campton
M2 (late teenage, middle-age) F4 (late 20s, 30s, middle-age, old). A prison cell. Fee code D

Six characters, sentenced for witchcraft, await death. The Calm Woman remains unmoved; she will not hang as the Devil looks after his own. The others beg her to tell them how they may gain Satan's protection. The Girl protests: they kill her and set on the Calm Woman also – fulfilling her prophecy. Period late 1600s-early 1700s
ISBN 978 0 573 12002 7

Afternoon at the Seaside. Play. Agatha Christie
M7 (25-elderly) F5 (25, 34, 52, 60). A beach. Fee code F

Inspector Foley arrives on the beach in pursuit of a stolen emerald necklace. It turns up in the trouser pocket of the timid Percy. An attempt to snatch the necklace from Percy is foiled by a disguised policewoman. The emeralds are paste; the real necklace is safely in the hands of the two most respectable-looking thieves.
ISBN 978 0 573 02004 9

Agamemnon. Play. Steven Berkoff
M4 F3. Greek Chorus. Fee code F
Adapted from Aeschylus' great tragedy and evolved over a long period of workshop sessions, the play is about heat and battle, fatigue, the marathon and the obscenity of modern and future wars.

Alas, Dear Reader. Play. Valerie Maskell
F5 (12, 18-40s). 1 male voice. A Victorian parlour. Fee code D. ISBN 978 0 573 13202 5

Alas, Poor Fred. Play. James Saunders
M1 (middle-age) F1 (middle-age). A drawing-room. Fee code E

The play begins with a peaceful armchair conversation between Ernest and Ethel, who are chatting about how funny it must be to get cut in half, as Fred was. The murder is placed in the past and these two conventional people talk about it as if it didn't interest them all that much. The fact is, it was Ernest that killed Fred ...

Albert. Comedy. Richard Harris
M2 (20s) F1 (20s). A sitting-room. Fee code C

If it were not for the thoughtfulness of the author who has kindly translated the dialogue of two of the characters into English, the audience would be as confused as the actors, who play a Finn, an Italian and an Englishman – none of whom speak a word of the other's languages. ISBN 978 0 573 12021 3

Albert Laddin. Minidrama. Richard Tydeman
M4 F6. Fee code B. ISBN 978 0 573 06617 7

Albert's Bridge. Play. Tom Stoppard
M10 F2. Composite setting. Fee code E

Albert is a painter who takes an immense pride in his work on a huge girdered railway bridge. To him it is 'his' bridge. The play follows, in a series of brief sequences, Albert's life at home and at work. The bridge eventually collapses under the tramping feet of an army of 'ordinary' people mounting it because 'it is the only direction left'.
ISBN 978 0 573 02321 0

Albert's Plot. Play. Bob Hartwell
M4 (40s-60s) F4 (teenage, 30-50s). An allotment, and a street. Fee code D.
ISBN 978 0 573 12024 4

Ali's Barbara. Minidrama. Richard Tydeman
M6 F7. Fee code B. ISBN 978 0 573 12006 0

All's Well That Ends As You Like It. A play for Coarse Actors. Michael Green

See the entry for *Four Plays for Coarse Actors.*

The Allotment. Play. Gillian Plowman
F5 (41, 50s, 65, 70). An allotment. Fee code D

Five women are serving community service orders working on an allotment. Marcie is convicted of dangerous driving; Norah is a serial shoplifter; Belle has blackmailed her boss and Lorna, an actress, is convicted of criminal damage. It is the first morning for Daisy, the new probation officer, and the tables are cleverly turned when a traumatic event in her past puts her on a par with the others.
ISBN 978 0 573 03395 7

Alternative Accommodation. Play. Pam Valentine
M1 (40s) F3 (40s, 70). A living-room. Fee code D

Recently widowed, Anna is visited by her three children who have decided that the family house must be sold and Anna moved to a residential home or sheltered housing. Their show of concern doesn't fool Anna. Far from suffering from dementia, Anna has organized a life in Florida that doesn't include any of them although it does encompass the new man in her life.
ISBN 978 0 573 02372 9

The American Dream. Play. Edward Albee
M2 (20, 30) F3 (45, 86). A living-room. Fee code F

In this vicious parable about America, Mommy and Daddy live in gilt-edged insecurity, Mommy ruling with an unholy vitality that has reduced Daddy to a terrible, contented impotence. Into the house strays a beautiful young man – an American dream – except that he can feel nothing because he is the twin of the child they killed years before.
ISBN 978 0 573 02007 0

And Go to Innisfree. Play. Jean Lennox Toddie
F3 (young, middle-age, older). A bare stage. Fee code D

A woman appears, her long skirt sweeping the sand of the deserted New England beach. She must make a decision, but will she make it alone? The middle-aged matron she was argues for the comfort of a retirement home. The child she was urges her to sit again and eat blackberries and to arise at long last and go to Innisfree.
ISBN 0 573 62620 0

And Tell Sad Stories of the Death of Queens. Play. Tennessee Williams.
M4 (young, 20s, 35). A living-room. Fee code E

Candy Delaney is a successful New Orleans interior decorator and also a drag queen approaching "her" 35th birthday. On the rebound from a seventeen-year relationship, Candy has picked up a rough sailor, Karl, on whom she lavishes money. On the day of the dreaded birthday, Karl walks out and it's left to the two queens who live upstairs, Alvin and Jerry, to comfort Candy.

Another Moon Called Earth. Play. Tom Stoppard
M3 F1. Various simple settings. Fee Code E

British astronauts have landed on the moon first, Penelope is plagued by a psychosomatic illness, receiving daily visits from a dubious doctor. The mysterious death of Penelope's nanny takes a back seat to philosophical musings on absolute truth. When the lunanaut discovers space he exposes the world's existence to be nothing more than a local custom, "because he has seen the edges where we stop".
ISBN 978 0 571 19428 5

Are You Normal, Mr Norman? Play. David Henry Wilson
M4 (27, 50s) F2 (20s). A dentist's waiting-room and surgery. Fee code C

Mr Norman Norman is waiting his turn to see the dentist when horrific screams are heard from the surgery. Confronted by a lunatic dentist who considers himself the Saviour, Norman soon realizes that much more than his teeth is at stake ... This stimulating play shows how the borderline between madness and normality is often fuzzy.

♦ **A bullet mark next to a title indicates that it is new to this edition of the Guide.**

As You Were. Farce. Johann Nestroy. Translated from the German and adapted by Geoffrey Skelton
M2 (young, middle-age) F2 (young, middle-age). An elegant living-room. Fee code D
ISBN 978 0 573 12138 8

Ashes to Ashes. Play. Harold Pinter
M1 (40s) F1 (40s). A living-room. Fee code G

B

A man interviews a woman. She has been sexually brutalized in the past; is he her torturer and her nation's political scourge? 'Pinter ... allies his fascination with isolation and separateness to his instinctive hatred of barbarism; he is exploring the apparent link between sexual and political fascism and the way one echoes, or even contradicts, the other.' *Guardian*. Running time approximately one hour.

Audience. Play. Michael Frayn
M6 (late teenage, middle-age, American 70s) F7 (17, middle-age, American 50s, 60s). Theatre stalls. Fee code F

In this amusing satire Michael Frayn turns the tables on us, the audience, and presents us with a picture of – an audience! A hapless playwright must contend with coughing fits, electronic watch alarms, noisy chocolate wrappers and latecomers as he tries to watch a performance of his play. ISBN 0 573 62068 7

Audience. Play. Václav Havel. Translated by Vera Blackwell
M2 (middle-age, any age). An office. Fee code E

Forming part of the *Vanek Plays* trilogy, *Audience* is a cleverly-constructed satire on power and those who wield it. Vanek is summoned to a meeting with the Head Maltster and offered promotion, but only if he informs on himself! NB. Please specify author when ordering this title. ISBN 978 0 573 04226 3

Auto-Da-Fé. Tragedy. Tennessee Williams
M1 (late 30s) F1 (elderly). A cottage porch. Fee code E

This is a tragic story of fanaticism. Madame Duvenet's son Eloi is wildly obsessed with the wickedness of the district in which they live. He rails against his mother's lodgers and tells her of an indecent picture which fell out of a envelope in the mail. His mother says he must burn it at once; he deliberately sets fire to the entire house.

Babysitting Calvin. Play. John H. Newmeir
M2 (baby, 40s) F3 (young, 40s). A living-room. Fee code E

Baby Calvin (acted by an adult) can remember his previous life when he was happily married to Laura. Calvin will lose his blissful memories when he reaches his first birthday – or speaks – so he determines not to talk! His babysitter is Laura but she has brought along lecherous Bob. Calvin sets about thwarting Bob but can he prevent the unthinkable happening ... without speaking? ISBN 0 573 12152 4

◆ **A bullet mark next to a title indicates that it is new to this edition of the Guide.**

B

The Bald Prima Donna. Anti-Play. Eugene Ionesco. Translated from the French by Donald Watson
M3 F3. A typical middle-class English interior. Fee code E

This is a hilariously maniacal assault on the banality of English suburbia. A family is discussed, every member of which is called Bobby Watson; a young couple is alarmed to find that they have been married for years. For such people, words can have no meaning. The play ends in a crescendo of non-sequiturs.
ISBN 978 0 573 02013 1

Bang, You're Dead! Comedy thriller. Paul Reakes
M2 (late 20s, early 40s) F2 (30s, 45). A living-room. Fee code D

Lydia and her boyfriend Marcus rehearse the murder of Theo, Lydia's husband, which they are to commit that evening. When the victim and 'perfect witness' arrive all goes according to plan except that Marcus kills Lydia. A ghastly mistake – or are there some deviations from the original plot? In reality Marcus is Theo's boyfriend and Lydia the intended victim all along.
ISBN 978 0 573 12023 7

Bar and Ger. Drama. Geraldine Aron
M1 (young) F1 (young). A rostrum with cushions. Fee code E

In brief flashes of dialogue the growing-up relationship of a brother and sister is traced through the years. At the beginning, Bar (Barry) is newborn, Geraldine (Ger) is about ten years old. The relationship is developed in a simple, realistic and tender style as they age gradually through the play – not necessarily at the same time – until Bar is seventeen.
ISBN 978 0 573 02368 2

The Basement. Play. Harold Pinter
M2 (middle age) F1 (young). Various simple settings. Fee code F

Tim a middle-aged bachelor, lives a comfortable life. One evening his former roommate and friend, Stott, pops by unexpectedly. Even more unexpected is Jane, the young woman he has brought along with him. Almost immediately Stott and Jane are naked and taking over Law's bed. As the boundaries of friendship and middle-aged sexual frustrations are explored, the flat is refurnished and their lives re-arranged.
ISBN 978 0 571 19383 7

The Bear. Play. Anton Chekhov. Adapted by Bernard Lawrence
M2 (middle age, old) F1 (middle age). A living-room. Fee code D

Glasgow, 1890. Andrew Baird calls upon Flora McNeil to settle a debt owed by her late husband. It is a bank holiday, however: no money! Baird is determined and refuses to leave; Flora has to resort to violence. Pistols are brought out for a duel; but first, Baird must teach her to shoot ... Period 1890
ISBN 978 0 573 12016 8

◆ **A bullet mark next to a title indicates that it is new to this edition of the Guide.**

Beata Beatrix. Play. Gillian Plowman
M3 (any age, middle-age). F4 (any age, young). An art gallery. Fee code D

Touring an art gallery, Beatrice notices a lone man, Jon, crying before a painting created out of remorse for a tragedy in the artist's life. Intrigued, Beatrice offers help, and it transpires that for Jon, whose wife had died of leukæmia while he was with another woman, the painting tells his own story. Beatrice, also, has her own haunting secret ...
ISBN 978 0 573 12136 4

Bed Among the Lentils. Monologue. Alan Bennett
F1 (40s). A kitchen. Fee code F

Susan is a failure when it comes to jam-making and flower-arranging and isn't at all sure about God; how unfortunate for her that she is married to Geoffrey, a popular and respected vicar who treats her in an intensely patronizing manner and expects her to conform to her role as vicar's wife. A bleakly hilarious, dark and painful monologue, packed with insights and sparkling satire.
ISBN 978 0 573 13224 7

Before Dawn. Play. Terence Rattigan
M3 (young, middle-age) F1 (early middle-age). A room in a castle. Fee code E

An hilarious retelling of the play and opera *Tosca*, with Scarpia as a swaggering villain who proves to be impotent, Tosca as a proud beauty and a Captain who gets confused as to whether Scarpia means that Tosca's lover should *really* be executed ... or only appear to be. Tosca's attempt to stab Scarpia is foiled by his knife-proof vest. Period 1800
ISBN 978 0 573 12017 1

The Better Half. Comedy. Noel Coward
M1 (30s) F2 (30s). A bedroom. Fee code E

A recently discovered play written two years before *The Vortex*, prior to Coward becoming famous. It was seen in a season of Grand Guignol plays staged at the Little Theatre in London's West End. Alice and David are in an unhappy married relationship; Marion is the understanding friend whom David wants to have an affair with. Alice tries to push David and Marion together by confessing to affairs of her own and David infuriates her by being so very *understanding* about it all! Period 1920s.

The Big Game. Play. Tennessee Williams.
M6 F2. A small hospital ward. Fee code E

Tony, a vigorous footballer, is to be discharged from hospital. The other occupants of the ward are a terminally ill youth, Dave, and Walton, a middle-aged patient about to undergo surgery for a brain tumour. When Tony leaves, Walton introduces Dave to the concept of eternity by looking at the stars. Walton dies during the operation and the play ends with Dave contemplating the stars.

Bill & Bob. Play. H. Connolly
M2 (40s) F2 (30s, 40s). Composite set: a workplace, a kitchen, a front room. Fee code E
ISBN 978 0 573 02369 9

Black Comedy. Comedy. Peter Shaffer
M5 (30s, middle-age) F3 (20s, middle-age). An apartment. Fee code H

In this play the usual conditions of light and dark are reversed: when the lights are 'on', we see nothing but darkness; when they are 'off', we see the characters behaving as if they were in a black-out. Carol and Brindsley have invited a millionaire to see Brindsley's sculpture and to impress him have 'borrowed' antiques from a neighbour. Carol's formidable father is also expected. The lights fuse, and the arrival of several unexpected visitors effectively wrecks the evening.
ISBN 978 0 573 02303 3

B

♦ **Blind Date.** Comedy. Peter Quilter (From *Duets*)
M1 F1. A living room. Fee code D

Jonathan and Wendy meet through a lonely hearts column and arrange to go on a blind date with a difference – in Jonathan's living-room. Neither of them has particularly high hopes, having had bad romantic experiences before, but gradually they overcome their nerves and awkwardness and agree to make it a proper date over dinner. May be performed individually or as the first act in *Duets*.
ISBN 978 0 573 11111 2

Blue. Play. Heather Dunmore
M1 F7 (playing various ages) or M1 F3 with doubling. A bare stage. Fee code D

Leo, a doctor, is suffering from depression and finds it hard to come to terms with his illness. Weaving through memories as a child and a father, Leo re-lives his suspicions, panic attacks and emotions, trying everything from hypnotism to art therapy to beat the blues. His mother, sister and wife offer insight into how depression affects those you love.
ISBN 978 0 573 02387 3

Blue Kettle. Play. Caryl Churchill
M2 (40, 70s) F6 (30, 50s-80s). Various simple settings. Fee code E

Derek, a con-man, approaches five different women and claims to be the illegitimate son they gave up for adoption. The hurt this engenders is mirrored in the gradual disintegration of the play's language as the words 'blue' and 'kettle' come to replace the words the characters mean to say. Together with *Heart's Desire*, this forms the double bill *Blue Heart* (see Section A).

Blue Suede Blues. Play. Diana Raffle
M2 (young) F4 (young, middle age, elderly) A sitting-room. Fee code D

Grace and Lily reside in a nursing home with little to do but witness a senile resident impersonating Elvis Presley. Grace is determined to break the tedium and inveigles the unwilling Lily into helping her kidnap the young care assistant, Pansy, for the ransom of a bottle of gin, some fags and a budgie, but things don't go quite according to plan – with hilarious results!
ISBN 978 0 573 02362 0

♦ **A bullet mark next to a title indicates that it is new to this edition of the Guide.**

Bookends. Play. Scott Perry
M2 (old). A park bench. Fee code E

Ron and Bill haven't met up for three weeks – Bill has been in Scarborough, reliving his honeymoon and Ron, having escaped from his old people's home, has been living it up on the ferry to Amsterdam. Funny and touching simultaneously, *Bookends* is a perceptive portrait of old age.
ISBN 978 0 573 14208 6

The Boundary. Comedy. Tom Stoppard and Clive Exton
M2 (elderly) F1. Extras. A lexicographer's library. Fee code E

Johnson is horrified to discover that his library, where he is working on his dictionary, appears to be ransacked. Paper is everywhere, so that even the body of his wife, Brenda, is hidden. With his collaborator Bunyon, he concludes that Brenda is responsible, but the true explanation lies beyond the window. Originally produced for television, this play combines wit, wordplay and a slight touch of comic absurdity.
ISBN 978 0 573 12046 6

The Bow of Ulysses. Play. Steven Berkoff
M1 F1. Fee code D
A highly-charged duologue in which a married couple examine their collapsing relationship with startling savagery.

The Brave Bugler or Up the Khyber Pass. Melodrama. Harry Austin
M4 F1. 1M Extra. Fee code B

Spurred on by the voluptuous Daphne, the diminutive but brave Bugler attempts to repulse single-handedly an attack on the British fort by marauding Indian tribesmen, only to lose Daphne to the suave officer who appears once the fighting is over. Playing time approximately 12-14 minutes. Contained in *The Little Lights of Kimberley*.
ISBN 978 0 573 10023 3

Breakfast for One. Comedy. David Foxton
M3 (young, middle age, old) F2 (young, middle age). A hall/dining-room. Fee code D

Marcel arrives at the Signac home hoping to see his beloved Marie-Céleste, a dancer. Instead he encounters the maid, Honorine, while Yvette, the lady of the house, mistakes Marcel for Claude, a marauding vagrant. A raucous, swiftly-moving comedy of mistaken identities, shotguns and confusion with an unexpectedly happy ending for all concerned. Period 1895
ISBN 978 0 573 02356 9

Brenton Versus Brenton. Comedy. David Tristram
M3 (middle-age) F3 (20s, middle-age). An office. Fee code E

What is the dark secret which inflames the Brenton family feud? Who is the mysterious Eddie? Why are Lana's shoulder-pads wider than the door? And just what was Deke Brenton doing down on the farm? All this, and more, is revealed in this outrageous spoof of American soaps and blockbuster mini-series, set in the manic world of Chicago's biggest advertising agency.

◆ **The Bride-to-be.** Comedy. Peter Quilter (From *Duets*)
M1 F1. A living-room. Fee code D

Angela is about to get married for the third time. Her brother Toby is on hand to escort her to the church when she gets terrible cold feet. Various things go wrong, but with some ingenuity Toby manages to overcome these "bad omens" and persuades Angela to take a chance on Husband Number Three. May be performed individually or as the final act in *Duets*.
ISBN 978 0 573 11111 2

Brighton Beach Scumbags. Play. Steven Berkoff
M4 F2. Fee code F
Two loud, racist, homophobic couples find that a trip to the seaside is not the idyll they'd hoped for. "We might call them yobs and laugh at their Neanderthal struggles with existence," Berkoff writes, "but within there is an awful sadness as they try to claw happiness out of their day."

The Browning Version. Play. Terence Rattigan
M5 (16, 22, middle-age) F2 (20, 30s). A living-room. Fee code F

Ill-health is forcing Andrew Crocker-Harris to retire from school-teaching. His wife despises him for being a failure and has been finding consolation with a master, Frank Hunter. As Andrew prepares to leave she openly taunts him. Frank, witnessing this, is disgusted and bitterly ashamed. As the full story of the marriage is revealed, he warms to Andrew. Millie knows she has lost Frank, but even more bitter is the realization that he is now Andrew's fast friend.
ISBN 978 0 573 02025 4

But Yesterday. Play. Jimmie Chinn
M2 F3. Extras 2M. A garden. Fee code D

A haunting, enigmatic play set in the fifties and before. Prior to leaving on a journey Robert comes back to the garden of his childhood and relives moments from his past, which become mingled with the present. Sound and light do much to evoke the atmosphere and we learn of Robert's gradual desertion of his childhood beliefs and hopes. Two men in shadow have accompanied him on this last visit and they escort him to his new life leaving behind a hurt, bewildered family.
ISBN 978 0 573 12048 0

Café Society. Play. Ayshe Raif
F4 (70s, any age). A café. Fee code D. ISBN 978 0 573 13218 6

The Cagebirds. Play. David Campton
8 characters. A room. Fee code D

In this allegorical play six birds live in a cage, each totally absorbed in her own particular characteristics. When the Wild One is introduced into their midst by their Mistress, she endeavours to persuade them to break out from their self-imposed dependence and imprisonment into the wider world outside – but her efforts result only in her own destruction at their hands.
ISBN 978 0 573 03366 7

Cahoot's Macbeth. Tom Stoppard

Please see the entry for *Dogg's Hamlet* in this section.

♦ **Calling.** Comedy. Colin and Mary Crowther
F6. Simple setting. Fee code D

Six very different young women (17-35) have come on a residential weekend to see if they have what it takes for the most difficult job in the world. All are convinced they are up to it, but watching their awkward interviews, disastrous attempts at teamwork and revealing private conversations, we begin to understand why so few women really have the calling ... to be a nun.
ISBN 978 0 573 03387 2

Camp Confidence. Comedy. Diana Raffle
F7 (29, 30s, 40s, 50s). A campsite . Fee Code D

Lacking in self esteem? Then enrol in Camp Confidence. That's what Maria (terrified of birds), Blanche (agoraphobic), Donna (single mum on probation) and Cherry (obsessive cleaner) have done. Led by the harrassed Julia and her assistant Fiona, the four learn a great deal about each other and themselves in this gentle, warm-hearted comedy, and emerge happier and more secure.
ISBN 978 0 573 02376 7

Can You Hear The Music? Play. David Campton
6 characters. A loft. Fee code D

Everyone has their dream, and this is no exception for the six mice living in the loft. Their dreams are conjured up by music as each hears a different tune played by an invisible Piper and each has to answer his call until only Tattymouse, who is completely deaf, is left. A highly original and thought-provoking play.
ISBN 978 0 573 12042 8

Cards, Cups and Crystal Ball. Play. David Campton
F5 (middle-age). A drawing-room. Fee code D

The Weerd sisters try to make ends meet through fortune-telling. When Lady M calls, Flora discovers she indeed has the gift of foresight, although she does not like what she sees. The sisters' fortunes are turned. Lady M returns to learn more but this time the truth is held back. Period late nineteenth-early twentieth century
ISBN 978 0 573 13215 5

♦ **Carrot.** Comedy. David Tristram
M2. Simple setting. Fee code B

The managing director of an ailing roofing bolt manufacturer has an unusual proposition for his union representative. Can he accept without compromising his principles? Contained in the volume *Duets* with *Peas.*

♦ **A bullet mark next to a title indicates that it is new to this edition of the Guide.**

◆ **Carry Me Kate.** Comedy. Rachel Musgrove
M3 or 6 (20s) F2 (20s). Various simple settings. Fee code D

When Kate and Dave meet at their mutual friend's Tupperware party, they have no idea that the chance encounter will change the course of their lives forever. After a disastrous first date and a drunken misunderstanding, Dave finds himself somehow engaged to Kate. This funny, insightful play explores the opposing reactions of men and women when romance comes their way.
ISBN 978 0 573 12036 7

B

Case of the Crushed Petunia. Play. Tennessee Williams
M2 (young) F2 (26, middle-age). A shop. Fee code E

Primanproper, Massachusetts: Dorothy owns a shop called Simple Notions which is barricaded behind a double row of petunias. One morning she is distraught to find the flowers trampled down. A young man admits he trod down the flowers, reluctant to live a full life. Finally she makes an assignation with him and changes the name of her shop to Tremendous Inspirations.

Cecily. Play. Gillian Plowman
F3. Interior setting. Fee code D

Intense complicated family relationships are put to the test when Cecily becomes brain damaged following a motor-cycle accident and the problems of carers are highlighted. Flashbacks of Cecily before the accident are shown, her lively personality contrasting cruelly with her wheelchair-bound reality. Fiery, forthright and honest, this moving play has three excellent roles for women.

Celebration. Play. Harold Pinter
M5 (30s-40s) F6 (30s-40s). A restaurant. Fee code F

In a fashionable restaurant, two gangsterish brothers, formerly from the East End but now "strategy consultants who enforce the peace", are celebrating a wedding anniversary with their wives, who are sisters. At the next table, a banker is dining with his wife, formerly his secretary. Violent, wildly funny, this play displays a vivid zest for life. " … an uproarious satire … " *Financial Times*

The Chairs. Tragic farce. Eugene Ionesco. Translated from the French by Donald Watson
M2 (45-50, 95) F1 (94). A room. Fee code E

An old man invites all the world to hear his message – the vindication of his existence. His wife has to bring in more and more chairs for the guests. The Orator arrives. The couple announce that their mission is completed and jump to their deaths. The voice of the Orator is that of a deaf mute.

Charity Begins ... Play. Bettine Manktelow
F4 (45, middle age, elderly). An office. Fee Code D

Teresa oversees a women's charity, smugly imagining that she dispenses invaluable advice to any with the temerity to walk through the door. So when dowdy, middle-aged Melanie turns up to volunteer, Teresa soon puts her straight. The arrival of patronizing Mrs Castle-Kettle, daughter of the charity's founder, ruffles even more feathers. And then along comes Angie: a quiet woman with a big secret ...
ISBN 978 0 573 03396 4

The Cherry Sisters. A play for Coarse Actors. Michael Green

See the entry for *The Coarse Acting Show 2.*

A Chip in the Sugar. Monologue from *Talking Heads*. Alan Bennett
M1 (middle-age). A bedroom. Fee code F

Graham, a middle-aged bachelor, emotionally retarded and chronically dependent on his mother, finds life difficult enough at the best of times; when Mother meets an old flame and seems set to marry him, however, Graham's old insecurities rear their ugly heads again. Fate, eventually, rescues Graham and he resumes his normal life of banal muddle under his mother's amnesiac tyranny.
ISBN 978 0 573 04212 6

Cinderella. A Play for Coarse Actors. Michael Green

See the entry for *Coarse Acting Strikes Back.*

Clara's on the Curtains! Comedy. Arthur Lovegrove
F10 (16, young, middle-age). A bare stage. Fee code D. ISBN 978 0 573 03352 0

Clearing The Colours. Play. James Vollmar
M2 (18, 60) F1 (60). A sitting-room, a snooker club. Fee Code E

Danny, a brilliant young snooker player, has a lot of pain in his past life which George, his manager, feels threatens his career. So George introduces him to Dora, a seaside landlady with special healing skills. Premiered at the Stephen Joseph Theatre, Scarborough.
ISBN 978 0 573 02378 1

Close to Croydon. Play. Gillian Plowman
M1 F1. M1 F1 voices only. An overturned railway carriage. Fee code D

Hugo, a PR consultant on his way to an important meeting, and Martha, a Museum Education Officer with a case full of liberty bodices, are trapped in an overturned railway carriage following a rail crash, waiting tensely to be rescued. A touching relationship begins to develop between them, but they are torn apart by tragedy.

◆ **A bullet mark next to a title indicates that it is new to this edition of the Guide.**

THE COARSE ACTING SHOW 2 (Further Plays for Coarse Actors). Michael Green
M9 F4. Extras. Various interior and exterior settings. Fee codes A, B, C and D.

The number of characters given above would be sufficient, with doubling, to cover the
presentation of all four plays by the same cast. Ages can vary from young to practically senile.
The Coarse Acting Show 2 contains further plays for Coarse Actors. Like the plays in the
previous volume, *Four Plays for Coarse Actors*, these four plays show different aspects of Coarse
Theatre. *Moby Dick*, (Fee code C) is a rather over-ambitious attempt to reduce the epic novel
(685 pages long) into a series of quick-fire scenes. *The Cherry Sisters*, (Fee code B) a hitherto
undiscovered fragment of Chekhov, is a desperately sincere piece, with a real tear-jerker of
an ending, spoiled only by the fact that someone has to die standing up in order to cope with
a faulty prop. *Last Call for Breakfast*, (Fee code A), is full of symbolism, a short avant-garde
piece made shorter by the simple mischance of one of the actors getting himself in the wrong
position during a black-out. *Henry the Tenth (Part Seven)*, (Fee code D) is a rarely-performed
masterpiece (from a suggestion by William Shakespeare) with battle scenes of which the Bard
would have been proud. In all four, everything which can conceivably go wrong does so: sets
collapse, actors fail to appear on stage, props fall to pieces – but the Coarse cast carry on, firmly
believing that the audience won't notice a thing.
ISBN 978 0 573 10005 2

COARSE ACTING STRIKES BACK (Further Plays for Coarse Actors). Michael Green
M5 F8. Extras. Various interior and exterior settings. Fee codes C and D.

In this fourth volume of Coarse plays, which has more parts for females than males (cheers!),
Michael Green builds on his previous offerings with a new crop of winners in the Art of Coarse
Acting and theatrical disaster. *Trapped!* (M3 F6. Fee code C) In a send-up of a traditional
English thriller, the cast find themselves *not* trapped when the over-energetic lead actor knocks
down doors that were meant to be locked. Adding to the fun is a corpse that walks – because
it cannot fall – through the jammed door and the Stage Manager who has to read in a part.
Oedocles, King of Thebes. (M2 F6 or M4 F4. Female chorus. Fee code C) The spoof Greek
tragedy presents a fine example of a Coarse Acting script, enhanced by Coarse management and
direction. While doom and disaster stalk the main characters, a Chorus of ill-assorted females,
spitting copiously, reduce the most tragic scenes to mirth. *Pride at Southanger Park.* (M5 F4.
Fee code D) The third play, written by Rupert Bean and edited by Michael Green, is supposedly
an adaptation of a long-lost Jane Austen novel, presenting a naturally developing and utterly
hilarious set of acting disasters. As the performance crumbles into low farce, the cast plough
on, determined to prove themselves the equal of any BBC adaptation. *Cinderella.* (M3 F6 or
M1 F8. Fee code D) The Prince is a stout older woman, the cat anything but cat-like, and the
slipper fits the Ugly Sisters. Not to mention a transformation scene which doesn't work and a
disastrous attempt to fly the Good Fairy.
ISBN 978 0 573 10009 3

The Collection. Play. Harold Pinter
M3 (28, 35, middle-age) F1 (35). Composite setting. Fee code F

Stella returns from her dress collection in Leeds to tell James, her husband, that she has been
unfaithful. James confronts Bill, pressing for the truth, already determined to believe the worst.
Bill confesses that he and Stella had only talked about spending the night together. It had amused
him to perpetuate Stella's story – to hurt his friend Harry. Is this the truth? Stella is silent.
ISBN 978 0 573 02036 0

◆ **A bullet mark next to a title indicates that it is new to this edition of the Guide.**

A Collier's Tuesday Tea. A Play for Coarse Actors. Michael Green

See the entry for *Four Plays for Coarse Actors*.

♦ **Come and Go.** Dramaticule. Samuel Beckett
F3. Simple set. Fee code B

Three women come together and reminisce about linking hands in the school playground. Each woman leaves the stage briefly and in each absence an appalling secret about the missing one is whispered by the other two, although the audience are not privy to the secret. Finally, the three link hands "in the old way" and Flo says: "I can feel the rings", although Beckett specifies there are no rings apparent.

Come into the Garden Maud. Comedy. Noël Coward
M2 (28, 55) F2 (late 40s, early 50s). A Swiss hotel suite. Fee code F

For years the affable Verner Conklin has placidly endured his ill-humoured wife, Anna-Mary. When one of her dinner guests falls ill she is left with thirteen at table; she orders Verner to dine in their suite. He has excellent company in Maud Caragnani. When Anna-Mary snappishly tells Verner to go away Verner complies – with Maud.
ISBN 978 0 573 02308 8

Costa del Packet! Farce. Anthony Booth
F5. A hut. Fee code D. ISBN 978 0 573 03357 5

A Cream Cracker Under the Settee. Monologue. Alan Bennett
F1(70s). 1 M, voice only. A living-room. Fee code F

Doris, a widow, lives alone. Refusing to relinquish her independence, she surreptitiously cleans when her home help, Zulema, is absent; when we meet her, she has just fallen over whilst attempting to dust a picture frame high on the wall. The day goes on; unable to get help, Doris reminisces about her quiet, uneventful life with its joys and sadnesses.
ISBN 978 0 573 13225 4

Crossing. Play. Reza de Wet
M1 (40-50) F3 (young; 30 and 50). A parlour. Fee code F

South Africa. Two sisters bury the bodies of fortune-seekers who fail to heed their warnings about the nearby river. They hold a séance to discover the name of a persistent young girl ghost. In flashback, twenty years earlier, the sisters were visited by Maestro, a hypnotist, and his assistant Ezmerelda who later drowned attempting to cross the river. Following the séance, Sussie invokes the power of the Maestro and walks out into the night as the river roars.

Crossways. Play. Jane Parry-Davis
F7 (20s, middle-age). A cottage sitting-room. Fee code D. ISBN 978 0 573 13228 5

Cruise Missile. Comedy. (From *Deckchairs III*) Jean McConnell
F2 (early 60s). A cruise liner deck. Fee code C

When Janet embarks on her first cruise, she finds herself overwhelmed by the array of delights on offer. However, there is a fellow passenger who is only too willing to be her guide and mentor. It is the flamboyant Goldie, who is familiar with all the wrinkles and most of the crew. But her instant friendship is something of a mixed blessing.
ISBN 978 0 573 10010 9

B

Cupboard Love. Play. (From *Deckchairs III*) Jean McConnell
F2. A seaside esplanade. Fee code C

Peggy and Jane come to rest after jogging. They find to their delight that they have much in common: both are excellent cooks; both are fighting the flab acquired through preparing rich meals for a new gentleman friend. But when they discover, to their horror, they share a passion for the same man, the two women devise their culinary revenge on the deceiver.
ISBN 978 0 573 10010 9

Curses, Foiled Again! Play. Evelyn Hood
M2 F4. A drawing-room. Fee code D

The eve-of-performance dress rehearsal of Henry's send-up of a Victorian tragedy is running anything but smoothly as the cast constantly step out of character to bicker. Feuds simmer beneath the surface and the pretty heroine cannot remember her lines! However, when all seems lost, and the play likely to be cancelled, the cast rally like true troopers for 'the show must go on'!
ISBN 978 0 573 12020 6

Cut and Dried. Play (from the double bill *Fiddlers Three*). Eric Chappell
M5 (20s, 30s, 40s, 50s) F2 (20s, 30s). Two adjoining offices. Fee code F

In the offices of Multiple Holdings, Rex, Harry and Osborne form an alliance against the management, as personified by the devious Fletcher. Rex has to re-apply for his job along with everyone else. Harry is better at ingratiating himself with the bosses and at the close seems well on the way to the top ...
ISBN 978 0 573 01980 7

A Cut in the Rates. Play. Alan Ayckbourn
M1 F3, may be played by M1 F2. A street, a study, a cellar. Fee code D

When Miss Pickhart visits Ratchet, an illusionist, at his home she discovers some dark, sinister secrets from his past. She is asked for help by Rosalinda's ghost, who died when they performed the saw-the-woman-in-half trick, but this means Miss Pickhart reliving that fateful night. Will she also meet a grim death?
ISBN 978 0 573 12084 8

Dancers. Comedy. Jean McConnell
F2 (middle-age). A seaside promenade. Fee code B

See the entry for *Deckchairs I*.

The Dark. Play. Jonathan Holloway. (From *Darkness Falls*)
M3 (30, 37, 40) F1 (30). A living-room. Fee code F

The perils of ambition lie at the heart of this supernatural tale. A successful novelist who has committed himself wholeheartedly to furthering his career meets his Mephistopheles and is dispatched to an uncertain and sinister fate.
ISBN 978 0 573 10002 4

The Dark Room. Play. Tennessee Williams
M1 (boy) F2 (middle-age). A kitchen. Fee code E

Miss Morgan, a social worker, is interviewing Mrs Pocciotti, whose daughter of fifteen, Tina, has remained shut in a dark room for six months after being jilted by a young German. Further surprises follow: the boy, Max, visits her regularly, the girl fights and screams if he does not arrive. The biggest surprise of all comes as the curtain slowly falls. Period 1946

Darlings, You Were Wonderful! Comedy. Derek Lomas
F6. 1 male voice. The dressing-room of a small theatre. Fee code D

The Amazon Theatre Group are to perform a little-known, passionate, Spanish drama in a festival. Amid multiple tensions and general chaos backstage, Lesley, the missing member, staggers in paralytically drunk and dressed in motorcycle gear. The adjudicator is impressed with the cast's seething passion and pronounces Lesley's motorcycle regalia a stroke of genius!
ISBN 978 0 573 13231 5

Day Trippers. Short play (From *Deckchairs II*). Jean McConnell
F2 (elderly). A seafront. Fee code C

Confident Beryl and prudish Doris, on an annual works outing, learn a little more about themselves and their work colleagues than they perhaps ought to. When they discover that they have come to a nudist beach, the result is a brilliantly funny scene of hilarious antics.
ISBN 978 0 573 10004 8

The Deadly Attachment. Comedy (from *Dad's Army*). Jimmy Perry and David Croft
M13. Extras. A church hall and office. Fee code E

The Walmington-on-Sea Home Guard platoon have to guard a captured U-Boat Captain and his crew. But fearless Captain Mainwaring incurs German displeasure when he orders the defiant prisoners be served soggy fish and chips! An hilarious episode from the classic BBC TV series *Dad's Army*. Period 1940
ISBN 978 0 573 10014 7

Death. Comedy. Woody Allen
M18 F2. Various settings on an open stage. Fee code F

Kleinman is awakened in the middle of the night and summoned to join a party of vigilantes hunting a murdering maniac. He finds himself in a series of encounters which become increasingly mystifying and menacing. Is he even suspected of being the maniac himself? When the strangler eventually appears he resembles Kleinman just as – oddly – one of the murdered had said the maniac resembled *him*.
ISBN 0 573 62129 2

The Death Artist. Play. David Henry Wilson
M2 (30s, 60s). One interior. Fee code C

The central issue of this thought-provoking play is death and punishment. Deliberately retreating from the world to avoid evil and injustice, the sinner, on the verge of monetary success, is visited by the death artist who instils the fear of dying into the victim's mind and leaves him a complete wreck.
ISBN 0 573 62364 3

B

Deckchairs I. Five short plays. Jean McConnell
F2. A seaside promenade. Fee code B per play. (For productions of two or more of these plays in one performance please apply for details)

These five twist-in-the-tail playlets for two women – all set on a seaside promenade – are by turns funny and poignant. In *Shoppers*, two well-to-do shopaholics have a rather surprising secret. *Early Blight* is a heart-breaking exploration of a doomed mother/daughter relationship. *Dancers* wittily dissects the tea-dancing world of two skittish widows. *Late Frost* is a drama in which a woman finds out her best friend had an affair with her late husband. And *Doggies* is an hilarious tale about two very different types of dog-owner. These delightful plays run for approximately fifteen minutes each and may be performed as a set or individually.
ISBN 978 0 573 10003 1

Deckchairs II. Four short plays. Jean McConnell
F2. Fee code C per play
See *Day Trippers, The Guilt Card, Short Changed, Theatrical Digs*

Deckchairs III. Three plays. Jean McConnell
F2. Fee code C per play
See *Cruise Missile, Cupboard Love, Last Post*

Deckchairs IV Four short plays. Jean McConnell
F2. Fee code C per play. See *Garden Pests, Grannies, Outdoor Pleasures, Remember Me*

This is Jean McConnell's fourth volume of *Deckchairs* plays, each with a cast of two women and requiring only a simple setting. Two are comedies, two dramas, and all display Jean McConnell's keen-eyed view of human nature and of the foibles and fancies of women in particular.
ISBN 978 0 573 10021 5

The Demon. Thriller. Martin Downing
M3 (30s, 40) F4 (20s, 30s). A lounge. Fee code D

Escaping a torrential rain-storm, six friends meet in a high-rise flat and hear a terrifying announcement: one of them may well be a serial killer, possessed by the Devil! This hypothesis is soon proved when one of their number meets a hideous death, and from then on the survivors embark on a desperate quest – to find and destroy the fiend in their midst before more blood is spilled.
IBSN 978 0 573 12090 9

Departure. Play. Stephen Smith
M1 (40s) F3 (20, 40s). An airport lounge. Fee code D

Stranded in an airport lounge during the delay of a holiday flight to Spain, Rosemary and her carbon-copy daughter, Mandy, draw the reluctant Dennis and Sheila Tippit into conversation. The comic tone of the play shifts continually between Rosemary's malapropisms and Dennis's grimly humorous bigotry with the close of the play finding Rosemary unmoved by the chaos she has caused and Dennis near to a nervous breakdown!
ISBN 978 0 573 12075 6

B

Dickens' Children. Play. Charles Dickens, adapted by Nick Warburton
7 actors (minimum cast). Simple settings. Fee code D

This is Charles Dickens the social reformer linking cameo child scenes from *Great Expectations, Nicholas Nickleby, Bleak House* and *David Copperfield*. One actor plays the adult Dickens and the main child part in each scene while the other 6 actors play a selection of roles, both adult and child, and act as narrators. Within one act, Nick Warburton conveys the humour, pathos and poetry of Dickens.
ISBN 978 0 573 02374 3

Distracted Globe. Comedy. Nick Warburton
M2 (40, middle-age) F4 (young). The set of *Hamlet*. Fee code D

A very funny completion to Nick Warburton's trilogy of the Drama Club's production of *Hamlet* (seen on stage in *Don't Blame It on the Boots* and backstage in *Easy Stages*) which progresses to the after-show party! Meticulous stage-manager Gerry, in charge of the refreshments and music, marshals poor Patsy into artistically arranging bridge rolls, to the accompaniment of *Peer Gynt*!
ISBN 978 0 573 12102 9

The Dock Brief. Play. John Mortimer
M2 (middle-age, old). A prison cell. Fee code E. ISBN 978 0 573 04209 6

Dog. Play. Steven Berkoff
M1. Fee code C
One man – trainers, track suit, his stomach sagging over his waistband – and his dog – a pitbull, violent and uncontrolled. In this hilarious monologue the man and the dog are shown as a paradigm of the "low-class yob culture" of "the pub, obsessive drunkenness, football and xenophobia".

A Dog's Life. Play. Pam Valentine
M4 F2 or M3 F3. An animal shelter. Fee code D

Four dogs lie in cages in an animal shelter. *A Dog's Life* depicts the moment when a woman comes to the shelter and has to choose between the dogs – a choice that literally means life or death to the oldest, Ben. This compassionate drama, easy to stage – dog costumes are not required – is an ideal festival play.
ISBN 978 0 573 12175 3

Doggies. Comedy. Jean McConnell
F2 (any age). A seaside promenade. Fee code B

See the entry for *Deckchairs I*.

Dogg's Hamlet, Cahoot's Macbeth. Tom Stoppard
Fee code M when performed as a double bill, fee code F when performed separately

Dogg's Hamlet is an exercise in nonsensical language for 22 characters (much doubling possible), which leads to *The Dogg's Troupe 15-Minute Hamlet* (available separately under the title *The Fifteen Minute Hamlet*)

Cahoot's Macbeth is a play for 19 characters (with doubling, M2 F3) dedicated to the Czechoslovakian playwright Pavel Kohout. At its core is a performance of *Macbeth* taking place in a private home because the actors have been forbidden to perform in public.

The Donahue Sisters. Play. Geraldine Aron
F3 (30s, 40s). An attic room. Fee code E

Gathered together the sisters talk of their unhappy lives into the night until the time comes for the ritual re-enactment of a disturbing incident from their childhood. Departing from the hitherto naturalistic style of the play the sisters in unison create the persona of Dominic and with this creation would appear to come an answer to their problems. A challenge to both actors and director.
ISBN 978 0 573 13234 6

Don't Blame It on the Boots. Comedy. N. J. Warburton
M1 (40) F3 (young, 30, 40). A stage, a dressing-room. Fee code D

No-one would have blamed it on the boots if only Kate had produced *Macbeth* instead of *Hamlet*; Ophelia hadn't been so attractively naïve; Eric had been blessed with smaller feet and wasn't the drama group's prize flirt; and Liz's father hadn't once trod the boards at Stratford in those self-same boots.
ISBN 978 0 573 12086 2

Don't Walk About with Nothing On. Farce. Georges Feydeau, translated by Peter Meyer
M4 (40s) F1 (30s). 1 boy (voice only). A drawing-room. Fee code E

Clarisse has removed her dress and donned a nightdress in daytime. A quick succession of unexpected influential visitors seems set to destroy her husband's promising political career – especially when a wasp stings Clarisse in a very delicate place. Translated from Feydeau's *Mais N'te Promène Donc Pas Toute Nue!* (see also *Put Some Clothes On, Clarisse!*). Period 1910

Double Dealing, or, **A Little Horse Play**. Melodrama. Brian J. Burton
M4 F2. Simple interior setting. Fee code B

A mini melodrama for inclusion in a Music Hall Evening, with the emphasis on comedy with a difference. Contained in *Foiled Again!*

♦ **A bullet mark next to a title indicates that it is new to this edition of the Guide.**

The Drag Factor. Play. Frank Vickery
M2 (youngish, mid 50s) F1 (mid 50s). A hospital corridor. Fee code D

Set in a hospital corridor, *The Drag Factor* is a poignant and blisteringly funny account of a husband and wife coming abruptly to terms with the fact that their son is gay. NB. *The Drag Factor* is Act I Scene 1 of Frank Vickery's full length play *Roots and Wings*.

Dreamjobs. Play. Graham Jones
F5 (15). A waiting-room. Fee code D

Waiting for interviews with a Youth Employment Service, five teenage girls dream of romantic, exciting jobs derived from sentimental television series and films. The dreams are enacted, and in each case there is a rude awakening. Finally Beverly, clearest-sighted, brings them down to earth, forcing them to realize that their characters and abilities will fit them for only the drabbest of occupations.
ISBN 978 0 573 03379 7

The Droitwich Discovery. Play. Nick Warburton
M2 (young) F4 (young, middle-age). An attic. Fee code D

Four thespian enthusiasts find themselves in a dusty attic in Droitwich. Their guide explains that Shakespeare, aged ten, lived there. Then there emerges a Tudor-looking man, the ghost of Terry Shakespeare, embittered by his brother William's literary thievery. To prove his point, he puts the visitors in a trance, making them perform scenes from the plays *he* had written.
ISBN 978 0 573 12146 3

♦ **Drunk Enough To Say I Love You.** Play. Caryl Churchill
M2. Simple setting. Fee code F

Jack would do anything for Sam. Sam would do anything. This series of fragmented duologues examines the "special" relationship between two men: deferential Brit Jack, who has left his wife and family for dominant Sam, who is American, which in turn serves as an allegory for the subservient attitude of Britain to America. This 45-minute play premiered at the Royal Court Theatre, London, in 2006.

The Drunkard's Wife or **The Tables Turned**. Melodrama. Brian J. Burton
M2 F2. One interior. Fee code D

A temperance drama, employing the Victorian device of the occasional overuse of long or obscure words, which it is doubtful if the actors understand, let alone the audience! Contained in *Three Hisses for Villainy*.

Duck Variations. Play. David Mamet
M2 (60s). A park. Fee code E

Two elderly gentlemen meet in a park and proceed to discuss life, death and ducks. The ducks form a sort of sounding-board from which their flights of fancy take off, providing parallels, analogies and equivalents for their more serious, or less worldly, topics. The play is presented in the form of fourteen variations with an interval between each variation to allow the actors to prepare.

The Dumb Waiter. Play. Harold Pinter
M2. A basement room. Fee code F

Gus and Ben are on the job, waiting and listening. Into the waiting silence rattles the dumb waiter with extraordinary demands for dishes they cannot supply – and who is operating the dumb waiter in an empty house? In a while their victim will come and they will know what to do.
ISBN 978 0 573 04210 2

The Dwarfs. Play. Harold Pinter
M3 (20s). Composite set. Fee code E

Len and Peter are drinking tea in Mark's flat at midnight. As Mark arrives the scene changes to Len's house. Len, a neurotic young man, is haunted by dwarfs. At great length he describes their extraordinary and seemingly nonsensical behaviour. The other two believe he gets too excited by life and his delusions. The explanation of Len's haunting is left in the air.

Early Blight. Play. Jean McConnell
F2 (middle age, elderly). A seaside promenade. Fee code B

See the entry for *Deckchairs I*.

Easy Stages. Comedy. N. J. Warburton
M3 (40s) F4 (30s) or M2 F5. A stage. Fee code D

This is an amusing, subtle parody of the backstage goings-on of an amateur dramatic society. While N. J. Warburton's play *Don't Blame It on the Boots* centred on the onstage difficulties of the amateur dramatic society's production of *Hamlet*, here we see the stage crew struggling to play their part against all the odds.
ISBN 978 0 573 12066 4

The Edge. Play. Steve Carley
M3 (any age, 50) or M2 F1. Composite set: 2 offices. Fee code E

Marcus Wade has found himself saddled with a curious gift: he can see into the future. At first he can use this power to his advantage but his pleasure turns to terror when he finds his vision only extends a certain distance into the future. What lies beyond 'the edge' he sees coming rapidly towards him?
ISBN 978 0 573 12151 7

Effie's Burning. Play. Valerie Windsor
F2 (20s, 60s). A hospital room, a space. Fee code E

Effie, who has lived in mental institutions since the age of thirteen, has been admitted to hospital with severe burns. Treating her is Dr Ruth Kovacs, who finds in Effie's extraordinary story of injustice and official callousness the key to her own suppressed anger and power. Taut and powerful, tender and often funny, *Effie's Burning* is an emotional switchback of a play, with a searing anger at its heart.
ISBN 978 0 573 13236 0

Eliza's House. Play. Brendan Murray
M1(10-13, 40) F1 (30s), 1 girl (11). A council-house room. Fee code F

Family poverty robs Eliza of her dream of becoming a violinist. She transfers her ambition on to her son but he does not wish to learn. After a long absence he returns for his violin unprepared for an encounter with a girl who has befriended his mother or the rush of memory this meeting produces. A delicate and moving drama. Running time approximately one hour.
ISBN 978 0 573 02367 5

Endgame. Play. Samuel Beckett
M3 F1. A bare interior. Fee code F

The world is coming to an end, and Hamm, a sightless despot, attended by Clov, his shambling slave, watch from their bleak cell. Hamm is flanked by two dustbins, inhabited by his legless parents, Nagg and Nell. Eventually Nell dies. In Beckett's vision, there is defeat and poetic despair but the whole is faintly illumined by a glimmer of salvation.

An Englishman Abroad. Play. Alan Bennett
M4 (20s, 50s) F1 (40s). A flat. Fee code F

Originally a television play, this forms part of the double bill *Single Spies* (see Section A) which was presented by the Royal National Theatre in 1988, winning the Laurence Olivier Award for Comedy of the Year. It is based on a true incident in the life of the actress Coral Browne and tells the witty, touching story of her meeting with Guy Burgess in Moscow in 1958.
ISBN 978 0 573 01891 6

Ernie's Incredible Illucinations. Play for young people. Alan Ayckbourn
22 characters. Extras. Doubling possible. A bare stage, waiting-room at one side. Fee code E

Ernie Fraser has a vivid imagination, but his thoughts have a disturbing habit of turning into reality. After a number of embarrassing episodes, Ernie's parents consult a doctor. When Ernie fails to produce a brass band on demand, the doctor diagnoses group hallucination. However, 'Ernie's incredible illucinations' aren't to be dismissed quite so lightly!
ISBN 978 0 573 12063 3

Escape. Play. Tennessee Williams.
M3. A chain-gang bunk-house. Fee code E

Three prisoners in a bunk-house play cards and listen while their cellmate makes a run to the rail tracks with guards and dogs in hot pursuit. Finally, they hear gunshots but when they see the guards return with a body they believe Billy's free at last.

The Escapologist. Play. David Henry Wilson
M2 (30s, middle-age) F1 (middle-age). A street. Fee code C

Joe, a passerby, becomes central in the act of Escalini, a street performer accompanied by a parrot-like wife. The show becomes a kaleidoscope of themes ranging from God to free will and, ultimately, death while the escapologist attempts to free himself from steel chains which – metaphorically – summarize man's fate.

B

Everyman. Morality play. Constance Cox
M7 F4 or F11. Extras optional. Choir. A market-place, dominated by a cross. Fee code A
ISBN 978 0 573 06248 3

Everywoman. Verse drama. Hugh Steadman Williams, from the fifteenth-century morality play *Everyman* and Hugo von Hofmannsthal's *Jedermann*
M8 F4 or M7 F5. Simple settings on an open stage. Fee code D

Everywoman is a ruthless, successful careerist who has sacrificed everything for her own advancement. When Death appears, her successes fail her; only Faith, her deserted husband, and Crystal, her child, remain by her. Her eyes are opened, she repents, and is saved.
ISBN 978 0 573 06253 6

The Exception and the Rule. Play. Bertolt Brecht
Translations: Ralph Manheim, music by Dessau
Tom Osborn, music by Frank Wagland
Eric Bentley
M9 F1. Several simple interiors. Fee code G for play, code C for music

Crossing the desert, an unscrupulous merchant and his maltreated coolie run short of water. The coolie generously offers what water he has but the merchant, mistrusting the coolie, thinks he is about to attack and shoots him. The merchant is tried but is acquitted when it is decided that, in present day society, to murder one's oppressor is the Rule, and to repay cruelty with kindness is the Exception.

The Extraordinary Revelations of Orca the Goldfish. Comedy. David Tristram
M1 (middle-age) F1 (middle-age). Simple settings. Fee code E

For Henry Smith life was rarely dull. For Alice Smith life was rarely anything else. Enter Michel – French waiter – tall, dark, and available. Exactly what happened next, no-one's quite sure ... A virtuoso piece for two talented and versatile actors – one female and one male – requiring minimal props and scenery and therefore ideal for festivals.

Family Voices. Play (from the triple bill *Other Places*). Harold Pinter
M2 (young, middle-age) F1 (middle-age). A bare stage. Fee code E

Written as a series of monologues featuring an exchange of letters between a mother and her absent son. The mother's desperate attempts to bring her son back to her from his lodgings in a sleazy London boarding house become more ill-attuned, serving only to accentuate the irreparable rift between them.
ISBN 978 0 573 12067 1

Fanny's Prayer, or, All Was Not Lost. Brian J. Burton
M4 (45, 65) F2 (18, 65). A farm labourer's cottage. Fee code B

A short melodrama for inclusion in a Music Hall evening. Little scenery is required and detailed production notes are given in the script. Contained with two other melodramas in *Cheers, Tears and Screamers*.

The Fat Lady Sings in Little Grimley. Comedy. David Tristram
M2 F2. A bare stage. Fee code D

Gordon, Margaret, Joyce and Bernard tackle another threat to their survival – this time it's a newly-formed rival am-dram, determined to upstage them with an award-winning musical. The querulous quartet pull together to devise an ingenious plan that doesn't go well. Could this finally be the end of their society? It's never over until the fat lady sings. This completes the Little Grimley trilogy.

B

The Fat Man's Wife. Play Tennessee Williams.
M2 (young, middle age) F1 (middle age). A bedroom. Fee code E

New Year's morning 1938. Vera and her husband Joe, an influential theatre producer, return from a party, at which a young playwright, Dennis, has paid court to Vera. Rather than compromise his art, Dennis has decided to quit New York for Acapulco and wants Vera to accompany him. But Vera sends him away; she is, after all, the fat man's wife.

♦ **Fatal Loins**. Comedy. Perry Pontac
M4 F3 or M3 F4. Various simple settings. Fee Code D

Subtitled *Romeo and Juliet reconsidered* – the question answered by the play is posed in the prologue: "If Juliet and Romeo survive/Will their eternal passion stay alive?". In the volume *Codpieces*, forming a triple bill with *Prince Lear* and *Hamlet Part II*. ". . . a gift to actors and a tonic for audiences." Alan Bennett.

Fawlty Towers. By John Cleese and Connie Booth

All 12 complete and unexpurgated scripts of the most celebrated TV sit-com ever are collected in this volume. Fawlty Towers is the best-loved bad hotel in the world and here we meet the snobbish, manic Basil; his over-coiffeured domineering wife, Sybil; the hopeless but ever-hopeful waiter Manuel; the calm and capable Polly – and, of course, the steady stream of abused guests. (Please note that the scripts have not been specifically adapted for the stage.)

A Touch of Class
M9 F4. Extras. The hotel reception, the dining-room, the town, the hotel bar. Fee code D

The Builders
M9 F4. The hotel reception, the dining-room, the forecourt, the drawing-room. Fee code D

The Wedding Party
M6 F7. The hotel bar, the Fawltys' bedroom, the lobby, the dining-room, a bedroom. Fee code D

The Hotel Inspectors
M7 F4. The hotel office and lobby. Fee code D

Gourmet Night
M9 F7. The hotel lobby, bar and dining-room. Fee code D

The Germans
M8 F8. A hospital room, hotel reception and dining-room. Fee code D

Communication Problems
M9 F5. The hotel lobby, bedroom and bar. Fee code D

The Psychiatrist
M6 F8. The hotel lobby, dining-room and upstairs corridor. Fee code D

Waldorf Salad
M7 F9. The hotel dining-room. Fee code D

The Kipper and the Corpse
M11 F7. The hotel bar, lobby, dining-room and bedroom. Fee code D

The Anniversary
M7 F8. The hotel kitchen, lobby and bar. Fee code D

Basil the Rat
M8 F6. The hotel forecourt, kitchen and a bedroom. Fee code D

The Fear of Heaven. Play. John Mortimer
M5 (young, middle-age) F2 (middle-age, elderly). A hospital ward. Fee code E
ISBN 978 0 573 12070 1

The Fifteen Minute Hamlet. Comedy. Tom Stoppard
M4 F2. An open stage. Fee code E

Following his success with *Rosencrantz and Guildenstern Are Dead*, Stoppard has taken the most well-known and best-loved lines from Shakespeare's play and condensed them into an hilarious version lasting approximately thirteen minutes, followed by an encore which consists of a two-minute version of the play! The vast multitude of characters is played by six actors with hectic doubling.
ISBN 978 0 573 02506 8

Figuring Things. Play. Michael Fosbrook
M2 (middle age) F2 (middle age). Various simple settings. Fee code D

For Dennis, cricket averages are everything. When the Statisticians' Circle accepts Pat, its first female member, however, Dennis's life takes a sharp turn. Contrary to Dennis's assumptions, Pat excels in the craft. They plan a trip to the Caribbean but Dennis's wife doesn't know that Pat is female, so when they meet this highly original satire on male-female relations is set for an explosive ending.
ISBN 978 0 573 12205 1

A Fish in Her Kettle. A play for Coarse Actors. Edited by Michael Green

See the entry for *The Third Great Coarse Acting Show*.

Five Kinds of Silence. Play. Shelagh Stephenson
M2 (middle age, any age) F4 (30s, any age), with trebling. Various simple settings. Fee code G

This highly-acclaimed stage version of the 1996 radio play is the story of a family in which control has become the driving force. Billy, himself abused as a child, has sexually abused his two daughters since their early teens. Now the adult daughters, with the connivance of their mother, attempt to free themselves, and kill him.

♦ **Flash, Bam, Alakazam**. Play. Sue Wilding
F1 (elderly). A living-room. Fee Code D

Elsie lives alone and avoids socialising with her neighbours. Newly arrived Kate and Adrian invite Elsie for tea and she strikes up a bond with their young son, James. Elsie is drafted in as babysitter but when James strays too near to the garden pond Elsie acts on her instincts but his parents are appalled. A prize-winning, poignant monologue.
ISBN 978 0 573 13243 8

Flood Warning. Play. Fay Weldon
M2 (30s, 50s) F3 (25, 35, 50s). A living-room. Fee code E

The local river has flooded Cynthia's and Step's antiques business. Cynthia, immobile, can only comment on the rising tide as her husband and daughter Angela move salvageable stock upstairs. Elder daughter, city exec Jane, and partner arrive to help, with Jane intent on organizing everyone. The animosity between the sisters is apparent and an announcement by Angela opens up a flood of family secrets!
ISBN 978 0 573 02361 3

Footprints in the Sand. Play. Colin Crowther
M1 (40s) F3 (15+, 50s, 60s). A beach. Fee code E

A man facing a protracted terminal illness comes to a deserted beach, despondent and raging. A mysterious woman tells him of the place's history: nearby, in the fifth century, Dwynwen, maid-in-waiting to the queen, deserted her faithless lover to live alone, away from deceitful humanity. Dwynwen appears with her nurse, who attempts to coax her home; in enlisting the man's support she opens his eyes to the love of others which will help him through his ordeal.
ISBN 978 0 573 02351 4

For Starters. Comedy. Nick Warburton
M1 (40s) F1 (20s). A hotel restaurant. Fee Code D

Daisy is a recently employed waitress at an hotel and Roland, a regular and rather particular customer, is getting more than he ordered. From polite conversation to an outright invasion of privacy, Daisy attends to Roland in her unique way. They realize they have something to learn from each other – Daisy needs to be less nosey and Roland learns how to accept change.
ISBN 978 0 573 02383 5

♦ **A bullet mark next to a title indicates that it is new to this edition of the Guide.**

Foreign Bodies. Play. Peter Nichols
M5 (25, middle-age, 60s) F2 (young, middle-age). Composite set: a study, a sitting-room. Fee code G

Swinging London meets bourgeois Shrewsbury in 1963 and the drinks are laced with cyanide. As the son of the household struggles to write his first play, a murder story is offered to him on a plate. Together with *A Game of Soldiers* this forms the double bill *Blue Murder* (see the entry in Section A).

B

The Form. Play. N. F. Simpson
M2 (23, 50s) F2 (20, middle-age). An art office. Fee code C

A parody of bureaucratic procedure occurs when a young man goes to be interviewed by a Mr Chacterson. When he approaches the secretary, it appears that she cannot help him until she takes on the persona of Mr Chacterson's receptionist, which will not be until Mr Chacterson rings for her. The interview takes place on consistently illogical lines.
ISBN 978 0 573 02076 6

Forty Winks Beauty. Minidrama. Richard Tydeman
M5 F7. Fee code B

A 'Potted Panto' with Beauty being awakened not by the prince, who's late, but by Charley Prince, a teddy boy. Luckily the day is saved, albeit unwittingly, by the wicked fairy Maud. Running time: 15-20 minutes
ISBN 978 0 573 06616 0

Forward to the Right. A play of Joan of Arc. Lily Ann Green
M1 F1. A gaol cell of a castle in Rouen. Fee code D

Joan of Arc, condemned to burn at the stake, is denied a rosary, cross or any form of service, but the guard becomes sympathetic and arranges for her to receive the last rites. In consequence he is imprisoned after Joan's death, refusing to acknowledge her powers as witchcraft.
ISBN 978 0 573 12057 2

FOUR PLAYS FOR COARSE ACTORS

Michael Green
M9 F3. Extras. Three living-rooms; a throne-room; a forest. Fee codes B and C

The number of characters given above would be sufficient to cover the presentation of all four plays by the same cast. Ages can vary from young to the practically senile.

The plays are presented as parodies of four dramatic styles, in the performance of which everything which can conceivably go wrong in a production does so. *Il Fornicazione*, (Fee code B) is a grim tale of operatic adultery, poison and mayhem. *Streuth*, (Fee code B) is a crime story which even Agatha Christie would never have dared to write. *A Collier's Tuesday Tea*, (Fee code B) combines the kitchen sink with the coal-mine, and with an irreverent glance at D.H. Lawrence. *All's Well That Ends As You Like It*, (Fee code C) ('from an idea by William Shakespeare' and set in 'the Forest of Solihull') pushes the genius of the Bard to its utmost limits, while managing to filch lines from most of his own plays. In all four, cues are missed, effects fail, props are lost or in the wrong place, furniture and scenery collapses – and one play, *Streuth*, gets itself into such confusion that it is doomed, apparently, to perpetual motion: but the Coarse Actors struggle gamefully on throughout. Apart from the essentials, the settings can be simple or elaborate, as facilities permit.
ISBN 978 0 573 00008 9

Four-Play. Play. Colin Smith
M2 (40s) F2 (40s). A sitting-room. Fee code D

Two perfectly ordinary couples – hosts David and Caroline, guests Helen and Edward – are enjoying a dinner party. David is having an affair with Helen and Caroline knows all about it. Once the cat is out of the bag there is no way to stop the evening developing into a battleground of recriminations, explanations and cruel home truths. Explosively and observantly written.
ISBN 978 0 573 12248 4

B

The Fourth Prisoner. Play. David Henry Wilson
M6 (20s, 40s, middle-age). 3 extras. Prison cell. Fee code C

Two veteran prisoners, Jack and Sean, are initiating newcomer Lamb into the cell routine. Each accepts his sentence in his own way. At night the cell is visited by Johnnie, the fourth prisoner, a sort of alter ego who gives them hope and strength to endure life behind the prison walls.

From Here to the Library. Play. Jimmie Chinn
M2 (middle-age, 70s) F1 (30s). A living-room. Fee code D

Beryl, a librarian, is dominated by her elderly and irascible father; the library is her only escape. So when Beryl throws an uncharacteristic fit of temper at work and doesn't return, her boss visits her to find out why. He succeeds in showing Beryl that she both needs and is needed by the world outside.
ISBN 978 0 573 12058 9

Fumed Oak. Comedy. Noël Coward
M1 (middle-age) F3 (14, 35, elderly). A drawing-room. Fee code C

For years Henry Gow has loathed his awful wife, their adenoidal child and his utterly repulsive mother-in-law. One evening Henry tells them all exactly what he thinks of them, announces he has saved £500 and that he is going to leave them. And off he goes, triumphantly slamming the door on three howling women. Period 1936
ISBN 978 0 573 02079 7

A Gaggle of Saints. Play. Neil LaBute
M1 F1. A bare stage. Fee code E

A young Mormon couple separately describe the events of an anniversary weekend in New York. As the events described entwine, the girl is blissfully unaware of the violence perpetrated by her fiancé. This play is from the triple bill *Bash – a* collection of three raw, dark, yet lyrically intense one-act plays which won the Time Out Critic's Choice Award. For details please see the entry in Section A.

A Galway Girl. Drama. Geraldine Aron
M1 F1. Simple set: a table and two chairs. Fee code E

A married couple reminisce about their life together. The characters are young to begin with, then middle-aged, then old, then one of them dies. The anecdotes they relate are both humorous and tragic. At the end the wife's muted gesture of affection conveys the love that can endure through years of household bickering and incompatibility.
ISBN 978 0 573 62204 3

A Game of Soldiers. Play. Peter Nichols
M5 (20s, middle-age, 60s) F2 (young, middle-age). An elegant room. Fee code G

A Game of Soldiers is a Whitehall farce set in St James's Palace in 1967. A young dramatist has brought his play to be censored but the Lord Chamberlain's Men have shameful secrets of their own to hide, including a priapic guardsman. With *Foreign Bodies* this forms the double bill *Blue Murder* (see the entry in Section A).

B

Garden Pests. Short play (From *Deckchairs IV*). Jean McConnell.
F2 (50+,). A garden. Fee code C

A comedy which focuses on two keen gardeners meeting in a magnificent garden from which neither intends to go home empty-handed.
ISBN 978 0 573 10021 5

Getting Along. Comedy. Charles Mander
M3 (ageing, elderly) F2 (middle-age, ageing). An interior. Fee code D. ISBN 978 0 573 12128 9

Ghost of a Chance. Play. Brian J. Burton
F5 (20, 40, 50, elderly). A room. Fee code C

When Mrs Dean learns one of her ancestors haunts a deserted house nearby, she arranges to spend the night there alone. As she watches, dramatic events of 1860 are re-enacted and she leaves supposedly having found the reason for the reputed haunting.

Ghosts of Bedlam. Play. Arthur Aldrich
M1 (40s) F3 (50s, elderly). Derelict hospital ward. Fee Code D

Royston is commissioned to film a documentary contrasting old-style mental health care with the improvement 1990s care-in-the-community has brought. Showing him around the derelict ward of a former mental hospital is nurse-turned-caretaker, Janet. Determined to show the reality of care-in-the-community, Janet introduces Milly, an old baglady and former inmate. Bu Royston experiences a flashback into his own life, he makes a life-changing decision.
ISBN 978 0 573 02377 8

Gizmo. Play. Alan Ayckbourn
M5 F3. Various simple settings. Fee code F

Ben suffers from post-traumatic paralysis, brought on by a shooting he witnessed. Doctors have developed an advanced new device, GIZMO; a microchip implanted in Ben's brain helps him walk by mimicking the movements of the GIZMO wearer. Then Ben falls into the hands of Lando, a hit man, who thinks he knows Ben from somewhere ... (Playing time: more than one hour.)
ISBN 978 0 573 15206 1

The Gnädiges Fräulein. Tennessee Williams

See the entry under *Slapstick Tragedy* in Section A

God. Play. Woody Allen
M20 F8. Extras. An amphitheatre. Fee code F

Athens, approximately 500 BC. The Actor and Writer are trying to work out the ending of a play. Suddenly the Writer asks if the audience have any suggestions. Alarming abysses open. What if the audience are characters in another play, and somebody is writing *them*? In the ensuing mêlée of shifting realities time and space become inextricably mixed.
ISBN 0 573 62201 9

B

The Godiva Affair. Comedy (from *Dad's Army*). Jimmy Perry and David Croft
M14 F3. Extras. A church hall and office. Fee code E

The platoon are rehearsing their Morris Dancing routine as part of a fund-raising carnival parade which will include a ride-past by Lady Godiva. Unfortunately for Mr Mainwaring, there's a last minute substitution for Godiva! An hilarious episode from the classic BBC TV series *Dad's Army*. Period 1940
ISBN 978 0 573 10014 7

Going Home. Play (from *Visiting Hour*). Richard Harris
M2 F4 (1 Black). A hospital ward. Fee code D

Taken from the full-length play *Visiting Hour* (see Section A), *Going Home* was seen in 1990 at the Duke's Head Theatre, Richmond, Surrey. It traces the lessons learned by a confrontation between a white woman patient and a black woman patient on the eve of their discharge from hospital.
ISBN 978 0 573 01925 8

Goodbye Iphigenia. Play. George MacEwan Green
M3 F3. A military camp. Fee code D

The legend of Iphigenia, sacrificed by her father King Agamemnon to the goddess Artemis in order to free the becalmed Greek fleet in the port of Aulis is here made more accessible for contemporary audiences by dramatizing an 'eye witness' account of the events given by Andreas, the soldier, who guarded the royal tent that fateful day.
ISBN 978 0 573 12097 8

Grannies. Short play (From *Deckchairs IV*). Jean McConnell.
F2 (40/50). A seafront. Fee code C

A drama which introduces us to Jenny, reluctantly looking after her teenage daughter's baby, and to Barbara, whose deep grandmotherly feelings have led her into a very strange situation.
ISBN 978 0 573 10021 5

The Green Eye of the Little Yellow Dog. Melodrama. Harry Austin
M6 F1 Fee code C

A stirring tale of true love, devotion to duty and stark staring stupidity on the part of Captain Quincey Hogg, newly arrived adjutant at the British fort just north of Katmandu, who falls foul of the curse of the green eye of the little yellow dog. Playing time approximately 20 minutes. Contained in *The Little Lights of Kimberley*.
ISBN 978 0 573 10023 3

Green Forms. Play. Alan Bennett
M2 (middle-age, 1 Black) F3 (30s, 40s). An office. Fee code F

Doris and Doreen are comfortably installed in an obscure department of a large organization. On a normal day the girls keep busy by flirting or pursuing their bitter feud over office supplies with the Personnel Department. Work is nowhere. However, a shadow falls across their tranquil lives. Is it redundancy?
ISBN 978 0 573 12087 9

B

The Guilt Card. Short play (From *Deckchairs II*). Jean McConnell
F2 (middle-age). A seafront. Fee code C

Marion discovers, by a cruel twist of fate, that her life has been blighted by the machinations and emotional blackmail of her sickly elder sister, Deborah.
ISBN 978 0 573 10004 8

The Gypsy Curse or The Flower of the Tribe. Melodrama. Brian J. Burton
M3 F3. One exterior. Fee code D

A gypsy romantic drama, telling the story, recounted by one of the gypsies in Maria Marten, of the events that were supposed to have occurred to William Corder before he met Maria and foully murdered her in the red barn. Contained in *Three Hisses for Villainy*.

Half an Idea. Comedy. Bob Larbey
M9 F18 (doubling possible). Composite set: three living rooms. Fee code G

The Writer types 'Curtain', completing his first play: a rage against life ... But when the script is enacted before his eyes it turns out to be a very funny piece. The hilarity must stop, the Writer commands, and so rewrites it as a funeral. But this, too, brought to life, becomes an hilarious comedy. The Writer vows he will re-cast!
ISBN 978 0 573 12132 6

Half-Life. Play. Katy Darby
M1 (50s) F1 (35). A hotel bedroom. Fee code D

Dirk, a former American movie star turned US Senator, is held hostage at gunpoint by English journalist Jay in a seedy hotel room. Is she an obsessive fan, an activist with a grudge, or something more sinister? Gradually Jay reveals her purpose and offers Dirk a deal which will guarantee both their places in history. But an unexpected twist will force Jay's hand ... Running time thirty minutes.
ISBN 978 0 573 02373 6

The Hamelin Incident. Play. Graham Walker
M13 F2. 8 children. Extras. Simple interior and exterior settings. Fee code E

This adaptation of the Pied Piper tale centres on the figure of Blankenfeld, the one member of the Town Council to feel a moral obligation towards the Piper once he has rid the town of rats. He alone is exempt from the doom the town brings upon itself by ignoring the Piper's demands for his payment.
ISBN 978 0 573 12092 3

◆ **Hamlet Part II**. Comedy. Perry Pontac
M3 F1. A platform. Fee Code D

Here Perry Pontac answers a question about Hamlet that has plagued scholars, readers and playgoers for over four hundred years: what happened next?. With *Prince Lear* and *Fatal Loins* this forms the triple bill *Codpieces*. "Perfectly crafted, wonderful fun." Daily Telegraph

Hands Across the Sea. Comedy. Noël Coward
M5 (young, middle-age) F4 (30s, middle-age). A drawing-room. Fee code E

On their world tour, Piggie Gilpin and Lady Dalborough invited all their kind hosts to see them when they returned to England. An unassuming couple from Malaya stray into the Gilpin flat, only to find themselves bewildered by Naval officers, smart and totally meaningless chatter, and a hostess who has forgotten who they are. Period 1936

◆ **Happy Birthday Me**. A comedy. Simon Williams
M2 (70s, young) F5 (young, 40s, 70s). A lounge. Fee Code D

A comedy based on the author's earlier play, *Laying the Ghost*. "It's my birthday. All I wanted was a bottle of claret and a couple of winners at Sandown". Instead, retired actress Margot receives three separate visitors – her ex-husband, his new wife and his latest mistress. In the ensuing fireworks Leo suffers a heart attack. Then the kissogram turns up . . .
ISBN 978 0 573 12093 0

The Happy Journey. Play. Thornton Wilder
M3 (13, middle-age) F3 (15, 22, middle-age). No scenery. Fee code C

An ordinary American family journeys to visit a married daughter in a distant town. Their extremely amusing encounters and discussions are interwoven with a tender philosophy and sincere faith as expressed by the mother and a kindly common sense in the father – a combination which gives the play a most satisfying quality.

Harlequinade. Farce. Terence Rattigan
M10 (20s-middle-age, old) F5 (young, middle-age, old). A stage set for *Romeo and Juliet*. Fee code F

Arthur and Edna Gosport are opening a Shakespearian tour. During the dress rehearsal of *Romeo and Juliet*, a pallid spectre turns up out of Arthur's past, claiming to be his daughter. In a few moments before the curtain rises, the harassed Arthur makes wild attempts to solve this imbroglio.
ISBN 978 0 573 02094 0

Harry's Christmas. Play. Steven Berkoff
M1. Fee code E
At the beginning of this moving and bitterly funny monologue, Harry is counting his Christmas cards. Six. This is the last time he will go though the agonies of Christmas alone. Berkoff writes: " ... no play I have done received so many responses from people who found in Harry's dilemma and, may I say agony, echoes in their own lives."

Heart's Desire. Play. Caryl Churchill
M2 F4 with doubling. Child extras. A kitchen. Fee code E

A family await the return of their daughter after a long sojourn in Australia. The moments before the arrival are re-enacted over and over again with increasingly wild variations in the course of which a crazy selection of visitors bursts upon the scene. Together with *Blue Kettle*, this forms the double bill *Blue Heart* (see Section A).

B

Hello from Bertha. Play. Tennessee Williams
F4 (young, middle-age). A bedroom. Fee code E

Bertha, a prostitute, is ill, probably fatally, and her room is needed by the other prostitutes. Despite her friend Goldie's protestations, she refuses to leave. Goldie suggests that Bertha should write to Charlie, one of Bertha's erstwhile customers, and ask for money to help her. Bertha dictates the letter – her last message – but it seems unlikely that it will ever be sent.

Henna Night. Play. Amy Rosenthal
F2 (20s-30s). A bedsit. Fee code E

Judith leaves her ex-boyfriend a message on his answerphone saying that she is not coping, that she has razor blades and henna in order to either slash her wrists or dye her hair and she might be pregnant. However, it is his new partner, Ros, who hears the message and rushes to Judith's bedsit. An evening of emotion and humour ensues, ending with the two women, despite their rivalry, finding friendship.
ISBN 978 0 573 03393 3

Henry the Tenth. (Part Seven). A play for Coarse Actors. Michael Green

See the entry for *The Coarse Acting Show 2*.

Her Big Chance. Monologue. Alan Bennett
F1 (early 30s). A room. Fee code F

Meet Lesley, an actress. She has just completed a video ('targeted chiefly on West Germany') in which she plays Travis, a career girl who enjoys life, spends a remarkable amount of time topless and shoots a man with a harpoon gun. She tells all, blind to the sinister undertones of her story as well as to her own self-delusions and gullibility.
ISBN 978 0 573 13241 4

The Hole. Play. N. F. Simpson
M5 F2. Around a hole dug in the road. Fee code E

There is a hole in the road, where men are working. Watchers gather, curious folk who wonder what is going on below, obsessed with the need to categorize what is happening. Each one sees a fantastic significance in the hole. Their theories are ingenious but contradictory, and each tries to impose his own interpretation on everyone else.
ISBN 978 0 573 02100 8

♦ **The Holiday.** Comedy. Peter Quilter (From *Duets*)
M1 F1. A living-room. Fee code D

Shelley and Bobby are getting divorced, but are having a final holiday together in Spain. Despite their best intentions to stay civilised, Shelley gets drunk and flirtatious and Bobby threatens to fly home early. Eventually nostalgia for the happy times they had together wins through, and they agree to end the holiday – and the marriage – amicably. May be performed individually or as the third act in *Duets*.
ISBN 978 0 573 11111 2

B

Hot Fudge. Play. Caryl Churchill
M5 F5 or M2 F3. Simple interior settings. Fee code E

The play was given a performance reading at the Royal Court Theatre Upstairs in 1989 and performed as a double bill with *Icecream* in New York in 1990. In this brief series of vignettes we meet various couples in a completely amoral world where money is all that matters and lies are the only truth.
ISBN 978 0 573 62234 5

How Much Is Your Iron? Play. Bertolt Brecht. Translated by Rose and Martin Kastner
M4 F2. An iron-dealer's shop. Fee code F

A sinister customer purchases iron from Svendson and later Svendson's neighbour the tobacconist, is murdered. The customer returns and barters belligerantly for iron with cigars (Svendson's weakness). Another neighbour's murdered but Svendson continues to supply the customer – after all, it's business. Finally, brandishing machine guns, the customer demands: "How much is your iron?" The iron-dealer stammers: "Nothing". Period 1938

How To Make Your Theatre Pay. Comedy. David Henry Wilson
M2 (middle age) F1 (young). A theatre. Fee code D

Rouse, a Council official, is visiting the theatre run by Mike Pemberton-Hawkesley, his mission to save the Council money. His brainwave is to turn the theatre into a storage facility for files; Mike is outraged. Mavis Dinwiddy intervenes and the hilarious absurdity of the situation, compounded by Rouse's very idiosyncratic verbal style, is maintained right up to end of this surprising and enigmatic play.
ISBN 978 0 573 02352 1

The Human Voice. Play. Jean Cocteau. New authorized English version by Anthony Wood
F1. A bedroom. Fee code F

A woman awaits and receives a phone call from her lover who has recently left her. 'The actress should give the impression that she is bleeding, losing her life's blood, like a wounded beast, finishing the play as if the bedroom is drenched in blood.'
ISBN 978 0 573 03381 0

Humour Helps. Play. Peter Barnes
M1 (any age) F1 (any age). A living-room. Fee code C

An actress hamfistedly tries to commit suicide, finally achieving her aim with the unwitting aid of a neighbour. May be presented as part of the full-length entertainment *Corpsing*. For details, see the entry in Section A.
ISBN 978 0 573 10006 2

I Do Solemnly Declare. Play. Simon Farquhar
M2 (mid teens, late 30s) F2 (mid teens, late 30s). A living-room. Fee code D
ISBN 978 0 573 12282 8

I Rise in Flame, Cried the Phoenix. Play. Tennessee Williams
M1 (40s) F2 (middle-age). A sun porch. Fee code E

This brief play, set at Vence in the Alps Maritimes, is an imaginary depiction of D. H. Lawrence's last moments, showing the intense love-hate relationship with his wife as, dying of consumption, he expresses his controversial views on art and sex, referring in particular to a recent exhibition of his paintings.

If Yer Take A Short Cut. Play. David Henry Wilson
M4 (young, elderly) F1 (elderly). Truthseekers' home. Fee code D

This perceptive play, centred on an elderly couple afflicted by boredom and despair, brings to mind Beckett's *Waiting for Godot*. Set in a hypothetical future which resembles only too well the present day, it follows the painful search for truth of Archibald, an aged man who cannot communicate any longer with his estranged wife.
ISBN 0 573 60108 8

If You're Glad I'll Be Frank. Play. Tom Stoppard
M7 (middle-age) F5 (young, middle-age). An open stage. Fee code E

Frank recognizes the voice of the GPO speaking clock as that of his long-lost wife. Determined to get her back, he forces his way into the inner sanctum of the Authorities to demand her release. Underlying the light-hearted story is a satiric comment on man's servitude to the clock.
ISBN 78 0 573 12112 8

Il Fornicazione. A play for Coarse Actors. Michael Green

See the entry for *Four Plays for Coarse Actors*.

In by the Half. Play. Jimmie Chinn
M1 F4, or F5 (young, 40s, elderly). A living-room. Fee code E

Madam, once a distinguished actress, lives in seclusion looked after by her ex-dresser. Their peaceful routine includes visits from the doctor and the insipid Sylvia, who takes acting lessons from Madam. But the initial acerbic comedy of the play gives way to a poignant drama with the arrival of Madam's estranged daughter who nurses a bitter secret.
ISBN 978 0 573 12126 5

In Need of Care. Play. David E. Rowley
M2 (teenage) F2 (teenage). A farm outbuilding. Fee code C

Shirley and Rita, having run away from school, are hiding. They are surprised by two boys who know who they are from the newspapers. The play follows the developing relations among the four, Jeff and Rita becoming immediately attracted to each other. The encounter and the resulting delay alters all their plans.
ISBN 978 0 573 02322 4

In Room Five Hundred and Four. Play. Jimmie Chinn
M2 (20s) F2 (20s, 60s). A room in a boarding-house. Fee code D. ISBN 978 0 573 12120 3

In the Penal Colony. Play. Adapted from Franz Kafka by Steven Berkoff
M4. Fee code D
Berkoff describes this as a "strange tale of torture and suffering". An officer describes the workings of an horrific machine of torture; later he puts himself in the machine hoping for redemption. A blackly comic, frightening moral play.

Indian Summer. Play. Lucy Maurice
F2 (20s). A railway station café. Fee code F

'Look at this place! You know, in here, all the secrets of the world exist.' Laura and Steph work, talk, laugh and cry in the station café. People come and go, each one sharing a moment, a hope, or a fear over a hot cup of coffee. Laura and Steph realize it is not only the cappuccino machine that's broken. This attractive two-hander is easily staged.

The Intruders. Comedy. Peter Horsler
M2 F2. A lounge. Fee code D. ISBN 978 0 573 12115 9

Iphegenia in Orem. Play. Neil LaBute
M1. Motel-room. Fee code E

A Utah businessman, in a Las Vegas motel room, confesses an especially chilling crime to a complete stranger. This play is from the triple bill *Bash* – a collection of three raw, dark, yet lyrically intense one-act plays which won the Time Out Critic's Choice Award. For details please see the entry in Section A.

Is It Something I Said? Play. Richard Harris
M2 (50s) F1 (40s). A hotel reception area/landing/bedroom. Fee code E

Intending to kill himself, Wallace books into an hotel run by Arthur and Stella. Wallace's plans, however, are repeatedly thwarted and his determination wavers. After he and Arthur discuss their hatred for their respective wives, Wallace is fired with new determination to end it all, leaving poor Arthur contemplating a similar approach to escape from the unpleasant Stella.
ISBN 978 0 573 12119 7

◆ **A bullet mark next to a title indicates that it is new to this edition of the Guide.**

Jabiru. Play. Margaret Johnson
M2 (black or Spanish 30s, 26) F1 (late 20s). A tourist hut. Fee Code D. ISBN 978 0 573 02355 2

The Janna Years. Play. Gillian Plowman
M2 (late 30s, middle-age) F3 (20s-40s). One interior setting. Fee code D

Ruby's boarding house is home to an odd mix of characters in this moving and well-observed play about four lonely people: Abe, the middle-aged divorcee, Chas, the Northerner forced to find work in the South, Fleur, put there by her social worker and Holly, struggling to save enough money to move out.
ISBN 978 0 573 12125 8

Joggers. Play. Geraldine Aron
M2 (40s) F2 (28, 40s). A beach and the lawns of an hotel. Fee code E
ISBN 978 0 573 12124 1

Johnny, Don't Jump. Satirical comedy. Alan Ogden
M5 (young, middle age) F3 (young, 20, 40s). A ledge round an office block. Fee code E

Johnny sits on a high ledge writing a suicide note. The building's caretaker, a young policeman, a priest and others – including his mum, and girlfriend Eileen – visit Johnny on his ledge and the conversations they have with him satirically demonstrate various degrees of hypocrisy and callousness. Observant and funny.
ISBN 978 0 573 12310 8

Joining the Club. Comedy. David Tristram
M1 F1. A living-room. Fee code C

Vicky is pregnant. Her husband Mark has been passed over for promotion and he's convinced it's because he's not a member of the 'baby club'. He has resigned from his job and roundly insulted his boss. When he hears Vicky's news Mark phones his boss to get his job back but Vicky, hearing him grovel, snatches the phone from him and reiterates Mark's original insult. They now face impending parenthood happily together!

A Jolly Sinister Jape. Play. Elliot Strange
M2 (young, 30s) F2 (young). An entrance hall. Fee code D

Lord Stubbs, Biffy Trubshaw and his actress wife Ophelia are stranded by a collapsed bridge in a mysterious house in a thunderstorm. As romance blossoms, someone locks the front door, trapping the three unfortunates. Who else is in the house? A fast-moving, madcap comedy, set in the 1920s, with a liberal sprinkling of hilarious period slang, along with mystery and thrills.

The Judge's Wife. Play. Caryl Churchill
M3 (young, 60s) F4 (20s, 50s, 60s). Various simple settings. Fee code D

A Judge passes a harsh sentence on a young man, Vernon Warren. Warren's brother kills the Judge. Caroline, the Judge's wife, explains her husband's reactionary behaviour, seeing his death as 'his way of committing suicide'; deliberately making himself a parody of a right-wing bigot, thereby giving his life for the oppressed, for the revolution.

Julius and Cleopatra. A play for Coarse Actors. Michael Green

See the entry for *The Third Great Coarse Acting Show*.

Just Passing. Play. Colin and Mary Crowther
M1 (40-70) F1 (40-70), 1 other M or F (50-60). A park. Fee code D

Love story or ghost story? This warm, wise and witty play shows a man and a woman meeting, apparently on a park bench, apparently to say goodbye. But who is leaving and why? It seems that for all their squabbling they were happily married once, until a road accident landed him in a nursing home. Now he must move away and she must move on. ISBN 978 0 573 12127 2

♦ **Just the Two of Us.** Comedy. Ros Moruzzi
M1 (40s) F6 (18,40s, 60s). A living room. Fee code D

Matt and Ruth's lives are turned upside-down by a visit from eighteen-year-old Freya and her mother. Freya has discovered that Matt is her biological father, having traced his "donation" to a clinic. As Ruth and Matt struggle to come to terms with this revelation, more visitors arrive, adding to the chaos. Hilariously explores the impact and repercussions of modern science.

Keeping Mum. Monologue from **Visiting Hour**. Richard Harris
F2 (middle-age). A hospital ward. Fee code D

First presented as a National Theatre Platform performance in the Cottesloe Theatre in 1987 and subsequently seen in a revised version at the Duke's Head Theatre, Richmond, Surrey in 1990, this poignant monologue sees Pauline sitting at the bedside of her dying mother. As she mulls over her own churning emotions she realizes a love that, it eventually transpires, is now too late to communicate.
ISBN 978 0 573 13291 9

A Kind of Alaska. Play (from the triple bill *Other Places*). Harold Pinter
M1 (60s) F2 (40s). A room. Fee code G

Deborah was a lively 16-year old and part of a close-knit family when she fell victim to sleeping sickness. Twenty-nine years later, having been watched over throughout by the same doctor, she comes to life and gradually tries to adjust to the world around her.
ISBN 978 0 573 12129 9

A Kind of Vesuvius. Play. Gillian Plowman
M3 (mid 30s). An empty sitting-room. Fee code D. ISBN 978 0 573 04229 4

Knightsbridge. Play. John Mortimer
M2 (middle-age) F2 (19, middle-age). A sitting-room. Fee code E

Francesca brings her lover, Henry, to her mother's flat to announce their intention to get married. While waiting for Mrs Stokes, Francesca answers a mysterious phone call. From what he overhears, Henry concludes that Mrs Stokes is a member of the oldest profession. It is later revealed that Mrs Stokes deals in nothing more erotic than antique furniture.
ISBN 978 0 573 12130 2

Knowing Constance Spry. Comedy. Mary Rensten
F6 (19, 30s, 40s, 50s, 60s). A village hall. Fee code D

Joyce has the thankless task of organizing the teas for the Floral Art Club. Thankless, because Mrs Cowper-Jones can only criticize others' efforts. Mrs Cowper-Jones arrives in full fault-finding flow, complete with large floral arrangement. But, today has more in store for Mrs Cowper-Jones than she could possibly imagine – lucky for her, and her audience, that she once met Constance Spry!
ISBN 978 0 573 03392 6

Krapp's Last Tape. Play. Samuel Beckett
M1 (old). A room. Fee code F

Krapp is alone in his room. Slowly, and with much fumbling, he selects the spools of recording tape he needs. Crouched over the recorder, and in moods of exaltation, he listens like a drowning man to the record of his past as preserved on the magnetic tapes.

Lady Bracknell's Confinement. Monologue. Paul Doust
M1 or F1, 3M 2F voices only. A hall. Fee code F. ISBN 978 0 573 12504 1

The Lady of Larkspur Lotion. Play. Tennessee Williams
M1 F2. A windowless room. Fee code E

Mrs Hardwicke-Moore lives in an imaginary past in which she supposedly owned a Brazilian rubber plantation; the Writer dreams of an equally imaginary future as a great literary figure. Mrs Hardwicke-Moore has a furious row with the landlady and the Writer complains of the disturbance to his work – or possibly his drunken stupor. The landlady jeers at them and they resume their absurd dreams.

A Lady of Letters. Monologue from *Talking Heads*. Alan Bennett
F1 (middle-age). A bleak suburban room. Fee code F

Miss Ruddock writes letters – not, unfortunately, social communications filled with harmless news, but letters of complaint, comment and, occasionally, officious praise to various businesses and government departments. She complains about the lack of care she assumes the child living opposite is receiving and ends up in prison. There, ironically, Miss Ruddock finds freedom and is, for possibly the first time, happy.
ISBN 978 0 573 03384 1

Landscape. Play. Harold Pinter
M1 (50s) F1 (40s). A kitchen. Fee code F

Duff, a handyman and chauffeur, and his wife, Beth, a housekeeper, sit talking in the kitchen of a large house. Duff tells her about his day and reminds her of his past infidelity. But Beth makes no response to him; she is absorbed in the memory of an old romantic encounter that may or may not have involved Duff. Either way, it matters little to them now.

The Last Bread Pudding. Comedy. Nick Warburton
M3 (middle-age) F4 (young, middle-age) or M2 F5. A room. Fee code D
ISBN 978 0 573 12145 6

Last Call For Breakfast. A play for Coarse Actors. Michael Green

See the entry for *The Coarse Acting Show 2*.

Last of My Solid Gold Watches. Play. Tennessee Williams
M3 (35, 70s (1 Black)). A hotel room. Fee code E

Charlie, an old-fashioned travelling salesman, is visited by Harper, a salesman of the modern style. As they talk together of their trade it becomes apparent that Charlie's bravado hides a poignant consciousness of the changes that come to everyone with the approach of old age.

The Last of the Last of the Mohicans. Comedy. Hugh Leonard
M3 (40, middle-age) F2 (30s, middle-age). M1 or F1 voice only. Fee code F

See entry for *Suburb of Babylon* in Section A.

Last Panto in Little Grimley. Comedy. David Tristram
M2 F2. A bare stage. Fee code D

This is a long overdue sequel to the tremendously popular *Last Tango in Little Grimley* and features the same characters. Even though this is a stand-alone story, societies who haven't yet produced the original might care to check it out first. Indeed, running both plays together makes for a full and very entertaining evening. An excellent choice for a festival.

Last Post. Play. (From *Deckchairs III*) Jean McConnell
F2 (40s, 60s). A garden. Fee code C

When the widow of a much-respected Army Colonel discovers that his past seems to include a secret child for whom he was paying maintenance, she is naturally very distressed. But she is determined to protect his reputation and retain her own dignity. Not so easy when the mother of the child in question arrives on her doorstep.
ISBN 978 0 573 10010 9

Last Tango in Little Grimley. Comedy. David Tristram
M2 F2. A simple stage. Fee code D

Membership of the local amateur drama society has dwindled to four. Time for dramatic action. There's only one thing that sells tickets these days – sex. But how will the locals react to the promise of a sizzling sex comedy? All is revealed in this fast-paced comedy of an Am-Dram in trouble. David Tristram's hilarious play requires only the simplest of props and no scenery.

Last Things. Play. Peter Barnes (In a volume).
M1 (elderly) F1 (elderly). An empty space. Fee code C

An elderly couple of thespians awake in bed to find themselves dead. Troupers that they are, they decide to go into the next world with their famous husband and wife sketch – to the applause of the heavenly host. May be presented as part of the full-length entertainment *Corpsing*. For details, please see the entry in Section A.
ISBN 978 0 573 10006 2

Late Entry. Comedy. David Tristram
M1 F1. Simple settings. Fee Code D

A short spoof monologue followed by a spoof adjudication, with a few twists! Not available in book form, but an electronic script, with permission to print out copies for your production only, may be purchased from www.flyingducks.biz. The script comes with a DVD of the play's première at the Golden Beak Comedy Festival. The performing licence must be obtained from Samuel French in the normal way.

B

Late Frost. Play. Jean McConnell
F2 (middle age). A seaside promenade. Fee code B

See the entry for *Deckchairs I*.

Leslie. Play (from *A Different Way Home*). Jimmie Chinn
M1 (middle-age). A living-room. Fee code H

Leslie, who has lived with his mother all his life in a small, closely-knit, North of England town, narrates the events leading up to her death, unwittingly revealing the extent of his loss and his bitterness towards his sister Maureen who lives nearby but is not in touch. This deeply-moving and astutely observed monologue has a running time of approximately 55 minutes.
ISBN 978 0 573 11092 4

The Lesson. Comic drama. Eugene Ionesco. Translated from the French by Donald Watson
M1 (middle-age) F2 (18, middle-age). A study. Fee code E

The Professor's private lesson begins well: his pupil seems remarkably gifted. Suddenly he discovers she cannot subtract. The lesson gets more frenzied as he persists in forcing her to understand subtraction. Maddened by her insensibility, he stabs her. The maid clucks with dismay. This, she complains, is the fortieth to be stabbed today.

Lifelines. Play. Amy Rosenthal
M1 (young) F1 (young). A split set; a bedroom, a kitchen. Fee code E

When Robert misdials, Annie is ready to hang up on what she thinks is a nuisance caller interrupting her indulgent sobbing. This accidental telephone call is the start of a distant, yet significant telephonic relationship. Both Robert and Annie are plagued by love troubles and enjoy the opportunity to let off steam, take a few tips and perhaps begin again.
ISBN 978 0 573 12139 5

A Light Lunch. Play. Bridget Derrett
M3 (30s, 40s, 50s) F1 (40s). A restaurant. Fee code D. ISBN 978 0 573 12314 6

The Little Lights of Kimberley. Melodrama. Harry Austin
M4 F1. Fee code B

A heart-warming tale of how young war widow Lulu Littlehampton is saved from the dishonourable designs of Captain Harvey Kneetrembler and Arkwright, the Pickled Onion King, by the timely return of her husband Walter, who is not only not dead, but also very rich, having stumbled upon a hidden diamond mine! Playing time approximately 16 minutes. Contained in *The Little Lights of Kimberley and Other Plays*.
ISBN 978 0 573 10023 3

LittleBro Morning and BigSis Afternoon. Play. Mike Tibbetts
M5 F5 or M4 F4, 1 boy 1 girl. Various simple settings. Fee code E. ISBN 978 0 573 12154 8

London Vertigo. Play. Brian Friel. Based on a play *The True Born Irishman,* or *The Irish Fine Lady* by Charles Macklin
M3 F2. A room. Fee code G

This is a superb satire on Irish Anglophiles. Nancy O'Doherty has been smitten by 'the London vertigo', a sudden, dizzy conviction that London is the only place for style, wit, good fortune and excitement. Her husband enlists the help of his brother-in-law to restore her to sanity and Irishness. Period eighteenth century

The Long Christmas Dinner. Play. Thornton Wilder
M5 F7. A dining-room. Fee code C

Ninety years are traversed in this play, which represents in accelerated motion ninety Christmas dinners in the Bayard household. Each member of the family ages with the passing years until finally they die and exit from the stage. We hear them comment on the development of the countryside, the enormous changes in manners and customs during this period of time. ISBN 978 0 573 02144 2

The Long Goodbye. Play. Tennessee Williams
M7 (young) F2 (young, middle-age). A tenement apartment. Fee code E

While Joe waits for the moving men to cart away his furnishings, he talks to a companion, Silva, about his past life – his mother who suffered from cancer and killed herself, and about his sister, strong-willed and attractive. Silva's inclination is to look forward, but to Joe life is 'just a long, long goodbye'.

The Long Stay Cut Short, or The Unsatisfactory Supper. Play. Tennessee Williams
M1 F2. A porch and sideyard. Fee code E

Baby Doll and Archie Lee have had their senile Aunt Rose staying with them, and are at the end of their tether. They argue that she should be sent to stay with other relatives, and eventually in a fury Archie Lee bursts out at her. Nature takes a hand in settling the matter.

The Loophole. Play. N. J. Warburton
M4. An office, a room. Fee code D

Mr Overall, the Junior Under Minister for Justice, has a special knack for finding legal loopholes. When Prisoner 604 is sentenced to death all his talent is brought to bear. Aided by the prison chaplain, he finds a way, only to be defeated by his officious assistant and the prison officer. But Overall is not quite convinced that the game is over. ISBN 978 0 573 04228 7

B

◆ **A bullet mark next to a title indicates that it is new to this edition of the Guide.**

Lord Byron's Love Letter. Play. Tennessee Williams
M1 F3 (middle-age, elderly). A parlour. Fee code E

In New Orleans the Old Woman and her granddaughter try to alleviate their poverty by displaying a love-letter supposedly written to the former by Lord Byron. When a couple arrive, the two women tell their story. The visitors hear the Mardi Gras parade arriving and dash out without paying. The Old Woman angrily accuses her granddaughter of dropping 'her grandfather's' letter on the floor.

B

The Love Course. Drama. A. R. Gurney
M2 F2. One interior set. Fee code E

A woman professor has been teaching a course on 'the literature of love' with a younger male colleague. She has fallen in love with him through the books and the experience of the classroom. Now, in the last year of the class, she is attempting to bring the course and their relationship to a climax and a conclusion.

The Lover. Play. Harold Pinter
M2 (30s) F1 (early 30s). Composite setting. Fee code F

Richard and Sarah have created fictional lovers, Max and Sarah. They indulge in erotic wish fulfilment and thus keep the marriage refreshed. Then Richard begins to upset the *status quo* by refusing to allow the distinct halves of their relationship to remain separate. The afternoons have been for Max, the evenings for Richard. This evening, Max encroaches on Richard's preserves.
ISBN 978 0 573 02148 0

Lovesick. Play. Caryl Churchill
M4 (25, 40) F2 (30). Various simple settings. Fee code D

Hodge, a psychiatrist, has successfully developed an aversion therapy. Ellen, a depressive patient, loves Kevin, a homosexual, while Hodge is strongly attracted to Ellen. He decides to use his therapy on her and Kevin to make Ellen fall in love with him and turn Kevin from his homosexuality. Kevin's brother Robert despises Hodge and secretly alters the treatment so that Ellen becomes a lesbian and Kevin falls madly in love with Hodge.

A Lovesome Thing. Play. Jean McConnell
F8 (middle-age). A conservatory. Fee code D. ISBN 978 0 573 13269 8

Luck of the Draw. Play. A. S. Robertson
M3 F1. A committee room. Fee Code D

In a locked room the Chairman, Treasurer and Organizer await the beleaguered Mr Pessel, a non-committee guest witness, to pick a winning Christmas Draw ticket for the Social Club. A humorous moral entanglement ensues when Pessel draws a ticket belonging to Mr Brooker, one of the richest men in the area and one belonging to someone more worthy of winning the prize hamper.
ISBN 978 0 573 02379 8

Lunch. Play. Steven Berkoff
M1 F1. Fee Code D
Two people meet on a bench in a park near the sea. It could be anywhere. The man sells the most humiliating item of uselessness that he could find to foist on to the public ... space.

Lunch Hour. Play. John Mortimer
M1 (40s) F2 (23, 40s). An hotel bedroom. Fee code E

Two lovers, a Man and a Girl, meet in a hotel room one lunch time for a hour. To preserve a façade of respectability he tells the Manageress he is expecting his wife, the mother of his three children. The Girl arrives and knowing nothing of the story is surprised by the sympathy of the Manageress but she soon comes to identify with the fictional tired mother and storms out.
ISBN 978 0 573 02149 7

Magic. Play (from *Visiting Hour*). Richard Harris
M2 (middle-age, elderly) F4 (early 20s (Black), 35, middle-age, elderly). A hospital ward. Fee code D

Brenda, a timid spinster awaiting a hysterectomy, suffers a visit from a crass work colleague and her appalling husband who performs very bad jokes and conjuring tricks. The play was seen as part of the full length play *Visiting Hour* (see Section A) which was presented in 1990 at the Duke's Head Theatre, Richmond, Surrey.
ISBN 978 0 573 01925 8

A Man of Letters. Play. Tim Firth
M2 (18, 54). A ledge. Fee code F

A truly outstanding, genuinely funny play, with a wry twist at the end, first seen at the Stephen Joseph Theatre in the Round Studio, Scarborough. Frank has erected signs for a commercial letterer for twenty-five years. With trainee Alan, he attempts to spell 'Forshaw's' – the letters collectively forming the play's third 'character'. He is nonplussed when the right letters do not appear and then realization dawns.
ISBN 978 0 573 04227 0

Maria Marten or **The Murder in the Red Barn**. Victorian Melodrama. Constance Cox
M5 F9. A garden or green. Fee code C

This is a version of the famous nineteenth-century crime in which an innocent young country girl is murdered by a local squire who had earlier seduced her and is now anxious to marry an heiress. Partly through the agency of a gypsy, however, retribution overtakes the villain. Ingeniously telescoped in time and place into one simple setting.
ISBN 978 0 573 02325 5

Massage. Play. Steven Berkoff
M2 (with doubling). Fee code F
A no-holds-barred sexual comedy. Berkoff writes:"The play is a bit of fun with the concept of the massage parlour as the sanctuary for men who come tormented and distraught and are sent away renewed by the dextrous hands of the woman who then reveals herself as a truly liberated female ..."

Matchstick Dreams. Comedy. Fiz Marcus
M3 (50s, 60s, any age) F1 (60s) or M2 F1 with doubling. A living-room. Fee code D
ISBN 978 0 573 12157 9

Maureen. Play (from *A Different Way Home*). Jimmie Chinn
F1 (middle age). A living-room. Fee code E

Maureen, living in a small, closely-knit, North of England town, relates how she felt rejected by family and friends because she married a Jew. She also feels betrayed for not being asked by her brother to help when their mother was dying. This astutely observed monologue conveys the need for families to communicate, and for love to transcend prejudice. Running time: approximately 35 minutes.
ISBN 978 0 573 11092 4

Mayhem at the Mill, or, **Fortune's Fate**. Brian J. Burton
M3 F1. A gloomy mill. Fee code B

A short melodrama for inclusion in a Music Hall Evening. Little scenery is required and detailed production notes are given in the script. Contained with two other melodramas in *Cheers, Tears and Screamers*.

Me and My Friend. Two one-act plays. Gillian Plowman
M2 and F2. Fee codes on application

The first act of this full-length play may be presented as a one-act play for men, the second as a one-act play for women. Please see the entry in Section A.
ISBN 978 0 573 01831 2

The Measures Taken (**The Decision**). Play. Bertolt Brecht
Translations: Carl Mueller
            John Willett
M4 F1. A concert platform. Fee code G

Four Communist agitators have killed a comrade while on a mission to China. A 'Control Chorus' instructs them to describe how this came about, so that a verdict may be pronounced. Their reasons for the deed are re-enacted: the victim, though a true Communist, had committed several serious errors in Communist practice and therefore agreed to his own death. They are praised by the Control Chorus for their successful work.

Meat and Two Veg. Comedy. Paul Beard
M2 (elderly) F1 (elderly). A living-room. Fee code D. ISBN 978 0 573 12165 4

Medea Redux. Play. Neil LaBute
F1. Simple setting. Fee code E

A tragic tale in which a woman recounts her relationship with a high school teacher and the lengths she finally goes to in order to exact revenge. This play is from the triple bill *Bash – a* collection of three raw, dark, yet lyrically intense one-act plays which won the Time Out Critic's Choice Award. For details please see the entry in Section A.

Melody. Comedy. Deirdre Kinahan
M1 (40s) F1 (40). Various simple settings. Fee Code D

Mr Kane and Kathleen meet eating lunch on a park bench, but they end up sharing more than just their sandwiches. They form a strong friendship which is tested by rumour and speculation, but together they learn to accept the blessings and face the challenges of love. This is a beautiful, funny and heart-warming play, certain to touch any audience.
ISBN 978 0 573 02385 9

B

Melons at the Parsonage. Comedy. Nick Warburton
M4 F4, 1M or F. A village hall stage. Fee code D

Two amateur drama groups become joint winners of a play festival. A tie-break involves the groups performing an extract from their own entry and then an excerpt from the opposing team's play, but the pieces are very different. They compete again with hilarious results but the outcome is still a tie. This time a rugby scrum will decide the winner!
ISBN 978 0 573 12159 3

Merry Regiment of Women. Comedy. Rae Shirley
M3 F6. A fragment from the old Globe Theatre. Fee code E

Shakespeare's great women and three extraordinary men meet and perform a totally contemporary play. Kate and Petruchio, Romeo and Juliet, daring Henry V, plus Lady Macbeth and Cleopatra, combine to produce a mad and merry, totally irreverent but particularly apt, tribute to the greatest writer of all! A triumph of irony in the iambic – yet warm of heart. Forsooth play on!

Millie's Tale. Play. Jean McConnell
M2 (50, 60) F4 (30, 40s, 50, 60). Main room in a rest home. Fee code D

When Millie, an elderly helper at Westway Rest Home, dies seemingly impoverished, the authorities refuse to pay funeral expenses. Eddie, Millie's friend, is enraged and alerts journalist, Lisa. Millie is pushed into the limelight when she's found to have won a million pounds. Immediately two money-grabbing relatives appear, but Lisa finds Millie's illegitimate daughter, uncovering a heartbreaking story which finally vindicates Millie.
ISBN 978 0 573 02375 0

Missing. Play. Reza de Wet. Translated by Steven Stead
M1 (30-40) F3 . A room with a trapdoor in the ceiling. Fee code F

Miem and her daughter, Meisie, live on a remote small-holding in South Africa. The circus is nearby. This night is the anniversary of mysterious disappearances of several young women and it is feared that the killer/abductor will strike again. Meisie, Miem and her friend Gertie lock themselves in, but they are visited by a blind constable who encourages Meisie to dance out into the night until she too is missing.

Mister Paradise. Play Tennessee Williams.
M1 (elderly) F1 (young). A room. Fee code E

An eager college girl visits the eponymous Mister Paradise in his squalid surroundings. Having discovered an early book of his poetry, she is determined to make him famous. Horrified, he explains that "Gabriel has not yet blown the horn" and his pen-name will only be famous when he is dead. He tells her to watch the obituaries, she promises his future is safe in her hands.

Moby Dick. A play for Coarse Actors. Michael Green

See the entry for *The Coarse Acting Show 2*.

Money Makes You Happy. Play. Francis Beckett
M3 (30s) F4 (late 20s, 30s). A living-room. Fee code D

Jeremy, a writer low on ideas and money, learns from his ex-girlfriend that he may well be a father and he needs financial stability pronto! Proving it's not what you know but who you know, he soon has three important clients eager to hire him but what are they really after? A funny, fast-paced, witty and modern play that comments on modern society.
ISBN 978 0 573 02388 0

Monologue. Play. Harold Pinter
M1. Simple set. Fee Code D

A man talks to an empty chair. It becomes clear that this chair holds the image of an old friend - one he hasn't seen for many years. They fell out after they both got involved with the same woman – one fell in love with her soul, the other, her body. Giving more clues than answers we learn about the frame of mind of the man and what happened between the characters.
ISBN 978 0 571 23223 9

The Monkey's Paw. Adapted by Jonathan Holloway, from the short story by W.W. Jacobs. (From *Darkness Falls*)
M4 (20s, 40s) F1 (40s) or M3 F1 with doubling. A kitchen/living-room. Fee code E

The perils of ambition lie at the heart of this supernatural tale. In *The Monkey's Paw* a working-class family in the 1940s is granted three wishes, all of which come true, but in a macabre and unexpected way.
ISBN 978 0 573 10002 4

Moony's Kid Don't Cry. Play. Tennessee Williams
M1 (25) F1 (young). A kitchen. Fee code E

A dawn quarrel in the middle of a slovenly kitchen between the frustrated labourer and his ailing wife boils up until she strikes him and he catches her by the throat. She tells him to go if he wants to, she will return to work but she insists he take the child with him and places it in his arms.

Mountain Language. Play. Harold Pinter
M5 F2. Various simple settings. Fee code F

'Focusing on the brutalities of a society which forbids a minority of its population to speak in their own language, it is a play of few words which add up to an eloquent indictment of the banning of any human utterance.' Paul Taylor in the *Independent*. It was presented by the National Theatre at the Lyttelton Theatre in 1988 starring Eileen Atkins, Michael Gambon and Miranda Richardson.
ISBN 978 0 573 12163 0

Mrs Meadowsweet. Play. David Campton
F6 (young, 30s-50s). A lounge in a guest house. Fee code D. ISBN 978 0 573 13282 7

Mum's Army. Comedy (from *Dad's Army*). Jimmy Perry and David Croft
M10 F8. Extras. Church hall and office, a railway station. Fee code E

The Home Guard are recruiting women but as Mrs Mainwaring "hasn't left the house since Munich", she won't be joining her husband's platoon. So when newcomer Mrs Gray joins, Captain Mainwaring is set for a brief encounter. An hilarious, touching episode from the classic BBC TV series *Dad's Army*. Period 1940
ISBN 978 0 573 10014 7

The Municipal Abattoir. Play. Tennessee Williams.
M2 F1. A pavement. Fee code E

In a dictatorship, a condemned clerk asks a student the way to the Municipal Abattoir. The student tells him to save himself but the clerk can't because he's been a Municipal Employee too long to disobey. The student changes tack and orders the clerk to shoot the general as his motorcade passes by. But the clerk is too cowed and asks the audience the way to the abattoir.

Music for Amelia. Play. Derek Rhodes
M2 (40s, 60s). 1M or F. An office. Fee code D

Max, an MP, comes to discuss a radio programme which will trace his life through his favourite music. The show's presenter, Amelia Cruikshank, is unavailable so Hector deputizes – but he is not what he purports to be. His questioning reveals the shocking details of a story from the past and their repercussions in the present day, leading to the final shattering moments of this intriguing play.
ISBN 978 0 573 02371 2

The Music Lovers. Farce. Georges Feydeau. Adapted by Reggie Oliver
M1 F4. An apartment salon. Fee code E

Set in 1890s Paris and very typically Feydeau in style, this lively and fast-moving play revolves around the idea of mistaken identity. Lucille awaits her new music teacher but the man who walks into her apartment is Edouard, in the mistaken belief that he is attending a rendezvous with his mistress. A series of hilarious misunderstandings and *double entendres* ensues.
ISBN 978 0 573 12169 2

The Mutilated. Tennessee Williams

See *Slapstick Tragedy* in Section A

Nasty Things, Murders. Play. Arthur Lovegrove
F5 (55, elderly). A lounge. Fee code D. ISBN 978 0 573 03354 4

♦ **A bullet mark next to a title indicates that it is new to this edition of the Guide.**

Nellie's Nightlights. Comedy melodrama. Harry Austin
M4 F3. Fee code E

A Victorian/Edwardian comedy melodrama in which young Nellie Larkin becomes the 'face that flickers in a thousand bedrooms', thanks to her invention of 'Nellie's Nightlights'. Playing time approximately 42 minutes. Contained in *The Little Lights Of Kimberley*.
ISBN 978 0 573 10023 3

The New World Order. Sketch. Harold Pinter
M2, 1M extra. A bare stage. Fee code A

Des and Lionel stand and discuss what they are going do with the prisoner who sits blindfolded on a chair before them. They taunt the silent victim with speculatory chit-chat that intimates the torture that is to follow. Lionel breaks down in tears because he loves his job so much, it makes him feel 'so pure'. Des replies he is 'keeping the world clean for democracy'.

The Night Before Christmas. Comedy. Anthony Neilson
M3 F1. A warehouse. Fee code G

It's Christmas Eve, and Gary summons Simon to their warehouse, which stores 'mostly legal' children's toys. A man in an elf suit has broken in, and is claiming to be a genuine employee of the 'International Gift Distribution Agency'. Cherry turns up, desperate to get hold of a Power Ranger for her son, and she and Simon torment the elf for inflicting Christmas on them. Meanwhile, he is suffering withdrawal symptoms from 'Christmas Spirit' and offers to grant them each a wish to release him.

A Night Out. Play. Harold Pinter
M10 (28, 50, 65) F5 (25, 55). Composite setting. Fee code E

Albert finds himself dominated by his mother. At an office party he is mercilessly teased by his colleagues and arrives home, his temper rising. When his mother nags he attacks and leaves her, gets picked up by a girl and is able to reduce her to humble servility. Yet, when he arrives home his mother is there fully recovered and ready to reassert her dominance. (*Please specify author when ordering*)
ISBN 978 0 573 02176 3

No Name in the Street. An Easter Play. Edward Murch
14 characters, may be played by 8 actors with doubling. A bare stage. Fee code D

The events leading up to the Crucifixion are seen by a mother searching for her son. When she comes to the Cross, she asks forgiveness, and we find she is not the mother of Jesus, as we had been led to believe, but the mother of Judas. Dramatic and powerful in its simplicity, the play is a tournament winner in Great Britain, a popular work in American church groups, and has been televised to great acclaim.

◆ **A bullet mark next to a title indicates that it is new to this edition of the Guide.**

Normal. Play. Anthony Neilson
M2 F1. Simple settings. Fee code G

Justus Wehner, an idealistic young lawyer, is interviewing Peter Kurten, the Dusseldorf ripper of 1931, whose conviction for the murders of nine people he has been appointed to appeal. Wehner initially believes that he can get Kurten off on a plea of insanity, but their sinister and graphic conversations reveal a man who is disturbingly sane and rational. Wehner finds himself becoming increasingly involved with Kurten's past and drawn to his wife, Frau Kurten. He begins to question his own morality and the concept of evil. Period 1930s.

B

Not Bobby. Play. N. J. Warburton
M1 F4, doubling possible. A living-room. Fee code D

Anxious to complete yesterday's newspaper crossword, Frank finds the page missing. His mother, Pam, confesses to using it in the newly acquired rabbit's cage. Extracting the page Frank is astonished to find the crossword is now complete. Could the rabbit, Bobby, be responsible ... ? A quirky, well-observed satire from the author of *Don't Blame It on the Boots*.
ISBN 978 0 573 12179 7

Not Not Not Not Not Enough Oxygen. Play. Caryl Churchill
M2 (19, 60) F1 (30). A room. Fee code D

The time is 2010. Mick and Vivian live in a tower block, protected from the violence and pollution outside where groups of 'fanatics' roam, setting fire to themselves in protest against wars and famine. Mick hopes his rich son will give him money to escape, but when Claude arrives they learn he has given his money away and is to join the 'fanatics' outside.

Nothing Personal. Play. Hugh Leonard
M2 (30s, 40) F1 (30s). Fee code C

See entry for *Suburb of Babylon* in Section A.

Oedocles, King of Thebes. A Play for Coarse Actors. Michael Green.

See the entry for *Coarse Acting Strikes Back*

Office Song. Play. Nick Warburton
M1 (20s-40s) F2 (20s-40s). A cloakroom. Fee code D

Brian is attempting to escape his firm's Christmas party when he is waylaid in the cloakroom by Claire, who soon discovers a secret about her unassuming colleague: at home, he likes to sing Doris Day songs. Claire tries to persuade Brian to take part in a talent contest; with her friend Wendy she sets about training Brian to sing in public.
ISBN 978 0 573 12174 6

◆ **A bullet mark next to a title indicates that it is new to this edition of the Guide.**

The Old One-Two. Drama. A. R. Gurney
M2 F1. Fee code E

A professor of Classics at an American university gets into an affair with a female student. Meanwhile the dean of the department has become involved in a sly relationship with the professor's mysterious wife. The play is saved from a tragic ending by a sudden surprising discovery.

B

Old Tyme Dancing and **The Whizzer**

Words by Joyce Grenfell. Music by Richard Addinsell
Fee code A for each sketch

One Careful Owner. Play. H. Connolly
M2 (late 20s, 55) F2 (young, late 20s). A sitting-room. Fee code D. ISBN 978 0 573 12160 9

One for the Road. Play. Harold Pinter (from the triple bill *Other Places*)
M2 (30s, 40s) F1 (30s) 1 boy (8). A room. Fee code F

This award-winning play about a torturer and the family he victimizes was premièred in 1984 and subsequently presented as part of the triple bill *Other Places* at the Duchess Theatre, London in 1985. 'It is a disturbing and brilliantly controlled little masterpiece of a play.' *Spectator.* ' ... dialogue that rings like a hammer blow.' *Guardian*
ISBN 978 0 573 12184 5

One Month Early. Farce. Georges Feydeau, translated by Peter Meyer from *Lèonie est en Avance*
M2 (38, middle-age) F4 (young, middle-age). A dining-room. Fee code E

Léonie is eight months pregnant and, it seems, going into labour. Toudoux, her husband, is torn between supporting Léonie and trying to eat as much as possible of his dinner. His in-laws and the midwife arrive and he is berated by everyone, until the midwife makes a stunning announcement. Period 1910

One Month to Pay or **The Sailor's Return**. Melodrama. Brian. J Burton
M3 F3. One interior. Fee code D

The traditional battle between a wicked landlord and the wife of his impecunious tenant, with 'Jolly Jack Tar', village simpletons and 'saintly child' themes thrown in for good measure. Virtue, of course, triumphs in the end. Contained in *Three Hisses for Villainy*.

One-Sided Triangle. Play. Stephen Smith
M2 (young, middle-age) F1 (30s). An hotel garden. Fee code D. ISBN 978 0 573 12153 1

◆ **A bullet mark next to a title indicates that it is new to this edition of the Guide.**

One Thing More or **Caedmon Construed.** Play. Christopher Fry
M10 F4 or M7 F3, with doubling. Extras. A bare stage. Fee code G

An account of the poet Caedmon isolated and silenced for thirty years by an immense personal grief. A person appears to him in a dream, makes him talk and tells him to sing. The miracle happens and Caedmon sings the 'Hymn Of Creation'. Fry's play was produced at Chelmsford Cathedral and broadcast on BBC Radio 4 in 1986.

One Was Nude and One Wore Tails. Farce. Dario Fo. Translated by Ed Emery
M5 F1. A street. Fee code E

A roadsweeper's comrade convinces him that in being a nothing, he is the beginning of everything, and thus divine. Guided by this principle, he helps a nude ambassador recover his evening dress, but the roadsweeper finds he is treated much better as an ambassador than when dressed for his own profession, which makes him no longer an absolute and therefore not divine at all.

The Open Couple. Comedy. Dario Fo and Franca Rame. Translated by Stuart Hood
M2 F1. An apartment. Fee code F

This hilarious comedy is typical of the biting satire for which Fo has become famous. Antonia has coped for years with her philandering husband and unsuccessfully tried various forms of suicide. The husband decides they should have an open marriage. Antonia agrees, gets herself a job – and a man. Now the tables are turned and the husband threatens suicide!

Open Secrets. Play. Katy Darby
M1 (30) F2 (20s, 30s). A tapas bar and kitchen. Fee code D

Tobias, struggling to pay tuition fees as he finishes his doctorate, works in a tapas bar. Casey is a waitress and T-shirt entrepreneur manqué who needs capital to realize her dreams. Monday is the deadest night of the week, but their luck looks about to change when Leila walks into the bar which is situated just down the road from MI6 …
ISBN 978 0 573 02370 5

The Orchestra. Play. Jean Anouilh. Translated by Miriam John
M1 F6. Extras 3M (2 of whom need not appear). A concert stage. Fee code F

As they play their little pieces of music, the ladies of the brasserie orchestra (and the solitary male pianist) reveal seething volcanoes under the placid exterior. Jealousy, gossip, boasting and thwarted emotions climax in one of them shooting herself in the toilets – but the music goes jauntily on.
ISBN 978 0 573 02343 9

An Ordinary Day. Play. Dario Fo and Franca Rame. Translated by Joe Farrell
M2 F1, several voices. A studio flat. Fee code G

The play opens with Julia making a video of herself for her husband to watch after she has killed herself. Her film-making attempts are foiled, however, by a series of phone calls from women mistaking her for an analyst. Despite the serious theme, this thought-provoking play has comic moments and a strong female central role.

Other People. Play. Geoff Saunders
M2 (early 20s, 30s) F2 (early 20s, mid-20s). A living-room. Fee code D

Neurotic Andrea, slobbish Stephen, efficient Hilary and meek Duncan share a flat and, given their very different characters, it is no surprise that they do not get on particularly well. *Other People* depicts half an hour in the life of this chaotic and argumentative household, in which tempers are lost, crockery is broken and tears are shed ...
ISBN 978 0 573 12183 8

B

♦ **Oubliette**. Play. David Foxton
M6 F9. 5 M or F. A room. Fee Code D

A tour guide is taking a group of visitors around a manor house, bringing them to a mysterious room with no windows or doors – an oubliette, from the French "to forget". The present-day visitors are unknowingly accompanied into the room by people from 500 years ago, including a servant girl, Anne, and Susan Makem, an eccentric loner rumoured to be a witch.
ISBN 978 0 573 12188 3

Out for the Count or How Would You Like Your Stake? Vampire yarn. Martin Downing
M5 (20s, middle-age) F4 (young, 19). A sitting-room. Fee code D. ISBN 978 0 573 12189 0

Outdoor Pleasures. Short play (From *Deckchairs IV*). Jean McConnell
F2 (40/50, 60+). A large garden. Fee code C

A comedy which finds long-suffering Deirdre waiting for an outdoor production of *Much Ado About Nothing* to start, accompanied by her awkward and far-from-enthusiastic Aunt Tottie.
ISBN 978 0 573 10021 5

The Palooka. Play. Tennessee Williams
M4 (or M2 with 2 off-stage voices). Boxing arena dressing-room. Fee code E

The Palooka is a spent boxer. Awaiting his first professional fight is a starry-eyed youngster who hopes to make it big like his hero, former champion Galveston Joe. The Kid supposes that Joe retired wealthy and glorious, and the Palooka wistfully agrees. But the Trainer gives the brutal truth: old timers in the crowd still recognize the has-been – despite changing his name

Parentcraft. Play. Stephen Smith
M1 (30s) F4 (20s, 30s, middle-age). A hospital room. Fee code D. ISBN 978 0 573 12214 9

♦ **Party.** Comedy. Tom Basden
M4 F2. A garden shed. Fee code F

In a humble garden shed in deepest Suburbia, four young idealists have decided to form a new political party to save the world from itself. The new fifth member, Duncan, sets about saving the world from them. *Party* is a comic play about small minds tackling big issues. This hilarious, critically-acclaimed comedy was seen at the Edinburgh Festival in 2009 and the Arts Theatre, London, in 2010.
ISBN 978 0 573 12202 6

Party Time. Play. Harold Pinter
M5 (20s, 40s-50) F4 (20s-30s, 70). A living-room. Fee code H

The streets are blockaded outside Gavin's upmarket flat, the result of a military occupation. Inside, Gavin hosts a party where the machinations between the guests are as potent and suffocating as any wider social upheaval. This play (first performed at the Almeida with *Mountain Language*) is sparse, but in typical Pinter style, it is bursting with confrontational contemporary themes.

B

Pastiche. Farce. Nick Hall
M2 (young, 50) F2 (young, 45). A sitting-room. Fee code E

Medford, a young servant, is setting an elegant supper table at which Sir Peter is shortly to entertain a young girl. However Sir Peter's wife Lady Alexandra unexpectedly arrives and with Medford's help hides under the table as Sir Peter and his guest arrive. This is only the start of fantastic plotting in which Medford and Lady Alexandra, in a variety of disguises, foil Sir Peter's plans for a quietly amorous evening.

The Patient. Play. Agatha Christie
M5 (26, 35, 45) F4 (20s, 38, middle-age). A consulting room. Fee code E

Mrs Wingfield fell over the balcony but no-one could be sure whether it was an accident, attempted murder or failed suicide. All her relatives are summoned to the nursing home and Mrs Wingfield is now unable to speak but with the aid of Dr Ginsberg's ingenious device the attempted murder is solved.
ISBN 978 0 573 02198 5

♦ **Peas.** Comedy by David Tristram
M1 F1. Simple set. Fee code D

Gerry and Daisy are the first to test out a new dating agency. They soon discover just how much they have in common. Contained in the volume *Duets* with *Carrot*.

Penalty. Play. Stephen Smith
M1 F1 (30s). A hotel room. Fee code D

In a hotel room in Azerbaijan, Howard wakes with a monster hangover. Proffering sympathy is ministry official, Yellena. Howard, who is to referee an important football match, has disgraced himself the previous evening at an official UEFA dinner. Or has he? Yellena first cajoles Howard then blackmails him into awarding a penalty to the Azerbaijan team. Just when Howard thinks he's gained control, Yellena springs another surprise ...
ISBN 978 0 573 02359 0

Penetrator. Play. Anthony Neilson
M3. A flat. Fee code G

Max and Alan are sitting in their rented flat, sharing a joint and playing cards. Tadge, Max's childhood friend, shows up in a manic frame of mind, having just been discharged from the army. Events take a frightening turn when Tadge produces a knife and Max is forced to revisit some uncomfortable memories. Explicit language and sexual imagery are a frequent feature of this powerful play. 'This superbly crafted play thrusts in the male psyche with a rigour and insight which is by turns hilarious and horrific but always compulsive.' *Glasgow Herald*

A Perfect Analysis Given by a Parrot. Comedy. Tennessee Williams
M3 (2 non-speaking) F2 (40s). A tavern. Fee code E

Flora and Bessie are members of the Women's Auxiliary of the Jackson Haggerty Post of the
Sons of Mars in Memphis and are in town for the National Convention. Having got separated
from 'the boys' they await them in the tavern, where they chat and gossip. Things get tearful
but luckily 'the boys' arrive and all ends in jubilation.

B

Perfect Partners. Play. Alan Richardson
M2 (20s) F2 (40s). An office. Fee code D. ISBN 978 0 573 12197 5

Permission to Cry. Play. David Campton
F5 or M1 F4 or M2 F3. A bare stage. Fee code D

Julia Gibbon, a junior minister, is thrown into turmoil by the conflict between private and
public morality. Her affair with Penelope Wright, a frank and forthright journalist, very much
a thorn-in-the-side of the Establishment, forces Julia to confront insecurities and doubts she
never knew she had. This is a compassionate play about love and politics in our hypocritical age.
ISBN 978 0 573 12208 8

A Phoenix Too Frequent. Play. Christopher Fry
M1 (young) F2 (young, any age). An underground tomb. Fee code F

Dynamene is ready to die from grief over the death of her husband and has immured herself,
fasting, in his tomb. After a 'brilliant parade of poetry, paradox, wit, humour and intellectual
discourse' she is diverted from her death-wish by the handsome soldier, Tegeus, and even offers
her husband's body to save Tegeus' life.

♦ **Pineapple**. A play. Robert Messik
M1 F1. A living-room. Fee Code D

An unremarkable Tuesday night. Jill and Peter Wilson live together in an immaculate, Ikea-
furnished flat in London. Jill is pregnant and has packed her suitcases. Peter has bought wine
and ordered pizza. Whilst Peter tries to outwit the delivery man to guarantee them a free pizza,
Jill tries to get him to attend to the matter of her imminent departure.
ISBN 978 0 573 12198 2

The Pink Bedroom. Play. Tennessee Williams
M1(middle age) F1 (30). 1M (young). A pink bedroom. Fee code E

The Woman berates her tedious, negligent lover whom she knows has two-timed her. As the
quarrel reaches a crescendo, she turns him out and slams the door on him. Then she calls to
his replacement, a younger man, who's waiting in the other room ...

♦ **A bullet mark next to a title indicates that it is new to this edition of the Guide.**

Pity About Kitty. Play. Jimmie Chinn
M1 (middle-age) F3 (40s). Simple interior. Fee code D
ISBN 978 0 573 12203 3

Pizzazz. Play. Hugh Leonard
M2 F3. A reception area. Fee code F. (In a volume)

Whilst waiting to hire out cabin cruisers on the River Shannon, two apparent strangers play an elaborate game, which involves re-enacting a marriage on the rocks, with the other people in the reception area as a supporting cast. But this is a Chinese box of a play and all is not what it seems ...
ISBN 978 0 573 01641 7

B

A Plan of Action. Play. Philip Ayckbourn
M2 (16, 40) F2 (16, 40). Two living-rooms. Fee Code D

Widowed Roger and separated Samantha have recently started dating, but their teenage children are far from impressed. So Liam, Roger's son, and Tabitha, Samantha's daughter, have devised a plan of action to break them up. This comic scheme involves everything from French and Italian impersonations to a sword ... but will it be enough? This fast-paced comedy was written for students studying English as a second language.
ISBN 978 0 573 02384 2

Plaster. Play (from *Visiting Hour*). Richard Harris
M1 F1 (middle-age). A hospital ward. Fee code D

Eric, hospitalized following a car accident, is visited with hilarious results by his canny wife! The play was seen as part of the full-length play *Visiting Hour* (see Section A) which was presented at the Duke's Head Theatre, Richmond, Surrey, in 1990.
ISBN 978 0 573 01925 8

Portrait of a Madonna. Play. Tennessee Williams
M4 (young, middle-age, old) F2 (middle-age). A living-room. Fee code E

Lucretia has been described as a Blanche DuBois with variations. She has been living in a state of utter neglect and disorder with her mind steadily giving way. The play depicts her last moments before being taken away to a mental institution, whilst she chatters on about her extraordinary fantasies.

Post Mortem. Play. Brian Clark
F1. M4 F1 voices only. An office. Fee code E

Helen arrives at the office to find in the post a tape from her boss, L. K. Halpin, saying he will not be in. As one business crisis after another develops Helen is never off the telephone, Halpin himself remaining unreachable. Then we see Halpin on a projected slide, dead in his bed at nine a.m. ...

Present Slaughter. A play for Coarse Actors. Edited by Michael Green

See the entry for *The Third Great Coarse Acting Show*.

Pride at Southanger Park. A play for Coarse Actors. Rupert Bean. Edited by Michael Green

See the entry for *Coarse Acting Strikes Back.*

♦ **Prince Lear**. Comedy. Perry Pontac
M2 F4. Palace state room. Fee Code D

Prince Lear, a prequel, addresses what took place just before the start of King Lear, setting in motion the improbable events of Act I, Scene 1. With *Hamlet Part II* and *Fatal Loins* this forms the tripe bill *Codpieces.* "Pontac's verse is bliss" *Independent on Sunday*

The Private Ear. Play. Peter Shaffer
M2 (20s) F1 (20). A bed-sitting room. Fee code F

Bob is a born loser: plain and shy he is no match for Ted whose facile charm impresses 'the birds'. Bob thinks he has found a different kind of girl and invites her to dinner. Ted bustles about, further reducing Bob's store of confidence. Doreen arrives. Her quiet poise is revealed as foolishness and she finds classical music as tedious as Bob's conversation.
ISBN 978 0 573 02215 9

Private View. Play. Václav Havel. Translated by Vera Blackwell
M2 F1. A living-room. Fee code E

Private View has the same irony and touch of comic absurdity as its two companion pieces in the Vanek trilogy. Invited by his ridiculous friends Michael and Vera, the mild-mannered writer, Vanek, endeavours to enthuse over their newly, pretentiously refurbished flat. But as the couple happily express the perfection of their marriage their tone gradually develops into a personal attack on Vanek.
ISBN 978 0 573 12212 5

The Public Eye. Play. Peter Shaffer
M2 (35, 40) F1 (22). An office. Fee code F

Charles and Belinda are an ill-assorted couple yet they were once in love. Insanely jealous, Charles engages a private eye, Julian, to follow her round London. Julian can only report that she is attached to someone. When the three meet it transpires that Belinda has fallen for Julian. Deciding to mend a marriage, rather than break it, Julian banishes Belinda to her wanderings but this time to be followed by Charles.
ISBN 978 0 573 12219 2

Pullman Car *Hiawatha*. Play. Thornton Wilder
M15 F9. Extras. No setting. Fee code D

In this composite picture of travellers in an American Pullman car, conversations and thoughts reveal their past lives and future hopes. Various characters representing the Weather, the Hours, the Planets and a Field bring to life the time and places through which the train is passing. There are even two archangels on the train, disguised as young men in serge suits.
ISBN 978 0 573 02220 3

The Purification. Play with music. Tennessee Williams
M6 F3. Chorus of M3 F3. A room. Fee code E

A play in verse, to be performed to guitar music. Set in the form of a trial, it tells of the death of a young girl, the love for her of her brother and the tragic act of a Rancher. The characters are Spanish Ranchers and American Indians. Period nineteenth century

Purvis. Comedy. Nick Warburton
M1 (indeterminate) F1 (younger). A vestry. Fee Code D

Rachel, the vicar's wife, chats to recently-widowed Mr Purvis and is cornered into offering him the post of the church's Health and Safety Officer. Purvis is keen but causes more problems than he solves, the vicar being the prime victim of his misguided attempts to make things safer. Funny, touching and wry, this play for two actors is an example of comedy writing at its very best.
ISBN 978 0 573 02381 1

Put Some Clothes On, Clarisse! Farce. Adapted by Reggie Oliver from *Mais N'te Promène Donc Pas Toute Nue!* by Georges Feydeau
M4 (40s) F1 (30s). A Parisian apartment. Fee code E

The troubles of Ventroux, parliamentary deputy, begin when his wife Clarisse insists it is so hot that she can only wear a négligé around the apartment. Hochepaix, a former political enemy, visits; Clarisse is stung in a most unfortunate place and pleads with Hochepaix and her husband to suck out the sting for her. When a reporter from *Le Figaro* kindly administers first aid in full view of the President it seems doubtful that poor Ventroux's political career will survive!
ISBN 978 0 573 12211 8

Putting the Kettle On. Play. Simon Brett
F1 (late 30s). A kitchen. Fee code E

Miggy, a "Sloane Ranger", has just been dumped by her boyfriend Roddy because she is "shallow" and does not care for the environment in the way his new love, Harmony, does. Miggy tells us her sorry story as she wrestles with the environmental issues presented by the act of putting the kettle on to make a reviving cup of tea.
ISBN 978 0 573 03391 9

A Question of Attribution. Play. Alan Bennett
M5 (20s, 40s-50s) F1. An office, a corridor. Fee code G

This forms the second part of the double bill *Single Spies* (see Section A) which was presented by the Royal National Theatre in 1988, winning the Laurence Olivier award for Comedy of the Year. Anthony Blunt, Surveyor of the Queen's Pictures, tries to solve the riddle of an enigmatic painting and is himself the subject of a more official investigation. Period 1980s
ISBN 978 0 573 01891 6

Rape of Bunny Stuntz. Play. A. R. Gurney
M1 (40) F2 (young, 35). A table, a chair. Fee code E

An efficient suburban matron, chairing an evening meeting, finds that she has to cope with an offstage intruder. The meeting degenerates into a wild party, and the lady confesses to the lure of a liaison with this representative from the underside of society. The meeting ends by coming to order under a new woman but the implications are that she must also undergo some sort of expiation.

The Rats. Play. Agatha Christie
M2 (29, 38) F2 (30s). A flat. Fee code E

Sandra and her lover David arrive for a non-existent party followed by Alec. A Kurdish knife attracts attention and is dropped over the balcony after Sandra and David have handled it. Alec leaves, locking them in the flat with the body of Sandra's husband and they realize that this is Alec's revenge for the death of a man for whom he had a crazed homosexual devotion.
ISBN 978 0 573 02223 4

The Reading Group. Play. Fay Weldon
M2 (30, middle-age) F5 (50, middle-age). A front parlour. Fee code E

A witty, astutely observed study of sexual politics in contemporary society which centres on an all-female reading group. Oriole wants to study contemporary authors, while Anne prefers well-known classics. Pondering the relative merits, the women reveal themselves, their personalities echoing the literary heroines. But not everyone is there for literature. Nefarious designs are uncovered and tensions rise to a dramatic climax.
ISBN 978 0 573 12227 9

The Real Inspector Hound. Play. Tom Stoppard
M5 (young, middle-age) F3 (20s, young, middle-age). A sitting-room with auditorium behind. Fee code H

Moon and Birdboot, two drama critics, arrive to watch the performance of a new detective play, a parody of the conventional stage thriller. However the private lives of the critics become inextricably mixed with those of the play's characters until Moon is shot dead and the real Inspector Hound proves to be …?
ISBN 978 0 573 02323 1

Receive This Light. Play. N. J. Warburton
M3 (30s, any age) F1. Interior setting. Fee code D. ISBN 978 0 573 06254 4

Red Peppers. Comedy with music. Noël Coward
M4 (young, 30s, middle-age) F2 (30s, middle-age). A theatre dressing-room/front-cloth. Fee code C

The Red Peppers – George and Lily – have a music hall act which is going none too well. They make a bad exit in the first house and have a row with the MD and Manager. Going on for the second house, Lily ends up throwing her hat at the MD because he is playing a number impossibly fast. Period 1936
ISBN 0 573 64242 9

Relics. Play. David Campton
F4 (middle-age). A bedsitting-room. Fee code D. ISBN 978 0 573 13302 2

Remember Me. Short play (From *Deckchairs IV*). Jean McConnell
F2 (40/50). A garden. Fee code C

A drama which takes place in a corner of a garden at a wedding reception. Elizabeth and Sarah, who shared a flat many years before, meet for the first time since then, and Sarah seizes her chance to let Elizabeth know what she feels about her actions in the past.
ISBN 978 0 573 10021 5

Remembering Things. Comedy. Michael Fosbrook
M1 (30) F2 (24, 70s-80s). A front room. Fee code D

Mrs Weston, an elderly widow, believes she has been robbed – the trouble is, she is very forgetful. Rosemary, a policewoman, investigates, helped by her jokey and somewhat ambiguous colleague, Derek, and they make extremely slow, confused progress with the old lady who always seems a couple of steps ahead of them. This delightful comedy ends still shrouded in mystery.
ISBN 978 0 573 12252 1

A Resounding Tinkle. Play. N. F. Simpson
M1 (young) F2 (young). A living-room. Fee code E

Bro and Middie Paradock are quite unperturbed by the presence of an elephant in their suburban front garden, but they are annoyed at being sent the wrong *size* of elephant. Uncle Ted arrives causing momentarily raised eyebrows as he has become an elegant 'she'. The Paradocks' talk satirizes suburbia, and amidst its anarchic comedy turns a ribald eye on us all.
ISBN 978 0 573 02229 6

A Respectable Funeral. Play. Jimmie Chinn
M1 (50s) F3 (50s). A living-room. Fee code E

Three middle-aged sisters are gathered at the house of their dead mother. Surprisingly, Charlie, their brother, who looked after their mother, has failed to turn up. From the sisters' gossip it appears that Mother was no saint. They have plans for Mother's money but then Charlie suddenly arrives with a request that will put paid to all their plans ... A sharp and often funny play.
ISBN 978 0 573 12232 3

The Rialto Prom. Play. Angela Wye
F5 (20s-30). A street, a cloakroom. Fee code E

Four friends meet at the Rialto Ballroom to go to the Saturday dance. One of them introduces a shy, gauche newcomer to their hardbitten world. They initiate her into the tough, not to say unscrupulous code of conduct of the dance hall, dressing her up to turn her from her usual retiring self into a sex-symbol – they hope. Period 1960s
ISBN 978 0 573 03358 2

Ringing For You. Play. Norman Stubbs
M5-7 (young, middle-age, ageing) F3 (young, middle-age). Various interior settings. Fee code D
ISBN 978 0 573 12226 2

A Ringing of Bells. "Conversational fantasy". Christopher Fry
M4 (young, middle age) F2 (young). A hotel foyer. Fee code D

A couple, unsure of their whereabouts on Millennium New Year's Eve, comes into a small village hotel, seeking directions. They are in Elstow, the birthplace of John Bunyan, the troubled author of *The Pilgrim's Progress*. As they converse with the hotel receptionist and the local bell-ringers, memories, history, religion and philosophical speculation converge.
ISBN 978 0 573 12207 1

Ritual for Dolls. Play. George MacEwan Green
M2 F2. An attic. Fee code D. ISBN 978 0 573 12231 2

Roman Fever. Play. Hugh Leonard, based on Edith Wharton's story
M1 F2. A terrace. Fee code D. (In a volume)

On a restaurant terrace in Rome, Mrs Slade and Mrs Ansley are reminiscing about a Roman holiday they had together many years before. Mrs Slade, envious of the other's daughter's engagement to a rich marchese cannot resist a spiteful jibe which demolishes a cherished memory. But in the end it is Mrs Slade's illusions that are shattered. Period 1930
ISBN 978 0 573 01641 7

The Room. Play. Harold Pinter
M4 (young, 40s (black), 50s, elderly) F2 (young, 60). A bedsitting-room. Fee code E

Rose and Bert rent a room that might almost be a paleolithic cave; the outside is terrifying and unknown. Rose never goes out, Bert only goes to drive his van with furious aggression. A young couple call, and then a blind black man. Bert comes home, massive with triumph at smashing every car that challenged his van. Finding the stranger he kicks him to death and Rose goes blind.
ISBN 978 0 573 02236 4

Save My Child! or, **Trapped by the Bottle**. Brian J. Burton
M2 (35, middle-age) F2 (12, 30). A wretched attic room. Fee code B

A short melodrama for inclusion in a Music Hall evening. Little scenery is required and detailed production notes are given in the script. Contained with two other melodramas in *Cheers, Tears and Screamers*.

Say Something Happened. Play. Alan Bennett
M1 (60s) F2 (20s, 60s). A hallway and living-room. Fee code F

Eager but green June is despatched by the Council to register elderly people in the area. Mam and Dad are elderly and therefore must be in need of registering – but the able-bodied, street-wise couple have no intention of being registered. Increasingly desperate, June resorts to Mr Farquharson's notes on Conduct of Interviews while no-nonsense Mam sorts her out!
ISBN 978 0 573 12246 0

Sea Side Trippers. Minidrama. Richard Tydeman
M or F16. Fee code B. ISBN 978 0 573 13305 3

Seagulls. Play. Caryl Churchill
M1 (young) F2 (middle-age). Simple exterior setting. Fee code D

Valery is to let off a firework at a public function–by power of thought. When the firework fails to ignite, Valery is afraid her extraordinary powers are waning. She is comforted by a fan who relates the Chinese parable of the seagulls who come to a man every time he goes to the beach, but on the one occasion he needs a seagull to come to him, none approach.

Seascape. Play. Tony Rushforth
M2 (17, late 50s) F2 (17, late 30s). 1 exterior. Fee Code D

In this moving play, set against the dramatic wartime backdrop of the Isle of Man internment camp, romances develop between a German internee and an English girl; and between a woman of Italian descent and a German Jew. The play raises issues about a little-recorded part of British domestic history. The characters are sustained by their hopes and dreams which we realise cannot be fulfilled. Period 1940.
ISBN 978 0 573 02382 8

♦ **Secretarial Skills.** Comedy. Peter Quilter (From *Duets*)
M1 F1. A living-room. Fee code D

It's Barrie's birthday party and PA Janet is helping him get ready. As they discuss getting older and love (or Janet's lack of it), it's clear she would happily settle down with Barrie. Unfortunately, Barrie is more interested in men, but he still books them both on a cruise as a birthday present to himself. May be performed individually or as the second act in *Duets*.
ISBN 978 0 573 11111 2

Semblance of Madness! Play. John H. Newmeir
F3 (20s, 40s). A psychiatric hospital. Fee code D

Three women in a psychiatric hospital meet for a therapeutic drama lesson. Jones, an ex-professional actress, adopts the role of teacher. The other two women – Dawn, a neurotic day-dreamer, and Hannah, an apparently "normal" dispassionate person – portray her students. From the outset we learn that the lesson is carefully controlled to extract information regarding a gruesome murder.
ISBN 978 0 573 03385 8

Señora Carrar's Rifles. Play. Bertolt Brecht. Translated by Wolfgang Sauerlander
M6 F3. Extras. Simple interior. Fee code G

Widow Carrar observes neutrality by refusing to let her sons join the Spanish Republican Army, or to let her brother have the rifles which were concealed by her husband before his death. When the elder son is killed by the rebels, mother and son decide to take the hidden rifles and leave with her brother for the front. (The play is a modern version of J. M. Synge's *Riders to the Sea*.)

A Separate Peace. Play. Tom Stoppard
M2 (40s) F4 (young, middle-age). A nursing-home ward and reception office. Fee code E

Mr Brown arrives at an expensive nursing home, apparently in no need of treatment. He takes a room, treats the place like a hotel, spends his time painting a vast mural but all the time remaining courteous. It is only the young nurse Maggie who can make contact with him.
ISBN 978 0 573 12254 5

Sequence of Events. George MacEwan Green
M3 (20s, middle-age) F2 (young, middle-age). Three acting areas. Fee code C

A hangman, a prostitute, a murderer and murderer's stricken parents are the ingredients in this taut drama. In a fascinating chopped time sequence they spin a strange web of sex and death.
Period Edwardian
ISBN 978 0 573 12239 2

Seven Stages of an Affair. Play. Lorraine Forrest-Turner
M1 (30s-40s) F1(30s-40s). Various simple settings. Fee code D

Caroline is married to dependable Robert, has two children and runs an employment agency. When Tony Brunetti comes for an interview, she is attracted by his charm. So begins an affair. With clandestine meetings and deceit piled upon deceit, they jeopardize both their marriages before they call a halt – but not without regrets. Runner-up in the National Drama Festival Association's George Taylor Memorial Award.
ISBN 978 0 573 02364 4

Sexual Perversity in Chicago. Comedy. David Mamet
M2 (20s) F2 (20s). Various simple settings. Fee code H

The play opens with a duologue between the two men in which they discuss various sexual adventures and then proceeds to further scenes in which their attitudes and those of the women are investigated. The scenes are brief, the settings very simply staged and may be indicated largely through effective lighting changes. Running time is approximately 90 minutes

Shadows of the Evening. Play. Noël Coward
M2 (28, 50s) F2 (45, 50). A private suite in a luxurious hotel. Fee code F

Linda, George's mistress and Anne, his estranged wife decide to settle their animosities for George's sake as he has now only a few months to live. He has to accept that he will go back with Anne, not only because he wants to see his children again but also because he has still continued to love her just as he will continue to love Linda.
ISBN 978 0 573 02309 1

Shindig. Play. Arthur Aldrich
F5 (30-40). An office. Fee code D. ISBN 978 0 573 03382 7

Shop for Charity. Comedy. Charles Mander
M1 (50s, 79) F4 (middle-age, 60s, 79). A charity shop. Fee code D

Are charity shops really there to help the Developing World or are they just a sop to the consciences of the middle-class people who run them? Easy to stage, thought-provoking and full of 'characters' this is a very amusing play about the nature of charity.
ISBN 978 0 573 12247 7

Shoppers. Comedy. Jean McConnell
F2 (middle age). A seaside promenade. Fee code B

See the entry for *Deckchairs I*.

Short Changed. Short play (From *Deckchairs II*). Jean McConnell
F2 (50, 80s). A garden. Fee code C

Miss Westlake, a retired headmistress, tries to retire peacefully to the prestigious residential home of Merrywinds, but finds that her earlier misdemeanours as a headmistress still haunt her. Julia, a social service official and ex-pupil of Miss Westlake has the ideal opportunity for revenge and justice.
ISBN 978 0 573 10004 8

Showbusiness. Play (from *Visiting Hour*). Richard Harris
M5 F9, may be played by M2 F4 (1 black). A hospital ward. Fee code D

We follow the satirical vagaries of a TV crew filming a documentary on the world's first quadruple transplant – until they discover they are pipped at the post by a transplant operation in another hospital! The play forms part of *Visiting Hour* (see Section A) which was presented at The Duke's Head Theatre, Richmond, Surrey, in 1990.
ISBN 978 0 573 01925 8

Silence. Play. Harold Pinter
M2 (30s, 40s) F1 (20s). Three areas. Fee code F

Silence consists of three monologues by Ellen, Rumsey and Bates. Ellen grew up in the country and Rumsey and Bates, who knew her as a child fell in love with her. Rumsey, ended their relationship, advising her to find younger men. Ellen may have gone away with Bates but, she loved Rumsey more. While Ellen and Bates lived unhappily in town, Rumsey lived in contentment in the country.

Sins of the Father. Play. Leo Smith
M1 F2. A bedroom representing two locations. Fee code D

Kevin, an upwardly mobile family man, is manipulated into an affair by the glamorous Kitty who then manoeuvres the pliable Kevin into confessing the affair to his wife. After an acrimonious scene, she takes the children and leaves. Each of the characters shows their true persona in revealing monologues, with the dark undertones of Kitty's real nature only surfacing at the play's climax.
ISBN 978 0 573 12253 8

Sister Mary Ignatius Explains It All for You. Play. Christopher Durang
M2 (30s) F3 (30s, 50s). 1 boy (8). A lecture platform. Fee code J

Please see the entry in Section A.

A Sleep of Prisoners. Play. Christopher Fry
M4. Church interior. Fee code F

An anti-war verse drama in the form of a modern Passion play. Four English soldiers are locked up for the night in a church turned into a prison camp. Privates King and Able fight and are separated by the other two. All four dream of the row, interpreting it in different Biblical ways.

A Slight Ache. Play. Harold Pinter
M2 (middle-age) F1 (middle-age). Composite setting. Fee code E

Flora and Edward invite the matchseller into their home. The matchseller is silent; faced with this silence, Edward destroys himself while Flora gains strength, until finally Flora turns Edward out with the tray of matches. The midsummer's day which began with Edward having a 'slight ache' ends in his total disintegration.
ISBN 978 0 573 02249 4

A Small Affair. Comedy. Bob Larbey
M5 F12. A rehearsal room. Fee code G

The television drama department is short of performing space. Director Guy's drama is shunted into a small room and he is beset with problems. The cast come to loggerheads but after a 'calming' break return to find their space double-booked by would-be contestants on an idiotic panel show. When the Head of Drama drops into the rehearsal the drama turns into a farce ...
ISBN 978 0 573 12135 7

B

A Small Family Murder. Play, Simon Brett
M3, M1 voice only, may be performed by M1 with doubling. An interview room. Fee code D

Valerie Trevelyan is murdered in her nursing home and her two sons are the prime suspects. As detectives interview them and their senile father the distinctive characters each tell a different story. Deep secrets from the past are uncovered and the clues begin to mount up. This can be performed as a male monologue.
ISBN 978 0 573 14220 8

♦ **The Sociable Plover**. Play. Tim Whitnall
M2. A hide. Fee code H

Nothing and nobody will stop Roy Tunt from spotting his wild birds and today, a stormy December morning on England's desolate east coast, he is about to make the last tick in his dog-eared notebook to have recorded all 567 species on the British List. But all is not as it seems. Who is the dark stranger battling through the flood waters towards him. . . ?
ISBN 978 0 573 14230 7

Sold to the Gypsies, or, **The Wicked Stepmother**. Melodrama. Brian J. Burton
M2 F7. A poor cottage. Fee code B

A mini melodrama for inclusion in a Music Hall Evening, with the emphasis on comedy with a difference. Contained in *Foiled Again!*

Soldiering On. Monologue from *Talking Heads*. Alan Bennett
F1 (50s). A room. Fee code F

Muriel's husband Ralph has just died, leaving her rather well off – until, that is, her son Giles gets his hands on the money and Muriel comes out the loser. Eventually, neglected by Giles and no longer needed by her disturbed daughter Margaret – whose state may well have been caused by Ralph himself – Muriel ends the play alone and poor.
ISBN 978 0 573 13311 4

Something Unspoken. Play. Tennessee Williams
F2 (40s, 60). A living-room. Fee code E

Between two spinsters, one, Cornelia, a grand, imperious, wealthy Daughter of the Revolution, and the other, Grace, her pale, fragile little secretary, there is a mysterious tension. As the play opens on a crucial afternoon, Cornelia upbraids Grace for having to impersonate her on the telephone – because she was asleep. Grace compares herself bitterly to a 'cobweb' but refuses to discuss what must 'remain unspoken'.

The Sound of Silence (*Le Bel Indifférent*). Play. Jean Cocteau. Translated by Anthony Wood
M1 F1 (middle-age). An hotel room. Fee code F. ISBN 978 0 573 12266 8

Sour Grapes and Ashes. Play. N. J. Warburton
M2 (30s, 40s) F3 (teenage, 30s). A hillside. Fee code D. ISBN 978 0 573 12244 6

Split Ends. Comedy. Frank Vickery
M2 F2 (young, middle-age). A living-room. Fee code D.

A very funny comedy, written with Frank Vickery's usual panache and style. Nancy and Cyril are to meet their son's girlfriend, Susan. Cyril, naturally bald, goes into hiding when his wig disappears, and reappears in disguise. But there are further problems when Susan loses a contact lens in the salad – Cyril is soon on his way to hospital wearing a dead kitten on his head! ISBN 978 0 573 12264 4

Spoonface Steinberg. Play. Lee Hall
F1. A bare stage. Fee code H

See the entry in Section A

Spring Song Singers. Minidrama. Richard Tydeman
M or F7-15. Fee code B

A rehearsal for a concert just prior to the performance turns out to be, to the consternation of many, a rehearsal twenty-four hours in advance. Running time: 15-20 minutes
ISBN 978 0 573 12234 7

Stalag 69. A play for Coarse Actors. Edited by Michael Green

See the entry for *The Third Great Coarse Acting Show*.

The Stanley Parkers. Play. Geraldine Aron
M2 (middle-age). A bedroom. Fee code E

Written in a clear and unpretentious blank verse, this play tells the story of Stanley and Dimitri, two middle-aged men who have lived together and loved each other for seventeen years. They speak directly to the audience, sharing their story with insight, humour and very obvious affection. The story ends sadly but our overriding impression is of the tenderness and warmth of a happy, unselfish relationship.
ISBN 978 0 573 04230 0

Starch. Monologue. Geoff Saunders
M1 (40s). Simple setting. Fee Code D

Charles, a company accountant, has been arrested for shoplifting. When a police officer asks him whether the offence was a "cry for help", he denies it; later he begins to wonder out loud whether, in fact, this first-ever act of rebellion is showing him that, rather than lamenting the loss of his job and the collapse of his marriage, he should be rejoicing – for he is free!
ISBN 978 0 573 14203 1

Still Life. Play. Noël Coward
M6 (30s) F5 (young, 30, middle-age). A station refreshment room. Fee code E

Laura, a married woman, starts a love affair with Alec Harvey. For several months they try to enjoy their love while they can but find they can't go on. Alec takes an appointment in South Africa and leaves with only a handshake. Period 1936
ISBN 978 0 573 02255 5

The Strangest Kind of Romance. Play. Tennessee Williams
M3 (35) F1 (40s). A room. Fee code E

The Little Man moves into lodgings where he finds an alley-cat which had been rescued from the street by a previous tenant. The lonely lodger finds warmth and comfort in this equally lonely animal. However on losing his job, he is forced to leave. Later he returns to ask for the cat. It is still alive but the result is not as he expected.

Streuth. A play for Coarse Actors. Michael Green

See the entry for *Four Plays for Coarse Actors.*

Sturm und Drang. Play. Steven Berkoff
M2 F1. Fee code F
Subtitled "Confessions of a Cad!", this is a comedy of manners for three performers in blank verse.

Suddenly Last Summer. Play. Tennessee Williams
M2 (young) F5 (young, middle-age). A patio and garden. Fee code H

Mrs Venables, in order to protect her dead son's reputation, wants Catherine, who witnessed the death, to be lobotomized. The doctor administers a truth serum and Catherine pours out the whole appalling story of the young man's homosexuality and corruption, of his being pursued by starving, naked young people and of the finding of his mutilated and partly eaten body.

Summer at the Lake. Play. Tennessee Williams
M1 (17) F2 (middle age, elderly). A living-room. Fee code E

Donald desperately seeks refuge from his hectoring mother who perpetually nags him on topics that seem alternately trivial and all too painfully pertinent to his future. At every available opportunity he flees to the lake where he swims alone. Finally, he doesn't return.

Sunbeams. Play. Rosemary Mason
M1 (middle-age) F2 (20s, 30s). A bedroom. Fee code D

Frances, a social worker, calls on the downstairs flat to find she is interrupting the end of a caller's session with a prostitute, Louise. Later she and Louise have a lengthy discussion where each states and develops her views on Louise's trade. Frances leaves her own job to 'help' Louise. It seems that trying to apply her own kind of philosophy might not always have the best results.

Swan Song. Play. Vanessa Brooks
M1 (50s-60s) F2 (50s-60s). An office. Fee code E. ISBN 978 0 573 02358 3

Take Your Medicine Like a Man. Farce. Georges Feydeau, translated by Peter Meyer from *On Purge Bébé*
M3 (30s, any age) F3 (30s, any age), 1 boy. A study. Fee code E

Follavoine, attempting to impress his guests with his unbreakable chamber pots, contends with his wife, Julie, who is panicking because their son, Toto, has constipation and won't take his medicine. Julie insults the guests, Follavoine is challenged to two duels and Toto cunningly avoids taking his laxative. Period 1910

Talk to Me Like the Rain and Let Me Listen. Play. Tennessee Williams
M1 (young) F1 (young). Child's voice. A room. Fee code E

It is a Sunday morning, for the Man a 'morning after' a drunken debauch. After he describes what he went through the Woman tells him she wants to leave him, and in a long reverie describes her vision of a perfect peace by the sea. He begs her to come back to bed with him and, as the curtain falls, she responds.

The Tea Dance. Play. Margaret Bower
F7 (middle-age). An hotel sitting-room. Fee code D

In the summer of 1936, Jean, Barbara and Olive hope for some excitement as they holiday in South Devon. It is Barbara who first spots the mysterious woman who wants to remain incognito, and Jean who overhears 'Mrs Chisholm' plotting a murder. Easy to stage and costume, this delightful play has a twist or two up its sleeve and a neat ending.
ISBN 978 0 573 13322 0

The Tea Party. Play. Harold Pinter
M6 F4. Simple settings. Fee Code F

Disson has everything he wants: a beautiful bride, a successful business, a gorgeous secretary and an upcoming holiday. But his seemingly perfect life begins to unravel. He starts to lose control over his family, his company, his situation and even his eyesight. Everything comes to a head when Disson organizes a tea party to celebrate his first wedding anniversary and things seem to have turned against him.
ISBN 978 0 571 19383 7

Teeth. Play. Tom Stoppard
M2 (30s) F3 (young, 30). A dentist's surgery. Fee Code E

When George has an affair with Harry's wife things become complicated. For Harry is George's dentist and George's wife is Harry's dental receptionist. Once George's secret has been discovered, he desperately tries to cover up the affair but complicates matters by inventing stories. Harry calmly but unprofessionally treats George's teeth and gums. Visual gags, witty lines and increasing absurdity add to the fun.
ISBN 978 0 571 19428 5

Theatrical Digs. Short play (From *Deckchairs II*). Jean McConnell
F2 (elderly). A seafront. Fee code C

Pascaline Holbein, a glamorous and conceited actress, who is playing in the end of pier show, meets her challenge in the elderly and eccentric Maggie Festoon. When Pascaline discovers that Maggie Festoon is also an actress, the result is a comical and farcical battle of work, agents and mobile phones.
ISBN 978 0 573 10004 8

B

Thank You, Kind Spirit. Play . Tennessee Williams
M4 F7. 1 girl. Extras. A spiritualist chapel. Fee code E

Mother Duclos is a spiritualist dispensing succour, on payment of a fee, to the troubled people who come to her chapel. But a woman incites everyone to turn against her, and they strip the chapel of its religious artefacts. Desolate, Mother Duclos is comforted finally by the crippled little girl who returns to say that she still believes.

There's None So Blind. Play. Gillian Plowman
M4 (20s, 40s) F3 (30, 30/40, 40). A treatment room and reception area. Fee code D

A letter to Geoffrey, a reflexologist who is blind, informs him that his wife is having an affair with a work colleague. His trip to the leisure centre where Alice works changes both their lives as he confronts the other man. Geoffrey's friend Anton also has an illuminating experience at the leisure centre where he meets Amaryllis, his longed-for ideal woman.
ISBN 978 0 573 12270 5

These Are the Stairs You Got to Watch. Play. Tennessee Williams
M5 F3. 2M optional extras. A cinema foyer. Fee code E

Carl, veteran usher at the third-rate Joy Rio Cinema, is showing the ropes to a newly hired schoolboy usher. The boy is introduced to the sleazy workings of the cinema and instructed not to let patrons go upstairs. However, the patrons are hell-bent on going upstairs, especially seductive Gladys who's determined to get the boy to follow her.

Think the Beautiful Thoughts. Play. Rae Shirley
F5 (middle-age, elderly). A living-room. Fee code D. ISBN 978 0 573 13321 3

◆ **A bullet mark next to a title indicates that it is new to this edition of the Guide.**

THE THIRD GREAT COARSE ACTING SHOW

Michael Green
ISBN 978 0 573 00030 0

M9 F5. Extras. Various interior and exterior settings

The number of characters given above would be sufficient to cover the presentation of all four plays by the same cast. Ages can vary from young to the practically senile. Fee codes: A Fish in Her Kettle: C; Present Slaughter: B; The Vagabond Prince: B and B (for music); Stalag 69: C; Julius and Cleopatra: C.

In this third volume of Coarse Plays, Michael Green defines a Coarse Acting Show as a 'closely observed imitation of stage disaster', and these five plays cover a range of disasters appalling enough to turn any show into a Coarse one. They are, also, of course, extremely entertaining. In **A Fish In Her Kettle**, it is the simple lack of a door handle which causes the disaster, as most of the cast find themselves trapped on stage when the door jams. The second play, **Present Slaughter**, collapses because of one unlucky slip by the leading man, who cuts his wrist when he collides with a tableful of glasses. **The Vagabond Prince** is an all-purpose Coarse Musical, with a roistering chorus of gypsies and earthy tavern men and women. The fourth play, **Stalag 69**, is, according to the director, 'a seminal investigation into the relationship between man and war', a noble concept somewhat marred by the fact that the set is upside down for the first run-through, and collapses completely during the second, revealing the stage staff enthusiastically producing a startling range of live sound effects. The final play, **Julius and Cleopatra**, a Roman spectacular, illustrates two of the Laws of Coarse Acting – one, that every person in a Coarse crowd is hideously deformed or crippled for some reason, and two, that when stabbed, all pain is always felt in the bowels, no matter where the wound is!

This Property Is Condemned. Play. Tennessee Williams
M1 F1 (13). A railroad embankment. Fee code E

Willie tells Tom, in what is virtually a monologue, the story of her upbringing in a house that took in railroad men. She speaks with pride of his sister Alva, now dead. All the clothes Willie now wears she inherited from Alva. As she leaves he hears her singing 'You're the only star in my blue Heaven'.

Thor, with Angels. Play. Christopher Fry
M9 F3. A Jutish farmstead. Fee code F

At the time of St Augustine's mission to Britain, a young Christian soldier, Hoel, is captured by the Jutes. He is threatened with death, and later crucified, but others are converted through these events to Christianity, forsaking the Norse gods such as Thor. As the play ends the voices of Augustine's men are heard singing in the distance. Period AD 596

Three More Sleepless Nights. Play. Caryl Churchill
M2 F2. A double bed. Fee code E

Three couples are viewed in bed in three successive scenes. The first, Margaret and Frank, have been married for ten years and row constantly. The second, Pete and Dawn, have muted exchanges as she drifts to eventual suicide while he recounts the plot of *Alien*. The third scene shows Pete and Margaret together, starting out happy but gradually falling into the same patterns of non-communication they experienced before.

Till We Meet Again. Play. Colin and Mary Crowther
M3 (young, middle age, old) F3 (young, middle age, old). Somewhere between heaven and earth. Fee code E

What would we do differently if we had the chance to live life over again? Nearing death, the play's hero revisits himself as a teenager, as a young man starting a career, as a disgruntled middle-aged husband and, in the final moments, as a newborn child and as the old man he'll never be. Running time approximately 45 minutes.
ISBN 978 0 573 02360 6

B

A Time of Wolves and Tigers. Play. Hugh Leonard
M1 (40s). M1 or F1 voice only. Fee code D

See the entry for *Suburb of Babylon* in Section A

Tippers. Play. Gillian Plowman
M3 (20s-40s) F2 (20s, 30s). A rubbish tip. Fee code D. ISBN 978 0 573 12262 0

To Have and To Hold. Play. Lorraine Forrest-Turner
F3 (33, 58, 63). 1 male voice. A dining-room, a bedroom. Fee code D

Shocked at her father's sudden death, Susan has returned to the family home and immediately she and her mother, Margaret, are at loggerheads. Even the arrival of Margaret's sister, can't melt Margaret's hardness. But as Susan recalls childhood memories, a shocking truth emerges. Cleverly interspersing thirty years past with the present this is a family drama with a warm heart.
ISBN 978 0 573 03394 0

Too Hot to Handle. Play. Jim Hawkins
M1 F2 (30s). Split setting: a kitchen, a lounge, a bedroom. Fee code D

Suzanne, neat, houseproud, and conventional, is astonished and horrified when she finds a collection of hard porn photos and magazines in her bank manager husband Peter's wardrobe. The shock leads to a vital discussion and examination of their whole attitude towards each other. It seems that a more satisfying, understanding and realistic future of intimacy may await them both.

Too Long an Autumn. Play. Jimmie Chinn
M3 (middle-age, elderly) F4 (middle-age, elderly). Various simple interior settings. Fee code E

Long Autumn is a retirement home for theatricals. Maisie May, a former music-hall star, arrives and initially copes with the rigours of Long Autumn in her ever-cheerful, irrepressible style. She becomes increasingly depressed, however, until a breezy impresario arrives with big plans for Maisie ...
ISBN 978 0 573 12274 3

◆ **A bullet mark next to a title indicates that it is new to this edition of the Guide.**

Too Much the Sun. Play. Nicholas Pierpan
M4 (21,middle age) Simple settings. Fee Code D

Fresh out of prison, a young man returns to his English coastal home village. He takes a job offered by the local eccentric, a clockmaker and a friend of his father. Storytelling, epilepsy, seafaring, lockpicking and espionage make this unique lyrical play a true delight. Seen at Oxford University as part of their Play Festival.
ISBN 978 0 573 02386 6

Top Table. Satirical comedy. Margaret Wood
M8 or F8 or mixed cast. Extras. A conference room. Fee code D

The delegates from many governments arrive in an atmosphere of suspect bonhomie. The two cleaners, backed by the troops and ordinary people, take over and announce a slight amendment to international law: in future a formal declaration of any war shall be by the public execution of all members of governments concerned.
ISBN 978 0 573 12275 0

A Touch of Rose Madder. Play. Jim O'Connor
M2 (20s-40s) F1 (70s). A bed-sitting-room. Fee code E

A funny, quietly moving character study. Rose, an elderly widow, has a surprise: her new Home Help is Leslie – a *man*. Leslie's care and humour eventually win Rose round. Rose's son Danny has to move further away and cannot visit her regularly, so lonely Leslie moves into a spare room to be on hand all the time.
ISBN 978 0 573 12289 9

Touching Tomorrow. Play. Gillian Plowman
M2 (50s, any age) F3 (20s, 50s). A sitting-room. Fee code D

Dorcas looks after her middle-aged brother Vincent who has learning difficulties. She has brought home Gemma, a homeless girl who says she has been raped, but is Gemma telling the truth? Surprisingly, it is Vincent who provides the possible way ahead for Gemma. A powerful one-act play which boldly tackles the subjects of homelessness, rape and disability with humour, honesty and warmth.
ISBN 978 0 573 02357 6

The Train. Play. Carl Slotboom. Translated by Dr Louis I. Leviticus
M2 (young, elderly) F2 (young, elderly). 1 male voice, 1 voice. 2 train compartments. Fee code D

Two elderly Jewish people, David and Clara, sit in a 1990s train whilst their younger selves are seen in a converted cattle wagon in the 1940s. The modern train has halted unexpectedly and the enforced wait sends David's thoughts back to that earlier train, also stationary, and the war memories it evokes ... Period 1995 and 1943
ISBN 978 0 573 12332 0

Trapped! A Play for Coarse Actors. Michael Green.

See the entry for *Coarse Acting Strikes Back*.

The Trial of Joan of Arc at Rouen, 1431. Play. Bertolt Brecht. Translated by Ralph Manheim and Wolfgang Sauerlander
M25 F9. Extras, children. Interior and exterior settings. Fee code G

Brecht's play is an adaptation of a radio play by Anna Seghers based on the original records of the trial of Joan of Arc. The play emphasizes the destruction of Joan as a common interest to both the occupying power and the collaborationist clergy, and the clash of interests between them.

B

The Trial of Lucullus. Radio play. Bertolt Brecht
Translations: Frank Jones
                      H. R. Hays
Fee code G

The great Roman General Lucullus is judged in the underworld by representatives of the living future. The figures from his triumphal frieze are called as witnesses to his victories but only his introduction of the cherry tree into Europe speaks for him. Thus his bloody hands are not entirely empty, but 80,000 dead is a high price to pay. Set in classical Rome.

Trip of a Lifetime. Comedy. Bill Cashmore and Andy Powrie
M2 F1. An empty stage. Fee code E

Recently divorced Barry, thirty-nine, sets off around the world on the trip of a lifetime. His travelling companions are his parents, whose cheery optimism, all-too-visible romantic attachment and parochial ways drive Barry to distraction. Paris, Egypt, and New York are among the many stops: all are suggested, on an otherwise empty stage, by three stools and a soundtrack of music and effects.
ISBN 978 0 573 02363 7

Trip's Cinch. Play. Phyllis Nagy
M1 (30s) F2 (30s, 40s). Simple settings. Fee code F

It's somewhere along the East Coast of America. The Accused: Benjamin Trip. Handsome, charming and well-groomed. The Victim: Lucy Parks. Good-looking, witty and self-assured. The Academic: Val Greco. Opinionated, formidable and charismatic. Phyllis Nagy's taut, precise dialogue cunningly treads a fine line between what we see and what we hear, bringing into sharp focus a world where pinning down words leads to lies and obfuscation.

A Trouble Shared, or, **Two to the Rescue**. Melodrama. Brian J. Burton
M2 F2 Simple exterior setting. Fee code B

A mini melodrama for inclusion in a Music Hall Evening, with the emphasis on comedy. Contained in *Foiled Again!*

Tryst. Play. Colin Crowther
M1(40-60) F2 (40-60), or M2 F1. Various simple settings. Fee code E

Tom, suffering from heart disease and aware that he does not have long to live, commissions Jan, an artist, to paint a picture that Tom can leave to his wife Brenda. From this simple premise Colin Crowther has created a many-layered, thoughtful play exploring illness, grief and the difficulties of caring for the dying, threaded with a lucid discussion of the redemptive power of art.
ISBN 978 0 573 12211 5

27 Wagons Full of Cotton. Comedy. Tennessee Williams
M2 (middle-age, 1 Latin) F1 (middle-age). A cottage porch. Fee code E

Jake, owner of a Mississippi cotton gin, burns down the mill of a competitor. Silva Vicarro, the man whose gin he destroyed and who is suspicious of the circumstances surrounding the fire, seduces and rapes Jake's wife. Finally, however, they all tacitly accept the position in the name of good neighbourliness.

Two Fat Men. Light-hearted drama. Gillian Plowman
M3 F5. A room. Fee code D

B

Duncan and George feel far from comfortable attending a Weight Busters meeting, surrounded as they are by women. Waiting for the meeting to start, they meet an old flame of George's – who bore him a child many years earlier – and Duncan strikes up an affecting romance with a sign language teacher. Line dancing and snatches of Gilbert and Sullivan enhance the jolly mood of this touching comedy-drama.
ISBN 978 0 573 12313 9

Two Summers. Play. Gillian Plowman
M4 (30s, 70s) F2 (30s, 70s). Two sitting-rooms. Fee code D
ISBN 978 0 573 12285 9

Two Wits to Woo. Play. John Kelly
M2 F1. A study. Fee code D

Facing financial ruin, widowed Lady Winsome is forced to sell the manor and fire Joe the gardener and James the chauffeur. However, James has been secretly using the estate's Rolls Royce for a taxi business and Joe has been profiting from the garden produce. The two desperately try to prevent Lady Winsome from discovering their illicit dealings and from selling up. But Lady Winsome isn't so naïve... Period 1934
ISBN 978 0 573 02365 1

Umjana Land. Play. Gillian Plowman
M3 (20s, 40s) F4 (20s-40s, any age). A living-room/study. Fee code D

Leah discovers her author husband Gordon is having an affair with Ursula. Meanwhile, Gordon remembers Umjana Land, the childhood dream world he inhabited with his sister Agnes, and determines to write. When Agnes appears, having written a Booker Prize-nominated book about Umjana Land, Gordon is left strangely alone as his daughter, Leah, Ursula and Agnes find a common bond.
ISBN 978 0 573 12140 1

Under the Twelfth Sign. Play. Enid Coles
M1 (middle-age) F4 (50s). A sitting-room. Fee code D. ISBN 978 0 573 12276 83

♦ **A bullet mark next to a title indicates that it is new to this edition of the Guide.**

Us and Them. Play. David Campton
Any number of characters. A bare stage. Fee code D

This play was written to be performed by a company of almost any size, of any age and of either sex. Two parties enter, A and B, from East and West. Each party plans to settle down, then sees each other. Instant suspicion. A dividing wall is built. After mutual spying war ensues and the wall is broken down.
ISBN 978 0 573 02346 0

B

The Vagabond Prince. A play for Coarse Actors. Edited by Michael Green

See the entry for *The Third Great Coarse Acting Show*.

Victoria Station. Play (from the triple bill *Other Places*). Harold Pinter
M2. A car, an office. Fee code D

The Controller of a radio-cab firm is trying to contact Driver 274 and get him to pick up a fare at Victoria Station. The Driver doesn't know where he is and professes not to know where Victoria Station is. 'Brilliantly funny' *Daily Telegraph*
ISBN 978 0 573 04225 6

The Victory of the Cross. Passion play. M. Creagh-Henry
M3 F4. A room. Fee code A. ISBN 978 0 573 06250 6

A View from the Obelisk. Hugh Leonard
M2 F1. A hilltop. Fee code D. (In a volume)

Owen insists on showing Rosemary the view from a hilltop near Dublin. He is exhausted after the climb and Rosemary goes off to summon a car. While she is gone a boy appears, and Owen strikes up a casual conversation with him. The boy goes, and it is only when Rosemary returns that Owen realizes why the boy seemed so familiar ...
ISBN 978 0 573 01641 7

The Virtuous Burglar. Farce. Dario Fo. Translated by Joe Farrell
M4 F3. A living-room. Fee code F

A burglar is discovered when the owner of the flat returns unexpectedly with his mistress. When the owner's wife arrives, the burglar is forced to pretend the mistress is his wife. A profusion of spouses and lovers appear and the burglar – apparently the only one not having an affair – is forced into pretending to have multiple wives. Then his own wife arrives!

A Visit from Miss Prothero. Play. Alan Bennett
M1 (60s) F1 (middle-age). A living-room. Fee code E

Mr Dodsworth has recently retired. Sitting at home he is contemplating his life and achievements with quiet satisfaction when there is a sharp ring at the door: his former secretary has come to ruin it all.
ISBN 978 0 573 12286 6

The Visitor. Thriller. Maureen Lee
F4 (30s, middle-age). A lounge. Fee code D

Ex-secretary and ex-mistress of a wealthy businessman who committed suicide, the unpleasant Laura complains to her neighbour that she would have inherited much more than her cottage if a certain will had not disappeared. The arrival of a strange woman with threats of blackmail results in Laura being deprived of her cottage – and more as she receives her full deserts.
ISBN 978 0 573 03372 8

B

The Voice of the Phoenix. Play. Carol Parkinson
M2 (35, elderly) F2 30s). A lounge. Fee Code D

Music journalist Sarah has been hugely influenced when a student by the late renowed opera singer Gabrielle Leaman. She meets Professor Parish, Gabrielle's intimate friend, to help her complete the draft of a biography. However, at the singer's former cottage, Sarah's world is crushed when Parish, in a series of flashbacks with Gabrielle, paints a very unsavoury portrait of the singer.
ISBN 978 0 573 12222 4

Waiting. Play (from *Visiting Hour*). Richard Harris
M1 (elderly) F1 (black). A hospital ward. Fee code D

A moving depiction of lonely old age which was seen as part of the full-length play *Visiting Hour* (see Section A) in 1990 at the Duke's Head Theatre, Richmond, Surrey. An old man sits in hospital awaiting visitors that never come and falls back on distant memories of his boyhood and the ups and downs of his married life.
ISBN 978 0 573 01925 8

Waiting for a Bus. Play. Peter Barnes
M2 F1. A bedroom. Fee code D. (In a volume)

A pair of lovers are interrupted in bed by the arrival of the husband – or arc they actors rehearsing a new comedy *Waiting for a Bus* about a pair of lovers disturbed by the husband's arrival ...? May be presented as part of the full-length entertainment *Corpsing*. For details, please see the entry in Section A.
ISBN 978 0 573 10006 2

The Wall. Play. David Henry Wilson
M2 (20s, elderly) F1 (20s). A wall. Fee code B

Chalked on a huge wall are the words: 'The Wall'. John-John and Doll pass by and try their best to replace the two words with more pregnant ones ranging from 'Shakespeare' to 'Sex'. An old man hobbles on stage: he is lonely and in need of help, but the big words on the wall stress the inexorability of his loneliness.
ISBN 0 573 60108 8

♦ **A bullet mark next to a title indicates that it is new to this edition of the Guide.**

Way Out West. Minidrama. Richard Tydeman
M6 F4. Extras M and F. Fee code B

When a Bad Man (Jake) marries a squaw and tells her his name is Joe (a Good Man) all manner of misunderstandings occur. Particularly when Running Water and Big Jake come looking for the errant bridegroom. Running time: 15-20 minutes
ISBN 978 0 573 12288 0

B

Ways and Means. Comedy. Noël Coward
M5 (young, 30s) F4 (young, middle-age). A bedroom. Fee code E

Toby and Stella find themselves as guests in a house on the Riviera with no money and an outstayed welcome. A burglar breaks in and Stella offers to direct him to a rich guest's stash if he will go halves. He agrees, obtains and hands over the loot, then leaves them bound and gagged to allay suspicion. Period 1936
ISBN 0 573 62577 8

We Don't Want To Lose You. Play (from the double bill *Fiddlers Three*). Eric Chappell
M4 (20s, 30s, 50s) F2 (20s, 30s). Two adjoining offices. Fee code F

In the offices of Multiple Holdings, Rex, Harry and Osborne form an alliance against the management, as personified by the devious Fletcher. Rex is ordered to sack Osborne, and, encouraged by Harry and Norma, offers Fletcher his resignation in protest – to his horror, it is accepted! Norma rescues Rex with a spot of blackmail.
ISBN 978 0 573 01980 7

Wendlebury Day. Play. David Henry Wilson
M1. A bare stage. Fee code C

A monologue by Tom Wendlebury, a middle-aged man, who presents five different accounts of his life stressing that companionship is the only key to survival.
ISBN 0 573 60108 8

What Are You Doing Here? Play. David Campton
M5 F5. Extras 1M or 1F. A bare stage. Fee code D

A large jeering crowd appears on stage. A Narrator tries to analyse why ordinary people can suddenly be turned into an ugly mob. He describes a series of everyday events that upset people who in turn upset someone else. He asks who upset the first man in the chain. It was the Narrator himself.
ISBN 978 0 573 12296 5

What Ho Within! Minidrama. Richard Tydeman
F4. Extras M and F. Fee code B. ISBN 978 0 573 12292 7

◆ **A bullet mark next to a title indicates that it is new to this edition of the Guide.**

What's for Pudding? Comedy. David Tristram
M3 (middle-age) F2 (middle-age). A living-room. Fee code D

Mary and Jack's dull Saturday evening is interrupted by the arrival of Maureen, Ted and Dennis. The occasion rapidly dissolves into a drunken gathering as Ted's intellect is likened to that of a paper clip, Maureen, his wife, reveals a liking for Jack, and Jack rapidly cultivates a taste for pouring whisky over his head.
ISBN 978 0 573 12305 4

B

Whence. Play. Leo Smith
M1 (young) F1 (middle-age). Underground. Fee code D

A play set in the distant future but very much for our time. Driven underground by the greenhouse effect of CFCs on the earth's atmosphere, a 'baby factory' earth-mother and a genetically engineered survivor eke out an existence in a wary partnership. At the end we realize all hope is not lost as a baby cries in the darkness.
ISBN 978 0 573 12300 9

The White Liars. Play. Peter Shaffer
M2 (young) F1 (47). A fortune-teller's parlour. Fee code E

Two pop singers, Frank and Tom, visit Sophie, a fortune-teller, for consultation. Frank says Tom is trying to lure away his girl; Tom says Frank's attitude rests on lies. Tom leaves Frank and reveals to Sophie the secret of his true relationship with his friend. Sophie herself reveals that her supposed high connections are lies. Lies surround the seedy trio.
ISBN 978 0 573 12302 3

Who Calls? Play. David Campton
F6 (30-60). A kitchen. Fee code D

Four servants sit solemnly in the kitchen of a large Victorian house. Their Mistress has died suddenly and the cook, discovering that the housekeeper and personal maid have stolen some of her jewellery, demands a share. Reluctantly they agree. Then the bell rings in the Mistress's room ... everyone is in the kitchen, so who calls? Period late-nineteenth century
ISBN 978 0 573 03345 9

Whodidit? Comedy. Neil Harrison
17 characters may be played by M3 F2. An empty stage. Fee code E

Whodidit? is an engaging spoof on the country house murder mystery story. With a nominal setting and mimed props, the focus is mainly on the richly drawn gallery of unusual characters, including a wheelchair-bound transvestite, a madman, and an invisible professor ... Impenetrably mysterious and packed with daft gags, this is a treat for everyone!
ISBN 978 0 573 12316 0

Whose Wedding Is It Anyway? Play. Margaret Bower
F5. A living-room. Fee code D. ISBN 978 0 573 03389 6

Why Do You Smoke So Much, Lily?. Play. Tennessee Williams
F2 (young, middle age). A voice. A fashionable apartment. Fee code E

Mrs Yorke struts and preens herself in the mirror of her fashionable apartment while daughter, Lily, does nothing but chain-smoke and make cynical comments. Driven to near insanity by her overbearing mother, Lily can hear her mother's fretful, incessant voice even when she's not there. Her entrapment is total; there is no escape.

The Window Cleaner. Play. Gillian Plowman
M1 F1. A sitting-room. Fee Code D

Jill has served time for killing her husband who abused her. Making a new start as a window cleaner, she disturbs Daryl, who is burgling an apartment. Panicking, Daryl holds Jill captive but she gets him talking about his life. In turn, Jill relates her tragic history and it becomes apparent they have much in common. A final twist throws them together in an unlikely partnership.
ISBN 978 0 573 02380 4

A Woman of No Importance. Monologue from *Talking Heads*. Alan Bennett
F1 (middle-age). A hospital room. Fee code F

At work Peggy has carved herself a comfortable niche. Once in hospital, she loses no time in establishing herself as Queen Bee, taking on several responsibilities. Persistently cheerful, blind to the feelings of others and, at heart, terribly lonely, Peggy is at once a richly comic and desperately moving creation, providing a rewarding challenge for a mature actress.
ISBN 978 0 573 03390 2

Womberang. Comedy. Sue Townsend
M1 (30s) F6 (young, middle-age, elderly, with doubling and trebling). A hospital outpatients' waiting-room. Fee code F

It is the afternoon gynaecology clinic and an assortment of patients sit in a grim hospital room. Rita Onions breezes in. Her verve and energy, combined with a complete lack of respect for authority, gradually spreads an infectious, joyous anarchy throughout the patients as she demolishes officious hospital staff and generally sorts out the patients' personal problems.

World Première. Comedy. Charles Mander
M3 (middle-age, ageing) F4 (young, middle-age). A village hall. Fee code D

A fast-paced comedy about an amateur dramatic society gathering for the technical rehearsal of a play by their producer Gordon. Minus the set, director and stage crew, new-recruit Val frantically tries to improvise. Matters become increasingly frenetic with the arrival of Gordon's dypsomaniac wife Ruth, and an assortment of people totally unconnected with the drama group!
ISBN 978 0 573 12284 2

◆ **A bullet mark next to a title indicates that it is new to this edition of the Guide.**

Zartan. Play. N. J. Warburton
M6 (20s, middle-age, elderly) F3 (20s, elderly), doubling possible. Extras. Various simple settings. Fee code D

Lord Greycoat lost his son when the boy's carrycot dropped from a plane over the African jungle. An expedition is mounted to find the adult Zartan, who suffers from a split personality and doubts about his extraordinary size in comparison to his ant 'parents'. Through Greycoat's secretary, Jane, Zartan discovers his true identity – and love.
ISBN 978 0 573 12304 7

The Zoo Story. Play. Edward Albee
M2 (middle-age). Central Park. Fee code E

To escape his wife, two daughters and two parakeets Peter sits on a bench in Central Park, reading and thinking. Jerry joins him, having just been to the zoo. He draws the unwilling Peter into conversation and extracts information from him. In return Jerry supplies Peter with a curious medley of information about his wanderings in New York. The outcome of the meeting is a willing death for one of them.
ISBN 978 0 573 04222 5

◆ **A bullet mark next to a title indicates that it is new to this edition of the Guide.**

Revue Sketches

B

Beyond the Fringe. Alan Bennett, Peter Cook, Jonathan Miller and Dudley Moore
Fee code for each sketch code A

A madhouse of hilarity in both London and New York. Their skits include one about an impassioned preacher whose emotion carries him so far from the text that he can't find his way back. There's a delicious spoof on Shakespeare in beautifully faked speech and a couple of panel scenes. A lucky dip of highly intellectual fun.

Steppes in the Right Direction. M4
Royal Box. M2
Man Bites God. M3
Fruits of Experience. M1
Bollard. M4
The Heat Death of the Universe. M1
Deutscher Chansons. M2
The Sadder and Wiser Beaver. M2
Words ... and Things. M3
T.V.P.M. M1
And the Same to You. M1
Aftermyth of War. M4
Civil War. M4
Real Class. M4
Little Miss Britten. M2
The Suspense is Killing Me. M4
Porn Shopping. M1
Studio 5. M4
Sitting on the Bench. M1
Bread Alone. M4
Take a Pew. M1
So That's the Way You Like It. M4
The End of the World. M4
Home Thoughts from Abroad. M4
The English Way of Death. M1
The Well Song. M1
The Great Train Robbery. M2
One Leg Too Few. M2
Portraits from Memory. M2
Death of Lord Nelson. M1
Interviews (Studio 5). M4
The Minor. M1

B

B

LISTEN TO THIS

Sketches and monologues by Michael Frayn
Fee code A for each sketch. ISBN 0 573 69179 7

A collection of seventeen monologues, dialogues and parodies, one written for *The Secret Policeman's Ball*, some culled from his *Observer* column and some written for Eleanor Bron's TV series, *Beyond a Joke*. This volume is a delight to read and offers a wonderful repertoire of comic performance pieces.

An Occasion of This Nature. Monologue
At the Sign of the Rupture Belt. M2 F2
Blots. Monologue
Confession. Monologue
Glycerine. M1 F1
Head to Head. Monologue
Heaven. M1 F1
Listen to This. M1 F1
A Little Peace and Quiet. M1 F1
The Messenger's Assistant. M2 F1
Never Mind the Weather. Monologue
A Pleasure Shared. Monologue
The Property Speculators. M2 F1
Sons and Customers. M2 F1
Through the Wilderness. M3 F1
Value for Money. Monologue
Who Do You Think You Are? M1 F1

NOËL COWARD REVUE SKETCHES

The sketches marked with an asterisk have songs. Please enquire for details of the music.

London Calling! (1923)
"Rain Before Seven –" (Love Matches). M1 F1. A hotel sitting-room. Fee code A
Early Mourning ("Sorry You've Been Troubled"). F2. A bedroom. Fee code A
The Swiss Family Whittlebot. M3 F1. Fee code A

On With the Dance (1925)
The Café de la Paix (Fin de Siécle)*. M10 F10. Extras. Outside the Café de la Paix. Fee code A
Oranges and Lemons. M4. A bedroom. Fee code C
Class. M4 F3. A squalid room, a dining-room. Fee code C
Travelling Light (A Thief in the Night). M2 F1. A train compartment. Fee code A

This Year of Grace! (Charles B. Cochrane's 1928 Revue)
A Tube Station (The Tube)*. M8 F5. Large chorus. An Underground booking-office. Fee code C
Ignorance is Bliss. M4 F4. 2 hotel bedrooms. Fee code A
The Lido Beach*. M7 F8. The Lido beach. Fee code C
The English Lido*. M6 F10. Extras. Fee code C
The Legend of the Lily of the Valley*. M3 F1. Extras. Fee code A
Rules of Three. M7 F5, doubling possible. Fee code C
Law and Order. M2 F3. A street. Fee code A
Love, Life and Laughter*. M3 F3. A French café exterior and interior. Fee code A
The Order of the Day. M1 F1. A street. Fee code A

Charles B. Cochrane's 1931 Revue
Half-caste Woman*. M4 F4. Male extras. A waterfront café. Fee code A

The Third Little Show (1931)
Cat's Cradle. F2. 2 adjoining gardens. Fee code A

Words and Music (1932)
Children's Hour*. M1 F4. A nursery. Fee code A
Journey's End. A musical version of "Journey's End" as produced by Erik Charell (with acknowledgements to Erik Charell and apologies to R. C. Sherriff)*. M5 F4. Extras. Fee code A
Fairy Whispers. M3 F8. A dining-room. Fee code A
Midnight Matinée*. M2 F12. Chorus. A drawing-room. Fee code C
The Party's Over Now*. M5 F4. Extras. A house exterior. Fee code A

Set to Music (1939)
Weary of it All*. M3 F2. A dressing-room. Fee code A
Secret Service. M8 F3. 1F. A café. Fee code A

Sigh No More (1945)
Pageant*. Large cast. Fee code C

Playlets, Additional Sketches and Early Pieces
What Next? M1 F1. A drawing-room. Fee code A
Women and Whisky. M2 F2. A lounge. Fee code C
Mild Oats. M1 F1. A study. Fee code E
Customs House, Dover*. M3 F2. Fee code C
Weatherwise. M3 F5. A drawing-room. Fee code E
Shop-Girls. M1 F5. A furniture showroom. Fee code C
Some Other Private Lives (parody of *Private Lives*). M1 F1. A sitting-room. Fee code A

ONE TO ANOTHER

John Mortimer, N. F. Simpson and Harold Pinter
Fee code A for each sketch. ISBN 0 573 07021 0

Triangle. M2 F1
The Waitress studies her two regulars – one timid and uncertain, the other forceful and decisive. They both have powers to charm and as she serves them she dreams of life in their respective homes – the only snag is they are quite unaware of her aspirations.

Gladly Otherwise. M2 F1
Into the lethargy of the Brandywine household comes the Man, a high-powered salesman. Within minutes he has them tied in knots, but when he removes his personality they sink back into domestic gloom.

The Black and White. F2
Two old women, down-and-outs from London's Embankment and back streets, regale themselves with bread and soup in the early hours of the morning.

Trouble in the Works. M2
Fibbs interviews Wills from the works and tries to plumb the mental depths of his engineering workers. After cutting his way through a jungle of technical jargon he discovers what they really want to make is brandyballs.

Cleaning Up Justice. M1 F1
The court usher and the charwoman deplore the shocking goings-on of their betters who are brought to court – how differently and how happily they themselves have lived since they committed bigamy.

Collector's Piece. M6 F4
When young Albert caught a Goat Moth in his father's garden it changed his life – in future he would study Nature. Unfortunately his life passes and death comes too quickly, for, at the end, all he has discovered is the Goat Moth.

Conference. M3
The Tycoon interviews Jones, but he is such a popular fellow and so tied up with his telephones that a frustrated Jones retreats to a call box and winds up their meeting by phone to his own if not to the Tycoon's satisfaction.

Can You Hear Me? M2
Crob and Hud are staying in a reputable hotel but find the amenities leave much to be desired. When Crob feels the urge to have a speaking tube it is some time before it is supplied and then he finds it difficult to control.

THREE SKETCHES BY HAROLD PINTER

Precisely
M2. Fee code A
Precisely was first performed in *The Big One* at the Apollo Theatre, London, in 1983 with Barry Foster and Martin Jarvis.

Press Conference
M1. Other parts M or F. Fee code A
Harold Pinter can sketch a world in a few lines which reveal the power of his vision focused on the horrors that have been and that are to come. *Press Conference* was first presented as part of an evening of sketches in February 2002 at the Royal National Theatre, London.

Tess
F1. Fee code A (Playscript on hire only)
This tense, funny, teasingly enigmatic monologue – with a sting in its tail – was first performed by Penelope Wilton at the Royal National Theatre in 2002.

Samuel French
Theatre Books Lists

Free lists are available of theatre books stocked in our bookshop

- Acting

- Audition material

- Circus, magic, comedy, clowns, pantomime and puppetry

- Costume and make-up

- Criticism

- Drama in education and drama training

- Mime, movement and dance

- Musical interest

- Production, stage management, directing and marketing

- Shakespeare

- Speech training

- Stagecraft, design and lighting

- Theatre biography

- Theatre

- Theatre history

- Writing, television and radio

Please enquire

Oberon Books and Samuel French Ltd

Several of the plays in Samuel French's catalogue are published by Oberon Books. We are taking this close relationship a step further by licensing, on behalf of Oberon Books, a selection of their titles for amateur performance. A licence application to Samuel French's amateur licensing department (e-mail: plays@samuelfrench-london.co.uk; tel: 020 7255 4302) will give you a quotation, and later a licence, issued on behalf of Oberon Books by Samuel French. The pink-coloured section which follows details the titles we are handling, at the time of going to press (February 2012) but more titles will be added in future months and these will be found on the Samuel French website (www.samuelfrench-london.co.uk), the Oberon website (www.oberonbooks.com) and also in our paper Supplements to *The Guide to Selecting Plays* (available free of charge through our mailing list)

CONTENTS

O
B

Alphabetical Listing

O
B

Full Length

African Gothic. Play. Reza de Wet
M2 (30s) F2 (34, 60). Farmhouse. Fee code L

In a decaying farmhouse in South Africa, brother and sister Sussie and Frikkie
face eviction by an officious lawyer after the death of their parents. Abandoned, they
endlessly enact the rituals of punishment once visited upon them by their parents. Widely
regarded as a milestone in South African theatre, this multi-award winning play tells the
story of their final 'dance macabre'. In a volume of three plays with *Good Heavens* and
Breathing In.
ISBN 978 1 840 02480 7

After Troy. Play. Glyn Maxwell
M4 F4. A cave and its surroundings. Fee code M

A modern play made from the fragments of two Greek tragedies, *Hecuba* and *Women of
Troy*. Troy is in ruins. Its men are dead. Its women are captives and the victorious Greeks are
camped in the ashes preparing to sail home. We find, among others, four quarrelling women
drawn together by grief and four exhausted soldiers who hate each other's guts.
ISBN 978 1 849 43026 5

All Hallows' Eve. Play. David Pinner
M2 (19, 50s) F3 (16, 2 x 40s). Simple domestic settings. Fee code L

A ghost story exploring family taboos. When Arthur, a limping stranger with a sinister
presence, opens Pandora's Box on All Hallows' Eve, sisters Francesca and Lucinda are
forced to face up to the erotic demons in their past; as they make this dark journey of
discovery they will all but destroy each other along the way. Available in a volume of two
plays with *Midsummer*.
ISBN 978 1 840 02336 7

Another Paradise. Play. Sayan Kent
M2 (30s, 50s) F3 (27, 40, 52). Various settings, requires computer or projection screen.
Fee code L

Set in a familiar world not so far in the future when identity cards are compulsory and
people are validated only by their digital ID in the National Identity Database. Five people's
work lives, homes lives, even their sex lives, are thrown into confusion when their official
identities vanish with surprising and hilarious results. "a thoroughly enjoyable play … a
good piece of wacky English radicalism" *The Scotsman*
ISBN 978 1 840 02920 8

Astrakhan (Winter). Play. Dic Edwards
M5 (includes a father and son) F5. A mountaintop, a prison, a room. Fee code L

Refugee Smerdyakov stays with Walker and his son Like. When he tells a fable from his
home country featuring a mythical tin cross, Like pursues the cross and in doing so repeats
the war crimes of his father.
ISBN 978 1 840 02596 5

Bashment. Play. Rikki Beadle-Blair
M9 F1 (early 20s). Various interior settings including a nightclub, police cell and prison.
Fee code L

Gay couple JJ and Orlando go to a nightclub and meet with the prejudice and violence
influenced by anti-gay lyrics in Jamaican music. An electrifying play – hard-hitting, tender
and painfully funny. Premiered at the Theatre Royal Stratford East. NB. Contains strong
language.
ISBN 978 1 840 02582 4

Bells. Play. Yasmin Khan
M3 (27, 35, 55) F2 (20, 53). South Asian courtesan club. Fee code L

Bells takes us into the seedy world of Mujra (courtesan) clubs, a centuries-old tradition in
Pakistan which is now growing in Britain. A butcher's shop by day and a brothel by night,
Bells has all the sparkle of Lollywood (the Pakistani film industry) but the glitz and glamour
is tarnished by the pain and degradation of secret lives.
Available in a volume of two plays with *Chaos* by Azma Dar.
ISBN 978 1 840 02554 5

Berlin Hanover Express. Ian Kennedy Martin.
M3 F1. Berlin 1942. Office. Fee code L

Ireland has declared itself neutral in the war, yet does this mean turning a blind eye to
atrocities? Inside the Irish consulate in Berlin officials try to carry on their routine business.
The truth about concentration camps is becoming known, so when the security services start
to uncover the Jewish origins of the consulate's German cook, will the staff step into protect
her or will their neutrality render them powerless? Contains nudity.
ISBN 978 1 840 02901 7

Black Crows. Play. Linda Brogan
F3 (15, 30, 45) and a string-controlled puppet. Various simple settings. Fee code L

The puppet is a young black boy who dances the shuffle better than anyone. Teenager Hazel,
older woman Leonora and his mother Queenie all fight for his attention and love to a bitter
end. Contains strong language.
ISBN 978 1 840 02737 2

Bloody Sunday. Play. Richard Norton-Taylor
M15 F5 (Various ages). Interior, courtroom setting. Fee code L

This play is a dramatic overview of testimony presented to the Saville Inquiry, a major
chapter in the Northern Ireland peace process. Established to re-examine the events
of Bloody Sunday, when 13 civil rights marchers were shot dead by British Soldiers,
the Inquiry heard evidence from over 1,000 witnesses, including civilians, soldiers,
paramilitaries, politicians and priests. This play has a large number of cast members, but
many of the spoken parts are brief and well within the reach of amateur or even first-time
actors.
ISBN 978 1 840 02568 2

O
B

Bodies Unfinished. Play. Lewis Hetherington
M1 (40s) F3 (40s, 20s, 70s). Various simple settings. Fee code L

Alan loves his work. He doesn't love his wife, his mother or his only child, so he aims to break free and live for himself. Alan's going to sort this mess out – this huge, horrific mess that is his life. He's going to stop playing the husband, the father, the son and find himself. A sad play about love, parenthood and responsibility.
ISBN 978 1 849 43129 3

Bonnie & Clyde. Play. Adam Peck
M1 F1 (20s-30s). Simple, single-location setting. Fee code L

A two-hander based on the legend of the infamous outlaw couple, set during the Great Depression of the 1930s in an unnamed southern state of the United States of America. The action unfolds in one self-contained scene in a disused barn, as the pair spend their final hours together on the run from the law. The pair's dialogue touches on a number of morbid, adult themes in particular criminality, poverty and destructive romantic entanglement.
ISBN 978 1 849 43123 1

Break Away. Play. Dameon Garnett
M2 (15, 45) F3 (17 x2, 40). Various simple settings. Fee code L

Leaving behind her home in Speke, teenager Barbie Jean heads off to the sun, sea and sand of Torquay, accompanied by her best friend Stella and fun-loving, larger than life Auntie Pauline. Each wants something different from their holiday break, though boys figure high on the agenda! However, matters are complicated by an unexpected arrival. Suddenly not only Barbie Jean's future, but her whole identity, is in question.
ISBN 978 1 840 02549 1

Breathing In. Play. Reza de Wet
M2 (20s, 40s) F2 (20s, 40s). A cowshed. Fee code L

On a stormy night in the last bitter months of the Second Anglo-Boer War, a seriously wounded General and his faithful Adjutant encounter a mysterious woman and her seductive other-worldly daughter, and are confronted with the subtle methods of survival these women have been forced to adopt. In a volume of three plays with *African Gothic* and *Good Heavens*.
ISBN 978 1 840 02480 7

Bright. Play. Polly Wiseman
M3 (25, 2 x 20s-30s) F2 (20, 40). Psychiatric ward of a London hospital. Fee code L

Clair is bright – too bright. Crackling with energy, she's suddenly lost her flat and boyfriend and been sectioned to a psychiatric ward. As she is assessed by hospital staff she tries to work out whether to comply with the system or defy it. She finally discharges herself and throws away her medication. Available in a volume of two plays with *Playing Fields* (Dolezalova).
ISBN 978 1 8400 2349 7

The Broken Pitcher. Play. Heinrich von Kleist, translated by Noel Clark
M6 F5. Courtroom. Fee code L

In this comedy a visiting judge comes to inspect a small village and finds it rife with corruption. A satire on those who seek and dispense justice. Set in a Dutch village in the early 19th-century. Available in a volume of three plays with *Prince Friedrich von Homburg* and *Ordeal by Fire*.
ISBN 978 1 840 02123 3

The Brothers. Play. Reza de Wet
M2 (29, 34) F1 (33). Squalid country cottage in the Ukraine. Fee code L

During a night-long vigil preceding the funeral of their brother Kostia, Anton and Aleksander Chekhov are drawn into an agonising and explosive confrontation with each other and with deeply hidden aspects of themselves.
ISBN 978 1 840 02235 3

Brothers Karamazov. Play. Richard Crane
M4.Simple settings. Fee code M

An adaptation of Dostoyevsky's novel, condensed and reduced to a cast of four. A box-office hit at the Edinburgh Festival in 1981. "a gripping,intelligent,…two-hour chamber-work that seizes on the family drama as a microcosm of the turmoil in Russian society…" *Guardian*. In *Russian Plays* with *Vanity*, *Gogol* and *Satan's Ball*.
ISBN 978 1 849 43092 0

Celaine. Play. Matt Parker
M3 (teen, 2 x 50s) F3-4 (20s, 3 x 50s). House. Riverside. Fee code L

A family's 22 year-old daughter (Celaine) has refused to come out of her bedroom for twelve years, communicating to her parents with notes and spilled slop buckets. Meanwhile her younger brother Craig is exhibiting worryingly similar symptoms of withdrawal himself. The cycle of co-dependency and fraught optimism becomes searingly disturbing when Celaine suddenly begins to speak from behind the door.
ISBN 978 1 840 02111 0

Chaos. Play. Azma Dar
M3 F2. Simple settings. Fee code L

Mr Rizvi's ambitions to become a local councillor are thrown into turmoil as his family reveals shocking secrets and world events spiral out of control. *Chaos* is a dark, frantic comedy about the collapse of understanding on a personal and political level and the disastrous consequences which follow. Available in a volume of two plays with *Bells* by Yasmin Khan.
ISBN 978 1 840 02554 5

O
B

The Colour of Justice. Play. Richard Norton-Taylor
M21 F8 (Various ages). Interior, courtroom setting. Fee code L

Based on harrowing verbatim transcripts, this is a dramatic reconstruction of the Stephen Lawrence Inquiry, which exposed the Metropolitan Police's mishandling of the original murder investigation. The play has a large number of cast members, but many of the spoken parts are brief and well within the reach of amateur or even first-time actors. The playscript includes a comprehensive chronology of events and editors' notes.
ISBN 978 1 840 02107 3

Concealment. Play. Reza de Wet
M1 (50) F2 (20s-30s). A steamship, an African house, a garden. Fee code L

In the early 1900s Amy and her repressive father Dr Frost travel to South Africa to retrieve Amy's recently widowed sister. They are disturbed to find her untouched by grief, unwilling to return and drawn instead to the wild, natural beauty of her moonlit garden. Convinced May is now mad Dr Frost sedates her so he can force her home. Available in a volume of two plays with *Fever*.
ISBN 978 1 840 02492 0

Conspirators. Play. Mérimée, translated by Paul Vaughan
M9 F2 (Mostly 30s and upwards). Simple period setting (dining room). Fee code L

Based on a short story by Prosper Mérimée, this is an elaborate drawing-room comedy about a bungled plot to overthrow the French government, with a farcical denouement. Satirises the incompetence of the Napoleonic aristocracy and lampoons contemporary conservative values.
ISBN 978 1 899 79110 1

Deadeye. Play. Amber Lone
M3 (2 x 20s, 50s) F3 (2 x 20s, 50s). Fee code L

Deema is a good daughter and a loving sister. It's her family that's the problem. In their back garden in Birmingham, her mum Zainab is nurturing plants from Kashmir and her dad Rafique is day-dreaming of million-pound homes in the Cotswolds. Meanwhile, out on the streets, her mixed up brother Tariq is involved with drugs. She's doing her best to hold it all together, but it's time for her to move out and leave them to it.
ISBN 978 1 840 02707 5

The Devil Inside Him. Play. John Osborne
M5 (40s,18, 50s x 2, 20) F3 (50s x 2, 20). Living room in a cottage. Fee code M

In a 1950s Welsh boarding house, the strait-laced Prossers, have a teenage son Huw, who is deemed soft in the head. He is bullied by his father and, when his erotic poems are discovered, he is subjected to sermons by the local preacher. But when left alone with the pretty, teasing servant girl his reaction is to murder her… An early play by Osborne available in the volume *Before Anger* with *Personal Enemy*.
ISBN 978 1 8400 2903 1

The Drums of Snow. Play. David Pinner
M17+ F3. Simple settings. Fee code L

Set in the 17th-century, *The Drums of Snow* focuses on the power struggle between Charles I and Oliver Cromwell, with John Lilburne, the Leveller, and the English people as their unwilling victims. The vicissitudes of the Civil War culminate in the royal despot's death and a Puritan dictatorship that changes the course of English history. Available in *Three Power Plays* with *Richelieu* and *Prince of Traitors*.
ISBN 978 1 840 02597 2

Familyman. Play. Rikki Beadle-Blair
M3 F4 (3 x teens, 2 x 30s, 2 older). Various simple settings. Fee code L

Caesar Ramsay works hard for his family. But the news his seventeen-year-old son Nelson reveals – that his girlfriend is pregnant – sends Caesar's seemingly ordinary life rapidly spinning out of his control! Fresh, insightful and delivered with razor-sharp wit, *Familyman* confirms what many of us know only too well – parenting is messy!
ISBN 978 1 840 02858 4

Fanghorn. Play. David Pinner
M2 (40s, 70s) F3 (16, 25, 30s). A study (varying times of day). Fee code L

Fanghorn is a lesbian vampire, who invades the household of Joseph King, who may, or may not, be the First Secretary to the Minister of Defence, and hilarious emasculation and murderous mayhem follow in her wake. A darkly-surrealistic comedy, which pokes fun at the Theatre of Cruelty. Available in *The Vampire Trilogy* with *Edred, The Vampyre* and *Lucifer's Fair*.
ISBN 978 1 849 43088 3

Fit. Play. Rikki Beadle-Blair
M5 F2 (teens). Various simple settings. Fee code L

A bold and groundbreaking play for young people, developed to address the growing problem of homophobic bullying in Britain's schools. *Fit* is about attempting to "fit" into a culture where everything from not liking sport to wearing the wrong trainers is "gay". Snappy dialogue combines with hip-hop dance and sparky comedy to make *Fit* an unforgettable piece of theatre. The text also includes a screenplay version of the play and teachers' notes.
ISBN 978 1 849 43080 7

The Forever Waltz. Play. Glyn Maxwell
M2 (20s-50s) F (20s). Simple setting. Fee code M

A man arrives in the underworld searching for his love, only to find a mysterious guitar-wielding guide who may or may not be able to help him. He begins to mistake the underworld for the real world, and is caught there until he wakes up to the reality of his choices and breaks a cycle of violence.
ISBN 978 1 840 02591 0

O
B

Franziska. Play. Frank Wedekind, adapted by Eleanor Brown
M5+ F4+. Various settings including palace, wood, theatre dressing-room. Fee code L

Franziska, a 'female Faust', is consumed by a deep thirst for self-knowledge. She makes a pact with a 'Mephistolean' impresario, who grants her two years of pleasure and a brilliantly successful musical career as long as she becomes a wife and vassal. But in a remarkable twist, Wedekind's heroine is not destined for tragedy or eternal damnation.
ISBN 978 1 840 02082 3

The Free State. Play. Janet Suzman
M9 F4 (2 x Teens, 4 x 20s, 2 x 50s, 3 x 60s, 80s, 1 x any age). Both interior and exterior settings on a rural African estate – nursery room, farmland, large kitchen, porch. Fee code L

This adaptation relocates Chekhov's *The Cherry Orchard* to post-apartheid South Africa. It is set in the Clocolan area of the Free State in September 1994, six months after the first multi-racial democratic elections. This is a heavyweight political play that examines race relations, political recrimination, and economic disenfranchisement in one of the most sharply divided societies in the world. "It is difficult to imagine a relocation which works as comprehensively as this." *Financial Times*.
ISBN 978 1 849 43133 0

Gilgamesh. Play. Derrek Hines
M8 F3. May be played by M4 F1."Eternity", "Almost Heaven", Desert, Trenches. Fee code L

Gilgamesh is one of the most powerful men in Iraq. A king, a demi-God and a fearsome tyrant, he thrives on the shame and suffering of his subjects. But when the Gods turn against him, an almighty battle of will ensues, and a defiant Gilgamesh is forced to learn love, friendship, empathy and, in the end, mortality. "Derrek Hines does [for Gilgamesh] what *West Side Story* did for Romeo and Juliet." *The Times*.
ISBN 978 1 840 02654 2

Gogol. Play. Richard Crane
M1. Simple settings. Fee code M

In this short one-man play inspired by Nabokov's *Nikolai Gogol*, Gogol has become the Final Demands Clerk in the London Electricity Board. "... depicts the plight of bureaucratic man and a vision of a world that is horrifyingly random..." *Scotsman*. In *Russian Plays* with B*rothers Karamazov*, *Vanity*, and *Satan's Ball*.
ISBN 978 1 849 43092 0

O B

Guantanamo: Honor Bound to Defend Freedom. Play. Victoria Brittain and Gillian Slovo
M13 F1 (May be played by M9 F1). Simple settings. Fee code L
Weaving together personal stories, legal opinion and political debate, *Guantanamo* looks at the questions surrounding the detentions in Guantanamo Bay, and asks how much damage is being done to Western democratic values during the "war on terror". First produced at the Tricycle Theatre in 2004. "The British Theatre, indeed every Briton should be proud of this play." *Sunday Times*.
ISBN 978 1 840 02474 6

Guilty Secret. Play. Roger Mortimer-Smith
M3 (20s, 2 x 40s) F1 (20s). Isolated farmhouse. Fee code L

A four-character thriller. Two East-End chancers, George and Lennie, have kidnapped
wealthy heiress Charlotte Chamberlain and taken her to a remote farmhouse. George is
confident her father will pay five million to get her back safely. But why did he insist
on renting the farmhouse in Lennie's name? Or is the kidnap only a feint to disguise an
infinitely more devious scheme? And who is really pulling the strings?
ISBN 978 1 849 43202 3

High Life. Play. Lizzy Dijeh
M5 F2. Simple interior settings. Fee code L

When two families living in East London reunite after a family tragedy their union exposes
a wealth of secret motives, jealousy, insecurities and some very different reflections on a
young girl's short life. A mother's loss turns into obsession, a father's ambition turns into
contradiction and a child's innocence is forever lost. *High Life* is an explosive domestic
drama set within East London's Nigerian community.
ISBN 978 1 840 02905 5

House of Desires. Play. Sor Juana Ines de la Cruz, translated by Catherine Boyle
M6 F3. Simple setting. Fee code L

Don Pedro loves Dona Leonor who loves Don Carlos, who is desired by Dona Ana but
betrothed to Don Juan…This 17th-century romantic farce is a wild tale of confusion and
mistaken identities complete with wily servants and groping suitors. *House of Desires*
examines the idea of free will for women at a time when a woman's role was subject to a
strict moral code. Written by one of the few female playwrights of the age, a poet, nun and
major baroque literary figure of Mexico.
ISBN 978 1 840 02444 9

Justifying War. Play. Richard Norton-Taylor
M12 F2 (Various ages). Interior, courtroom setting. Fee code L

A verbatim play based on transcripts from the Hutton Inquiry, examining the controversial
circumstances surrounding the suicide of Dr David Kelly, one of the government's chief
advisors on chemical and biological weapons. Also focuses on the workings of the MoD and
strength the Government's case for war in Iraq based on the existence of 'weapons of mass
destruction'. A topical piece of documentary theatre, that can be staged very simply. This
play has a large number of cast members, but many of the spoken parts are brief and well
within the reach of amateur or even first-time actors.
ISBN 978 1 840 02417 3

O
B

The Kindness of Strangers. Play. Tony Green
M9 (3 x 30s, 3 x 20s, 40s, 2 x 50s) F3 (20s). Various settings including domestic interiors,
market, pub. Fee code L

A set of interweaving stories bringing together different characters in Liverpool: a group
of Iranian refugees, a prostitute with three children, students and a scheming landlord.
Hope blurs with survival, love with commerce, and sometimes kindness can be found in the
strangest of places.
ISBN 978 1 840 02496 8

Knock Down Ginger. Play. Mark Norfolk
M4 (teenage, 30s, 60s) F1 (30s). Various simple settings. Fee code L

Luke is 15 and looking for respect. Growing up on a council estate isn't easy, especially when your mother's got a new man in her life. In a place where fast cars and fast money are the ultimate status, Luke befriends Nelson who wants to teach him that fear breeds respect. Charlie, an old friend of the family, tries to persuade Luke to give up and play straight.
ISBN 978 1 840 02379 4

Lady Day. Play. David Pinner
M3 (2 x 40s, 20) F3 (2 x 40s, 19). A wood in the home counties. Fee code L

When Katya discovers her husband is having an affair with her best friend she hibernates to a derelict lake-side cottage, to reinvent her life in the depths of winter. But being a hermit proves difficult as she's pursued by her husband, her friend's husband and her daughter's boyfriend, all desperate to win her hand. Comic mayhem ensues as the men duel to the death for the illusive Lady. Available in a volume of two plays with *Revelations*.
ISBN 978 1 840 02385 5

Lenin in Love. Play. David Pinner
M3 (30s) F3 (17, 2 x30s). Set in various sparsely furnished houses. Fee code L

Set in various European cities in the early 20th Century, this comedy focusing on Lenin's complex and often stormy relationship with his wife Krupskaya, his French mistress Inessa Armand, and their complex troika. Lenin is portrayed as a frenzied character: romantic and often cruel. Available as a single play, and in *The Stalin Trilogy* with *The Teddy Bears' Picnic* and *The Potsdam Quartet*.
ISBN 978 1 840 02202 5

Liberty. Play. Glyn Maxwell
M14 F3 (may be played by M5 F3). Simple settings. Fee code M

April 1793, the French Revolution is four years old and the Committee of Public Safety under Robespierre finds threats to national liberty at home and abroad. When Gamelin, an ambitious and idealistic young magistrate, is given power over life and death, how long will ties of love and affection last? How long until a new republic plunges from high idealism to mob rule and state terror?
ISBN 978 1 840 02869 0

The Lifeblood. Play. Glyn Maxwell
M7 F1 (may be played by M4 F1). Simple setting. Fee code M

Set in 1587-88 *The Lifeblood* depicts the last days of Mary Queen of Scots, as four men weave about her a web of love and hatred. Available in *Glyn Maxwell Plays One* with *Wolfpit* and *The Only Girl in the World*.
ISBN 978 1 840 02590 3

The Lower Depths. Play. Maxim Gorky, adapted by Phil Willmott
M8 F4. A doss house. Fee code L

Set amongst the whores, alcoholics, cynics and doss house dreamers of a Russia on the brink of revolution, *The Lower Depths* is a harrowing, violent and uncompromising portrayal of the human spirit at its lowest ebb, with destitution and death an ever-present spectre. With no easy answers, neat plot twists or satisfying resolution, this depiction of an underclass without hope shocked audiences at its infamous Moscow, London and Berlin premieres.
ISBN 978 1 840 02894 2

Lucifer. Play. Joost van den Vondel, translated by Noel Clark
M8. Set in the heavens. Fee code L

Apollion the Angel returns from Eden, his wings singed by the sheer beauty of Adam and Eve's world, his spirit longing for the pleasures of their flesh. Jealousy and discontent among the angels lead to a rebellion led by Lucifer against the Creator. Banned when first performed in Holland in 1654. In rhyming verse.
ISBN 978 0 9482 3037 0

Lucifer's Fair. Play. David Pinner
M4 (11, 20s, 2 x 30+) F3 (11, 2 x40s). Entrance to a fair. Fee code L

Lucifer's Fair is the family Hallowe'en musical play, about a fair run by the Devil to entrap unwary children. Lucifer is aided by Fangs, who is a bovver boy by day, but an incompetent vampire by night. Simultaneously scary and funny, *Lucifer's Fair*, with its comic spills, thrills and chills, highlights the unreliability of grownups, both the living and the undead. Available in *The Vampire Trilogy* with *Fanghorn* and *Edred, the Vampyre*.
ISBN 978 1 849 43088 3

The Marriage of Figaro. Play. De Beaumarchais. Translated and adapted by Robert Cogo-Fawcett and Braham Murray
M11 F4. Various indoor and outdoor settings, including "sumptuously furnished bedroom." Fee code L

The servant Figaro is full of an irrepressible *joie de vivre*, and set to marry his beloved Suzanna. He determinedly outwits the cast of villains' mountebanks and rivals who seek to bring about his downfall. Set in 18th century France, Figaro's survival is a signal to the world that the common man has rights and that the world must change if he is to be allowed to enjoy them.
ISBN 978 1 840 02377 0

The Meaning of Waiting. Play. Victoria Brittain
M1 F1 (20s/30s). Various simple settings, Screen (for CCTV footage). Fee code L

Eight women tell their stories of the unseen fallout of the war on terror in Britain. These are stories of real women, from varied cultures who came to the UK as refugees, or married refugees here. After 9/11 the world they loved here vanished almost overnight and they were engulfed by isolation and private terror. A powerful work of verbatim theatre.
ISBN 978 1 849 43051 7

O
B

Meeting Myself Coming Back. Play. Kerry Hood
M1 (43) F3 (21,33,10). Various simple settings. Fee code L

It is Catherine's twenty-first birthday. She has not spoken for eight years, but when she revisits her childhood home, the hoarded words of those eight years come tumbling out, revealing a shocking story of child abuse and murder. A tragic and funny play about isolation, identity and the search for a language of survival.
ISBN 978 1 840 02335 0

Midsummer. Play. David Pinner
M5 (20s, 3 x 40s, 60s) F3 (19, 20s 40s). Various outdoor settings (grass, woods). Fee code L

In this modern homage to *A Midsummer Night's Dream*, two pairs of lovers believe they can transform themselves, with the help of two mysterious strangers. But the Midsummer Night transformations affect others too, and the last Stalinist trades-unionist in England is turned into more than just an ass. When night falls in the wood it is nature which proves the greatest enchanter of all. Available in a volume of two plays with *All Hallows' Eve*.
ISBN 978 1 840 02336 7

Mimi and the Stalker. Play. Glyn Maxwell
M2 (30s) F1 (30s). Simple settings. Fee code M

Snatched from obscurity and thrust into the spotlight, schoolgirl Michelle Latchford was transformed into Hollywood's hottest property: Mimi Luck. Now the reclusive Mimi is barricaded in her rural hideaway as a paparazzo lurks outside, scrutinised by her watchful agent, and haunted by the memory of the boy all the other kids called God.
ISBN 978 1 840 02884 3

Miracle. Play. Reza de Wet
M3 (65, 28, 40) F3 (60, 20s, 50). An abandoned church. Fee code L

Set in 1936 during the Great Depression. When a run-down troupe of actors decide to stage *Everyman* in an old church, they are themselves drawn into their own moral dilemma. Available in a volume of three plays by Reza de Wet.
ISBN 978 1 840 02145 5

The Mirror for Princes – Kalila wa Dimna. Play. Sulayman Al Bassam
M14 F1. Various settings including a house, a "palace fever", a road. Fee code L

The Kalila wa Dimna, one of the masterpieces of Eastern culture, is a collection of subtle and philosophical animal fables which carry immense significance to Arab and Persian society. This drama explores the creation of the fables in Iraq circa 750AD amidst the tragedy that unfolds around the author, Al-Muqaffa, as he battles for reform in the midst of fervent revolutionaries, heretic poets, religious propagandists, and a despotic ruler.
ISBN 978 1 840 02670 2

O
B

Musik. Play. Frank Wedekind translated and adapted by Neil Fleming
M4 (40s, 30s) F4 (19, 40s). May be played by M3 F3. An apartment with piano, a prison, an attic. Fee code L

Klara lives with her singing teacher, Josef Reissner, and his wife, but the relationship between Reissner and Klara is uncovered when she seeks the help of an abortionist. Klara then suffers arrest, the death of her baby and madness, while Reissner emerges with his reputation intact. Set in Munich in 1906.
ISBN 978 1 840 02550 7

Naked Soldiers. Play. Mark Norfolk
M3 (15, 17, 50s) F1 (30s). Burnt-out attic room. Fee code L

There's been a near fatal stabbing in a local park. Seventeen-year-old Tony has been accused of what has been called a racially motivated crime and goes on the run. But he has chosen to hide out in a place where Jamal, an African refugee is also hiding. The two fugitives must each set aside their preconceived prejudices as they discover things about themselves as human beings.
ISBN 978 1 849 43019 7

Nathan the Wise. Play. Gotthold Lessing, translated by Noel Clark
M7 F3, doubling-up possible. Various simple settings. Fee code L

In the Holy Land at the time of the Third Crusade (1192) Jews, Moslems and Christians are struggling to live alongside one another. Nathan tries to mediate using as central to his philosophy the Parable of the Ring, teaching that all religions should respect and tolerate one another. Available in *Two Jewish Plays* with *The Jews*.
ISBN 978 1 840 02208 7

Not in My Name. Play. Alice Bartlett
M11 (teens, 20s,30s) F6 (teens, 20s,30s). May be played by M4 F4. Various simple settings. Fee code L

A play using verbatim interviews to realistically portray the aftermath of a fictional terror attack from the perspective of over thirty young characters. Suitable for performance by young people or adults, this is a bold and challenging play. With comprehensive Teachers' Notes to aid adults working with young people. "a powerful resource for schools and community groups in the years to come" Lancashire Constabulary.
ISBN 978 1 840 02949 9

Oh to be in England. Play. David Pinner
M3 (18, 30s, 40s) F2 (29, 40). A comfortable lounge/dining room. Fee code L

A middle-aged Englishman, bred to believe in his innate superiority as a birthright of class, race, and gender, loses his job in the City. Left floundering impotently in a world that is no longer cricket, his family, security, and sanity follow close behind. Written in 1973, premiered at the Finborough Theatre in 2011.
ISBN 978 1 849 43056 2

O
B

Oikos. Play. Simon Wu
M1 F2 with doubling (2 x 40s, 1 x teen). Potentially complex staging, involving a flooding stage and various media projections. Fee code L

A high-flying, Indian-born financier returns late one night to his riverside home in London to find his life in chaos. His wife accuses him of having an affair and his teenage daughter has gone missing. A storm raging outside turns into a deluge and their family home begins to flood. Has a strong environmental message but the deepening crisis also serves as a forum for the domestic recriminations of the three main protagonists. Some challenging staging requirements, in particular simulating floodwater. The original production of the play also featured film footage and other multimedia elements.
ISBN 978 1 849 43005 0

The Only Girl in the World. Play. Glyn Maxwell
M1(30) F1 (23) (and possibly a musician). Various simple settings. Fee code M

Mary Kelly was the last victim of Jack the Ripper. This play, set in Whitechapel in 1888, imagines Mary finding love with Joe, a foreman at Billingsgate fish market. Available in *Glyn Maxwell Plays One* with *The Lifeblood* and *Wolfpit*.
ISBN 978 1 840 02590 3

Ordeal by Fire. Play. Heinrich von Kleist, translated by Noel Clark
M19 F8. Various settings, including an underground cavern and a forest. Fee code L

An enigmatic play set in the Middle Ages. The Count von Strahl feels passionately for the local blacksmith's daughter, Katie. However, the class division between them means he will never act on his feelings – until a journey and a discovery about Katie's true origins brings them together. Available in a volume of three plays with *Prince Friedrich von Homburg* and *The Broken Pitcher*.
ISBN 978 1 840 02123 3

Personal Enemy. Play. John Osborne
M6 F3. Family home. Fee code M

Set in the early 1950s in Langley Springs, USA, the play follows Mrs Constant, a mother and a pillar of the community. Her allegiance to her Country and her God is tested by her loyalty to her sons when they are both accused of being 'communists' and 'homosexuals', and put themselves in mortal danger for their beliefs. An early play by Osborne available in the volume *Before Anger* with *The Devil Inside Him*.
ISBN 978 1 840 02903 1

The Phoenix of Madrid. Play. Pedro Calderon de la Barca, translated by Laurence Boswell
M6 F3 (Mostly 40s-50s, 3 x 20s). Simple settings, both interior and exterior. Fee code L

A three-act comedy from the Spanish Golden Age. Plot centres on Don Pedro, a wealthy courtier, who must marry off his three headstrong young daughters, who are already romantically involved with a variety of extravagant suitors. The play has a fairly complex plot but each actor has frequent asides to the audience to explain their motivations and intentions. Poetic language with many long, lyrical passages. Has a light, satirical edge that pokes fun at the pomposity and neuroses of 17th-century aristocracy, but remains at its heart a gentle romantic comedy with a happy resolution.
ISBN 978 1 849 43134 7

Playing Fields. Play. Neela Dolezalova
M3 (16,17,18) F2 (16,18). Simple settings. Uses film and video material. Fee code L

Follows the lives of a group of teenagers as they transition to adulthood. Thyme is in a
lesbian relationship with Flea, who is busy campaigning to save the local playing fields.
Kieran is a nervy teenager, festering in a world of fish 'n' chips. Pete is filming everybody's
lives, and Justin has a lot to learn. When Thyme falls pregnant their dreamy adolescent
world is destabilised. Available in a volume of two plays with *Bright* by Polly Wiseman.
ISBN 978 1 840 02349 X

The Potsdam Quartet. Play. David Pinner
M5. (20s, 4 x 40s). A conference room. Fee code L

1945. At the Potsdam Conference the "big four" of Stalin, Truman, Churchill and Atlee are
"dividing up the world" offstage. Onstage are the four embittered musicians who are there
to provide the background music to the conference. The play explores the personal and
professional conflicts of a string quartet who have been playing together for many years, but
are on the point of disintegrating. Available in *The Stalin Trilogy* with *Lenin in Love* and *The
Teddy Bear's Picnic*.
ISBN 978 1 840 02446 3

Prince Friedrich von Homburg. Play. Heinrich von Kleist, translated by Noel Clark
M13 F2. Various indoor and outdoor settings. Fee code L

Set in the world of 17th-century Prussian militarism. The young cavalry general of the title
achieves swift victory in the field, only to be sentenced to death for rash disobedience.
Available in a volume of three plays with *The Broken Pitcher* and *Ordeal by Fire*.
ISBN 978 1 840 02123 3

Prince of Traitors. Play. David Pinner
M5 F1. "Set consists mainly of coat stands and tailor's dummies". Fee code L

An epic play set in 17th-century France for six actors, most of whom play several roles.
It is a sardonic comedy about the achievements of a witty, club-footed Anglophile Bishop
who manages to outlive Robespierre. After becoming Napoleon's First Minister, Talleyrand
helps bring about the Emperor's downfall, claiming that 'treachery is noble when its target is
tyranny'. Available in *Three Power Plays* with *Drums of Snow* and *Richelieu*.
ISBN 978 1 840 02597 2

Revelations. Play. David Pinner
M5 F3 (30s+). Graveyard, beach. Fee code L

O
B

A miraculous stranger comes to the aid of a desolate cliff-top village that is ravaged by
devastating storms and erosion. The villagers soon proclaim him the new Messiah, even
though the stranger protests that he is an atheist. He enjoys his power without accepting
responsibility for his actions, until he meets his spiritual nemesis in the storm of the century.
Available in a volume of two plays with *Lady Day*.
ISBN 978 1 840 02385 5

Richelieu. Play. David Pinner
M14+ F3. Bare stage, mirrors, smoke. Fee code L

Set in 17th-century France, explores the rise of the tormented Catholic Cardinal, Richelieu, who elevates Louis XIII to god-like status in order to pacify war-torn France. Richelieu sacrifices himself to a secure but repressive royal kingdom and unwittingly sows the seeds of the French Revolution. Available in *Three Power Plays* with *Drums of Snow* and *Prince of Traitors*.
ISBN 978 1 840 02597 2

Rose Rage. Play. Edward Hall & Roger Warren
11+. Parliament, various palaces and castles. Fee code L

A startling adaptation of Shakespeare's Henry VI trilogy, premiered at the Watermill Theatre, Newbury in 2001. It tells the exciting collapse of Henry V's empire and the chaos of the Wars of the Roses, from which arises the anarchic figure of the future Richard III.
ISBN 978 1 840 02213 1

Satan's Ball. Play. Richard Crane
15 (M/F variable). "The Tower of State". Fee code M

A stage adaptation of Bulgakov's novel *The Master and Margarita*, staged spectacularly at the Edinburgh Festival Fringe in 1977. "…an extraordinary assimilation of styles and influences: expressionism, morality, fairy tale, bureaucratic satire, political nightmare…" *Guardian*. In *Russian Plays* with *Brothers Karamazov*, *Vanity*, and *Gogol*.
ISBN 978 1 849 43092 0

Shadow Language. Play. Kelly Stuart
M4 F4 with doubling (Various ages). Various interior and moving exterior settings, such as cafés, hotels, buses and trains. Fee code L

A play set in Turkey, which follows an American woman in her search for a missing Kurdish man. Playfully satirises the cultural differences between America and Turkey. Includes shadow puppetry based on the Ottoman tradition, with puppets pressed up against a screen. A degree of improvisation is encouraged in the puppet show, and each actor has a puppet double.
ISBN 978 1 840 02842 3

Shalom Baby. Play. Rikki Beadle-Blair
M5 F2. Various interior and exterior settings. Basketball court, Concentration camp. Fee code L

In 1930s Berlin the daughter of a Jewish family falls in love with their black shabbes goy. Fast-forward to the tale of a mixed-race couple in seemingly unprejudiced modern-day Brooklyn, where the same family is coping with a number of calamities. A touching and funny exploration of love, family and friendship.
"Wildly ambitious and entertaining ... I love the way the play is stroppy and soppy, bold and bashful all at the same time" *Guardian*
ISBN 978 1 849 43213 9

Soap. Play. Sarah Woods
M4 F4. Various settings including a pub and a beach. Fee code L

A comedy with two sets, making fun of the familiar world of soap operas. Just as it seemed that Aussie heart-throb Thorn's future is all mapped out, the unscripted arrival of attractive East End pub landlady Lorna sends him into a spin. As storylines begin to merge and unravel, the characters start questioning their roles.
ISBN 978 1 840 02510 1

Swankiller. Play. David Drane
20+ various ages. Rural and urban settings, including scene of an aeroplane crash; dirty alley. Fee code L

An impoverished family are evicted from their country smallholding. They agree to separate for five years, then to meet again to reassess their fortunes. Swankiller, the eldest son, tries his luck in the big city. Homeless, jobless, penniless and eventually alone, he discovers the brutal undertow beneath the city's beguiling surface. A genuinely epic play, it was performed with a cast of fifty at Snape Maltings, Aldeburgh in 1996.
ISBN 978 1 840 02100 4

Tactical Questioning: Scenes from the Baha Mousa Inquiry. Play. Richard Norton-Taylor
M11 (various ages). Interior, courtroom setting. Fee code L

A documentary play which reconstructs the public inquiry into the death in custody of Baha Mousa, an Iraqi man arrested and detained by the British Army in Basra. It uses edited transcripts of witness testimony to paint a picture of institutionalised brutality in the British Army. This play has a large number of cast members, but many of the spoken parts are brief and well within the reach of amateur or even first-time actors.
ISBN 978 1 849 43031 9

The Teddy Bears' Picnic. Play. David Pinner
M13 F2. Various rooms in Stalin's dacha. Fee code L

An ironic comedy which shows Stalin playing relaxed host and bon viveur in his country retreat in 1938. The smiling, malignant 'Uncle Joe' torments his Politburo with brash insults, crude practical jokes and the ever-lurking threat of being 'purged'. Act Two follows up in the same setting in the 1950s. Available in *The Stalin Trilogy* with *Lenin in Love* and *The Potsdam Quartet*.
ISBN 978 1 840 02446 3

Trips. Play. Sarah Woods
M3 F3. A lounge, a night club. Uses video footage on screens. Fee code L

An imaginative account of six Birmingham housemates on a night out, searching for love, excitement and one infallible business idea, encountering more than they ever thought possible. Premiered at The Door, Birmingham Rep in 1999.
ISBN 978 1 840 02110 3

O
B

The Triumph of Love. Play. Marivaux. Translated by Braham Murray and Katherine Sand
M4 F3. A garden. Fee code L

In the tightly-structured, erotically-charged fable a young princess, conscious that her claim
to the throne is less than honorable, disguises herself as a man in order to dupe her enemies
and persuade the rightful ruler to return. Available in a volume of two Marivaux plays with
The Game of Love and *Chance*.
ISBN 978 1 840 02746 4

Turcaret. Play. Alain-René Lesage, translated and adapted by John Norman
M7 F5. May be played by M5 F3. Simple settings. Fee code L

In this early 18th-century French comedy Turcaret is a scheming financier. In a society
corrupted by fraud, theft, extortion and sexual exploitation, he stands to make a fortune. A
society which sells off and farms out the power of taxation into private hands reaps its own
harvest… "a fascinating cynical comedy…Norman's adaptation is full of twentieth century
colloquialisms and … would probably work well in modern dress." *Daily Telegraph*.
ISBN 978 0 948 23018 9

Untitled. Play. Inua Ellams
M1. A forest, a city. Fee code L

Untitled is a magical realist story set in Nigeria and England, of identical twin boys
separated at infancy. In the quarrel after the marred naming ceremony, the mother grabs
the titled child and flees, leaving the unnamed brother to lead an impetuous, chaotic,
blasphemous existence until the spirits of the land make their stand.
ISBN 978 1 849 43117 0

Vanity. Play. Richard Crane
M2F1. Various settings including countryside, on horseback, at a ball. Fee code M

A response to Pushkin's *Eugene Onegin*, this verse play tells the story of Russian dandy,
Onegin. Dismissing the love of Tatyana, Onegin flirts with his friend's fiancée and then
kills him in a duel. He travels away in remorse, only to return some years later to feel a
strong attraction to Tatyana, who, now married, rebuffs him. In *Russian Plays* with *Brothers
Karamazov*, *Gogol* and *Satan's Ball*.
ISBN 978 1 849 43092 0

Visible. Play. Sarah Woods
M4 (30s-40s) F2 (30s-40s). A suburban house. Fee code L

In their mock Georgian house on an exclusive estate, Rob and Hattie are preparing Sunday
lunch for friends and neighbours – but all is not going to plan. Their seemingly cosy world
of comfort and safety is about to explode, when they find themselves with a dead cat, a
surreal game show and an Albanian refugee. "Sarah Woods's script is light as a sponge but
has the density to ensure this show is always more than it seems" *Guardian*.
ISBN 978 1 840 02665 8

O
B

Washboard Blues. Play. Do Shaw
M5 F13 (Mostly 30s-40s, 2 x teenage girls, 1 x teenage boy and 1 x schoolgirl). Simple, flexible interior settings. Fee code L

Set in the 1950s in a municipal washhouse and a local Working Men's Club. A group of friends meet and talk their way through the weekly laundry, but one of them still dreams of becoming a famous clubland singer. Ideal for community theatre groups, it has a large cast, music and dancing. Features songs of the period which can be performed by talented actors rather than trained singers. Thirteen speaking parts for women and five for men. There can be as many non-speaking but all-singing people in the washhouse as are willing to get involved.
ISBN 978 1 840 02636 8

We're Gonna Make You Whole. Play. Yasmine Van Wilt
M1 F3 (all 20s-30s). Simple settings. Fee code L

Based loosely on the testimonies of more than one hundred Gulf of Mexico residents, *We're Gonna Make You Whole* is a passionate magical-real political drama that follows the lives of five people brought together by environmental tragedy. Set in Louisiana, the play examines how the petrochemical industries have forever altered the lives and livelihoods of the people of the Gulf of Mexico.
ISBN 978 1 849 43131 6

The Wedding. Play. Wyspianski, translated by Noel Clark
M15 F12 (various ages). Living room of a country farm-house. Fee code L

Poland 1900. In the haunted atmosphere of a country manor, peasants, gentry and phantoms of the past mingle uneasily at the wedding of a city-bred poet and a country girl. As night falls and the guests grow drowsy from drink and dancing, the Strawman is invited in…
ISBN 978 1 840 02041 0

Where the Flowers Grow. Play. Mark Norfolk
M2 (40s, teenager) F1 (40s). Suburban home. Fee code L

Vernon has fulfilled his ambitions: he has a good job and a suburban lifestyle with his wife and teenage son. But things change when austerity measures put his job under threat and soon Vernon begins to neglect his family whilst fighting redundancy. When a tragedy at work forces him to look closer to home, he discovers that communicating with loved ones in a postmodern technological age is not as easy as he thinks.
ISBN 978 1 849 43046 3

Wittgenstein's Daughter. Play. Dic Edwards
F1 (40s) M3 (20s, 50s, ancient). Hotel room, bedroom, a graveyard. Fee code L

Alma Wittgenstein, bored by her neo-fascist husband, goes to Cambridge to investigate the values of her long-lost father, Ludwig. There she meets an old friend of her Father's, the 100-year-old ex-boxer Beckett and a strange bandaged man claiming to be his ex-student. Her enquiries lead to the uncovering of a conspiracy at the heart of Western philosophy and the consequent disinterment of her Father's bones.
ISBN 978 1 870 25935 4

O
B

Wolfpit. Play. Glyn Maxwell
M7 F3. Simple settings. Fee code M

A play set in the 13th-century based on the story of two children who appeared in a Suffolk village in strange clothes, unable to speak English. Available in *Glyn Maxwell Plays One* with *The Lifeblood* and *The Only Girl in the World*.
ISBN 978 1 840 02590 3

O
B

One Act

Best Man Speech. Play. Glyn Maxwell
M1 (30s). Simple setting. Fee code E

Bailey takes revenge on the bridegroom in a long and revelatory best man speech. First performed at the Edinburgh Festival in 2004. Available in *Glyn Maxwell Plays Two* with *Broken Journey* and *The Last Valentine*.
ISBN 978 1 840 02615 3

Broken Journey. Play. Glyn Maxwell
M3 (15, 2 x 20s) F2 (20s, 40+). Roadside, police station. Fee code E

A car breaks down in a quiet place in the small hours. Soon a man is dead, a woman traumatised, another man accused. But who really knows what happened? An adaptation of the short story *In a Grove* by Ryunosuke Akutagawa. Available in *Glyn Maxwell Plays Two* with *Best Man Speech* and *The Last Valentine*.
ISBN 978 1 840 02615 3

Cake. Play. Sarah Woods
M1 F1 (and animators). A kitchen counter. Fee code E

A surreal comedy exploring the extraordinary upside and the dark downside of motherhood, using performance and animated kitchen utensils. Today Mum is going to make a cake, but in this world Mum only has vague memories of who she was before motherhood, nothing gets completed and even the interruptions are interrupted. A tiny moment contains the most intense love she's ever felt, as well as the most intense frustration. Available in a volume of two plays with *Grace*.
ISBN 978 1 840 02425 8

Casanova Undone. Play. Dic Edwards
M1 F2. Bedroom with four-poster bed. Fee code E

At the Height of the Terror, we find the legendary Casanova scheming in his room in revolutionary France. Premiered at The Citizens Theatre, Glasgow in 1992. Contains sexually explicit scenes and language. Available in *Three Plays by Dic Edwards* with *Looking for the World* and *Long to Rain Over Us*.
ISBN 978 1 870 25929 3

Chère Maître. Play. Peter Eyre
M1 (40s) F1 (60s). Simple settings. Fee code E

A dramatization of the letters between George Sand and Gustave Flaubert. After George Sand's spirited defence of Flaubert's novel *Salammbô* in 1863, the two writers became friends. Both were excited by the attentions of the other, despite their difference in age, and their affection developed into eager and frequent correspondence.
ISBN 978 1 840 02305 3

O
B

The Demon Box. Play. Steve Hennessy
M3 (40s) F1 (20s). Various simple interior settings. Fee code E

A play about Richard Dadd, an artist who murdered his father after suffering a mental breakdown, and spent the rest of his life at Broadmoor. Part of *Lullabies of Broadmoor, A Broadmoor Quartet*. (see *The Demon Box*; *The Murder Club*; *Wilderness*)
ISBN 978 1 849 43162 0

Edred, the Vampyre. Play. David Pinner
M2 (18, 30+) F1 (18). A church. Fee code E

Edred is a thousand-year-old Anglo-Saxon bisexual vampire, who slept with Shakespeare, but never bit him. Breaking all Bram Stoker's vampire laws, Edred loves garlic and crucifixes, so he lives in the village church where he is confronted by two students who Googled him. But soon the students wish they hadn't. Available in *The Vampire Trilogy* with *Fanghorn* and *Lucifer's Fair*.
ISBN 978 1 849 43088 3

Fever. Play. Reza de Wet
F2 (29, 30). Simple settings (split stage) Fee code E

Follows the correspondence between Emma, who has gone to teach English in South Africa, and her sister Katy back in England. When Emma dies Katy discovers her hidden diary and learns the full and terrible extent of Katie's yearning and isolation. Set in the early 19th-century. Available in a volume of two plays with *Concealment*.
ISBN 978 1 840 02492 0

Franco's Bastard. Play. Dic Edwards
M2 (40s, 20s) F2 (20s). A fishmonger's yard, a home. Fee code E

A play exploring nationalism and terrorism, set in small country on the fringe of Europe.
ISBN 978 1 840 02306 0

Good Heavens. Play. Reza de Wet
M1 (30) F4 (60s, 38, 36, 20s). Simple settings. Fee code E

Set in South Africa sometime in the first half of the 20th Century. In this dark comic thriller two spinster sisters, with their ailing mother and simple-minded brother, await the annual visit of their youngest sister. Deeply envious of her beauty and youth, they hatch a diabolical plot to rid themselves of her forever. In a volume of three plays with *African Gothic* and *Breathing In*.
ISBN 978 1 840 02480 7

Grace. Play. Sarah Woods
M2 F1. Various domestic settings. Fee code E

Bombarded by choices and pressures and plagued by the ticking of her biological clock, Grace is about to turn thirty. She can have it all – if she can only remember what she wants. A fast-moving comedy for one woman and two men in cupboards, written before Bridget Jones hit the scene. Available in a volume of two plays with *Cake*.
ISBN 978 1 840 02425 8

I Heart Maths. Play. James Ley
M3 F1 with doubling (20s, 30s or 40s). Disco, karaoke bars. Fee code E

A short one-act play for 2-4 actors with potential for doubling one of the parts. A gay biomathematics lecturer attempts to devise a testable genetic model for homosexuality. A high-energy romantic comedy based around a love triangle in Manchester's hedonistic gay quarter. Includes karaoke sing-alongs. Available as part of a collection entitled *The Ego Plays*, along with *Spain* and *Up*.
ISBN 978 1 849 43230 6

The Jews. One-act Play. Gotthold Lessing, translated by Noel Clark
M5 F2. The Baron's Estate in Prussia. Fee code E

A short exuberant play satirizing anti-semitism in mid 18th-century Prussia.
Available in *Two Jewish Plays* with *Nathan The Wise*.
ISBN 978 1 840 02208 7

The Last Valentine. Play. Glyn Maxwell
M4 F3 (teens). Simple settings. Fee code E

A cruel trick goes seriously wrong for a gang of schoolfriends when they send a Valentine to a mysterious new boy. Available in *Glyn Maxwell Plays Two* with *Broken Journey* and *Best Man Speech*.
ISBN 978 1 840 02615 3

Lola Brecht. Play. Dic Edwards
M3 (40s) F1 (30s) (may be played by M1 F2). Various simple settings. Fee code E

Peter and Lola Brecht's arguments eventually end in death. Set in an imaginary enclave engulfed by war in the heartland of Europe's turbulent present.
ISBN 978 1 840 02306 0

Long to Rain Over Us. Play. Dic Edwards
M4 (2 x 20s, 30s, 50s) F1 (20s). A field, a barn. Fee code E

In a prisoner of war camp in England Dangerfield, a scorned pacifist, comes to face with fanatical nationalists – Nazis, Fascists and jingoistic British alike. A powerful and disturbing play. Available in *Three Plays by Dic Edwards* with *Looking for the World* and *Casanova Undone*.
ISBN 978 1 870 25929 3

Looking for the World. Play. Dic Edwards
M3 (55,45, 20) F3 (55,45, any). A town square on a Greek island in the Aegean. Fee code E

When Paddy and Sylvia visit a Greek island for their holiday they discover the dark side of a country under control of a military junta. Late 1960s. Available in *Three Plays by Dic Edwards* with *Casanova Undone* and *Long to Rain Over Us*.
ISBN 978 1 870 25929 3

O
B

The Murder Club. Play. Steve Hennessy
M3 F1. Simple setting. Fee code E

1922. Murder is in the air. Two notorious murderers meet up for the first time at Broadmoor to plan an evening of entertainment in the prison. *Part of Lullabies of Broadmoor, A Broadmoor Quartet*. (See *The Demon Box*; *Venus at Broadmoor*; *Wilderness*)
ISBN 978 1 849 43162 0

Off Camera. Play. Marcia Layne
M2 F3 (all 20s). Bedroom, beach. Fee code L

Two London girls visit Jamaica for a holiday and for romance. Babs wants to know if her romance with Passion, a guy from last year, is for keeps. Anisha is there for different reasons, but she isn't saying what they are – yet. *Off Camera* premiered at the West Yorkshire Playhouse in 2003, and was winner of the Alfred Fagon Prize. Uses a mix of English and Jamaican patois.
ISBN 978 1 840 02381 7

On the Lake. One-act Play. Reza de Wet
F5 (20s, 30s x2, 40s, 50s). Fee code E

A tragic-comic dream play which revolves around a re-staging of the Symbolist play-within-a-play performed in Chekhov's *The Seagull*. Nina's need to free herself from the constraints of her naturalistic role exposes the tensions beneath the surface. Available in *A Russian Trilogy* with *Three Sisters Two* and *Yelena*.
ISBN 978 1 840 02168 4

Over Milk Wood. Play. Dic Edwards
M5 F4, may be played by M2F2. 20s+. Various settings: railway station, ship, port, hospital. Fee code E

We follow Hugh Pugh, a character from the work of Dylan Thomas, as he heads into the Bronx, trying to exorcise the curse of being portrayed as a murderer. Available in a volume of two plays with *Utah Blue*. "mischievously splendid" *New Welsh Review*.
ISBN 978 1 840 02159 2

The Pimp. Play. Dic Edwards
M2 (21, 50s) F2 (late 20s, 50s). A Paris apartment. Fee code E

A biographical play about the poet Charles Baudelaire. An elegant dance of death is set in motion involving Baudelaire, his mixed-race mistress, his respectable and repressed mother and his hypocritical legal advisor. Set in 1842.
ISBN 978 1 840 02813 3

OB

Snapshots. Play. Fiona Padfield
M2 F2 (30s). Simple domestic settings. Fce code E

Lian and Catherine are sisters and the rivalry between them goes back to their earliest days. Shifting between the fantastical world of childhood, and the pressures of the adult world, *Snapshots* explores the sisters' complex relationship as Lian and her egotistical husband James chart the rough waters of early parenthood. Available in a volume of two plays with *Strip*.
ISBN 978 1 840 02166 0

Solitude. Play. Dic Edwards
M2 (early 20s, 40s), F1 (teen). A pub. A barge. Fee code E

The blocked writer Trecci wishes to be left alone on his barge, only stepping out for a riotous visit to the pub and an occasional sexual encounter with his neighbour's one-legged wife. But when his friend brings round a potential conquest – an attractive young man who turns out to be a young woman – Trecci is drawn back into the world outside.
ISBN 978 1 840 02813 3

Spain. Play. James Ley
M1 (40s). Various interior settings: lecture theatre, bedroom, café and karaoke bar/disco. Fee code E

This is a colourful monologue about an ex-pat Scot who has led a promiscuous gay lifestyle in the Canary Islands for two decades, but is approaching a mid-life crisis at the age of 42. He is suddenly thrown into an existentialist crisis and forced to begin a long journey home. Requires the performer to impersonate a number of other characters and switch seamlessly back and forth between them. Available as part of a collection entitled *The Ego Plays*, along with *Up* and *I Heart Maths*.
ISBN 978 1 849 43230 6

Strip. Play. Fiona Padfield
M1 F1. Simple settings. Fee code E

Set against a background of Soho strip clubs, *Strip* is the story of a stripper, and her relationship with her sado-masochistic lover. Jo and Gunter are drawn to one another, each hoping to find fulfilment of their dangerous dreams. What transpires between them is surprisingly tender and as they tell their separate stories we learn how their relationship has transformed their lives. Contains strong language. Available in a volume of two plays with *Snapshots*.
ISBN 978 1 840 02166 0

O
B

Up. Play. James Ley
M1 (20s). Single scene, set in a hospital bedroom. Fee code E

A short monologue to be performed by a young actor, which deals with the mental turmoil and paranoia of a patient sectioned in a psychiatric hospital. The production requires a prerecorded 'relaxation tape', which the actor plays for the audience and talks over. This an intimate, unsettling piece in which the actor speaks a number of direct asides to the audience. Available as part of a collection entitled *The Ego Plays*, along with *Spain* and *I Heart Maths*.
ISBN 978 1 849 43230 6

Utah Blue. Play. Dic Edwards
M2 (20s) F2 (19, 50s). Interior settings with two beds. Fee code E

A powerful reworking of the story of Gary Gilmore, the American who killed two black men and then famously insisted the state carry out the death penalty it had imposed upon him. Available in a volume of two plays with *Over Milk Wood*.
ISBN 978 1 840 02159 2

Venus at Broadmoor. Play. Steve Hennessy
F1 (40s) M3 (40s). Various simple interior settings. Fee code E

Explores the relationship between a Broadmoor inmate, Christiana Edmunds, and the prison staff. Part of *Lullabies of Broadmoor, A Broadmoor Quartet*. (see *The Demon Box*; *The Murder Club*; *Wilderness*).
ISBN 978 1 849 431620

Wilderness. One-act Play. Steve Hennessy
M3 F1. Various simple settings. Fee code E

This is the story of William Chester Minor, one time surgeon in the American Union Army. After murdering a complete stranger in Lambeth in 1872 he was incarcerated in Broadmoor, where he became a major contributor to the Oxford English Dictionary. Part of *Lullabies of Broadmoor, A Broadmoor Quartet*. (see *The Demon Box*; *Venus at Broadmoor*; *The Murder Club*)
ISBN 978 1 849 43162 0

Yelena. Play. Reza de Wet
M3 (45, 52, 68) F2 (30, 35, 68). Country house. Fee code E

Set in 1905, eight years after Chekhov's *Uncle Vanya* with the same characters. It focuses on the destructive effects that love can have on a small group of people connected by marriage and blood. Available in *A Russian Trilogy* with *Three Sisters Two* and *On the Lake*.
ISBN 978 1 840 02168 4

O
B

Authors' Index

Entries in italics refer to novels by well-known authors which have been dramatized either under their own name or under another title which is given in parenthesis.

O
B

Al Bassam, Sulayman
The Mirror for Princes – Kalila wa Dimna

Bartlett, Alice
Not in My Name

Beadle-Blair, Rikki
Bashment
Familyman
Fit
Shalom Baby

Boswell, Laurence
The Phoenix of Madrid (trans.)

Boyle, Catherine
House of Desires (trans.)

Brogan, Linda
Black Crows

Brown, Eleanor
Franziska (adapt.)

Brittain, Victoria
The Meaning of Waiting

Brittain, Victoria and Slovo, Gillian
Guantanamo: Honor Bound to Defend
Freedom

Bulgakov, Mikhail
The Master and Margarita (Satan's Ball)

Calderon de la Barca, Pedro
The Phoenix of Madrid

Clark, Noel
The Broken Pitcher (trans.)
The Jews (trans.)
Lucifer (trans.)
Nathan the Wise (trans.)
Ordeal by Fire (trans.)
Prince Friedrich von Homburg (trans.)
The Wedding (trans.)

Cogo-Fawcett, Robert and Murray, Braham
The Marriage of Figaro (trans. and adapt.)

Crane, Richard
Brothers Karamazov (adapt.)
Gogol
Satan's Ball (adapt.)
Vanity

Dar, Azma
Chaos

De Beaumarchais, Pierre
The Marriage of Figaro

De la Cruz, Juana Inés
House of Desires

De Wet, Reza
African Gothic
Breathing In
The Brothers
Concealment
Fever
Good Heavens
Miracle
On the Lake
Yelena

Dijeh, Lizzy
High Life

Dolezalova, Neela
Playing Fields

Dostoyevsky, Fyodor
Brothers Karamazov

Drane, David
Swankiller

Edwards, Dic
Astrakhan (Winter)
Casanova Undone
Franco's Bastard
Lola Brecht
Long to Rain Over Us
Looking for the World
Over Milk Wood
The Pimp
Solitude
Utah Blue
Wittgenstein's Daughter

Ellams, Inua
Untitled

Eyre, Peter
Chère Maître

Fleming, Neil
Musik (trans. and adapt.)

Garnett, Dameon
Break Away

O
B

Gorky, Maxim
The Lower Depths

Green, Tony
The Kindness of Strangers

Hall, Edward and Warren, Roger
Rose Rage

Hennessy, Steve
The Demon Box
The Murder Club
Venus at Broadmoor
Wilderness

Hetherington, Lewis
Bodies Unfinished

Hines, Derrek
Gilgamesh

Hood, Kerry
Meeting Myself Coming Back

Kent, Sayan
Another Paradise

Khan, Yasmin
Bells

Layne, Marcia
Off Camera

Lesage, Alain-René
Turcaret

Lessing, Gotthold
The Jews
Nathan the Wise

Ley, James
I Heart Maths
Spain
Up

Lone, Amber
Deadeye

Marivaux
The Triumph of Love

Martin, Ian Kennedy
Berlin Hanover Express

Maxwell, Glyn
After Troy
Best Man Speech
Broken Journey
The Forever Waltz
The Last Valentine
Liberty
The Lifeblood
Mimi and the Stalker
The Only Girl in the World
Wolfpit

Mérimée, Prosper
Conspirators

Mortimer-Smith, Roger
Guilty Secret

Murray, Braham and Sand, Katherine
The Triumph of Love (trans.)

Norfolk, Mark
Knock Down Ginger
Naked Soldiers
Where the Flowers Grow

Norman, John
Turcaret (trans. and adapt.)

Norton-Taylor, Richard
Bloody Sunday
The Colour of Justice
Justifying War
Tactical Questioning: Scenes from the
Baha Mousa Inquiry

Osborne, John
The Devil Inside Him
Personal Enemy

Padfield, Fiona
Snapshots
Strip

Parker, Matt
Celaine

Peck, Adam
Bonnie & Clyde

O
B

Pinner, David
All Hallows' Eve
The Drums of Snow
Edred, the Vampyre
Fanghorn
Lady Day
Lenin in Love
Lucifer's Fair
Midsummer
Oh to be in England
The Potsdam Quartet
Prince of Traitors
Revelations
Richelieu
The Teddy Bears' Picnic

Shaw, Do
Washboard Blues

Stuart, Kelly
Shadow Language

Suzman, Janet
The Free State

Van den Vondel, Joost
Lucifer

Van Wilt, Yasmine
We're Gonna Make You Whole

Vaughan, Paul
Conspirators (trans.)

Von Kleist, Heinrich
The Broken Pitcher
Ordeal by Fire
Prince Friedrich von Homburg

Wedekind, Frank
Franziska
Musik

Willmott, Phil
The Lower Depths (adapt.)

Wiseman, Polly
Bright

Woods, Sarah
Cake
Grace
Soap
Trips
Visible

Wu, Simon
Oikos

Wyspianski
The Wedding

O
B

SECTION C
Plays for Children, Youth Groups and Students

C

CONTENTS

Play Ideas

A selection of plays we've chosen for students and youth groups. Please check General Title Index to locate full details

Student Plays
(full length and short length)

Full length

Actor – Steven Berkoff
Advice to Iraqi Women – Martin Crimp
After Miss Julie – Patrick Marber
Agamemnon – Steven Berkoff, adapted from Aeschylus
Alone it Stands – John Breen
Amongst Barbarians – Michael Wall
At Break of Day – Noël Greig
Attempts on her Life – Martin Crimp
Baby Doll – Tennessee Williams
Bad Company – Simon Bent
Bash – Neil LaBute
The Beauty Queen of Leenane – Martin McDonagh
Bent – Martin Sherman
Birdy – Naomi Wallace
Blue/Orange – Joe Penhall
Blue Remembered Hills – Dennis Potter
The Blue Room – David Hare
Brighton Beach Scumbags – Steven Berkoff
Can't Pay? Won't Pay! – Dario Fo
Carpe Jugulum – Terry Pratchett
Cleo, Camping, Emmanuelle and Dick – Terry Johnson
Closer – Patrick Marber
Comedians – Trevor Griffiths
Cooking with Elvis – Lee Hall
The Country – Martin Crimp
Cracks – Martin Sherman
Dahling You Were Marvellous – Steven Berkoff
Dealer's Choice – Patrick Marber
Dealing with Clair – Martin Crimp
Disappeared – Phyllis Nagy
Don Juan in Soho – Patrick Marber
Edward Gant's Amazing Feats of Loneliness – Anthony Neilson
Eigengrau – Penelope Skinner
Entertaining Mr Sloane – Joe Orton
The Fall of the House of Usher – Steven Berkoff
Fallout – Roy Williams

The False Servant – Pierre Marivaux. New translation by Martin Crimp
Fewer Emergencies – Martin Crimp
Gasping – Ben Elton
Getting Attention – Martin Crimp
Greek – Steven Berkoff
Harry's Christmas – Steven Berkoff
The History Boys – Alan Bennett
I Dreamt I Dwelt in Marble Halls – Ade Morris
In the Penal Colony – Adapted from Franz Kafka by Steven Berkoff
The Jewish Wife – Bertolt Brecht. English text by Martin Crimp
Killers – Adam Pernak
Kvetch – Steven Berkoff
The Long Road – Shelagh Stephenson
Loot – Joe Orton
Lunch – Steven Berkoff
The Lying Kind – Anthony Neilson
Massage – Steven Berkoff
Messiah – Steven Berkoff
Metamorphosis – Steven Berkoff, adapted from Franz Kafka
The Misanthrope – Martin Crimp, from Molière
My Mother Said I Never Should – Charlotte Keatley
My Zinc Bed – David Hare
Oedipus – Steven Berkoff
Our Boys – Jonathan Lewis
Penetrator – Anthony Neilson
Posh – Laura Wade
The Rise and Fall of Little Voice – Jim Cartwright
Road – Jim Cartwright
Rock 'n' Roll – Tom Stoppard
Rope – Patrick Hamilton
Saucy Jack and the Space Vixens – Charlotte Mann and Michael Fidler
The Seagull – Anton Chekhov, in a version by Martin Crimp
The Secret Diary of Adrian Mole, Aged 13¾ – Sue Townsend
The Secret Love Life of Ophelia – Steven Berkoff
Serious Money – Caryl Churchill. Songs by Ian Dury, Micky Gallacher and Chas Jankel

Sink the Belgrano! – Steven Berkoff
Sturm und Drang – Steven Berkoff
The Sugar Syndrome – Lucy Prebble
Taking Care of Baby – Dennis Kelly
That Face – Polly Stenham
TheThreefold Cord – Scott Marshall
The Trial – Stephen Berkoff, adapted from Franz Kafka
Two – Jim Cartwright
Vita and Virginia – Eileen Atkins, adapted from correspondence between Virginia Woolf and Vita Sackville-West
The Wonderful World of Dissocia – Anthony Neilson
Yellow Moon – David Greig

Short length:

Another Moon Called Earth – Tom Stoppard
As We Forgive Those – Andrew Smith
Blackout – Davey Anderson
Carry Me Kate – Rachel Musgrove
Drunk Enough to Say I Love You – Caryl Churchill
A Gaggle of Saints – Neil LaBute
Half Life – Katy Darby
Iphegenia in Orem – Neil LaBute
Medea Redux – Neil LaBute
Lions and Donkeys – Steve Harper
Open Secrets – Katy Darby
Other People – Geoff Saunders

Youth Group Plays
(full length and short length)

Full length:

Brenda Bly: Teen Detective – Kevin Hammonds
Dark River – Alexa Romanes
The Demon Headmaster – Based on the novel *The Demon Headmaster* by Gillian Cross. Book by Paul James. Lyrics by Iain Halstead and Paul James. Music by Eric Angus and Cathy Shostak
The Late Sleepers – Eric Angus and Paul James
Like a Virgin – Gordon Steel
Punk Rock – Simon Stephens
Sparkleshark – Philip Ridley
Virgins – John Retallack
The Wall – D.C. Jackson
Zombie Prom – John Dempsey and Dana P. Rowe

Short length:

After Juliet – Sharman MacDonald
As We Forgive Those – Andrew Smth
Burn – Deborah Gearing
Chatroom – Enda Walsh
Citizenship – Mark Ravenhill
The Queen Must Die – David Farr
Taking Breath – Sarah Daniels
Totally Over You – Mark Ravenhill

Longer Plays
Plays which have an approximate running time of more than one hour

Non-Musical Plays For Children

Alice's Adventures in Wonderland (Pearn)
Angelica ... and the Monstrous Monster of
  the Deep
Babe, the Sheep-Pig
BFG
Boy Who Fell Into a Book
Callisto Five
Champion of Paribanou
Dandelion Time
Danny the Champion of the World
Difficult Unicorn
Eliza's House
Fantastic Mr Fox
Firebird (Duffield)
Gargling With Jelly. The Play!
Good King Wenceslas and the Chancellor
  of Bohemia
Horse and his Boy
House That Sailed Away
Hundred and One Dalmatians
Invisible Friends
James and the Giant Peach
Jump for Your Life
Jungle Book
Lion, the Witch and the Wardrobe
Little Women
Magician's Nephew
More Adventures of Noddy
More Grimm Tales
Mr A's Amazing Maze Plays
Mr Macaroni and the Exploding Pizza Pie
My Very Own Story
Nativity
Noddy
Peter Pan
Phantom Tollbooth
Play of the Royal Astrologers
Railway Children
Ramayana
Real Story of Puss in Boots
Right Christmas Caper
Scatterbrained Scarecrow of Oz
Secret Garden
Smashed Eggs
Snatching of Horrible Harold
Snow Queen

Telling Wilde Tales
13 Clocks
Thwarting of Baron Bolligrew
Tom's Midnight Garden
Twits
Utter Garbage
Voyage of the Dawn Treader
Wind in the Willows (Morley)
Winnie-the-Pooh
Witches
Wizard of Oz

Non-Musical Plays For Young People
(ages 14-21 approximately)

Adventures of Jason and the Argonauts
After Juliet
At Break of Day
A Bad Dream
Do We Ever See Grace?
Emperor's New Clothes
Hannah and Hanna
Junk
Little Mermaid
Monkey in the Stars
Oedipus Plays
Playing With My Heart
Punk Rock
Rainbow's Ending
Sing Yer Heart Out for the Lads
Sparkleshark
Stags and Hens
This Is Where We Came In
Virgins
Wall
Whale

Musical Plays For Children

Alice in Wonderland and Through the
  Looking Glass
Around the Pond in 80 Days
Babe, the Sheep-Pig
Bad Day at Black Frog Creek
Big Al

Burston Drum
Christopher Columbus
Curious Quest for the Sandman's Sand
Dazzle
Demon Headmaster
Dinosaurs and All That Rubbish
Dracula Spectacula
Dreams of Anne Frank
Fawkes – the Quiet Guy
Flibberty and the Penguin
Frankenstein Monster Show
Gingerbread Man
Giraffe and the Pelly and Me
Grimm Tales
Happy Prince
Henry the Tudor Dude
Hiawatha
Hijack Over Hygenia
How to Eat Like a Child
Ideal Gnome Expedition
Jeremy and the Thinking Machine
Joshua's Egg
Little Princess
Mammoth Sails Tonight!
Meg and Mog Show
Mothers and Daughters
Mystery of Dumsey Meadow
Nell's Belles
Nightingale and the Emperor
Nutcracker Sweet
Old Father Time
Old Man of Lochnagar
Our Day Out
Owl and the Pussycat Went to See…
Pandemonium! (a Greek Myth-adventure)
Papertown Paperchase
Peter Pan (Chater-Robinson)
Pied Piper
Plotters of Cabbage Patch Corner
Quest for the Whooperdink
Railway Children
Robin Hood
Rockasocka
Rosie and the Bad, Bad Apples
Rumpelstiltskin Racket
Rupert and the Green Dragon
Sammy's Magic Garden
Save the Human
See-Saw Tree
Selfish Shellfish
Seven Golden Dragons
Skool & Crossbones
Some Canterbury Tales

Space Junk
Spot's Birthday Party
Surgical Sensation at St Sennapod's
Sweeney Todd Shock 'n' Roll Show
Tales of Hans Andersen
There Was an Old Woman
Think of the Magic
Tinder Box
Toad of Toad Hall
Tom Kitten and His Friends
Voyage of the Jumblies
Water Babies
Whenever
Where the Rainbow Ends
Wind in the Willows (Bennett)
Wind in the Willows (Hall)
Worzel Gummidge

Musical Plays For Young People
(ages 14-21 approximately)

Brenda Bly: Teen Detective
Dark River
Fawkes – the Quiet Guy
Henry the Tudor Dude
Late Sleepers
Nell's Belles
Mammoth Sails Tonight!
Orvin – Champion of Champions
Rumpelstiltskin Racket
Shake, Ripple & Roll
Siege
Summer in the Park
Surgical Sensations at St Sennapod's
Tracy Beaker Gets Real

Shorter Plays

Plays which have an approximate running time of less than one hour

Non-Musical Plays for Children

Adventure Camp*
All the World's a Stage
Blood Brothers (play version)
Captain Blackboot and the
  Wallamagrumba
Captain Blackboot's Island
Children's Ward*
Dawn on our Darkness
Domby-Dom
Ernie's Incredible Illucinations
Horatians and the Curiatians
I Read the News Today
Noah's Ark
Our Day Out (shorter version)
Papa Panov's Magic Christmas
Percival the Performing Pig
Press Gang*
Real Spirit of Christmas
Round the World with Class 6
Six Primroses Each
Stone Soup
Ugly Duckling

Non-Musical Plays for Young People

(ages 14-21 approximately)

Blackout
Boy with a Transistor Radio
Burn
Chatroom
Citizenship
Colour of Compassion*
Dickens' Children
DNA
Dreamjobs
Flatmates*
Ghost Writer
Hallo, Is That You?*
A Handbag
In Need of Care
In Service*
Madam Has a Combination Skin*
Musicians
Queen Must Die
Rabbit
Shadows*
Spider and the Bird
Strawberry Tea*
Taking Breath
Terraces
Totally Over You
You, Me and Mrs Jones

Musical Plays for Children

Daniel and the Lions
Future Perfect
Giant's Giant Pizza
River Witch
Selfish Giant
Tickle

* See *Six Primroses Each* and Other Plays

Authors' Index

Entries in italics refer to novels by well-known authors which have been dramatized either under their own name or under another title which is given in parenthesis

Alcott, Louisa May
Little Women

Andersen, Hans Christian
Little Mermaid
Nightingale and the Emperor
Snow Queen
Tinder Box
(See also *Tales of Hans Andersen*)

Anderson, Davey
Blackout

Ayckbourn, Alan
Boy Who Fell Into a Book
Callisto 5
Champion of Paribanou
Ernie's Incredible Illucinations
Invisible Friends
Mr A's Amazing Maze Plays
My Very Own Story
Orvin – Champion of Champions
This Is Where We Came In
Whenever

Barrie, J. M.
Peter Pan

Baum, Frank L.
Wizard of Oz

Bennett, Alan
Wind in the Willows (*adapt.*)

Blyton, Enid
Noddy stories

Bogdanov, Michael
Hiawatha

Bolt, Robert
Thwarting of Baron Bolligrew

Bradley, Alfred
Nightingale and the Emperor (*adapt.*)
Scatterbrained Scarecrow of Oz (*adapt.*)
Wizard of Oz (*adapt.*)

Brecht, Bertolt
Horatians and Curiatians

Brett, Simon
Bad Dream

Browning, Robert
Pied Piper

Burgess, Melvin
Junk

Burnett, Frances Hodgson
Little Princess
Secret Garden

Carroll, Lewis
Alice's Adventures in Wonderland
Through the Looking Glass and What Alice Found There

Chater-Robinson, Piers
Peter Pan (*adapt.*)

Chaucer, Geoffrey
Canterbury Tales (see *Some Canterbury Tales*)

Clarke, David
River Witch

Cole, Keith R
Ulysses

Cregan, David
Difficult Unicorn

Crocker, John and Hampton, Tim
Frankenstein Monster Show

Cross, Gillian
Demon Headmaster

Crowther, Colin and Mary
Noah's Ark

Culling, Dave
Daniel and the Lions

Dahl, Roald
BFG
Danny the Champion of the World
Fantastic Mr Fox
Giraffe and the Pelly and Me
James and the Giant Peach
Twits
Witches

Dane, Clemence
Alice's Adventures in Wonderland and Through the Looking Glass (*adapt.*)

Daniels, Sarah
Taking Breath

Dickens, Charles
Christmas Carol
Oliver Twist
(see also *Dickens' Children*)

Dobbs, Georgia
Spider and the Bird

Dryden, Ellen
Adventure Camp
Children's Ward
Colour of Compassion
Flatmates
Hallo, Is That You?
In Service
Madam Has a Combination Skin
Press Gang
Shadows
Six Primroses Each
Strawberry Tea

Dryden, Ellen and Taylor, Don
Burston Drum
Summer in the Park

Duffy, Carol Ann
Grimm Tales (*adapt.*)
More Grimm Tales (*adapt.*)

Duffield, Neil
Firebird
Secret Garden (*adapt.*)

Ellison, Les
Space Junk
Utter Garbage

Ephron, Delia, Foster, John and Kahan, Judith
How to Eat a Like a Child

Farr, David
Nativity
Queen Must Die

Foreman, Michael
Dinosaurs and All That Rubbish

Foxton, David
Emperor's New Clothes
Rabbit
Real Story of Puss in Boots

Free *see* Shrubshall and Free

Gardiner, John
Big Al
Dazzle
Dracula Spectacula
Rockasocka

Gardiner, John and Coleman, Fiz
Bad Day at Black Frog Creek
Mr Macaroni and the Exploding Pizza Pie
Snatching of Horrible Harold
Surgical Sensations at St Sennapod's, or Dr
    Scalpel's Missing Bit

Garner, Julian
Giant's Giant Pizza

Gavin, Jamila
Monkey in the Stars

Gearing, Deborah
Burn

Gems, Pam
Little Mermaid (*adapt.*)

Grahame, Kenneth
Wind in the Willows
(see also *Toad of Toad Hall*)

Greig, Noël
At Break of Day
Do We Ever See Grace?
Rainbow's Ending

Grimm, Brothers
Tales (see *Grimm Tales, More Grimm Tales*)

Hall, Valerie
Rosie and the Bad, Bad Apples

Hall, Willis
Play of the Royal Astrologers
Right Christmas Caper
Treasure Island (*adapt.*)
Water Babies (*adapt.*)
Wind in the Willows (*adapt.*)

Hammonds, Kevin
Brenda Bly: Teen Detective

Hartoch, John
Jungle Book (*adapt.*)

Holman, David
Whale

Horitz, Tony
Good King Wenceslas and the Chancellor
  of Bohemia
You, Me and Mrs Jones

Horowitz, Anthony
Handbag

H.R.H. The Prince of Wales
Old Man of Lochnagar

Hutchins, Pat
House That Sailed Away

Ireland, Vicky
Giraffe and the Pelly and Me (*adapt.*)

Jackson, D. C.
Wall

James, Paul et al.
Demon Headmaster (*adapt.*)
Late Sleepers

Jones, Graham
Dreamjobs

Juster, Norton
Phantom Tolbooth

Kelly, Dennis
DNA

King-Smith, Dick
(see *Babe, the Sheep-Pig*)

Kingsley, Charles
Water Babies

Kipling, Rudyard
Jungle Book stories

Kops, Bernard
Dreams of Anne Frank

Lewis, C. S.
Horse and his Boy
Lion, the Witch and the Wardrobe
Magician's Nephew
Voyage of the Dawn Treader

Lewton, Randall
Seven Golden Dragons
(*see also* Miller, Peter)

Lowe, Frank
13 Clocks (*adapt.*)

MacDonald, Sharman
After Juliet

Macalpine, Joan
Christopher Columbus

Magee, Wes
Real Spirit of Christmas

Marber, Patrick
Musicians

Meakin, Pete
Tales of Hans Andersen (*adapt.*)

Miller, Peter and Lewton, Randall
Sweeney Todd Shock 'n' Roll Show

Mills, Clifford and Ramsay, John
Where the Rainbow Ends

Milne, A. A.
Toad of Toad Hall
Ugly Duckling
Winnie-the-Pooh

Mitchell, Adrian
Mammoth Sails Tonight!
Pied Piper (*adapt.*)
Siege
Tom Kitten and His Friends (*adapt.*)

Morley, John
Wind in the Willows (*adapt.*)

Morris, Mary
Tracy Beaker Gets Real

Murray, Brendan
Eliza's House

Nanus, Susan
Phantom Tolbooth (*adapt.*)

Neipris, Janet and Greenberg, Barbara
Jeremy and the Thinking Machine

Nesbit, E.
Railway Children (play and musical)

Nicol, Ron
Snow Queen (*adapt.*)

Nicoll, Helen and Pienkowski, Jan
Meg and Mog books

Olding, Grant
Tracy Beaker Gets Real

Oswald, Peter
Ramayana

Owen, Dilys
Percival the Performing Pig

Patten, Brian
Gargling With Jelly. The Play!

Pearce, Philippa
Tom's Midnight Garden

Pearn, V.A.
Alice's Adventures in Wonderland

Perkins, David
Selfish Giant (*adapt.*)
(*see also* Toksvig, Jenifer)

Perkins, David and Dooley, Caroline
Happy Prince (adapt.)
Mystery of Dumsey Meadow

Pickering, Ken
Some Canterbury Tales (*adapt.*)

Pickering, Ken and Cole, Keith
Mothers and Daughters

Porter, Phil
Smashed Eggs

Poskitt, Kjartan
Fawkes – the Quiet Guy
Henry the Tudor Dude
Nell's Belles
The Rumpelstiltskin Racket
Sammy's Magic Garden

Potter, Beatrix
Tom Kitten stories (see *Tom Kitten and his Friends*)

Prendergast, Shaun
Playing With My Heart

Ravenhill, Mark
Citizenship
Totally Over You

Reader, Caroline
Oedipus Plays (*adapt.*)

Reeves, Emma
Little Women (*adapt.*)

Retallack, John
Hannah and Hanna
Junk (*adapt.*)
Virgins

Ridley, Philip
Sparkleshark

Robbins, Glyn
Horse and his Boy (*adapt.*)
Hundred and One Dalmatians (*adapt.*)
Lion, the Witch and the Wardrobe (*adapt.*)
Magician's Nephew (*adapt.*)
Voyage of the Dawn Treader (*adapt.*)
Winnie-the-Pooh (*adapt.*)

Roberts, Belinda
Angelica! ... and the Monstrous Monster of the Deep

Rodgers, Frank
Think of the Magic

Romanes, Alexa
Dark River

Rowley, David E.
In Need of Care

Ruskin, S.
Owl and the Pussycat Went to See ...

Russell, Willy
Blood Brothers (*non-musical*)
Boy with the Transistor Radio
I Read the News Today
Our Day Out (*musical and non-musical version*)
Stags and Hens
Terraces

Sanderson, Bill
(*See* Thwaite, Emily)

Sayer, Philip Freeman
Voyage of the Jumblies

Simpson, Dave
Railway Children (*adapt.*)

Smith, Dodie
Hundred and One Dalmatians

Shapiro, Jacqui
Joshua's Egg

Shrubshall and Free
Around the Pond in 80 Days

Sophocles
Oedipus the King
Oedipus at Colonus
Antigone
(*See* Oedipus Plays)

Stephens, Simon
Punk Rock

Stevenson, Robert Louis
Treasure Island

Supple, Tim
Grimm Tales (dram.)
More Grimm Tales (dram.)

Tasca, Jules
Telling Wilde Tales (*adapt.*)

Teacey, A. H.
Quest for the Whooperdink

Thain, Paul
Papa Panov's Magic Christmas (*adapt.*)
Stone Soup

Thwaite, Emily and Sanderson, Bill
Future Perfect

Thurber, James
13 Clocks

Toksvig, Jenifer and Perkins, David
Curious Quest for the Sandman's Sand
Pandemonium! (a Greek Myth-adventure)
Shake, Ripple & Roll
Skool & Crossbones

Todd, Barbara Euphan
Worzel Gummidge characters

Tolstoy, Leo
Papa Panov's Magic Christmas

Tourtel, Mary and Bestall, Alfred
Rupert stories

Tydeman, Richard
Dawn on Our Darkness

Vivis, Anthony
Horatians and Curiatians (*trans.*)

Walsh, Enda
Chatroom

Warburton, Nick
Dickens' Children (*adapt.*)
Domby-Dom
Ghost Writer
Round the World with Class 6

Waterhouse, Keith and Hall, Willis
Worzel Gummidge (adapt.)

Whelan, Peter
Tinder Box (*adapt.*)

Whitmore, Ken
Jump for Your Life

Wild, Michael
Little Princess (adapt.)

Wilde, Oscar
Happy Prince
Selfish Giant
Seven Fairy Tales (see *Telling Wilde Tales*)

Williams, Roy
Sing Yer Heart Out for the Lads

Willmott, Phil
Adventures of Jason and the Argonauts

Wilson, David Henry
All the World's a Stage

Wilson, Jacqueline
Tracy Beaker

Wood, David
Babe, the Sheep-Pig (*adapt.*)
BFG (*adapt.*)
Danny the Champion of the World (*adapt.*)
Dinosaurs and All That Rubbish (*adapt.*)
Fantastic Mr Fox (*adapt.*)
Flibberty and the Penguin
Gingerbread Man
Hijack Over Hygenia
Ideal Gnome Expedition
James and the Giant Peach (*adapt.*)

Meg and Mog Show (*adapt.*)
More Adventures of Noddy (*adapt.*)
Noddy (*adapt.*)
Nutcracker Sweet
Old Father Time
Old Man of Lochnagar (*adapt.*)
Papertown Paperchase
Plotters of Cabbage Patch Corner
Rupert and the Green Dragon (*adapt.*)
Save the Human
See-Saw Tree
Selfish Shellfish
Spot's Birthday Party
There Was an Old Woman ...
Tickle
Tom's Midnight Garden (*adapt.*)
Twits (*adapt.*)
Witches (*adapt.*)

Wood, David and Arthur, Dave and Toni
Pied Piper (*adapt.*)
Robin Hood

Wood, David and Ruskin, Sheila
Owl and the Pussycat Went to See ...

Wood, Patricia
Captain Blackboot and the Wallamagrumba
Captain Blackboot's Island
Dandelion Time

Woolford, Julian
Railway Children (*adapt.*)

C

Plays for Children and Young People

C

The plays are listed alphabetically with marks to indicate the playing time of the individual titles and whether they are for performance by children, young people or adults to children. Please note the classifications are only suggestions and the playing times are approximate.

Key to symbols

A = Adults
C = Children
Y = Young people

S = playing time of under 60 minutes approximately
L = playing time of over 60 minutes approximately

Example marks:

A L = adults to perform to children; playing time longer than 60 minutes (approx.)

C/Y S = to be performed by children or young people; playing time shorter than 60 minutes (approx.)

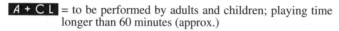 = to be performed by adults and children; playing time longer than 60 minutes (approx.)

♦ **The Adventures of Jason and the Argonauts.** Play freely adapted from the ancient myths by Phil Willmott **Y L**

M7-12, F5-8. A city square. Fee code K. Period Ancient Greece
Join Prince Jason, plucky Princess Medea, Hercules and all the gang for a lively re-telling of the greatest adventure story ever told! Our heroes must overcome monsters, tricksters and tempests if they are to capture the Golden Fleece, defeat Jason's evil uncle and win back the kingdom. A light-hearted romp where humour and easy puppetry overcome the difficulties of a fire-breathing bull, a dragon and an army of skeletons!
ISBN 978 0 573 15039 5

After Juliet. Play. Sharman MacDonald **A/Y L**
M7 (teenage) F6 (teenage, 30s). 2 extras. Simple set. Fee code H

A tense truce holds between the Capulets and the Montagues after the deaths of Romeo and Juliet. Benvolio, Romeo's best friend, is in love with Rosaline, Juliet's cousin; but Rosaline is bent on revenge. *After Juliet* was specially commissioned by the Royal National Theatre for the BT National Connections Scheme for young people. There is an original score – the use of which is not mandatory – for sampler, drums and flute by Caleb Knightley and Adrian Howgate.

C

Alice's Adventures in Wonderland. Play. V. A. Pearn **C/Y L**
Any number of characters. Composite setting. Fee code C

This longer adaptation of Lewis Carroll's story is designed for children of a slightly older age group. Playing time about 90 minutes

Alice's Adventures in Wonderland and Through the Looking Glass. Musical play. Clemence Dane. Music by Richard Addinsell
Any number of characters. Composite setting. Fee code H **A/C L**

The first act tells of Alice's adventures in Wonderland, of the people she meets there, including the White Rabbit, Mad Hatter and March Hare, and of her escape into the Looking Glass land of the second act, where she finds the rest of Lewis Carroll's well-loved people.
ISBN 978 0 573 05001 9

All the World's a Stage. Morality play. David Henry Wilson **Y S**
Any number of characters. An empty stage. Fee code B

The children assemble on the stage and are given neither script nor plot. The parts chosen include a nurse, a shop assistant, a mother, a policeman, a politician and a rich man. The Producer's instructions are explained but fighting breaks out. The Producer's son tries to persuade everyone to play a better part. He is killed but returns to give his advice.

Angelica! ... and the Monstrous Monster of the Deep. Play. Belinda Roberts **A + Y L**
14 characters. Various simple settings. Fee code E

The Monstrous Monster of the Deep, a giant eel, captures young Cornet in revenge for the eels he has caught. Cornet's inventor sister, Angelica, sets off underwater to rescue Cornet and eventually, aided by Coral and Co. of the Military School of Fish, achieves her goal and makes an unexpected friend. This is a charming and funny play for young people, full of quirky characters and a touch of surrealism.
ISBN 978 0 573 05124 1

Around the Pond in 80 Days. A musical by Shrubshall and Free **C L**
Large mixed cast of children. Fee by arrangement

Can Phileas Frog (aided by his faithful friend, Pass) get round the pond in eighty days? Travelling by foot, boat and balloon the intrepid adventurers face many trials and make lots of friends. Catchy songs, imaginative staging and numerous excellent frog jokes make this joyful musical a feast of fun for actors and audience alike.
ISBN 978 0 573 08130 9

At Break of Day. Play. Noël Greig **Y L**
17 characters. Various interior and exterior settings suggested on a bare stage. Fee code K

Two soldiers make an epic, dreamlike journey home after a long war, encountering many different people on the way and travelling through a whole century and its conflicts. One of them records his thoughts in a notebook. Interwoven with this story is that of a young woman who has made her own journey to a distant land, to discover what happened to her great-grandfather, searching the battered notebook that once belonged to him for clues.
ISBN 978 0 573 05135 7

Babe, the Sheep-Pig. Play. David Wood. Based on the book by Dick King-Smith **A L**
10 actors, with doubling. Various simple settings. Fee code M (play) code D (music – optional)

This is a tale of high adventure in the farmyard; of humble beginnings and courageous triumphs. This is the story of one piglet's rise to become the world famous "sheep-pig", hero of the Grand Challenge Sheep-dog Trials. The play is suitable for everyone from 5 years upwards. Incidental music by Peter Pontzen is available separately on hire.
ISBN 978 0 573 05115 9

Bad Day at Black Frog Creek. Musical play. John Gardiner and Fiz Coleman **C L**
M5 F4. Extras. A saloon. Fee code E

One Christmas Eve, the Muldoon Mob arrive in Black Frog Creek, bent on retrieving the diamond which saloon-keeper Lil has had cemented into one of her teeth. They get the diamond, only to be foiled yet again by Filthy Frank. The play may be adapted quite simply to suit any period of celebration – not just Christmas. Approximate playing time 90 minutes.
ISBN 978 0 573 05249 1

A Bad Dream. Play. Simon Brett **Y L**
M8 F12. A committee room. Fee code K

Please see the entry in Section A.

The BFG (Big Friendly Giant). Play. Roald Dahl, adapted for the stage by David Wood **A L**
30 roles may be played by M4 F4. A playroom/bedroom, a cave, Dream Country, Buckingham Palace. Fee code M

Roald Dahl's book about a twenty-four-feet-high giant and a little girl is recreated faithfully for the stage by David Wood. The play begins in Sophie's playroom at her birthday party when family and friends act out the story of The BFG using props, objects and puppets to tell the tale in an improvisatory manner.
ISBN 978 0 573 05094 7

Big Al. Musical play. Book and lyrics by John Gardiner. Music by Andrew Parr `C + Y`
M57 F57, can be played by M10 F10. Composite setting. Fee by arrangement

This lively musical, originally written for teenagers and young people, is based on the life and times of Al Capone, the infamous Chicago gangster. Although there are 114 characters appearing in this musical the parts can be divided between a minimum cast of twenty. The set comprises a standing construction of scaffolding which is used to represent different areas in Chicago.
ISBN 978 0 573 08048 7

♦ **Blackout.** Play. Davey Anderson `Y S`
Any number of actors. Simple setting. Fee code E

A hard-hitting play about 'getting bullied, fighting back, trying to make a name for yourself, turning vicious, doing something stupid, losing everything, then finding your way again.' Can be performed as a monologue or with any number of actors; staging can be as simple or elaborate as desired. Presented to critical acclaim at the National Theatre as part of their New Connections programme.
ISBN 978 0 573 05258 3

Blood Brothers (play version). Play. Willy Russell `C/Y S`
13 characters, doubling possible. Various simple settings. Fee Code F

Blood Brothers (play version) is the non-musical version of the hugely successful musical which is currently being performed professionally, and thus is not available for performance.. It tells of twin brothers and what happens when their mother decides to have one of them adopted. Their contrasting upbringing and the hand fate deals them is fast moving, perceptive and ultimately tragic. This original version is simple to stage, rewarding to act, and is ideal for a large mixed cast.
ISBN 0 7487 0182 6

The Boy Who Fell Into a Book. Play. Alan Ayckbourn `A + C`
M3 F2, 1 boy. Various simple settings. Fee code M

Rockfist Slim's enemies have plunged him into another desperate situation when Kevin has to close his detective book and go to sleep. But his own adventure is only just beginning. Fast-moving, fun and full of special effects, Ayckbourn's latest work for children brings alive several well-known children's books as Kevin and Rockfist Slim escape the baddies by plunging into and becoming part of *Kidnapped*, *Grimm's Tales*, *Chess for Beginners* and many other stories.

Boy with the Transistor Radio. Play. Willy Russell `Y S`
M7 F3. Extras. Simple settings. Fee code D

Terry is leaving school with few prospects in his native Liverpool. His father finds him a job in a local warehouse, but Terry has other ideas. Living in a dream world promulgated by a radio DJ to whom he listens constantly, Terry is convinced there is something better and he makes an angry escape bid. This compelling, compassionate play was transmitted on Thames Television.

♦ **A bullet mark next to a title indicates that it is new to this edition of the Guide.**

Brenda Bly: Teen Detective. Book and lyrics by Kevin Hammonds
Music by Charles Miller
M3-9 F9-13. Various simple settings. Fee by arrangement 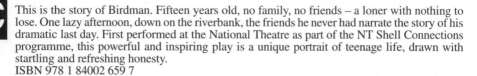 Y L

It's 1958 – a time of rock and roll, space discovery, and great hope for a bright future. But trouble is brewing at the Whitney Ellis Private School For Girls. Only days away from the opening night of the end of term musical, "Rocket Girl", the leading lady is knocked unconscious with a sandbag. Once again it is up to our favourite teenage sleuth, Brenda Bly, to solve the crime, catch the crook and save the day. Period 1958.
ISBN 978 0 573 08128 6

Burn. Play. Deborah Gearing
M5 (teens) F8 (9,teens). Various simple settings. Fee Code F Y S

This is the story of Birdman. Fifteen years old, no family, no friends – a loner with nothing to lose. One lazy afternoon, down on the riverbank, the friends he never had narrate the story of his dramatic last day. First performed at the National Theatre as part of the NT Shell Connections programme, this powerful and inspiring play is a unique portrait of teenage life, drawn with startling and refreshing honesty.
ISBN 978 1 84002 659 7

The Burston Drum. Musical for young people. Book by Ellen Dryden, lyrics by Don Taylor, music by Charles Young
M14 F11. Children. Extras. Three simple settings. Fee by arrangement Y L
ISBN 978 0 573 08082 1

Callisto 5. Play. Alan Ayckbourn A L
M3 (17, 30s, any age) F1 (30s) or M2 F2, 2 M or F voices. A space station interior. Fee code M

Jem is alone on space station Callisto 5 with Damaris, a babysitting robot, and Iris, the all-powerful computer, as his only company. Jem is bored with the childish amusements provided by the computer and despairs increasingly at Damaris's instability. Jem has to do battle with The Thing, a marauding alien that can only be seen through a video camera, and finds his efforts rewarded in a very surprising way ...
ISBN 978 0 573 05107 4

Captain Blackboot and the Wallamagrumba. Play. Patricia Wood C S
M15 F9. A desert island. Fee code D

The sequel to *Captain Blackboot's Island* opens with the Captain and his crew puzzling over the whereabouts of their octopus, Oliver. Luckily James, Sally and Victoria arrive, overhear some wreckers plotting and discover that Oliver is to be made into an octopus stew! A happy ending is assured, however, following their victorious battle with the wreckers, and when Oliver appears from the sea, it seems that the Wallamagrumba may not be so bad after all.
ISBN 978 0 573 15223 8

♦ **A bullet mark next to a title indicates that it is new to this edition of the Guide.**

Captain Blackboot's Island. Play for children. Patricia Wood **C S**
Mixed cast of children. A desert island. Fee code D

Captain Blackboot and crew have been living on the desert island for months and he has worked out a Treasure Trail hoping his island will become famous. Three young seekers arrive followed by Wicked Pirates and even the Captain's wife and children. Real treasure is found and a battle results.
ISBN 978 0 573 15208 5

The Champion of Paribanou. Play. Alan Ayckbourn **A L**
M7 F3 with doubling. Various simple settings. Fee code M

Murganah loves Ahmed, the Sultan's youngest son, but feeling herself rejected, she invokes the help of dark supernatural forces to regain him. When she finally loses him to another she seeks a terrible revenge. Alan Ayckbourn writes: 'For the first time in a children's play, I've strayed into the grey area of individual choice. Are any of us ever born good or bad? Or do we only grow that way as a result of the circumstances we face and the choices we make?' ISBN 978 0 573 05123 4

Chatroom. Play. Enda Walsh **Y S**
M3 (15) F3 (15). A bare stage. Fee Code F

The six teenage characters in *Chatroom* never meet each other, they just communicate via the internet. Conversations range in subject from Britney Spears to Willy Wonka to – suicide: Jim is depressed and talks of ending his life and Eva and William decide to do their utmost to persuade him to carry out his threat. From this chilling premise Enda Walsh has forged a funny, compelling and uplifting play that tackles some of the issues of teenage life head-on and with great understanding.
ISBN 978 0 573 05256 9

Christopher Columbus. Play. Joan Macalpine. Music by Peter Durrent **Y L**
18 named parts. Large cast can be involved. Various locations. Fee code G.
ISBN 978 0 573 05102 9

Citizenship. Play. Mark Ravenhill **Y S**
M7 F6. Simple settings. Fee Code F

A funny, outspoken drama, focusing on teenager Tom, who dreams of kissing someone but can't tell whether they're female or male. Is he gay? "Gay Gary", his schoolfriend, is gay by nickname only. deClerk, the young Citizenship teacher, is gay but stressed out and professionally cautious; Amy, Tom's self-harming best friend, has sex with him as an experiment … then Tom meets Martin, who helps him to answer some questions while raising others.
ISBN 978 0 573 05255 2

The Curious Quest for the Sandman's Sand. Children's Musical. Book and lyrics by Jenifer Toksvig. Music by David Perkins
11 principals. Chorus. Various simple settings. Fee by arrangement **C L**

Three children embark on an eventful journey into the mysterious world of silver-tongued Harry, the Sandman, to retrieve the magical sand. Along the way they meet extraordinary creatures – Snoodle Werps, the Trash Trump, Litter Bugs to name but a few – before their final showdown with Jewels, the Witch and the awesome Gump Grump. A colourful, fun-packed adventure musical for children between the ages of 7 and 13. Running time: approximately one hour.
ISBN 978 0 573 08109 5

Dandelion Time. Fantasy. Patricia Wood C L
43 characters, doubling possible. Extras. Composite setting. Fee code J
ISBN 978 0 573 05043 5

Daniel and the Lions. Children's musical. Book, music and lyrics by Dave Culling C S
Large flexible cast. Various simple settings. Fee by arrangement

This charming one-act musical, based on the story of Daniel, King Darius's trusted advisor in ancient Babylon, is written for Key Stage 2 students or children of similar age to perform. It features a cast of delightful characters, including an amusing group of Noël Coward-esque lions. The show can be accompanied live with piano or by recorded backing tracks.
ISBN 978 0 573 08126 2

Danny the Champion of the World. Roald Dahl, adapted for the stage by David Wood
7 or 8 actors minimum. Various simple settings. Fee code M A L

Young Danny lives happily in a gypsy caravan with his devoted father and works in their small village petrol station. When his father fails to return from a poaching expedition on the wealthy estate of nasty, greedy, Victor Hazell, Danny fears for his father and sets off on a courageous journey, masterminding the most incredible rescue. Although written for seven actors with doubling, a larger cast is possible and could enhance the "community" feel.
ISBN 978 0 573 15016 6

Dark River. Play with music. Alexa Romanes C/Y L
25 principal characters, doubling possible. Extras. Various simple settings. Fee code J for play, code A for music

Alexa Romanes' play for young people traces the fortunes of the poorest of the human chain in Victorian London, from the mudlarks who scour the Thames mud for a pittance, to the crossing sweepers, costers and pickpockets. Into their midst comes a mysterious stranger, Sal, a maid-of-all-work from the country who is running from her Rotherhithe employer. An unsentimental yet sensitive play with a large cast of well-drawn characters. The music is available separately.
ISBN 978 0 573 05137 1

Dawn on Our Darkness. Play. Richard Tydeman C / Y
M9 F1. Extras. An acting area. Fee code C. ISBN 978 0 573 16603 7

Dazzle. Musical Space-tacular! Book and lyrics by John Gardiner. Music by Andrew Parr
M5 F4. Chorus. 12 named parts plus extras and chorus. Simple settings. Fee by arrangement

With brilliantly funny parodies of *Star Trek*, *Dazzle* charts a voyage of the starship Sunburster One on its highly important first mission under the control of the dashingly handsome (and doesn't he know it!) Captain Sam Galactic. The musical has flexible casting, settings and costumes are easily achieved and extensive notes are given in the text for these, together with suggestions for lighting, sound and special effects.
ISBN 978 0 573 08088 3 – Libretto
ISBN 0 573 08591 9 – Vocal Score C + Y

The Demon Headmaster. Musical. Based on the novel by Gillian Cross. Music by Eric Angus and Cathy Shostak. Lyrics by Iain Halstead and Paul James. Book by Paul James **A + YL**
15 principals with doubling, plus large chorus. Various simple settings. Fee by arrangement

This musical is fun, exciting and a little bit scary. The pupils of St Campion's Comprehensive, ultra-disciplined exam machines, are devoted to their headmaster. But something strange is going on and the worst class in the world – 6Z – are going to get to the bottom of this mystery and expose the DEMON HEADMASTER! Originally commissioned by Brent Music Service.
ISBN 978 0 573 08116 3

Dickens' Children. Play. Charles Dickens, adapted by Nick Warburton **A + Y**

Please see the entry in Section B.

The Difficult Unicorn. Children's Play. David Cregan **A L**

M5 (21, middle age, elderly) F3 (21, middle age, elderly) Optional extras for Unicorn or M3 F3 (with doubling). Various simple settings. Fee code L. ISBN 978 0 573 05134 0

Dinosaurs and All That Rubbish. Musical play. David Wood and Peter Pontzen. Based on the book by Michael Foreman
Flexible casting. Various simple exterior settings. Fee code F **A + C**

Man destroys his own world through misuse and disrespect, only to search for a replacement in the stars. In his absence the Dinosaurs restore the Earth to its former beauty. Ironically when man returns he tries to lay claim to this new blooming planet, but is reminded that it is the same decaying Earth he had abandoned. The final note of this lively play is that Earth belongs to everyone and should be respected.
ISBN 978 0 573 15205 4 – Libretto
ISBN 0 573 08584 6 – Vocal Score

DNA. Play. Dennis Kelly **Y S**
11 main parts. A street, a field, a wood. Fee code F

Some teenagers do something bad, really bad, then panic and cover the whole thing up. But when they find that the cover-up unites them and brings harmony to their once fractious lives, where's the incentive to put things right? Commissioned by NT Education as part of its Connection project, the play was first performed in the Cottesloe Theatre of the National Theatre in 2008.

Do We Ever See Grace? Play. Noël Greig **C/YL**
Large ensemble playing many roles. A bare stage. Fee code J

This play is presented as a 'clown show' in which most of the actors wear clown-style costumes, creating a kaleidoscope of impressions around the central character of Grace, representing all those people who are scorned in this world but who develop a resistance to such injustice. An intelligent and searching contemporary play of ideas, ideal for school groups and young people.
ISBN 978 0 573 05118 0

> ◆ **A bullet mark next to a title indicates that it is new to this edition of the Guide.**

Domby-Dom. Comedy. Nick Warburton C + Y
Flexible, minimum of 12 actors. A stage. Fee code D. ISBN 978 0 573 12221 7

The Dracula Spectacula. A spooky musical. Book and lyrics by John Gardiner. Music by Andrew Parr
24 characters. Large supporting cast. Various interior and exterior settings. Fee by arrangement. Vocal score available separately Y L

In this bubbling modern extravaganza for the young, the immaculate Miss Nadia and her three pupils are swung into riotous Transylvanian happenings with the irrepressible Count and his gruesome acolytes. Plenty of good parts, a sizzling score and a fresh hilarious script make this an attractive enterprise for a young company.
ISBN 978 0 573 18013 2

Dreamjobs. Play. Graham Jones Y S
F5. A waiting-room. Fee code D

While waiting for interviews with Youth Employment Service, five teenage girls dream of the romantic, exciting jobs they would like to do. The dreams are enacted by all the girls together. Each has a rude awakening. Beverly eventually brings them down to earth. They are only fit for the drabbest of jobs.
ISBN 978 0 573 03379 7

Dreams of Anne Frank. Play. Bernard Kops Y L
M4 (16, middle-age) F4 (13, 18, middle-age). Simple set. Fee code H for play, B for music

Bernard Kops's play, with music by David Burman, was premièred at the Polka Theatre, London, in 1992 and won the *Time Out* award for best children's production. Using a cinematograph approach with minimal scenery, it tells the famous story of how two Jewish families hid from the Nazis for two years in a cramped Amsterdam attic and the fantasy world the adolescent Anne Frank created to escape her incarceration.
ISBN 978 0 573 05101 2

Eliza's House. Play. Brendan Murray A/Y L

Please see the full entry in Section B.

♦ **The Emperor's New Clothes** or **Five Beans for Jack**. Play. David Foxton
11 Principals. Extras. Various simple settings. Fee Code K

David Foxton merges two popular pantomimes with hilarious results and plenty of audience participation. The town crier makes a mistake in announcing that the Emperor's birthday will be celebrated *every* Friday. The town is nearly bankrupt from the continuous celebrations, with Sly and Wily (who have relieved Jack of his cow in exchange for five magic beans) urging more expenditure on a new outfit which only intelligent and powerful people can see.
ISBN 978 0 573 15011 1

♦ **A bullet mark next to a title indicates that it is new to this edition of the Guide.**

Ernie's Incredible Illucinations. Play for young people. Alan Ayckbourn C / Y
22 characters, doubling possible. Extras. A bare stage, waiting-room at one side. Fee code E

This bright comedy based on the extraordinary powers of Ernie Fraser, a daydreamer with a difference, shows his thoughts having a disturbing habit of turning into reality. After some embarrassments, Ernie's parents consult a doctor. Many of Ernie's adventures are acted out in flashback. When Ernie fails to produce a Brass Band, group hallucination is diagnosed. Ernie's 'illucinations' aren't to be dismissed quite so lightly ...
ISBN 978 0 573 12063 3

Fantastic Mr Fox. Roald Dahl, adapted for the stage by David Wood A L
8 characters (can be played by 6), 4 children. Supernumerary animals. Supernumerary human beings. Various settings on an open stage. Fee code M

When Mr Fox steals one chicken too many from a local farm, the farmers decide the only cure is to rid themselves of him by any means possible. Outwitted at every turn, the farmers' ploys backfire, and all the animals celebrate a feast at their expense. This enthralling story can be performed by a small company of experienced actors supported by community and child actors.
ISBN 978 0 573 05133 3

Fawkes – the Quiet Guy. Musical. Kjartan Poskitt Y L
M26 F15 (doubling/tripling possible). Various simple settings. Fee by arrangement

Welcome to Catesby's Cabaret Club, your hostess for the evening is Miss Catherine Wheel ... It is the reign of King James I, a time of religious unrest, double-crossing and treachery. A secret plot is afoot, Sir Robert Catesby has invited a willing band of conspirators to his "happening" club to plan an explosive solution to their problems – the great Gunpowder Plot of 1605. Kjartan Poskitt combines witty songs with an energetic approach to history, in this easily staged piece. Period 1603-05
ISBN 978 0 573 08107 1 – Libretto
ISBN 0 573 08604 4 – Vocal score

The Firebird. Play. Neil Duffield
M5 F6 played by M2 F3. Various simple settings. Fee code L A/Y L
ISBN 978 0 573 05136 4

Flibberty and the Penguin. Musical play for children. David Wood A L
M10 F2, some M characters can be played by F. Five exterior, two interior simple settings. Fee code J. ISBN 978 0 573 05033 6

The Frankenstein Monster Show. Book by John Crocker and Tim Hampton. Music by Ken Bolam. Lyrics by Les Scott
M10 F3. Extras. Various simple settings. Fee by arrangement Y L

This inventive and exuberant musical brings the old Frankenstein story bang up-to-date – right into the computer age in fact. When Frank Enstein arrives at Enstein hall from the USA, he continues the reanimation experiments of his deceased great-great uncle. Frank's expertise in computer robotics and the timely arrival of Burke and Hare, two rather suspicious undertakers, soon have remote-controlled monsters rolling off the production line.
ISBN 978 0 573 08057 7

Future Perfect. Play. Emily Thwaite and Bill Sanderson. Music by Phil Andrews C + Y
Large cast. Various settings. Fee code D (play), A (music). Music available separately on hire.

Future Perfect imagines a future where a town which is 'Under the Edge' has a connection with a world above it – 'Over the Edge' – but is destroying itself with pollution – until the children decide to save the day. The play was devised with a group of twenty-five children aged between seven and fourteen; it is intended as a blueprint for further improvisation and adaptation. (Cast up to 70.)
ISBN 978 0 573 15230 6

Gargling With Jelly. The Play! Play. Brian Patten. Based on poems from his book *Gargling With Jelly*
11 characters, doubling possible. Various simple settings. Fee code L A L
ISBN 978 0 573 05092 3

Ghost Writer. Play. N. J. Warburton
M13 F8, doubling possible. The writer's study and the Colonel's lounge. Fee code D Y S
ISBN 978 0 573 15216 0

A Giant's Giant Pizza. Play. Julian Garner C + Y
Large cast. Various simple settings. Fee code G

A Giant's Giant Pizza offers opportunities for about thirty young actors (aged 8 to 13). Giant Rumblebottom is about to destroy the kingdom. Our unlikely hero, Olaf, who thinks he's ugly, wins the lottery and has plastic surgery. With his increased confidence he asks the king's daughter for a date, but alas, the Giant comes between them, kidnaps the princess and demands a giant pizza. It falls to Olaf to win the day! The play has five delightful songs.
ISBN 978 0 573 05126 5

The Gingerbread Man. Musical play. Book, music and lyrics by David Wood A L
M4 F2. A kitchen dresser. Fee code M. Vocal score available separately

While the 'Big Ones' are asleep plenty of activity is taking place on the kitchen dresser. The cuckoo clock has lost his voice and might be threatened with the dustbin in the morning if he doesn't recover it. The efforts of the salt cellar and the pepper-mill to help him regain it involve them in confrontation with the Old Tea-Bag ... but all is resolved by morning.
ISBN 978 0 573 05042 8

The Giraffe and the Pelly and Me. Play with music. Adapted by Vicky Ireland from the story by Roald Dahl
M5 F1, 1 boy (12). Various simple settings. Fee code H A L

Billy and a strange trio of animals, the Giraffe, the Pelly and the Monkey, known as 'The Ladderless Window-Cleaning Company', set off to clean the many windows at the Duke of Hampshire's house, and have a tense encounter with cat burglar 'Cobra' Clive. For performance to children aged five to nine, with music and a host of special effects! (NB. The music is available separately from The Polka Theatre.)
ISBN 978 0 573 05109 8

♦ **A bullet mark next to a title indicates that it is new to this edition of the Guide.**

Good King Wenceslas and the Chancellor of Bohemia. Play. Tony Horitz `C L`
M5 F2, 8M or F (minimum). Interior and exterior settings. Fee code F

Please see the entry in Section D.

Grimm Tales. Play with music, adapted from the Brothers Grimm by Carol Ann Duffy, dramatized by Tim Supple
Large cast may be played by M4 F3. Various simple settings. Fee code M `A L`

Eight stories from the Brothers Grimm, presented in different and exciting styles with an emphasis on the horror, grotesquerie and savage farce of the originals: *Hansel and Gretel*; *The Golden Goose*; *Ashputtel; A Riddling Tale*; *The Mouse, the Bird and the Sausage; Iron Hans*; *The Lady and the Lion*; and *The Magic Table, the Gold-Donkey and the Cudgel in the Sack*.

♦ **A Handbag.** Play. Anthony Horowitz `Y S`
M4 F2, all 18 - 22. A room. Fee code E

A funny, poignant play commissioned for the National Theatre's New Connections programme. As a group of young people rehearse *The Importance of Being Earnest*, a play which is alien to them, it becomes apparent that their surroundings are not normal. Gradually, as tensions mount, squabbles ensue and each young person's story starts to emerge, the location is found to be an institution.
ISBN 978 0 573 05257 6

Hannah and Hanna. Play. John Retallack `A/Y L`
F2. Various interior and exterior settings on a bare stage. Fee code L

It is 1999. Hannah is sixteen. She loves karaoke and her bloke Bullfrog; she hates her home town of Margate and the Kosovan asylum-seekers who have come to live there. Hanna is also sixteen. She loves karaoke, loves Margate – and is one of the asylum-seekers. Slowly and unexpectedly, the two become friends, Hannah being forced to face up to her prejudices. This play for two young women addresses important issues through comedy, personal drama and the uniting power of music.
ISBN 978 0 573 03023 9

Oscar Wilde's **The Happy Prince.** Children's musical. Music by David Perkins. Adaptation, book and lyrics by Caroline Dooley and David Perkins
16 prinicipals. Chorus. Unit set. Fee by arrangement `C/Y L`

A touching musical from the well-loved story by Oscar Wilde. The golden statue of the Happy Prince overlooks the misery and poverty of the city. Desperate to bring hope and happiness to the poor, he asks a swallow to distribute his gold and jewels to them and his generosity, combined with the courage of the swallow, help to overcome the greed of the powerful mayor. "... a rich and varied piece." Madeline Clements, *Surrey Advertiser*
ISBN 978 0 573 66237 9

♦ **A bullet mark next to a title indicates that it is new to this edition of the Guide.**

Henry the Tudor Dude. Musical for young people. Kjartan Poskitt **Y L**
50 named parts, doubling possible. Various interior and exterior settings. Fee by arrangement

Henry VIII believes in the Divine Right of Kings – he looks Divine and he's always Right! His first wife fails to bear him a son and he cannot divorce her in Roman Catholic law, so he creates the Church of England, divorces his wife, and tries again – five times! *Henry the Tudor Dude* has all these and hilarious dialogue, witty songs and more than a touch of playful cynicism. History has never been such fun!
ISBN 978 0 573 08096 8 – Libretto
ISBN 0 573 08595 1 – Vocal score

Hiawatha. Play. Michael Bogdanov **C/Y L**

Please see the entry in Section A

Hijack Over Hygenia. Children's play with music. David Wood **A L**
M8 F4, with doubling. An aeroplane interior, a roof, a throne room, a bedroom. Fee code K

Hygenia is the cleanest kingdom in the world. Disease is unknown, but one day a villainous Measle enters illegally and starts bringing the inhabitants out in spots. It is all the plot of Doctor Spicknspan who, owing to prevailing healthiness is always out of work. Things look serious, but the plot is foiled by the gallantry of the Royal staff: peace, health and cleanliness are restored.
ISBN 978 0 573 05034 3

The Horatians and the Curiatians. A didactic play for children. Bertolt Brecht. Translated by Anthony Vivis **Y S**
Fee code G

The Curiatii decide to attack the city of the Horatii; both sides organize their armies. Thanks to better weapons the Curiatii win the bowmen's and pikemen's engagements, and in the engagement between the swordsmen the Horatii run away. But the pursuit splits up the Curiatii, so that the Horatian swordsmen can engage them singly and beat them.

The Horse and his Boy. C. S. Lewis. Adapted by Glyn Robbins
M23 F3 or M11 F2 with doubling. Extras. Various simple settings. Fee code M **A + C L**

This enthralling adaptation of one of C. S. Lewis's Chronicles of Narnia blends drama, fantasy and humour. To escape the clutches of the evil warlord Rabadash, the horse, Bree and the boy, Shasta, run away together from the cruel land of Calormen. When they discover that Rabadash has plans to invade Narnia and neighbouring Archenland, they race ahead to warn the people of Narnia. The play can be very simply staged.
ISBN 978 0 573 05095 4

♦ **A bullet mark next to a title indicates that it is new to this edition of the Guide.**

The House That Sailed Away. Play. Pat Hutchins
M7 F4, 1 boy. 1M or F. Various simple settings. Fee code L **A + C L**

It's rained every day since Grandma arrived. Mother makes a shocking discovery: the house is half-way down the street and heading out to sea! In the exciting adventures that follow, the family find themselves at the centre of a dangerous international plot to steal the Crown Jewels. Please note that no specific music exists for the play and the author would like companies to create suitable music of their own.

How to Eat Like a Child. Musical revue **C/Y L**
Book by Delia Ephron, John Forster and Judith Kahan. Music and lyrics by John Forster. Based on the book by Delia Ephron

Children give 23 lessons gleaned from the heady experiences of being young – "how to wait for a hamburger", "how to stay home from school", and "how to express an opinion" among them. The pace is fast, the tone subversive, and the recognition instant among adults and children. On stage and as a highly praised television special, *How to Eat Like a Child* has an unbroken record of delighting audiences.
ISBN 978 0 573 68133 2

The Hundred and One Dalmatians. Play. Dodie Smith. Adapted by Glyn Robbins **A L**
20 characters, extras. May be played by a cast of 9, plus extras. Simple interior and exterior settings. Fee code M

Pongo, a Dalmatian dog, and his Missis are expecting their first litter. They become jittery when obsessive fur collector Mrs Cruella de Vil arrives. When Missis produces fifteen puppies, Cruella is enraptured and has the Badduns kidnap the litter. Distraught, Pongo and Missis enlist support on the Twilight Barking and encounter many adventures before rescuing their own pups – and a great many more!
ISBN 978 0 573 05114 2

I Read the News Today. Play. Willy Russell **A / Y**
M4, 3M or F. Split set: radio station and police station. Fee code D

This telling tale from the author of *Educating Rita* relates the night that the local radio station's late-night broadcast is interrupted by the arrival of Ronnie, who has escaped from police custody. Ronnie's act of 'vandalism', for which he has been convicted, was in reality a one-man stand against the lies told by advertisers and DJs. Ronnie is led away for psychiatric tests, but who is disturbed – Ronnie or the dream merchants?
ISBN 978 0 573 15222 1

The Ideal Gnome Expedition. Musical play. David Wood **A L**
6 characters M or F. A back yard, an alley, an adventure playground, a street, a traffic island. Fee code M

After rescuing a toy duck from the dustbin in their back yard, Mr Fisher and Mr Wheeler, two temporarily nomadic garden gnomes, decide to venture into the big wide world. Their object is to find a holiday island, just like the 'Big Ones', but being unused to the hazards of the town, they almost don't make it. Although nothing turns out quite as expected, they all agree that it is the best holiday they've ever had.
ISBN 978 0 573 05061 9

In Need of Care. Play. David E. Rowley
M2 F2. A derelict barn. Fee code C

Two girls on the run from an approved school take shelter in an old barn where they are discovered by two boys of their own age. The resulting delay prevents their escape from their followers, but one of the girls, at least, has benefited from the encounter.
ISBN 978 0 573 02322 4

Invisible Friends. A play. Alan Ayckbourn
M4 F3. Composite setting. Fee code M

Lucy is a very ordinary, straightforward teenager. With her father glued to the telly, her mother preoccupied with gossip and her brother enclosed in his ear-phones, no-one wants to know about her place in the swimming team. Lucy revives her childhood fantasy friend, Zara. However, Zara materializes, bringing with her an idealized father and brother. The moral of this cautionary tale is clearly spelt out – that when you get what you want it's not what you wanted: Lucy's dream family is a nightmare.

James and the Giant Peach. Play. Roald Dahl, adapted for the stage by David Wood
6 actors (with doubling and trebling). Extras. Various settings. Fee code M

Orphan James is sent to live with his aunts who treat him horribly. He meets an old man who gives him a bag containing the strongest magic in the world. When James accidentally spills it near the old peach tree the most marvellous things happen and so start his adventures with his new friends as he journeys in the Giant Peach to New York. David Wood's adaptation proves a worthy companion to his other Dahl dramatizations.
ISBN 978 0 573 05138 8

Jenny and the Lucky Bags. Musical play for children. Book and lyrics by Helen Murdoch. Music by Ethel McCracken
M4 (boys, middle-age) F5 (young, middle-age, elderly). Extras. A street, a shop, an open space. Fee code K. Vocal score available separately

Jenny's sweet shop is very popular, but she cannot get any sweets to sell. However, with the help of PC Spearmint and Jenny's pretty niece, following a magic trip and a thrilling encounter with the wicked Sugar Sorceress, Jenny's sweet stock is marvellously multiplied in time for the local fair.
ISBN 978 0 573 05059 3

Jeremy and the Thinking Machine. Play with music. Book and lyrics by Janet Neipris and Barbara Greenberg. Based on a story by Barbara Greenberg. Music by Janet Neipris
8 characters. Extras. Fee code G

Jeremy is the only child of the King and Queen of Jamboreen, but everyone agrees, including Jeremy, that he is not the brightest of princes. So, his fairy godmother gives him a thinking machine and he turns into a kind of genius. But does the machine require batteries? Will he be able to rescue his mother and defy his evil uncle? The music for the twelve easy songs is available separately on hire and the play has a running time of about one hour.
ISBN 978 0 573 05139 5

Joshua's Egg. Play. Jacqui Shapiro, music by Andrew Dodge **A L**
M3 F4, may be played by M1 F2 with doubling. Various simple settings. Fee code G (play), code B (music). ISBN 978 0 573 05119 7

Jump for Your Life. A dangerous play for children. Ken Whitmore **C L**
M6 F2, with doubling. Composite setting. Fee code L. ISBN 978 0 573 05049 7

The Jungle Book. Play. John Hartoch. Adapted from stories by Rudyard Kipling **C L**
Minimum 13 with doubling. Various simple jungle settings. Fee code M

Mowgli, the 'man-cub', lost in the jungle, is rescued from the clutches of the fearsome tiger, Shere Khan, by Baloo the bear and Bagheera the black panther. Brought up with a family of wolf-cubs, the time eventually comes for Mowgli to return to the world of Man. But Mowgli is not finished with the jungle, for one day he returns to settle the score with Shere Khan ...
ISBN 978 0 573 05077 0

C

Junk. Play. Melvin Burgess, adapted for the stage by John Retallack **A + Y L**
M8 F7 (doubling possible). Various simple settings. Fee code K

Junk caused a storm of controversy when it was published in 1996, due to its graphic descriptions of underage sex, hard drug abuse and prostitution. John Retallack's adaptation for the stage shows *Junk* as the love story that it is, a celebration of nonconformist youth culture emerging from punk and other alternative lifestyles. Tar loves Gemma, but Gemma doesn't want to be tied down; she wants to fly. But no-one can fly forever. One day you have to come down.

The Late Sleepers. Musical. Book and lyrics by Paul James. Music by Eric Angus **Y/L**
19 principals. Chorus. Simple setting. Fee by arrangement

An energetic, original rock musical for young people that was premièred by the National Youth Music Theatre. In a junk-strewn wasteland a gang of young people – self-styled vampires with bright dyed hair – scrape a strange existence on the outskirts of a walled city. With show-stopping numbers, a high gothic wedding, drama and betrayal, and, ultimately, heart-breaking bravery, this is a fascinating romp through the world of the Undead, of popular culture, and of teenage rebellion.
ISBN 978 0 573 18040 8 (libretto)

The Lion, the Witch and the Wardrobe. Play by Glyn Robbins. Adapted from the book by C. S. Lewis
M8 F5, with doubling. Extras. Various simple settings. Fee code M **A + C L**

Peter, Susan, Edmund and Lucy embark on a magical mystery tour to the Land of Narnia through the wardrobe. There they encounter the wicked White Witch, representing the forces of evil, and the King of the Beasts, Aslan the lion, representing all that is good and right. The White Witch is destroyed, allowing good to triumph over evil in the time-honoured way.
ISBN 978 0 573 05081 7

◆ **A bullet mark next to a title indicates that it is new to this edition of the Guide.**

The Little Mermaid. Hans Christian Andersen. Adapted by Pam Gems **C/Y L**
M5 F9 may be played by M2 F4. Various interior and exterior settings. Fee Code L

After falling in love with a prince on her very first journey to the surface, the Little Mermaid braves a journey to the evil Sea-Witch. Exchanging her voice and her mermaid's tail for legs, she heads for the surface once more, but any bargain with the Sea-Witch comes at a price ...

A Little Princess. Musical play. Michael Wild, from the novel by Frances Hodgson Burnett M10 F16. Extras. Various settings on an open stage. Fee by arrangement. Vocal score on hire. Period nineteenth-century **A + C L**

Little Women. Play. Louisa May Alcott, adapted for the stage by Emma Reeves **A + Y L**

Please see the entry in Section A.

The Magician's Nephew. Play. Glyn Robbins. Adapted from the book by C. S. Lewis M9 F4, with doubling. Various simple interior and exterior settings. Fee code M **A + C L**

Digory is concerned about his ill mother and about his Uncle Andrew, who seems very strange indeed. When Digory and his friend are tricked by Uncle Andrew into embarking on a series of magical adventures, they are brought into contact with the forces of both evil and good. Digory is set a task, which he completes successfully, and the safety of Narnia and the restored health of his mother are thereby ensured.
ISBN 978 0 573 15013 5

The Mammoth Sails Tonight! Play with songs. Adrian Mitchell. Music by Peter Moser **Y L**
Large mixed cast. Various settings. Fee code J for play, D for music. Music on hire

The Mammoth is the greatest sailing ship ever built. It is to carry Princess Alysoun from Noroway to Scotland, where she is to marry King Andrew the Bold. But she falls in love with Sir Patrick Spens, the bravest captain to sail the seven seas. He takes her on a wild adventure that involves timewarps, icebergs, trolls and skulduggery. A passionate, funny, subversive celebration!

Meg and Mog Show. Book, music and lyrics by David Wood. Based on Meg and Mog books by Helen Nicoll and Jan Pienkowski **A L**
15 characters, may be played by F1 and 6 or 7 M or F. Extras optional. Various simple settings. Fee code M

Ingeniously combining stories from five of the books we see Meg, Mog and Owl set off on an adventure to find the ingredients for a getting-rid-of-Steggy spell – an adventure that takes them to a medieval castle, zoo, and the moon! Lively songs and plenty of audience participation ensure a production to enchant all ages!
ISBN 978 0 573 05065 7

♦ **A bullet mark next to a title indicates that it is new to this edition of the Guide.**

Monkey in the Stars. Play. Jamila Gavin **A / Y**
M8 F6. Extras. Can be played by M3 F2 with doubling. Various simple interior and exterior settings. Fee code L

First performed at the Polka Theatre, Wimbledon, in 2000, this tells a story from the Indian epic poem *The Ramayana*. From Rama's banishment to his triumph, helped by an army of monkeys, over the ten-headed demon king, Ravana, this is a stirring and magical tale, framed by scenes set in the present in which a family prepares for Diwali, the traditional celebration of the return of Rama and Sita to safety.
ISBN 978 0 573 05128 1

More Adventures of Noddy. Enid Blyton. Adapted for the stage by David Wood **A L**
17 characters may be played by 10 actors. Simple settings. Fee code M (full length play), code G for each separate part

This is David Wood's second adaptation of Enid Blyton's classic children's stories. In two acts it may be performed as a full length play or each act may be performed separately as a one-act play. 'David Wood, the country's top children's dramatist has adapted some of Enid Blyton's charming Noddy stories and created another delightful, colourful show packed with fun, excitement and plenty of audience participation.' *What's On in London*
ISBN 978 0 573 05117 3

More Grimm Tales. The Brothers Grimm. Adapted by Carol Ann Duffy. Dramatized by Tim Supple and the Young Vic Company
Large cast, may be played by 9 actors. Simple settings. Fee code M **A L**

Funny, magical, cruel and wondrous, the folk classics *Little Red Riding Hood*, *Snow White*, *Rumpelstiltskin* and others from the brothers Grimm are presented here in acclaimed poet Carol Ann Duffy's enchantingly fresh adaptation, with a beguiling and vigorous dramatization by Tim Supple. 'The best demonstration all year of the living power of theatre, the children squealed with delight and so did I.' *Observer*

Mothers and Daughters. Books and lyrics by Ken Pickering. Music and lyrics by Keith Cole
6 to 200 characters. A bare stage. Fee by arrangement. Libretto and vocal score on hire **Y L**

'It is a characteristic of the human race that the most satisfactory relationships are those in which mother and daughter relationships achieve the transition into friendship ...' This highly entertaining musical presents mother/daughter relationships in a pastiche of situations which encompass school, exams, driving tests, budding romance, dreams, disillusionment, unemployment and employment.

Mr A's Amazing Maze Plays. Play. Alan Ayckbourn **A L**
M6 F2. Various simple settings. Fee code L

An ingeniously constructed play in which Suzy's mother buys her a small puppy to keep her company while she works hard to earn a living for them. A strange man– Mr Accousticus – moves into the empty house opposite their cottage; he charms Suzy's mother but frightens Suzy and her puppy Neville. Odd things start to happen ... Suzy is convinced that Mr Accousticus is responsible. She and Neville have to find out and how they do this depends on decisions taken by the audience aided by the Narrators!
ISBN 978 0 573 05098 5

Mr Macaroni and the Exploding Pizza Pie. Play for children. John Gardiner and Fiz Coleman
16 characters, doubling possible. Various simple settings on an open stage. Fee code K **C L**
ISBN 978 0 573 05062 6

The Musicians. Play. Patrick Marber **Y S**
Large flexible cast. A concert hall stage. Fee code E

The orchestra of Ridley Road, a state school, is to give a concert in Moscow at the European
Festival of Youth, playing Tchaikovsky's Fourth Symphony before an audience of cultural
bigwigs. But their instruments have been impounded by Customs. Luckily, Alex, the Russian
boy who cleans the hall, is a devout *Pinball Wizard* fan who comes up with a plan that saves
everyone. Written for the National Theatre's new writing programme for teenagers, it was
performed in the Cottesloe Theatre in 2004.
ISBN 978 0 573 05253 8

My Very Own Story. Play. Alan Ayckbourn **A L**
M8 F5, with doubling. A stage. Fee code M

Time for Percy Parton's Very Own Story, a gothic tale about a young man called Rupert who,
in the midst of a deep, dark and snow-laden wood, comes across a mysterious family whose
lives have been made wretched by the terrible spell that hangs over them. But wait a moment,
this tale can't be Percy Parton's because Peter Patchett claims it's his! But it can't be Peter
Patchett's, for according to Paul Peel, it's his! As the three story-tellers squabble a macabre,
darkly humorous morality tale is brought to life.
ISBN 978 0 573 05105 0

The Mystery of Dumsey Meadow. A Musical play. Music by David Perkins. Book and lyrics
by Caroline Dooley.
Large mixed cast. Fee by arrangement. Material on hire only **A + C L**

Deep in the heart of the English countryside the children of St Winifred's and St Albert's schools
find themselves caught up in a curious mystery when they go on a camping trip to the beautiful
Dumsey Meadow. Why did the Dumsey apple harvest fail for the first time in 300 years? Who
is the hooded woman with the horrible cackle . . . .

The Nativity. Play. Adapted by David Farr **A + C L**
Large mixed cast. Various simple settings. Fee code M

Joseph, the Carpenter, seems destined never to find love, until one day a beautiful girl enters
his workshop to escape from a storm. Her name is Mary, and three months later they are
married. But on their wedding night Mary tells Joseph that she is already pregnant. So begins
a remarkable journey involving giants, shepherds, kings, devils and angels, a journey covering
hundreds of miles and ending in a divine miracle.

◆ **A bullet mark next to a title indicates that it is new to this edition of the Guide.**

Nell's Belles. Musical. Kjartan Poskitt `Y L`
35 speaking parts (played by 15 with doubling). Chorus. Various simple settings. Fee by arrangement. Piano score on hire

It's the swinging 1660s. Charles II wants nothing too heavy: politics are a bore. When Nell and her friends from the local bawdy house join the Drury Lane Theatre, Charles is delighted by their saucy antics. A whole army of Charladies and seventeenth-century characters takes us through the story of Nell's and Charles' love affair, the Great Fire of London and recovery from the plague. An hilarious, easily-staged musical with a rock and roll score that should make learning history fun!
ISBN 978 0 573 08118 7 – Libretto

The Nightingale and the Emperor. Play for children. Alfred Bradley, after the story by Hans Christian Andersen `A L`
M6 (young, middle-age, elderly) F2 (young, middle-age). A palace throne-room, a kitchen, a wood. Fee code G. ISBN 978 0 573 05079 4

C

Noah's Ark. Play. Colin and Mary Crowther `C S`
Large cast. Various simple settings. Fee code D

This dramatization of the Bible story gives twenty to thirty 7-10 year olds a chance to practise their acting skills. Miming actions and props and using their voices for songs and sound effects, they learn how to relax, stand still and work together as a chorus. The moral lesson of the play won't go amiss either, as the Noah family battle with hostility and intolerance from Nasty Neighbours to create the Ark saving themselves and the Animals from the Flood.
ISBN 978 0 573 06255 1

Noddy. Enid Blyton, adapted for the stage by David Wood `A L`
18 characters may be played by M5 F3. Various simple settings. Fee code M

Exploiting the excitement of live theatre with imaginative staging, music, light, puppetry and lots of audience participation, this play will be a hit with all, whether they know Noddy or not. The plot may be familiar enough – Noddy and his friends pitched against the sneering goblins and a greedy witch – but the treatment is fresh, funny and inventive.
ISBN 978 0 573 05104 3

Nutcracker Sweet. Family musical. David Wood `A L`
M3 F3. Extra 1M or F. Fairground booths on an open stage. Fee code M

The Nuts, led by the imposing Kernel Walnut, decide to show that Nuts need not be 'nutty'. Unfortunately William the Conker seems to prove the opposite and falls under the spell of the wicked Professor Jelly, who is always on the look-out for nuts to 'glaze'. Together they almost succeed in glazing all our hero nuts, but the day is saved when Professor Jelly is imprisoned in his own glaze and turned into a large chocolate.
ISBN 978 0 573 15002 9

◆ **A bullet mark next to a title indicates that it is new to this edition of the Guide.**

The Oedipus Plays. Play. Caroline Reader, adapted from the plays by Sophocles
22 named characters. Extras. Composite setting. Fee code K. ISBN 978 0 573 05130 2

Old Father Time. Musical play. Book, music and lyrics by David Wood
Up to 30 characters but can be played by a cast of 12 with doubling and trebling. Four simple settings. Fee code M

Old Father Time lives in Big Ben and makes sure things happen on time. One day the inconceivable happens and Big Ben stops! The action of the play chases across the centuries through prehistoric times and near and far history until, with the help of some not-too-bright buskers and a wicked sorceress, Big Ben is started once more.
ISBN 978 0 573 05046 6

The Old Man of Lochnagar. Musical play by David Wood, based on the book by H.R.H. The Prince of Wales
16 characters, may be played by 12 actors with doubling. Various settings. Fee code M

The Gorms are responsible for spraying the Highland heather purple so why is there only white heather? The Gorms have gone to ground because Giant Gormless (a not very big giant) is trying to capture them for his performing circus. So, the Old Man of Lochnagar sets off determined to save the Gorms and bring the colour back to the Highlands!

Orvin – Champion of Champions. A musical by Alan Ayckbourn. Music by Denis King
M16 F8 plus chorus. Simple settings. Fee by arangement

An epic musical of accidental heroism. The gods set out to relate the tale of the Great Ulmar, legendary warrior of Sollistis. But their narrative suffers a major technical hitch when Orvin, Ulmar's hopeless squire, oversleeps on the eve of battle. What follows proves a challenge even to such seasoned storytellers as the gods themselves as they vainly attempt to re-write history with only the help of Orvin, the unlikeliest, most reluctant of last-minute replacement champions.

Our Day Out. Play. Willy Russell
M10 F4. 7 boys. 3 girls. Extras. Various simple interior and exterior settings. Fee code H. In the volume *Act I*

This play by award-winning Willy Russell was first seen on BBC2 in 1977 and has now been specially edited for practical use by schools, colleges and groups. Sad, humorous and true to life, it tells the story of a bunch of underprivileged, remedial Liverpool schoolchildren who are taken on a day's outing by their teachers.

Our Day Out. Book by Willy Russell. Songs and music by Bob Eaton, Chris Mellor and Willy Russell
M6 F3 (may be played by M3 F2). 16-20 children. Various simple interior and exterior settings. Fee by arrangement

Some underprivileged schoolchildren are taken on a day's outing by their teachers. The children boisterously rampage through a roadside café, a zoo, Conway Castle and a beach. A joyous celebration of the joys and agonies of growing up, but also a sharp pointer to the depressing present and empty future, for a day out is as much as these children can expect.
ISBN 978 0 573 08058 6

The Owl and the Pussycat Went to See ... Musical play for children. David Wood and Sheila Ruskin `A L`
M9 F5. Extras. One basic setting. Fee code M

The story based on the adventures of Lear's Owl and Pussycat who went to sea in a beautiful pea-green boat; of the Pig with a Ring through its Nose; of the villainous Plum Pudding Flea and others. These are interlinked with songs and mimed interludes. After many adventures, the Plum Pudding Flea is foiled and the two protagonists are married and live happily ever after.
ISBN 978 0 573 05027 5

Pandemonium! (a Greek Myth-adventure). Book and lyrics by Jenifer Toksvig. Music by David Perkins `A / Y`
22 Principals, Greek Chorus (variable number). Simple settings. Fee by arrangement

Welcome to Ancient Greece and the wedding of Pandora and Epimetheus! Pandora's a gift from Zeus, the king of the gods. A strange box appears amongst the wedding presents, and curiosity compels Pandora to open it. All manner of evil is released into the world! She grabs the box and runs away. This wasn't part of Zeus's plan! Follow the gods, goddesses, nymphs and mortals in their mad race to find Pandora and the box ...
ISBN 978 0 573 08117 0

Papa Panov's Magic Christmas. Play. Paul Thain. From a story by Leo Tolstoy `C S`

Please see the entry in Section D.

The Papertown Paperchase. Musical play for children. David Wood `A L`
12 characters, doubling possible. Extras. Nine simple settings. Fee code J

The Salamander is in trouble with the Fireflies because he is unable to breathe fire. To redeem himself he is sent on a mission to burn down Papertown. The townspeople gather their resources to meet the threat: even the two petty criminals, Blotch and Carbon, are released to join forces. In the end Salamander, who has fallen for timid little Tishoo, helps to thwart the Fireflies, and Papertown is saved from destruction.
ISBN 978 0 573 05032 9

Percival the Performing Pig. Play. Dilys Owen `C S`
21 characters, doubling possible. Extras. A bare stage. Fee code C

On old MacDonald's farm there lived a pig with a truly wonderful voice. Animals came from miles around to hear him sing; and so did Hiram J. Potter who bought him and took him off to London for a career in Grand Opera. But Percival wasn't keen on London so he planned to get home to the farm.
ISBN 978 0 573 15224 5

Peter Pan. Fantasy. J. M. Barrie `A + C/Y L`

For a full synopsis please see the entry in Section D.

Peter Pan. Book, music and lyrics by Piers Chater-Robinson. Adapted from the play by J. M. Barrie **A + C/Y L**
30 named parts. Extras. Fee by arrangement

The everlasting classic account of the children who follow Peter Pan and the fairy Tinker Bell into Never Land where children never grow old and where Captain Hook is outwitted, is here set to a delightful score. The addition of such songs as 'The Darlings', 'What Happens When you're Grown Up', 'Rich, Damp Cake' and 'You've Gotta Believe' enhances the play and will win new audiences everywhere.
ISBN 978 0 573 08059 3

The Phantom Tollbooth. Children's play. Susan Nanus. Based on the book by Norton Juster
Maximum of 37 roles for 19 performers. Several simple settings. Fee code K **A L**

Milo's adventures begin when he opens a large package and drives his small toy car through the tollbooth into a new world. He learns of the great argument between King Azaz of Dictionopolis and his brother the Mathe-magician of Digitopolis. Milo also has to rescue the Princesses Sweet Rhyme and Pure Reason, from the Land of Ignorance. Milo realizes his attitude toward learning will never again be the same.

The Pied Piper. Play with music. Adrian Mitchell, devised by Alan Cohen. Music by Dominic Muldowney. From the poem by Robert Browning **A/C L**
M8 F4, with doubling. Children. Various interior and exterior settings. Fee code H for play. Separate fee code for music (NB. The music is now leased by Samuel French Ltd)

Hamelin is infested with rats and the town's avaricious Mayor employs the Pied Piper, who solves the problem. But when cheated of his reward, the Piper spirits away the children, guiding them through a mountainous region of fearsome monsters and lonely knights until they reach a children's paradise. (Please specify author when ordering.)

The Pied Piper. Musical play. David Wood and Dave and Toni Arthur **A/C L**
M5 F3 (minimum). 20 children. A street. Fee code M

The Piper, as a modern busker, delights the childen with his music. Their parents soon put a stop to the energetic dancing. Music has been banned on this street for hundreds of years. The townsfolk act out the story of the Pied Piper, but the Piper once again enchants the children with his music. It is only when the Piper receives his fee promised by the medieval townsfolk that he frees Hamelin from the curse. (Please specify author when ordering.)
ISBN 978 0 573 15007 4 (Libretto)
ISBN 978 0 573 08587 1 (Vocal Score)

♦ **Playing With My Heart**. A comedy by Shaun Prendergast **A/Y S**
M7 F7 (may be played by M5 F4). Simple setting. Fee Code D

A group of adolescents and their teacher are on a visit to Gateshead. With their coach delayed, squabbles and jealousies break out, requiring the Angel of the North to come down from her lofty height . . . When a rival school comes on the scene, their jeers and taunts meld the group, goading them into a football penalty shoot-out giving Ella the chance to redeem herself.
ISBN 978 0 573 05260 6

The Play of the Royal Astrologers. Play. Willis Hall **A L**
20 characters, doubling possible. Extras. Various simple settings. Fee code M.
ISBN 978 0 573 05091 6

The Plotters of Cabbage Patch Corner. Musical play for children. David Wood **A L**
M6 F4. 1M 1F voices only. A garden. Fee code M

The insects in the garden are overshadowed by humans – the Big Ones. Infuriated by constant 'spraying', Slug, Greenfly and Maggot call for rebellion and ruination of the garden. The others oppose this, and war is declared. The garden goes to ruin, and the Big Ones decide to build a garage on it. The insects combine forces to restore the garden to its original beauty and thus preserve their home.
ISBN 978 0 573 05030 5

♦ **Punk Rock.** Play. Simon Stephens **Y L**
M5 (teens;middle-aged) F4 (teens). School Library. Hospital room. Fee Code M

William Carlisle has the world at his feet but its weight on his shoulders. In the library of a fee-paying grammar school, William and his fellow sixth-formers are preparing for their mock A-levels while navigating the pressures of teenage life. They are educated and aspirational young people, but step-by-step, the dislocation, disjunction and latent aggression is revealed. Premiered at the Lyric, Hammersmith in 2009. "powerful and compelling . . . evokes the twilight world of the teenager with scary vividness. . . " *Independent*
ISBN 978 1 408 12636 3

The Queen Must Die. Comedy. David Farr **Y S**
M4 (teens) F3 (teens). 1F Voice. Various simple settings. Fee code F

On the eve of the Golden Jubilee celebrations a papier-mâché statue of Queen Elizabeth II stands in Margaret Chivers' living-room in preparation for the Jubilee parade. Two factions converge on the house with the aim of vandalizing the statue – three girls who want to escape the embarrassment of dancing in the parade, and three lads wishing to make an anti-monarchist statement. Politics, friendship, Oliver Cromwell and Britney Spears feature in this ingenious comedy.
ISBN 978 0 573 05254 5

Quest for the Whooperdink. Play with music. A. H. Teacey **A L**
M3 F2, 4 others M or F. Extras. Various simple settings. Fee code H. ISBN 978 0 573 05070 1

Rabbit. Play. David Foxton **Y S**
15 characters (M and F). Simple settings on a bare stage. Fee code D

This perceptive play, set ten years 'after the Bomb', portrays with frightening clarity the destruction of the human character, as compassion and social standards become lost in the struggle for power and survival. Fifteen teenagers struggle to make sense of their world's desolation. Ironically, they soon begin to repeat their parents' mistakes, with the play ending in a thought-provoking clash of personalities.
ISBN 978 0 573 15240 5

The Railway Children. E. Nesbit. Adapted by Dave Simpson $\boxed{A + C\ L}$
M5 F5. 5 girls. 5 boys. Extras. A country railway station, a cottage, a railway tunnel. Fee code M

Set in and around a country railway station at the turn of the twentieth century, the plight of the Railway Children grappling with their new environment is imaginatively brought to life for a modern audience while losing nothing of the original spirit of humour, tension, adventure and the final triumph of good over evil.
ISBN 978 0 573 05083 1

The Railway Children. Musical. Book and lyrics by Julian Woolford. Music by Richard John. From the novel by E. Nesbit $\boxed{A + C/Y\ L}$

A superb adaptation for the musical stage of E. Nesbit's quintessentially English classic. An idyllic Edwardian family Christmas is interrupted by a knock at the door and a family's life is changed forever. Father is wrongfully arrested and Mother and the three children, Roberta (Bobbie), Peter and Phyllis, are forced to move to the country. Discovering a railway near their new house is just the beginning of a series of adventures set over one long summer.
ISBN 978 0 573 18032 3 (libretto).
978 0 573 19006 3 (song book).
978 0 573 18532 8 (vocal score)

Rainbow's Ending. Play. Noël Greig $\boxed{C/Y\ L}$
Large ensemble playing many roles. A bare stage. Fee code J

This is a modern fable which tells the story of a world in the grip of two giants whose insatiable appetite is driving it, apparently inevitably, to utter devastation. How a society and its individuals react to such a threat is the subject of this multi-faceted play, whose 'storytelling' style encourages inventive and imaginative approaches to dramatic work with the performer acting as both character and narrator.
ISBN 978 0 573 15243 6

The Ramayana. Play of the Hindu epic. Peter Oswald $\boxed{Y\ L}$

Please see the entry in Section A.

The Real Spirit of Christmas. Christmas play for children. Wes Magee $\boxed{C\ S}$

Please see the entry in Section D.

The Real Story of Puss in Boots. Play. David Foxton $\boxed{A + C + Y\ L}$
M6 F3 or M7 F4. Various simple settings. Fee code K

The story of *Puss in Boots* is ingeniously combined with that of *Cinderella* in this hilarious show. Puss in Boots transforms humble Colin Miller into Prince Charming. Cinderella's Fairy Godmother helps her to become Princess Priscilla, despite her meddling stepsisters. The two marry, providing two happy endings. Outrageous characters, a wealth of jokes and a fast-paced plot make this a hugely likeable show, which can be performed by a small cast without songs.
ISBN 978 0 573 06497 5

A Right Christmas Caper. Play. Willis Hall ▉A L▉

For a full synopsis please see the entry in Section D.

The Attack Upon and Defence of the Old Elvish Kingdom of Vassia Against **The River Witch** and Her Grim Horde. A play. David Clarke ▉C S▉
28 speaking parts. Extras. An open space. Fee code G. Optional score available separately.
ISBN 978 0 573 15241 2

Robin Hood. Musical celebration. David Wood and Dave and Toni Arthur ▉A L▉

For a full synopsis please see the entry in Section A.

Rockasocka. Musical play. Book and lyrics by John Gardiner. Music by Andrew Parr ▉Y L▉
M9 F9. Minimum of 25 for other parts. Extras. Simple settings. Fee by arrangement
ISBN 978 0 573 08091 3 (Libretto)
ISBN 978 0 573 08590 1 (Vocal score)

Rosie and the Bad, Bad Apples. Children's musical. Book and lyrics by Valerie Hall. Music by Paul Whittington ▉A + C▉
M8 F5. Large Chorus with various small roles. Various simple settings. Fee by arrangement.
Vocal score available separately. ISBN 978 0 573 08113 2 (Libretto)

Round the World with Class 6. Play for children. Nick Warburton ▉C S▉
7 children or more. A classroom. Fee code D

Class 6 are well-behaved, hard-working ... and bored. Every day is much the same – and then Mr Parker, the supply teacher, sets them an interesting project: to re-enact Sir Francis Drake's circumnavigation of the world in 1577. Within minutes the room is transformed into an Elizabethan sailing ship and the brave adventurers set sail!
ISBN 978 0 573 15239 9

The Rumpelstiltskin Racket. Musical. Kjartan Poskitt ▉Y L▉
11 named parts, doubling possible. Various interior and exterior settings. Fee by arrangement

An inventive and highly individual presentation of the well-loved fairy tale. The palace is bustling and the hacks from the Daily Slur are hard at work. Will Miranda manage to spin straw into gold, or will she be flogged by the jealous Madam Inquisitor? Only her mysterious visitor can help, but at what cost? A humorous, tuneful excursion into a world of love, intrigue, deception and the magical mischief of the manikin with no name.
ISBN 978 0 573 08103 3 (Libretto)
ISBN 978 0 573 08597 0 (Vocal score)

♦ **A bullet mark next to a title indicates that it is new to this edition of the Guide.**

Rupert and the Green Dragon. Musical play. David Wood
Based on the *Rupert* stories by Mary Tourtel and Alfred Bestall
16 characters. May be played by M5 F5. Various simple settings. Fee code M

Edward Trunk wishes for a sunny day for his birthday, but Nutwood is currently experiencing only winter weather. Rupert goes to see the Clerk of the Weather. The friendly Green Dragon is a great help but Zita, the Ice Maid, has to be foiled first! Songs take the place of rhyming couplets and there is a chance for the audience to help in the adventure.
ISBN 978 0 573 05113 5 (Libretto)
ISBN 978 0 573 08598 7 (Vocal score)

Sammy's Magic Garden. Play with music. Kjartan Poskitt **A / Y**
10 characters, doubling possible. Extras. Various interior and exterior settings. Fee code L

An enormously entertaining and funny musical comedy/ghost story. Sammy has just moved into a new house, overseen by 'housekeeper' Miss Nettles and a bumbling gardener, Compost. Weird things start happening! Sammy and his friend Alice find proof that Miss Nettles is a witch and that the garden is filled with enchanted Flower-children put under a spell by her. But it's Sammy and Alice, with some help from Compost, who save the day and the children are released.
ISBN 978 0 573 15015 9

Save the Human. Play with music. Based on the story by Tony Husband and David Wood. Book and lyrics by David Wood. Music by Peter Pontzen and David Wood. Lyrics for 'Rock 'n' Roar' by Tony Husband **A L**
Large flexible cast, minimum of 8 or 11 actors possible. Various simple settings. Fee code M

'It seems that long, long ago human beings ruled the world but made a terrible mess of it. They kept having wars and polluting the earth. They nearly succeeded in killing themselves off completely ... ' Now the animals are in charge. A worldwide campaign is started to SAVE THE HUMAN from extinction.
ISBN 978 0 573 05090 9

The Scatterbrained Scarecrow of Oz. Play for children. Alfred Bradley **A L**
M10 F5, or a mixed cast of 9 with doubling. An open stage. Fee code F. ISBN 978 0 573 05057 2

The Secret Garden. Frances Hodgson Burnett. Adapted by Neil Duffield **A + Y L**
M1 or 2 F2. 2 boys, 1 girl (with doubling). Various simple settings. Fee code L

Orphan Mary Lennox, snobbish and aloof, is sent to stay with her reclusive uncle at Misselthwaite Manor in Yorkshire. She makes friends with Dickon, who understands animals and nature, and discovers a secret garden that she can tend. As the garden is transformed, Mary, her invalid cousin Colin, and then his grieving father, feel the power of the magic of new life and growth. Period early 20th century
ISBN 978 0 573 05120 3

♦ **The Secret Garden (Spring version)** Book and lyrics by Marsha Norman. Music by Lucy Simon. Based on the novel by Frances Hodgson Burnett
Please see the entry in Section E.

The See-Saw Tree. Musical play. David Wood **A L**
16 characters, doubling possible. Various simple settings. Fee code M

An ancient Oak stands on ground which is ear-marked for development into a children's playground by Mr Jay. A public meeting is held to discuss his proposals, which include cutting down the three-hundred-year-old tree. The members of the council are then seen inside the tree in their equivalent animal forms to show us the devastating effect such plans would have on the inhabitants of the tree. In the end, the audience is asked to vote whether the See-Saw Tree should be saved or not.
ISBN 978 0 573 15017 3 (Libretto)
ISBN 978 0 573 08583 3 (Vocal score)

The Selfish Giant. A children's musical based on the short story by Oscar Wilde. Music, lyrics and adaptation by David Perkins. Additional lyrics by Caroline Dooley **C S**
Large variable cast. Simple settings. Fee by arrangement

From the composer of the popular children's musical *Shake, Ripple & Roll* comes this skilful sung-through musical written specially for a large cast of young people. It has great opportunity for lots of chorus and solo work, which can be easily adapted according to how many children are available. Running time approximately fifty-five minutes
ISBN 978 0 573 08122 4

The Selfish Shellfish. Play with music. David Wood **A L**
7 characters. A rockpool. Fee code M

In this play, the serious contemporary issue of oil pollution is looked at from the point of view of shellfish directly involved. The fight of Urchin, Mussel, Starfish, Seagull and the shellfish himself, H. C., to avoid becoming the innocent victims of pollution caused by the collison of two ships at sea, is delightfully told, with the audience being encouraged to participate in the battles with Sludge and The Great Slick.
ISBN 978 0 573 05069 5

Seven Golden Dragons. Play with music. Book and lyrics by Randall Lewton. Music by Peter Miller
34 named characters. Extras. Various simple interior and exterior settings. Fee code L **Y L**
ISBN 978 0 573 05089 3

Shake, Ripple & Roll. Musical for young people. Book and lyrics by Jenifer Toksvig. Music by David Perkins
13 principals. Chorus. An ice-cream parlour. Fee by arrangement. Vocal score on hire **C/Y L**

Another hectic day at Angelo's New York ice cream parlour when suddenly the phone rings – Angelo is dead! In walks glamorous Deanna la Domme, claiming to be his only living relative and announcing she's going to sell to Crazy Flavours. It is time to call Dirk Manley – private detective – to find the will double quick. An exuberant musical, with a glitzy rock'n'roll score, and a running time of approximately one hour. Period 1950s
ISBN 978 0 573 08112 5 (Libretto)

The Siege. Play with songs. Book by Adrian Mitchell. Music by Andrew Dickson **Y L**
Large flexible cast. Various simple settings. Fee code K (for play) code C (for music)

Adrian Mitchell has created a vibrant and topical text with songs. War breaks out and the town of Arden is under siege. On their sixteenth birthday and liable for military call-up, Betsy and Arlo Swados decide to flee to a neutral country but on the journey Arlo is killed. Betsy and the townspeople rebel against the racist gangster who has taken over the town and Arlo's funeral turns into a celebration for peace.

Sing Yer Heart Out for the Lads. Play by Roy Williams **A + Y L**
Please see the entry in Section A.

SIX PRIMROSES EACH & OTHER PLAYS FOR YOUNG ACTORS. Ellen Dryden

The eleven plays in this volume were written for Chiswick Youth Theatre, and they were in regular workshop and performance use by young actors between the ages of eleven and eighteen. The plays cover the whole range of secondary education, with good parts and dramatic situations for everyone between the playing ages of ten and twenty. They are particularly suitable for National Curriculum Key Stages 3 and 4. But they are not just teaching material; all are entertaining plays, and the best are as succinct and dramatically powerful as one act plays can be.

Six Primroses Each
F1 (young) 4 boys, 5 girls. A church hall. Fee code C **C + Y S**

Seven schoolchildren are evacuated to the country from the war-torn East End of London. Fearful, miserable and apprehensive, they wait in the village hall to be sorted for billeting. Their fears are hardly allayed by Angela, an evacuee from Manchester, who airily warns them of the horrors they can expect. Period 1940

Adventure Camp
12 girls. Two tents. Fee code C **Y S**

A school is holidaying at an adventure camp. In the girls' tents the conversation centres on the harshness of the routine and the appalling food. Sophie, acutely homesick, continually cries and Lottie, whose parents made a donation to a charity fund which enabled the others to attend the camp, is finding it hard to make friends. But rebellion is in the air ...

The Children's Ward
F1, 4 boys (teenage). A ward. Fee code C **Y S**

Four boys in a hospital ward, some of them long-stay patients, struggle to come to terms with each other and the death of one of their inmates in the ward.

The Press Gang
4 boys, 6 girls. A classroom. Fee code D **Y S**

The committee of a school magazine meets for a report on the first issue. Unfortunately the treasurer announces the profits have gone astray. Tensions rise as the co-founder, Mandy, confronts her once friend and fellow founder Suzi. It seems that not only the magazine will fold.

In Service
1 boy (12), 5 girls (14, slightly older). An attic, a kitchen. Fee code C **C + Y S**

In a large London house the maids awake to their duties on a freezing winter morning: they have only had a few hours' sleep. Lavinia, used to being well-treated in the country house where she was a nursery maid, finds it hard to adjust to the cruel way of her new life in London. Period 1890

The Colour of Compassion. The Story of Mary Seacole
F25, 1 M extra, may be played by a cast of 9. Fee code D **Y S**

Mary Seacole, a Creole born in Jamaica, dreamt of becoming a doctress but prejudice against her sex and colour thwarted her ambition. Refused permission to join Florence Nightingale's nurses because of her colour, she made her own way to the Crimea where she cared for many. Period early to mid 19th century

The Strawberry Tea
M2 F3. A school library. Fee code C **Y S**

A group of sixth formers at a comprehensive school are arranging the annual school OAP Strawberry Tea. This year will be worse than usual since the guest of honour is Miss Allenbury, an ex-teacher, now retired, a stickler for protocol who doesn't like boys. But, it seems, Miss Allenbury won't be attending the tea to celebrate her eightieth birthday ...

Flatmates
M3 F2. A sitting-room. Fee code D **Y S**

Students Tom and Lyn share the flat that Steve's wealthy parents bought for him. Steve arranges for a prospective flatmate, Coralie, to come for an interview to take Tom's room – without telling Tom. Tom discovers what's happening and meekly agrees to take a smaller room. Lyn has had enough and says she's leaving. Steve's not too worried, though – he's got Coralie now.

Shadows
M1 F3. An empty stage. Fee code B **Y S**

A man, David, emerges from the shadows of an empty theatre. Soon he is joined by Peggy, fresh from drama school who has come to audition for the part of Cordelia. Peggy begins to perform her audition speech and David joins her, playing the part of Lear. When Peggy asks who he is he replies, "Just – a jobbing actor." A mysterious, haunting drama.

Hallo, Is That You?
F1 (19). A bedsit. Fee code A **Y S**

Selina returns to her bedsit exhausted and in a high state of nervous tension. There has been a power cut. Selina sits awaiting a phone call from the hospital where her mother and estranged father sit at the bedside of her nine-year-old sister, Mel, who lies in a coma after a road accident which followed a bitter row Selina had with Mel.

Madam Has A Combination Skin
F1 (late teens). A sitting-room. Fee code A **Y S**

Sally is bursting with excitement and eager to tell her flatmate, Gemma, about her new job as a Rose Angel Beauty Philosopher. But Gemma is in the bath. Undeterred, Sally continues talking until the phone rings. It's for Gemma. Sally's mood changes to one of fury: "No, I won't get her. Because I'm the Rose Angel Beauty Philosopher for this area."

Skool & Crossbones. Caribbean-style musical for children. Book and lyrics by Jenifer Toksvig. Music by David Perkins
8 principals, chorus. One simple setting. Fee by arrangement. Score on hire **C + Y L**

Sizzling with Caribbean-style music, this show, written for 7-14 year olds to perform, is a toe-tapping treat for the whole family. When a group of children on a school boating trip force their headmistress to walk the plank, all hell breaks loose. The pirates attempt to take over a tranquil Caribbean island – will they succeed or will the islanders, with the help of the gods, conjure up something powerful?
ISBN 978 0 573 08124 8

Smashed Eggs. Play for 8-11 year olds by Phil Porter **A + C L**
M2 F2. A house interior, a wood, a hill path. Fee code L. ISBN 978 0 573 05132 6

The Snatching of Horrible Harold. Play for children. John Gardiner and Fiz Coleman
M4 F5. Extra 1M or F. Composite setting. Fee code K **A + C L**
ISBN 978 0 573 05074 9

The Snow Queen. Play. Ron Nicol. Based on the story by Hans Christian Andersen
Large mixed cast. Much doubling and trebling possible. Various simple settings.
Fee code K **A + C + Y L**

Skilfully adapted from the famous original story by Hans Christian Andersen, this is the story of Gerda, a little girl who seaches for her friend Kai when he is bewitched and imprisoned by the Snow Queen in her ice palace. Gerda's innocence charms all good people and animals she meets on the way. They help her to the royal court, and on to Lapland, where good conquers evil and the children are reunited.
ISBN 978 0 573 16503 0

Some Canterbury Tales. Freely adapted from Geoffrey Chaucer by Ken Pickering. Music by Derek Hyde
Variable cast, 7 named roles. Extras. Flexible settings. Fee by arrangement **Y L**

Six of Chaucer's best known Canterbury Tales – the Knight's, the Wife of Bath's, the Pardoner's, the Franklin's, the Nun's Priest's and the Miller's – are here freely adapted for the stage. Original and adapted music to suit the period has been added. The style of the play is that of a spontaneous telling of a story by a group of strolling players, with all the Company taking various parts in enacting the different tales.
ISBN 978 0 573 08077 7

Space Junk. Play. Les Ellison
Large mixed cast. Various simple settings. Fee code G (play), code B (music) **C + Y L**
ISBN 978 0 573 05121 0

◆ **A bullet mark next to a title indicates that it is new to this edition of the Guide.**

Sparkleshark. Play. Philip Ridley
M6 (14-15) F3 (14-15). A rooftop. Fee code H **Y L**

Fourteen-year-old Jake, the classroom "geek", takes refuge on the roof of a tower block in order to write his stories. Before long other young people join him and the taunting begins. Although at first he endeavours to hide he learns to fight back in the only way he knows how – storytelling. Soon the whole group is enmeshed in the story, enacting a fantastic tale which resonates with the dynamics of their own friendships and enmities.
ISBN 978 0 573 05122 7

The Spider and the Bird. Play. Georgia Dobbs **Y S**
20 named parts. Extras. Various simple settings. Fee code E

School gang-leader Sonia regains consciousness, having been attacked in a drugs-related gang war. Recuperating in hospital she re-evaluates her life, opting for freedom and a life away from drugs, gangs and power. By example, she persuades her friends to follow her. With a large cast and simple settings, this topical play is ideal for schools. The actors are encouraged to create their own soliloquies, thus providing a basis for further discussion.
ISBN 978 0 573 12259 0

Spot's Birthday Party. David Wood. Based on the books by Eric Hill **C L**
M5 F1. Simple settings.. Fee Code M

Adapting the popular *Spot* books for the stage, David Wood has created an exciting introduction to theatre for small children. Using the simple plot of a birthday party, complete with entertainer, the puppy and his animal friends teach and reflect children's early experiences such as guests arriving, present giving, game playing and going home thank-yous. Plenty of fun for the actors, too, with singing, character movement and, optionally, some acrobatic skills to show off!
ISBN 978 0 573 05129 6

Stags and Hens (the Re-Mix). Comedy. Willy Russell **Y L**
M6 (one non-speaking) F5. The Ladies' and Gents' toilets in a dance hall. Fee code M

Dave gets legless on a mix of drinks, while his mates demonstrate a combination of fear, lust and bravado. Linda's chums, alternately sentimental and sceptical about marriage, turn nasty when the bride starts dancing with an ex-lover, Peter. Whether Peter's worldly wisdom persuades Linda to flee an unsuitable marriage or merely makes her more prepared for the drudgery to come, is left unsaid.
ISBN 978 0 573 01609 7

Stone Soup (revised). Play. Paul Thain **A/C S**
12 named parts. Extras. A bare stage. Fee code E

The wise Sophia enters a starving village and declares she will feed everyone with her magical stone soup, and thus encourages the villagers to share their own hoarded goods for the benefit of the community. However, when Sophia philosophizes about peace and justice she is labelled a subversive by the autocratic government figure, General Mayhem. Despite this, the spirit of sharing and co-operation prevails in this heart-warming tale.
ISBN 978 0 573 15242 9

Summer in the Park. Musical. Book by Ellen Dryden, lyrics by Don Taylor, music by Charles Young
Large, flexible cast. Secluded area in a park. Fee by arrangement Y L

A derelict park is threatened by developers and a group of young people try to rescue it by writing and performing a play. But the project soon falters: the developers hover, the cast bicker and the hot weather breaks with a violent storm. But the park exercises a strange hold over them. A subtle, touching story combining an accurate, amusing account of producing a play with lively, realistic characterization and a memorable score.
ISBN 978 0 573 08089 0

Surgical Sensations at St Sennapod's, or Dr Scalpel's Missing Bit. Play with music. John Gardiner and Fiz Coleman. Music arranged by James R. Pearson
19 characters, doubling possible. Extras. A hospital ward. Fee code K Y L

A top surgeon has disappeared from St Sennapod's Hospital leaving young Dr Boldly in charge of Ward 10. Sinister Dr Scalpel arrives, trying to corner the market in spare-part surgery by snipping off spare parts wherever he can. However, Orderly Jim Pill and the hospital staff succeed in foiling Scalpel's dastardly plans and all ends happily. This fun-filled, fast-moving play for children is easily staged and allows plenty of opportunity for audience participation.
ISBN 978 0 573 05087 9

The Sweeney Todd Shock 'n' Roll Show. Musical play. Peter Miller and Randall Lewton Y L
20 main speaking parts, large supporting cast. Various interior and exterior settings. Fee by arrangement. Vocal score available separately

Billy and Tommy encounter the Demon Barber and his murderous accomplice Mrs Lovett. When Billy decides he needs a shave before travelling home to give his Susan a string of pearls the scene is set for musical mayhem with plenty of blood, pies and horrible murder thrown in for good measure!
ISBN 978 0 573 18030 9 (Libretto)

Taking Breath. Play for young people. Sarah Daniels Y S
M4 (16-20) F6 (14-19). Extra: 1M voice only. Various simple settings. Fee code H

Elliot, an eco-warrior, has fallen from a tree-top and now lies comatose in a hospital bed. When he fell, he slipped into the past, meeting Lucy, a suffragette from 1913. Alana, excluded from school, passionately follows all Elliot's TV news coverage and, by strange coincidence, it becomes evident that Lucy was Alana's great-grandmother. Alana is able to assist Elliot's recovery as well as using the past to find peace for herself. Period 1913 and present day.
ISBN 978 0 573 05252 1

The Tales of Hans Andersen. Play. A dramatization by Pete Meakin Y + C L
57 named characters, can be played by M5 F5. Narrators. Simple settings. Fee code L

A flexible adaptation of the haunting stories of Hans Christian Andersen, comprising *The Little Match Girl*, *The Brave Tin Soldier* and *The Snow Queen*. There are 57 named characters with many more numbered characters acting as narrators. The acclaimed original production at the Derby Playhouse used a cast of 10 but it can be played by as many as 100 or more. If required, the original score by Tony Coffey can be hired from the Derby Playhouse. With simple settings and a minimum of props this is an ideal choice of seasonal play.
ISBN 978 0 573 05131 9

Telling Wilde Tales. Seven Fairy Tales of Oscar Wilde. Adapted for the stage by Jules Tasca Flexible cast. An open stage. Fee code L for complete play. Individual plays are each on fee code B **A L**

If all seven plays are performed together they can be played by M4 F3 (minimum) although each play can be performed separately

Jules Tasca offers brilliant adaptations of some of the most endearing fairy tales ever written. This full evening's entertainment includes *The Birthday of the Infanta*, *The Star Child*, *The Happy Prince*, *The Nightingale and the Rose*, *The Devoted Friend*, *The Fisherman and his Soul*, *The Young King*.

Terraces. Play. Willy Russell **Y S**
M6 F6. 2 children. Simple settings. Fee code D

The local football team has reached the final and when Danny facetiously remarks on painting the street in support his friends take up the idea with fervour and paint their terraced houses yellow – the team's colour. But Danny refuses and when the family are ostracized by the community Danny's wife leaves him. Is he just stubborn and awkward or is he right to assert his independence?

There Was an Old Woman ... Family musical. David Wood **A L**
6 main characters. Children. A glade, a hilltop. Fee code M

Happily crowded to the laces of the shoe they live in, Mother Shipton and her family are faced with eviction as the Giant, whose shoe it was originally, has now come looking for it. The Great Boon arrives and attempts to save the family from the Giant. However, after a lot of adventures, muddles and magic all ends happily. There is even a circus – with all the acts provided by Mother Shipton's clever children.
ISBN 978 0 573 05051 0

Think of the Magic. Book, music and lyrics by Frank Rodgers **Y L**
M14 F10, with doubling. Extras. Various simple interior and exterior settings. Fee by arrangement

This chirpy, cheeky, exuberant musical has everything from rock 'n' roll to punchy pop as well as a glut of evil, scheming characters, a street gang led by an irrepressible ten-year-old tomboy, lovesick teenagers and a local housing officer whose shattering news that the Carrs' family home is to be demolished sets the ball rolling or rather a Genie to appear from an old electric kettle!
ISBN 978 0 573 08069 2

The 13 Clocks. James Thurber. Adapted for the stage by Frank Lowe **A L**
M13 F2, with doubling. Extras. Various simple interior and exterior sets. Fee code K

Prince Zorn, weary of his frivolous life, disguises himself as a ragged minstrel and travels the land learning the life of the lowly, and perhaps slaying a dragon or two. He hears of the matchless beauty of Princess Saralinda who is held captive by the evil Duke and resolves he must win her hand despite the staggering perils imposed on her suitors. The Golux arrives to help the Prince and eventually with the aid of a magic rose the Prince and Princess emerge victorious over the Duke.

◆ **A bullet mark next to a title indicates that it is new to this edition of the Guide.**

This Is Where We Came In. Play. Alan Ayckbourn **A / Y**
M6 (young, old) F4 (young, old). A bare stage. Fee code M

Fred sits ... somewhere or other ... next to a sign which reads 'Stories told here today'. A group of actors, the StoryPlayers, arrives. They are followed by the ageing StoryTellers, who create characters and the plots for the StoryPlayers to act out. What the StoryPlayers would really like, however, is to make up their own stories and they enlist Fred's help to free them.
ISBN 978 0 573 05106 7

The Thwarting of Baron Bolligrew. Comedy for children. Robert Bolt **A / Y**
M16. Extras M and F. Composite setting. Fee code M

Oblong is far too conscientious for the Duke and the rest of his knights, who want a rest from succouring the poor and needy. So he is persuaded to go on a mission to the Bolligrew Islands to subdue the wicked Baron who tyrannizes the peasants and pulls down churches. Eventually, of course, Right triumphs, the Baron departs to hunt dragons in the North, and Oblong rules in his place.
ISBN 978 0 573 05020 6

Tickle. Play with music. David Wood **A S**
Minimum cast of 6 players, of either sex. A bare stage. Fee code E. ISBN 0 573 05247 6

The Tinder Box. Play with music. Peter Whelan, adapted from a story by Hans Christian Andersen
M5 F5. Extras. Various simple interior and exterior settings. Fee code L **A L**

Peter Whelan's fine play adaptation (with songs) of Hans Christian Andersen's famous story is intelligent, funny and witty, ideal for performance to children by adults or young people. A common soldier meets varied fortunes as he gains and then loses a vast wealth, is sorely tested by many evils and finally marries the King's daughter and finds the peace and happiness he has sought.
ISBN 978 0 573 05108 1

Toad of Toad Hall. Musical play. A. A. Milne. Music by H. Fraser-Simson **A / Y**
Any number of characters. Six interiors, four exteriors. Fee code M. Band parts on hire

A dramatization of Kenneth Grahame's *Wind in the Willows*, with the kindly Rat, wise Badger, gentle Mole, and conceited, foolish Toad, who is always in trouble. His addiction to firstly caravanning, and then cars, his subsequent imprisonment, and the fight with the weasels and stoats are all included.
ISBN 978 0 573 05019 0

Tom Kitten and His Friends. Play with songs. Book by Adrian Mitchell. Music by Stephen McNeff. Based on stories by Beatrix Potter **A + C L**
May be played by a cast of 9. Various interior and exterior settings. Fee code G (for play) code C (for music)

A delightful adaptation of four Beatrix Potter stories suitable for the entertainment of younger children: *The Story of Miss Moppet, The Tale of Two Bad Mice, The Story of a Fierce Bad Rabbit* and *The Tale of Tom Kitten*.
ISBN 978 0 573 05116 6

Tom's Midnight Garden. Play. Adapted for the stage by David Wood from the book by Philippa Pearce
M5 F3, with doubling. Various interior and exterior settings. Fee code M $\boxed{A + C + Y L}$

This 1950s classic is here brilliantly adapted for the stage by David Wood. Quarantined in his aunt's and uncle's flat, Tom is bored. Startled to hear the grandfather clock strike thirteen, he goes to what in his time is a concrete backyard, and discovers a beautiful 1880's Victorian garden. He meets the unhappy orphan, Hatty, and visits her each night. Although Tom stays the same exuberant ten-year-old, Hatty grows into a young woman, until finally the truth is revealed in a touching denouement. Period 1880s/1890s, 1950s. **Available 1st February 2006**
ISBN 978 0 573 05127 2

Totally Over You. Play. Mark Ravenhill $\boxed{Y S}$
M7 (14-16) F7 (14-16). Extras. A bare stage. Fee code H

Suggested by Molière's *Les Preciéuse Ridicules*, the play concerns four girls who decide to become famous by marrying celebrities, so they dump their current boyfriends. The four boyfriends, and their school's drama class, set up a witty scenario designed to fool the girls into thinking that they should never have called off their relationships – because one day soon the lads will be the world-famous boyband *Awesome.* Our obsession with celebrity is satirized with the lightest of touches in this intelligent comedy.
ISBN 978 0 573 05251 4

♦ **Tracy Beaker Gets Real** Book by Mary Morris. Music by Grant Olding. Lyrics by Mary Morris. Based on the book by Jacqueline Wilson
Please see the full entry in Section E.

The Twits. Roald Dahl. Adapted for the stage by David Wood $\boxed{A + C L}$
8 characters. Children. A circus tent, a caravan, a cage, a tree. Fee code M

Bored with playing schoolkiddish tricks on one another, the grotesque, satisfyingly revolting couple Mr and Mrs Twit turn their attentions to capturing and training a family of monkeys for a circus act. The monkey's cruel incarceration in a cage is avenged when the birds trick the Twits into believing the world has turned upside-down. The Twits join in, aided by the birds, and the audience is encouraged to play their part in freeing the monkeys.
ISBN 978 0 573 05125 8

The Ugly Duckling. Comedy. A. A. Milne $\boxed{C/Y S}$
M4 F3. A throne-room. Fee code C

To prevent the Princess growing vain, her fairy godmother has withheld the gift of beauty from her – until the day she falls in love.
ISBN 978 0 573 05238 5

Utter Garbage. Play. Les Ellison $\boxed{A L}$
7 characters, 5 extras. A rubbish dump. Fee code G (play) Fee code A (song)

Dumpster, an idealistic young rat who lives in a rubbish dump, dreams of a brighter, better world. But his dreams are dashed daily by His Ignoble Ratship The Lord Vermin, Ruler of the Refuse, Defender of the Dump and Guardian of the Garbage, who has plans to turn every park and every garden into Utter Garbage! A delightful play about our environment for performance to children, with plenty of opportunities for lively audience participation!
ISBN 978 0 573 05112 8

Virgins. Play. John Retallack
M2 (17, 40) F2 (15, 40). Simple settings. Fee Code L

Suzy works extremely long hours so Nick has taken on the parenting role during their children's teenage years. One Sunday, Nick overhears his teenage son telling a girl he thinks he has contracted an STI from her at a party. So intense are the feelings generated, the family threatens to disintegrate but each member has the urge to keep the family together and what they cannot articulate, they say through dance.

The Voyage of the Dawn Treader. Play. Glyn Robbins. Adapted from the book by C. S. Lewis
M11 F2, with doubling. Various simple interior and exterior settings. Fee code M A L

This enthralling adaptation of one of C. S. Lewis's Narnian stories tells the adventures of the *Dawn Treader,* a dragon-ship led by Caspian, King of Narnia. The story is a traditional quest and the marvels include dragons, invisible islanders and a lake that turns everything to gold. The play can be very simply staged with few scenic requirements and no elaborate props.
ISBN 978 0 573 05085 5

The Voyage of the Jumblies. Play with music. Philip Freeman Sayer C L
19 characters, doubling possible. Extras. Various simple settings. Fee code H

An original, highly-imaginative and stimulating entertainment for children, whether as actors or members of the audience. Based on the classic characters created by Edward Lear in his nonsense poetry the two-act play, with a running time of ninety minutes, has simple settings, offers excellent, flexible casting opportunities for children, and is complemented by Edward Lear's verse set to music adapted from traditional folk tunes.

The Wall. Play. D.C. Jackson Y L
M2 (16, 17) F2 (14, 15). A wall. Fee code H

In the small Ayrshire town of Stewarton, the school holidays are like a microwave. So much happens so fast. Norma has got a problem and will be in big trouble if her dad finds out. Her big brother Barry's no use. He's in love for the first time. Michelle loves Barry too, but her family won't let them be together. This summer, everything's changing.

The Water Babies. Play with music. Willis Hall. Songs by John Cooper. Based on the story by Charles Kingsley A L
19 characters, can be played by M3 F6. Extras. Various simple settings. Fee by arrangement

Charles Kingsley's well-loved story of the Water Babies is enchantingly brought to life in this adaptation by Willis Hall. The tale of young Tom, apprentice to the unpleasant chimney sweep Mr Grimes, and his underwater journey to the End-of-Nowhere, is interspersed with delightful songs by John Cooper.
ISBN 978 0 573 08076 0

◆ **A bullet mark next to a title indicates that it is new to this edition of the Guide.**

Whale. Play. David Holman ▐Y L▐
51 characters, doubling possible. Various interior and exterior settings. Fee code M

In October 1988 three grey whales were trapped under the spreading ice-cap of an Arctic winter in Alaska. The story of Pitu, Siku and K'nik aroused international sympathy and support for the rescue operation which brought together the Americans, Russians and Inuits. Legend has it that the whales are trapped in Sedna's hair and only when she combs it will they be free. 'The juvenile audience gave every sign of being enthralled and it would be a hard-hearted adult who wasn't moved too.' *Sunday Telegraph*

Whenever. Musical play for children. Alan Ayckbourn. Music by Denis King ▐A + C L▐
26 characters. Doubling possible: M5F4 (minimum). Various simple settings. Fee by arrangement

Beginning in 1886, this historical-futuristic musical finds Emily's good Uncle Martin inventing a time-machine that wicked Uncle Lucas wants to get his hands on. So Emily must journey to the end of time to ensure evil does not prevail and she picks up three travelling companions from different eras. With the charming music of Denis King this is fine family entertainment.

C

Where the Rainbow Ends. Play with music. Clifford Mills and John Ramsay ▐A L▐
18 characters. Dancers. Extras. One interior, six exterior settings. Fee code H

Since their mother and father were shipwrecked, Crispian and Rosamund Carey have been living with their aunt and uncle. Rosamund discovers in a book that all lost loved ones are to be found in the land where the rainbow ends. Together with a Genie of a magic carpet found in the library and two friends, the children set out on their search.
ISBN 978 0 573 05021 3

The Wind in the Willows. Kenneth Grahame. Adapted for the stage by Alan Bennett. Music by Jeremy Sams ▐A L▐
24 characters. Extras. Various settings. Fee code M (play) code C (music)

For a full synopsis please see the entry in Section A.

The Wind in the Willows. Family entertainment by John Morley, adapted from the novel by Kenneth Grahame ▐A L▐

For a full synopsis please see the entry in Section A.

The Wind in the Willows. Musical play based on Kenneth Grahame's novel. Book and lyrics by Willis Hall. Music by Denis King ▐A L▐
15 characters. Extras. Various settings. Fee by arrangement

A delightful dramatization, with enchanting songs, of Kenneth Grahame's classic tale of river-bank animals. Toad finds himself in prison but manages to escape, but not before Toad Hall, his pride and joy, has been overrun by the wicked Weasels. Thanks to the efforts of his kind and concerned friends, however, all ends happily, after an exciting battle to regain Toad's home. (Please specify author when ordering this title.)
ISBN 978 0 573 08070 8

Winnie-the-Pooh. Play. Glyn Robbins. Adapted from the novel by A. A. Milne
M7 F4. A nursery, a wood. Fee code M

We are introduced to all A. A. Milne's well-loved characters – Christopher Robin, Kanga, Roo, Piglet, Tigger, Eeyore and Owl, not forgetting the Bear of Very Little Brain himself, Pooh – and follow their adventures involving bees, balloons, boats and birthdays in the 100 Aker Wood. ' ... hard to imagine a more faithful adaptation ... translates so effortlessly you could almost imagine you were reading it.' *Oxford Mail*
ISBN 978 0 573 05086 4

The Witches. Roald Dahl. Adapted for the stage by David Wood A L
21 characters, may be doubled by M4 F6 plus 15 witches (extras) doubling as Diners. Various interior and exterior settings. Fee code M

Roald Dahl's story is magically adapted for the stage by David Wood. It toured extensively before a successful West End season at the Duke of York's Theatre. ' ... while the kids will be thrilled by the dazzling illusions and the complex puppetry, their parents will be no less engaged by the sly humour that lurks within this ostensibly frivolous confection.' *What's On*
ISBN 978 0 573 05099 2

The Wizard of Oz. Alfred Bradley. From the story by L. Frank Baum C L
M6 F7, doubling possible. An open stage. Fee code K

This version can be produced very simply. It needs no stage and may be performed on the floor of a school hall. Alternatively a more ambitious production could use back-projection, flash-boxes, and all the magic of a proscenium stage, provided all the settings are kept simple. By doubling, the cast can be reduced to a total of nine players.
ISBN 978 0 573 05058 9

Worzel Gummidge. Book and lyrics by Keith Waterhouse and Willis Hall. Music by Denis King. Based on the characters created by Barbara Euphan Todd A + C + L
M12, doubling possible, F4. 1 boy, 1 girl. Extras. Various interior and exterior settings. Fee by arrangement. ISBN 978 0 573 18031 6

You, Me and Mrs Jones. Comedy. Tony Horitz Y S
M10 F9, doubling possible. Various simple settings. Fee code E

This comedy centres on two unemployed teenagers, uncertain about themselves and the world around them. They are sent on a mission to find 'heroes to save the day'. They encounter a hotchpotch of humanity from violent street gangs to a family of vagrants. And surprisingly it is in this final encounter that they find their 'heroes'. This is a fast-moving comedy yet it makes a serious statement too.
ISBN 978 0 573 12272 9

SECTION D
Pantomimes and Christmas Plays

CONTENTS

D

Pantomimes Full Length

Pantomime by Julia Banks

Hercules – the Panto!
M4 F8, 1M or F. Large chorus. Various settings. Fee code L
ISBN 978 0 573 16440 8

Pantomimes by Simon Brett

Sleeping Beauty. Book and lyrics by Simon Brett. Music by Sarah Travis. M4 F4, 2M or F. Extras. Fee by arrangement. ISBN 0 573 08110 7 (libretto). Piano/vocal score on hire

The Tale of Little Red Riding Hood. A Untraditional Pantomime. Simon Brett (book and lyrics), Sarah Travis (music). 8 principals. Chorus. Various simple settings. Fee by arrangement. ISBN 978 0 573 08106 4 (libretto). Piano/vocal score on hire. Optional violin score

Pantomimes by Alan Brown

Alan Brown's pantomimes recreate those of Victorian times, blending traditional elements – including Harlequin interludes and suggestions for period songs – with subtle updatings to suit modern young audiences.

Aladdin and His Wonderful Lamp
Mixed cast of 21. Various interior and exterior settings. Fee code M
ISBN 978 0 573 06486 9

The Babes in the Wood
Mixed cast of 25. Extras. Various simple exterior and interior scenes. Fee code M
ISBN 978 0 573 16432 3

Cinderella
17 Principals, with doubling. Extras. Various interior and exterior settings. Fee code M
ISBN 978 0 573 06475 3

Dick Whittington
Mixed cast of 22. Extras. Various interior and exterior settings. Fee code M
ISBN 978 0 573 06478 4

Sleeping Beauty
Mixed cast of 23. Various interior and exterior settings. Fee code M
ISBN 978 0 573 06491 3

◆ **A bullet mark next to a title indicates that it is new to this edition of the Guide.**

Pantomimes by David Cregan with music by Brian Protheroe

These pantomimes were written for the Theatre Royal, Stratford East, and combine all the traditional elements with original characterizations, imaginative and innovative staging ideas and witty, melodic songs.

Aladdin
15 Characters. Various interior and exterior settings. Fee code K
ISBN 978 0 573 16404 0

Beauty and the Beast
12 Characters. Various simple interior settings. Fee code K
ISBN 978 0 573 06481 4

Cinderella
13 Characters. Various simple interior and exterior settings. Fee code K
ISBN 978 0 573 06488 3

Jack and the Beanstalk
19 Characters. Various interior and exterior settings. Fee code K
ISBN 978 0 573 06477 6

Red Riding-hood
M7 F5, with doubling. Various interior and exterior settings. Fee code K
ISBN 978 0 573 06474 6

Sleeping Beauty
12 Principals. Extras. Various simple settings. Fee code K
ISBN 978 0 573 06472 2

Pantomimes by John Crocker

Small cast pantomimes with a choice of music left to the director. "John Crocker, whose scripts have always been as traditional as turkey and Christmas pudding ... still ahead of the field with traditional fare ... These splendid scripts, all of which run under two hours, have enjoyed very successful professional productions at the Northcott, Exeter, and the Theatre Royal, Winchester." *Amateur Stage*

Aladdin
11 Principals. Various interior and exterior settings. Fee code K. Manuscript on hire

Babes in the Wood
13 Principals. Various interior and exterior settings. Fee code K
Manuscript on hire

Cinderella
10 Principals, can be played by a cast of 9. Various interior and exterior settings. Fee code K.
Manuscript on hire

Dick Whittington
11 Principals, can be played by a cast of 10. Various interior and exterior settings. Fee code K. Manuscript on hire

Mother Goose
10 Principals. Various interior and exterior settings. Fee code K. Manuscript on hire

Sleeping Beauty
10 Principals, can be played by a cast of 9. Various interior and exterior settings. Fee code K. Manuscript on hire

Pantomimes by Crocker and Gilder
Books by John Crocker, music and lyrics by Eric Gilder

These are full length pantomimes, entirely traditional with lots of humour. Each has its own original and delightful score which is available separately. The large number of both amateur and professional groups who present Crocker and Gilder pantomimes regularly every year is unmistakable proof of their success.

Aladdin
14 Principals. Chorus. 8 Interiors. 4 Exteriors. Fee code L
ISBN 978 0 573 06471 5

Babes in the Wood
13 Principals. Chorus. 5 Interiors. 5 Exteriors. Fee code L
ISBN 978 0 573 16409 6

Cinderella
15 Principals. Chorus. 7 Interiors. 4 Exteriors. Fee code L
ISBN 978 0 573 16457 6

Dick Whittington
12 Principals. Chorus. 4 Interiors. 8 Exteriors. Fee code L
ISBN 978 0 573 06465 4

Humpty Dumpty
15 Principals. Chorus. 4 Interiors. 7 Exteriors. Fee code L
ISBN 978 0 573 16413 3

Jack and the Beanstalk
14 Principals. Chorus. 6 Interiors. 7 Exteriors. Fee code L
ISBN 978 0 573 16454 5

Mother Goose
16 Principals. Chorus. 4 Interiors. 6 Exteriors. Fee code L
ISBN 978 0 573 16424 8

Puss in Boots
16 Principals. Chorus. 5 Interiors. 5 Exteriors. Fee code L
ISBN 978 0 573 16446 0

Queen of Hearts
14 Principals. Chorus. 5 Interiors. 6 Exteriors. Fee code L
ISBN 978 0 573 16438 5

Red Riding Hood
13 Principals. Chorus. 5 Interiors. 5 Exteriors. Fee code L
ISBN 978 0 573 16433 0

Robinson Crusoe
12 Principals. Chorus. 2 Interiors. 7 Exteriors. Fee code L
ISBN 978 0 573 06473 9

Sinbad the Sailor
15 Principals. Chorus. 3 Interiors. 8 Exteriors. Fee code L
ISBN 978 0 573 16411 8

The Sleeping Beauty
12 Principals. Chorus. 3 Interiors. 4 Exteriors. Fee code L

Pantomimes by Richard Lloyd

Arabian Knights – The Panto!
14 principals. Extras. Various interior and exterior settings. Fee code K

In the Holy Land, a shapely-legged Richard the Lionheart meets eunuchs, spaced-out assassins, suspiciously masculine English dames, pantomime camels, flying carpets and genies in this hilarious, original pantomime.
ISBN 978 0 573 16412 5

The Christmas Cavalier
M7 F5, Children. Various simple settings. Fee code K

All the traditional elements are intact in this new pantomime which is set just after the English Civil War, when the Puritan Witchfinder General is trying to stamp out Christmas jollifications and meeting spirited opposition.
ISBN 978 0 573 06510 1

Smut's Saga or Santa and the Vikings
M14 F4. Various interior and exterior settings. Fee code K

Smut's Saga is a tale of war, pillage and raucous innuendo set in the days when Vikings plundered the Scandinavian coastline, stealing booty, kidnapping women and generally causing havoc, with a scandalous disregard for personal hygiene.
ISBN 978 0 573 16502 3

The Three Musketeers – Le Panteau!
20 principals. Extras. Various settings. Fee code K

Alexandre Dumas's rip-roaring yarn of derring-do, palace intrigue, and slushy amour has now been fully and seamlessly transplanted into pantoland!
ISBN 978 0 573 16416 3

Treasure Island, the Panto
19 characters. Extras. Various simple settings. Fee code K

A swashbuckling tale of skulduggery upon the high seas, treasure on a desert island, a Guatemalan crimson parakeet going by the name of Cap'n Haddock, Dame Ladd's fisherman's pies and – death by chocolate.
ISBN 978 0 573 06496 2

Pantomimes by Verne Morgan

Verne Morgan's pantomimes are clear and straightforward, following the traditional stories closely. Choice of music for songs and dances is left to the director.

Babes in the Wood
M12 F4. Extras. Several simple sets. Fee code H
ISBN 978 0 573 16414 9

Dick Whittington
12 Principals. 6 Small Parts. Chorus. Dancers. Children. 5 simple settings. Fee code H
ISBN 978 0 573 16422 4

Old King Cole or King Cole in Space. Pantomime space oddity
13 Principals. Extras. Children. Dancers. Chorus. Various simple settings. Fee code H
ISBN 978 0 573 06470 8

Pantomimes by John Morley

D

John Morley's pantomimes are full of fun and originality and can be produced very lavishly or simply, depending on the company's resources, without in any way affecting the comedy routines or the telling of the story. The choice of music is left to the director.

Aladdin
19 Principals. Dancers. Chorus. Extras. Various front-cloth and full-stage sets. Fee code L
ISBN 978 0 573 06462 2

Dick Whittington
12 Principals. 5 Small parts. Chorus. Dancers. Children. Various simple settings. Fee code L
ISBN 978 0 573 16435 4

Goldilocks and the Three Bears
10 Principals. Dancers. Chorus. Various simple settings. Fee code L
ISBN 978 0 573 06464 7

Jack and the Beanstalk
14 Principals. Extras. Singers. Dancers. Various interior and exterior settings. Fee code K
ISBN 978 0 573 06463 0

Robinson Crusoe
16 Principals. Chorus. Various simple settings. Fee code K. (Revised version 1997)
ISBN 978 0 573 06468 5

Sinbad the Sailor
11 Principals. 8 Small parts (all M or F). Chorus. Simple outdoor settings. Fee code L
ISBN 978 0 573 16441 5

Pantomime by Tony Nicholls

Old Mother Hubbard. Pantomime. Tony Nicholls
16 Principals. Chorus. Several simple settings. Fee Code K

After enduring centuries of bone-free cupboards, Old Mother Hubbard has decided that she and her dog deserve a break so she arranges for her daughter Polly to marry the very rich, though very unpleasant, Duke Ferdinand. Polly, however, is in love with Dick, the poor woodchopper's son, so they run away to seek their fortune. Unfortunately they fall into the clutches of the evil Witch Hepzibah …Choice of music is left to the individual director.
ISBN 978 0 573 16451 4

Pantomimes by Paul Reakes

Paul Reakes' pantomimes include many original twists to the familiar stories, with plenty of audience participation. They can be staged as simply or as elaborately as desired.

Babes in the Wood
14 Principals. Chorus. Extras. Various interior and exterior settings. Fee code K
ISBN 978 0 573 06487 6

Bluebeard
12 Principals. Chorus. Extras. Dancers. Children. Various simple settings. Fee code K
ISBN 978 0 573 16450 7

Cinderella. 16 principals. Chorus. Several simple settings. Fee code L
ISBN 978 0 573 16428 6

Dick Turpin
14 characters. Extras. Various interior and exterior settings. Fee code K
ISBN 978 0 573 06494 4

Goody Two Shoes
10 Principals. Chorus. Extras. Various settings. Fee code K
ISBN 978 0 573 16455 2

King Arthur. A pantomime adventure in Camelot
M6 F4, plus children, chorus and dancers. Various simple settings. Fee code K
ISBN 978 0 573 06498 2

King Humpty Dumpty
12 Principals. Chorus. Dancers. Children. Various simple settings. Fee code K
ISBN 978 0 573 16401 9

♦ **Little Bo Peep**
12 Principals. Chorus. Various settings. Fee Code K
ISBN 978 0 573 16431 6

Little Jack Horner
13 Principals. Chorus. Children. Fee code K
ISBN 978 0 573 06484 5

Little Miss Muffet
13 Principals. Chorus. Children. Various simple settings. Fee code K
ISBN 978 0 573 06480 7

Little Red Riding Hood
11 Principals. Chorus. Extras. Dancers. Various simple settings. Fee code K
ISBN 978 0 573 16434 7

Little Tommy Tucker
12 Principals. Chorus. Extras. Dancers. Various simple settings. Fee code K
ISBN 978 0 573 16445 3

Old Mother Hubbard
19 Principals. Chorus. Children. Various simple settings. Fee code K
ISBN 978 0 573 06492 0

Robinson Crusoe and the Pirates
M9 F3, with doubling. Chorus. Various interior and exterior settings. Fee code K
ISBN 978 0 573 16443 9

Santa in Space
14 Principals. Chorus. Children. Various settings. Fee code K
ISBN 978 0 573 06509 5

Sinbad the Sailor
17 Principals. Chorus. Children. Various interior and exterior settings. Fee code K
ISBN 978 0 573 06482 1

◆ **Tom Thumb**
15 Principals. Chorus. Various simple settings. Fee Code K. ISBN 978 0 573 16444 6

Pantomimes by Norman Robbins

Norman Robbins' fun-packed pantomimes tell the traditional stories in a clear fast-moving style
and can be staged simply or elaborately, as required. The choice of music is left to the director.

Aladdin
Mixed cast of 10. Children. Extras. Various simple interior and exterior settings. Fee code K
ISBN 978 0 573 16442 2

Ali Baba and the Forty Thieves
13 Characters. Chorus. Various simple interior and exterior settings. Fee code L
ISBN 978 0 573 06485 2

Babes in the Wood
M11 F3. Extras. Chorus. Various simple settings. Fee code L
ISBN 978 0 573 06493 7

Cinderella
12 Characters. Chorus. Various simple settings. Fee code L
ISBN 978 0 573 16417 0

Dick Whittington
12 Principals. Extras. Chorus. Dancers. Junior Chorus. Various simple settings. Fee code L
ISBN 978 0 573 06483 8

The Grand Old Duke of York
M8 F5. Chorus. Various simple interior and exterior settings. Fee code K
ISBN 978 0 573 16423 1

Hansel and Gretel
13 Principals. Chorus. Dancers. Various simple settings. Fee code L
ISBN 978 0 573 16402 6

Hickory Dickory Dock
M10 F8 (some interchangeable). Extras. Various simple settings on an open stage. Fee code J
ISBN 978 0 573 06460 9

Humpty Dumpty
M9 F5. Chorus. Various simple settings. Fee code J
ISBN 978 0 573 16430 9

Jack and Jill
14 principals. Chorus. Extras. Dancers. Various simple settings. Fee code L
ISBN 978 0 573 16426 2

Jack and the Beanstalk
M5 F3. Extras. Chorus. Various interior and exterior settings. Fee code L
ISBN 978 0 573 06490 6

The Old Woman Who Lived in a Shoe
M9 F5. Various simple settings. Fee code L
ISBN 978 0 573 16436 1

Puss in Boots
13 Principals. Extras. Various interior and exterior settings. Fee code L
ISBN 978 0 573 06489 0

Red Riding Hood. M7 F4. Chorus. Dancers. Children. Various simple settings. Fee code L.
ISBN 978 0 573 06499 9

Rumpelstiltzkin
M9 or 10, F2 or 3. Extras. Various simple settings. Fee code L
ISBN 978 0 573 06459 3

Sing a Song of Sixpence
M8 F9. Extras. Various simple settings. Fee code J
ISBN 978 0 573 06458 6

The Sleeping Beauty
11 Principals. Chorus. Various simple interior and exterior settings. Fee code K
ISBN 978 0 573 06479 1

Snow White
15 characters. Chorus. Various simple settings. Fee code L
ISBN 978 0 573 06495 1

D

Tom, the Piper's Son
17 Principals. Extras. Chorus. Various simple settings. Fee code K
ISBN978 0 573 06469 2

The White Cat
15 principals. Dancers. Chorus. Various frontcloth and full stage settings. Fee code L
ISBN 978 0 573 16425 5

The Wonderful Story of Mother Goose
11 Principals. Extras. Chorus. Various simple settings. Fee code K
ISBN 978 0 573 06476 0

Pantomime by David Tristram

Cinders: The True Story
9 Principals. Chorus. Various simple settings. Fee code L

Pantomime One Act

Potty Pantomime. Book by John Crocker. Lyrics and music by Eric Gilder
M8 or F8. With doubling may be played by M2 F1. A bare stage. Fee code B

A delightful, potty panto which is a pithy pot-pourri of popular pantomime plots!
ISBN 978 0 573 16606 8

Potted Panto-Parody in Rhyme by C. R. Cook

A one-act pantomime on a well-known theme – with a difference. Fee code C

Ali the Barber
9 Principals. Chorus. 5 Scenes
ISBN 978 0 573 06601 6

Minidramas by Richard Tydeman

All of these plays last 15-20 minutes, need little or no rehearsal, and use only the simplest of costumes and properties. There is no reason why they should not be performed entirely by men or entirely by women, if a mixed cast is not available. For full synopses see the entries in Section B.

Albert Laddin. M4 F6   ISBN 978 0 573 06617 7
Forty Winks Beauty. M5 F7   ISBN 978 0 573 06616 0

Family Musicals by David Wood

David Wood has adapted these fairy tales into musical plays rather than conventional pantomimes. Comedy, adventure and lively original songs combine to make these unusual plays sure-fire hits with family audiences.

Aladdin
15 Principals (doubling possible). Children. Various interior and exterior settings. Fee code M
ISBN 978 0 573 16403 3

Babes in the Magic Wood
Mixed cast of 12. Various interior and exterior settings. Fee code M
ISBN 978 0 573 06506 4

Cinderella
16M or F (variable). Extras. Various interior and exterior scenes. Fee code M
ISBN 978 0 573 16427 9

Dick Whittington and Wondercat
Flexible cast, minimum of M8 F5. Extra 1M or F. Chorus of adults or children. Several interior and exterior settings. Fee code M
ISBN 978 0 573 06507 1

Jack and The Giant
Mixed cast of 12. Various simple settings. Fee code M
ISBN 978 0 573 05080 0

Mother Goose's Golden Christmas
M6 F6, with doubling. Fee code M
ISBN 978 0 573 06504 0

Old Mother Hubbard
M10 F10, doubling, and some M and F interchangeable. A street, a forest, a well, a cave. Fee code M
ISBN 978 0 573 06449 4

D

◆ **A bullet mark next to a title indicates that it is new to this edition of the Guide.**

Christmas Plays
Full Length

The Ash Girl. Play. Timberlake Wertenbaker
M4 F6, 8M or F (with doubling). A house, a palace, a forest. Fee code M

Please see the entry in Section A.

Bad Day at Black Frog Creek. Musical play. John Gardner and Fiz Coleman

For a full synopsis see the entry in Section C.

A Child's Christmas in Wales. Christmas musical. Jeremy Brooks and Adrian Mitchell. Based on the poem by Dylan Thomas
M15 F7. Extras. Various simple settings. Fee code M

This enchanting play with music uses a variety of carols and well-known Welsh songs to conjure up the pure magic of Christmas for the enjoyment of an audience of all ages. The main course of events takes place on Christmas Eve itself, when the Thomas family are host to their relatives. Apart from a potentially major hiccup when the turkey catches fire, the traditional yuletide celebrations are enjoyed by all.

A Christmas Carol. Musical play. Book by Christopher Bedloe, adaptation and lyrics by James Wood, music by Malcolm Shapcott from the story by Charles Dickens
39 characters, with doubling can be staged by a cast of 18-20. Extras. Fee by arrangement. Vocal score available separately

A wealth of pretty, singable music, witty lyrics and plenty of scope for dancing and colourful staging make this musical version of a well-loved story a real piece of Christmas cheer. Period nineteenth century
ISBN 0 573 08050 X

A Christmas Carol. Play. Adapted by John Mortimer from the story by Charles Dickens
Large mixed cast, doubling possible. Various simple settings. Fee code M

Charles Dickens' famous tale of Ebenezer Scrooge's transformation from embittered skinflint to generous benefactor has been dramatized by John Mortimer with typical flair and wit in this definitive adaptation, first performed by the Royal Shakespeare Company. Retaining Dickens' own ironic point of view through the use of a Chorus, Mortimer has created a panoramic view of Victorian London with all the much-loved characters in place. There is plenty of scope for imaginative doubling, and the staging requirements are flexible. Period nineteenth century
ISBN 0 573 01733 6

A Christmas Carol. Christmas play. Shaun Sutton. From the story by Charles Dickens
M24 F15. Composite setting: an office, a street, a parlour. Fee code K

This version of the famous story contains nearly forty characters, but with reasonable doubling it can be performed by a cast of twenty – 10 men, 6 women, 2 boys and girls. The story of Scrooge's conversion from miserliness to benevolence contains scenes that elaborate a Christmas play into a simple form of Christmas pantomime. Period nineteenth century
ISBN 0 573 01070 6

The Christmas Story. Nativity play. David Wood
Large cast. Various simple settings. Fee code G

David Wood writes: 'This version of the nativity story was written at the request of several teachers who wanted a play which revealed the human side of the great event. I have tried to combine the traditional elements of the holy story with reverent humour'. Christmas carols and hymns are used to further the story and there are many opportunities for good acting parts as well as middle-sized parts and walk-on parts for younger children.

Good King Wenceslas and the Chancellor of Bohemia. Play. Tony Horitz
M5 F2, 8M or F (minimum). Various interior and exterior settings. Fee code F.
ISBN 0 573 16501 7

The Great Santa Kidnap. Christmas Play. Roy Chatfield
12 named characters. Extras. Various interior and exterior settings. Fee code J

It is Christmas Eve and Fergus, Santa Claus's Chief Forebrownie, is bustling about preparing Santa's sleigh. However, three goblins – Sneergripe, Snottle and Bug – are plotting to kidnap Santa Claus and hold him to ransom! The goblins stage the kidnap and it is up to Tommy and Anna to find Santa and safeguard Christmas for the children of the world. Playing time 90 minutes.
ISBN 0 573 06623 X

The Merry Gentleman. Book and lyrics by Dorothy Reynolds and Julian Slade. Music by Julian Slade
M12 F8. A drawing room, the rooftops, Christmasland. Fee by arrangement

Julian Slade writes: 'The intention behind this show is to present as many of the aspects of Christmas as possible, warmth, nostalgia and at times magic or absurdity or both.' Confusion arises when the real Father Christmas drops in on a Christmas night party in 1910. The guests soon find themselves in Christmasland on a very special treasure-hunt – a search for true happiness. The show has many enchanting and delightful songs and ends happily in the best of traditions.

The Nativity. Play. Adapted by David Farr
Large mixed cast. Various simple settings. Fee code M

Joseph, the Carpenter, seems never to find love, until one day a beautiful girl enters his workshop to escape from a storm. Her name is Mary, and three months later they are married. But on their wedding night Mary tells Joseph that she is already pregnant. So begins the remarkable journey involving giants, shepherds, kings, devils and angels, a journey covering hundreds of miles and ending in a divine miracle.

An O. Henry Christmas. O. Henry. Adaptation, music and lyrics by Peter Ekstrom

Please see the entries for *The Gift of the Magi* and *The Last Leaf* under Christmas Plays One Act in Section D.

◆ **A bullet mark next to a title indicates that it is new to this edition of the Guide.**

Peter Pan. Fantasy. J. M. Barrie
25 characters. Nursery, The Never Land, a ship. Fee code M

The everlasting classic account of two boys and a girl who follow Peter Pan and the invisible fairy, Tinker Bell, into The Never Land where children never grow old and where Captain Hook and his pirates are outwitted. Samuel French handles this play on behalf of the Hospital for Children, Great Ormond Street.
ISBN 0 573 05041 4

Peter Pan. Book, music and lyrics by Piers Chater-Robinson. Adapted from the play by J. M. Barrie

Please see the entry in Section C.

Pinocchio. Family entertainment. John Morley
Flexible casting: 9 to 14 Principals, adult and/or junior Chorus. One permanent set with three or four frontcloths. Fee code L

This delightful dramatization of Collodi's story *Pinocchio* has all the charm of the original. The story is simple to stage with many music and production suggestions, and the cast is flexible for both large and small companies.
ISBN 0 573 11345 9

Quest for the Whooperdink. Play with music. A. H. Teacey

For a full synopsis see the entry in Section C.

The Real Story of Puss in Boots. Play. David Foxton.

See the entry in Section A.

A Right Christmas Caper. Play. Willis Hall
M7 F2. Four simple settings. Fee code L
ISBN 0 573 05044 9

Robin Hood – The Truth Behind the Green Tights. Play. David Neilson
M7 F2, with doubling. Various interior and exterior settings. Fee code L

For a full synopsis see the entry in Section A.

The Snow Queen. Play. Ron Nicol. Based on the story by Hans Christian Andersen
Large mixed cast. Much doubling and trebling possible. Various simple settings. Fee code K

Please see the entry in Section C.

The Thwarting of Baron Bolligrew. Comedy for children. Robert Bolt

Please see the entry in Section C.

Treasure Island. Freely adapted for male and female pirates by Phil Willmott, from the novel by Robert Louis Stevenson
Flexible casting, can be played by M13 F8. Extras. Various simple settings. Period 1772. Fee Code K

This is a unique adaptation of *Treasure Island* with great parts for both male and female performers. Inspired by real-life female adventurers, Phil Willmott has changed the gender of several of the central characters without compromising the spirit of Stevenson's classic novel. Simply staged, and suitable for performance by children or adults, this refreshing version can be adapted to suit both large and small companies.
ISBN 978 1 84002 692 4

The Wind in the Willows. Kenneth Grahame. Adapted for the stage by Alan Bennett. Music by Jeremy Sams
24 characters. Extras. Various settings. Fee code M (play) code C (music)

For a full synopsis please see the entry in Section A.

D

The Wind in the Willows. Family entertainment by John Morley, adapted from the novel by Kenneth Grahame

Please see the entry in Section A.

Worzel Gummidge. Book and lyrics by Keith Waterhouse and Willis Hall. Music by Denis King

Please see the entry in Section C.

Christmas Plays
One Act

Dawn on Our Darkness. Play. Richard Tydeman
M9 F1. Extras. An acting area. Fee code C

An unusual treatment of the Nativity story, designed for performances in church or hall, by actors of any age. Richard Tydeman's skill in conveying the true meaning of Christmas is here exploited to the full.

The Gift of the Magi. Christmas play. O. Henry. Adaptation, music and lyrics by Peter Ekstrom
M1 (young) F1 (young). A shabby one-room flat. Fee by arrangement

This tells the classic O. Henry short story, through music and lyrics, of the young couple in New York on Christmas Eve 1905, who loved each other so much that each sold his most prized possession to buy the other a Christmas present. Their special gifts bring a touching reaffirmation of their unselfish love.
ISBN 0 573 68132 5

The Last Leaf. Christmas play. O. Henry. Adaptation, music and lyrics by Peter Ekstrom
M2 (30s, elderly) F2 (20s). A garret/studio. Fee by arrangement

This tells of two impoverished young women, Sue and Johnsy, struggling to become established artists in Greenwich Village, New York, in 1905 and how their aspirations are threatened when one is stricken with pneumonia. A combination of faith, prayer and strong chicken broth turns the tide, but not before a life allows itself to be selflessly given up in place of another.
ISBN 0 573 69572 5

Papa Panov's Magic Christmas. Play. Paul Thain. From a story by Leo Tolstoy
21 characters. Extras. A workshop. Fee code C

This adaptation of a story by Leo Tolstoy, narrated by a Storyteller and involving an unlimited cast of children, is a perfect play for Christmas. In a small Russian village an old shoemaker, now almost too blind to thread a needle, has a dream that Jesus will visit him on Christmas Day.
ISBN 0 573 06622 1

The Real Spirit of Christmas. Play for children. Wes Magee
48 children (M or F). An open stage. Fee code D

Alfie Ruffcutt is a spoil-sport and a bully, who does not believe in Father Christmas, so his brothers and sisters ask Father Christmas to bring Alfie 'the real spirit of Christmas'. Two spirits duly take Alfie on a star-ship trip, showing him a variety of Christmas wonders which transforms him into a happy, lovable boy.
ISBN 0 573 06613 2

The Soldier and the Woman. Play. Elaine Morgan
M3 (26, 30s) F1 (24). A stable. Fee code E

Rachel, whose baby son has been killed in the massacre of the innocents, is filled with hatred for the wounded officer she finds in her stable. Simon, her husband, is frightened of the consequences should the officer die; Rachel, eventually, is unable to watch him die. Period Biblical
ISBN 0 573 06234 X

SECTION E
Musical Plays

This section of the Guide gives brief details of the Musical Plays controlled for performance by Samuel French Ltd. Full details – casting, orchestration, etc. – can be found in the catalogue of Musical Plays, published separately. Information about individual titles can, of course, be given by letter, fax or over the telephone.

Please also see under the relevant headings in Section A (Full Length Plays), Section C (Children's Plays and Plays for Young People) and Section D (Pantomimes and Christmas Plays) of this Guide for full details of other Musical Plays and Plays with Music that are available for performance.

All for Your Delight. Book, music and lyrics by Roger Parsley.

And So to Bed. J. B. Fagan. Lyrics and music by Vivian Ellis.

Andy Capp. Book by Trevor Peacock. Music by Alan Price. Lyrics by Trevor Peacock and Alan Price.

Anne of Green Gables. From the novel by L. M. Montgomery. Adapted by Donald Harron. Lyrics by Donald Harron and Norman Campbell. Additional lyrics by Mavor Moore and Elaine Campbell. Music by Norman Campbell.

The Arcadians. Book by Mark Ambient, A. M. Thompson and Robert Courtneidge. Lyrics by Arthur Wimperis. Music by Lionel Monckton and Howard Talbot.

Around the Pond in 80 Days. Shrubshall and Free.

Around the World in Eighty Days. Freely adapted from the novel by Jules Verne. Book, lyrics and music by Phil Willmott. Music arranged by Annemarie Lewis Thomas.

Balalaika. Book and lyrics by Eric Maschwitz. Music by George Posford and Bernard Grun.

Bashville. Book by David William and Benny Green. Music by Denis King. Lyrics by Benny Green. Adapted from *The Admirable Bashville* by Bernard Shaw.

The Belle of New York. Book by Hugh Morton. New book by Bernard Dunn and Emile Littler. Music by Gustave Kerker.

The Best Little Whorehouse in Texas. Book by Larry L. King and Peter Masterson. Music and lyrics by Carol Hall.

Big Al. Book and Lyrics by John Gardiner. Music by Andrew Parr.

The Biograph Girl. Book by Warner Brown. Lyrics by Warner Brown and David Heneker. Music by David Heneker.

Bitter Sweet. An operetta by Noël Coward.

Bless the Bride. Book and lyrics by A. P. Herbert. Music by Vivian Ellis.

Blossom Time. Adapted by Sydney Box. Music arranged and derived from Franz Schubert by G. H. Clutsam. Lyrics by G.H. Clutsam, John Drinkwater and H. V. Purcell.

The Boy Friend. Book, music and lyrics by Sandy Wilson.

Brenda Bly: Teen Detective. Book and lyrics by Kevin Hammonds. Music by Charles Miller.

The Buccaneer. Book, music and lyrics by Sandy Wilson.

The Burston Drum. Book by Ellen Dryden. Lyrics by Don Taylor. Music by Charles Young.

La Cage aux Folles. Book by Harvey Fierstein. Music and lyrics by Jerry Herman. Based on the play by Jean Poiret.

The Canterville Ghost. Adapted from the original story by Oscar Wilde. Book and lyrics by Peter Quilter. Music by Charles Miller.

Careless Rapture. Ivor Novello. Lyrics by Christopher Hassall.

Carissima. Book and lyrics by Eric Maschwitz. From the story by Armin Robinson. Music by Hans May.

Chess. Lyrics by Tim Rice. Music by Björn Ulvaeus and Benny Andersson.

Chrysanthemum. Book and lyrics by Neville Philips and Robin Chancellor. Music by Rob Stewart.

Chu Chin Chow. Book by Oscar Asche. Music by Frederick Norton.

Clue. The Musical. Book by Peter DePietro. Music by Galen Blum, Wayne Barker and Vinnie Martucci. Lyrics by Tom Chiodo. Based on the Parker Brothers' Board Game.

Cole. An entertainment based on the words and music of Cole Porter. Devised by Benny Green and Alan Strachan.

Cowardy Custard. An entertainment devised by Gerald Frow, Alan Strachan and Wendy Toye featuring the words and music of Noël Coward.

The Curious Quest for the Sandman's Sand. Book and lyrics by Jenifer Toksvig. Music by David Perkins.

Dames at Sea. Book and lyrics by George Haimsohn and Robin Miller. Music by Jim Wise.

The Dancing Years. Devised, written and composed by Ivor Novello. Lyrics by Christopher Hassall.

The Dancing Years. A revised version for the theatre by Cecil Clarke and Tom Arnold of the original musical by Ivor Novello and Christopher Hassall.

Daniel and the Lions. Book, music and lyrics by Dave Culling

Dazzle. Book and lyrics by John Gardiner. Music by Andrew Parr.

The Demon Headmaster. Based on the novel by Gillian Cross. Music by Eric Angus and Cathy Shostak. Lyrics by Iain Halstead and Paul James. Book by Paul James.

Divorce Me Darling! Book, music and lyrics by Sandy Wilson.

Dreams from a Summer House. Words by Alan Ayckbourn. Music by John Pattison.

The Dubarry. Adapted by Eric Maschwitz from the play by Paul Knelpler and J. Welleminsky. Lyrics by Rowland Leigh. Additional lyrics by Eric Maschwitz. Music by Karl Milloecker. Arranged by Theo Makeben. Adapted and augmented by Bernard Grun.

The Duenna. Adapted by Lionel Harris from the operetta by Richard Brinsley Sheridan. Music by Julian Slade.

Eating Raoul. Book by Paul Bartel, adapted from his screenplay. Lyrics by Boyd Graham. Music by Jed Feuer.

Elegies for Angels, Punks and Raging Queens. By Bill Russell. Music by Janet Hood.

The End of the Pier Show. Book, music and lyrics by Roger Parsley.

The Farndale Avenue Housing Estate Townswomen's Guild Operatic Society's Production of *The Mikado*. By David McGillivray and Walter Zerlin Jnr. Based on *The Mikado* or *The Town of Titipu* by W. S. Gilbert and Arthur Sullivan. Music arranged by Sue Van Colle.

Fawkes – The Quiet Guy. Kjartan Poskitt.

Fings Ain't Wot They Used T'Be. Book by Frank Norman. Music and lyrics by Lionel Bart.

First Impressions. Book by Abe Burrows. Music and lyrics by Robert Goldman, Glenn Paxton and George Weiss.

Follow That Girl. Book and lyrics by Dorothy Reynolds and Julian Slade. Music by Julian Slade. Adapted by Bernard Dunn from the original production by Dennis Carey.

Free As Air. Book and lyrics by Dorothy Reynolds and Julian Slade. Music by Julian Slade.

Gay's the Word. Book and music by Ivor Novello. Lyrics by Alan Melville.

The Geisha. Book by Owen Hall. Lyrics by Harry Greenbank. Music by Sidney J. Jones.

Glamorous Night. Book and music by Ivor Novello. Lyrics by Christopher Hassall.

Godspell. Conceived and originally directed by John-Michael Tebelak. Music and new lyrics by Stephen Schwartz.

Goodnight Vienna. Book and lyrics by Eric Maschwitz. Music by George Posford. Additional material by Harold Purcell and Sydney Box.

The Grand Tour. Jerry Herman, Michael Stewart and Mark Bramble, based on S. N. Behrman's adaptation of Franz Werfel's play *Jacobowsky and the Colonel*.

The Great American Backstage Musical. Book by Bill Solly and Donald Ward. Music and lyrics by Bill Solly.

♦ **Happy Days.** Book by Garry Marshall. Music and lyrics by Paul Williams. Based on the Paramount Pictures TV series "Happy Days". Created by Garry Marshall.

Oscar Wilde's **The Happy Prince.** Music by David Perkins. Adaptation, book and lyrics by Caroline Dooley and David Perkins

Henry the Tudor Dude. A musical play by Kjartan Poskitt.

Henry's Wives (The much-married musical). Book, music and lyrics by Leslie Bricusse.

The Hired Man. Book by Melvyn Bragg. Music and lyrics by Howard Goodall.

How to Eat Like a Child. Book by Delia Ephron, John Forster and Judith Kahan. Music and lyrics by John Foster. Written by Judith Kahan. Based on the book by Delia Ephron.

The Hunchback of Notre Dame. Book and lyrics by Gary Sullivan. Music by John Trent Wallace. Based on *Notre Dame de Paris* by Victor Hugo.

I'm Getting My Act Together and Taking It on the Road. Gretchen Cryer and Nancy Ford.

Jack the Ripper. Book and lyrics by Ron Pember and Denis de Marne. Music by Ron Pember.

King's Rhapsody. Devised, written and composed by Ivor Novello. Lyrics by Christopher Hassall.

Kiss of the Spiderwoman. Book by Terrence McNally. Music by John Kander. Lyrics by Fred Ebb. Based on the novel by Manuel Puig.

The Late Sleepers. Book and lyrics by Paul James. Music by Eric Angus

Large as Life. Book by Richard Harris. Music by Keith Strachan. Lyrics by Richard Harris and Keith Strachan.

The Lion, the Witch and the Wardrobe. C.S. Lewis. Dramatized by Adrian Mitchell. Music by Shaun Davey

Little Mary Sunshine. Book, music and lyrics by Rick Besoyan.

A Little Princess. Michael Wild. Adapted from the novel by Frances Hodgson Burnett.

Lock Up Your Daughters. Adapted from Henry Fielding's comedy *Rape Upon Rape* by Bernard Miles. Lyrics by Lionel Bart. Music by Laurie Johnson.

Love from Judy. Music by Hugh Martin. Book by Eric Maschwitz and Jean Webster. Lyrics by Hugh Martin and Jack Gray.

Love Off the Shelf. Book by Roger Hall. Lyrics by A. K. Grant. Music by Philip Norman.

Lust. Book, music and lyrics by The Heather Brothers, based on William Wycherley's *The Country Wife*.

Lust 'n' Rust. The Trailer Park Musical. Frank Haney, Carol Kimball and Dave Stratton.

Mack and Mabel. Book by Michael Stewart. Music and lyrics by Jerry Herman. Based on an idea by Leonard Spigelglass. Revisions by Francine Pascal. **Restricted, please enquire.**

Magyar Melody. Adapted by Eric Maschwitz and George Posford from the play by Eric Maschwitz, Fred Thompson and Guy Bolton. Music by George Posford and Bernard Grun.

Maid of the Mountains. Book by Frederick Lonsdale, with revisions by Emile Maschwitz, Fred Thompson and Guy Bolton. Music by George Posford and Bernard Grun.

Make Me an Offer. Book by Wolf Mankowitz. Music and lyrics by David Heneker and Monty Norman.

The Matchgirls. Book and lyrics by Bill Owen. Music by Tony Russell.

Me and My Girl. Book and lyrics by L. Arthur Rose and Douglas Furber. Music by Noel Gay. Book revised by Stephen Fry, contributions to revisions by Mike Ockrent.. **Restricted, please enquire.**

The Merry Gentleman. Book and lyrics by Dorothy Reynolds and Julian Slade.

Moll Flanders. Book by Claire Luckham, lyrics by Paul Leigh. Music by George Stiles. Based on the novel by Daniel Defoe.

The Musical Importance of Being Earnest. A musical adaptation of Oscar Wilde's classic by John Sean O'Mahoney.

The Musical of Musicals. The Musical! Music by Eric Rockwell. Lyrics by Joanne Bogart. Book by Eric Rockwell and Joanne Bogart.

Nell's Belles. A musical play by Kjartan Poskitt.

Nine. Book by Arthur Kopit. Music, adaptation and lyrics by Maury Yeston. Adapted from the Italian by Mario Fratti.

Noël and Gertie. Devised by Sheridan Morley. Words and music by Noël Coward. Arrangements by Jonathan Cohen.

Nunsense. Dan Goggin.

Nymph Errant. Book by Steve Mackes and Michael Whaley. Music and lyrics by Cole Porter.

An O. Henry Christmas. A Christmas Musical. Adaptation, music and lyrics by Peter Ekstrom.

Oh, Brother! Book and lyrics by Donald Driver. Music by Michael Valenti.

Joan Littlewood's musical entertainment **Oh What a Lovely War.** By Theatre Workshop, Charles Chilton, Gerry Raffles and members of the original cast. Title suggested by Ted Allan.

Old Chelsea. Walter Ellis. Music by Richard Tauber. Additional numbers by Bernard Grun. Lyrics by Fred S. Tysh and Walter Ellis.

On the Twentieth Century. Book and lyrics by Betty Comden and Adolph Green. Music by Cy Coleman.

Orvin – Champion of Champions. Alan Ayckbourn. Music by Denis King.

Pandemonium! (a Greek Myth-adventure). Book and lyrics by Jenifer Toksvig. Music by David Perkins.

Pageant. Book and lyrics by Bill Russell and Frank Kelly. Music by Albert Evans. Conveived by Robert Longbottom.

Perchance to Dream. By Ivor Novello.

Personals. Words by David Crane, Seth Friedman and Marta Kauffman. Music by William Dreskin, Joel Phillip Friedman, Seth Friedman, Alan Menken, Stephen Schwartz and Michael Skloff.

Peter Pan. Adapted from the play by J. M. Barrie. Book, music and lyrics by Piers Chater-Robinson.

The Phantom of the Opera. Based on the novel by Gaston Leroux. Book and lyrics by Ken Hill. Arrangements and incidental music by Alasdair MacNeill.

Pickwick. Based on *Posthumous Papers of the Pickwick Club* by Charles Dickens. Book by Wolf Mankowitz, lyrics by Leslie Bricusse, music by Cyril Ornadel.

Pink Champagne. Adapted by Eric Maschwitz and Bernard Grun from *Die Fledermaus* by Johann Strauss.

Poppy. Book and lyrics by Peter Nichols. Music by Monty Norman.

Pump Boys and Dinettes. Conceived and written by John Foley, Mark Hardwick, Debra Monk, Cass Morgan, John Schimmel and Jim Wann.

The Quaker Girl. (Original version) Book by James T. Tanner and Emile Littler. Lyrics by Adrian Ross and Percy Greenbank. Music by Lionel Monckton.

The Quaker Girl. Freely adapted and arranged by Andrew Nicklin and Philip Beeson, from the original version.

Radio Times. Music by Noel Gay. Book by Abi Grant. Book devised by Robin Miller. Original conception by Alex Armitage. Additional material and book revisions by Paul Alexander and Alex Armitage.

The Railway Children. Book and lyrics by Julian Woolford. Music by Richard John. From the novel by E. Nesbit.

The Revenge of Sherlock Holmes. Book, music and lyrics by Leslie Bricusse. Based on characters created by Sir Arthur Conan Doyle.

The Rink. Book by Terence McNally. Music by John Kander. Lyrics by Fred Ebb.

Rio Rita. Book by Guy Bolton and Fred Thompson. Lyrics by Joseph McCarthy. Music by Harry Tierney.

Robert and Elizabeth. Book and lyrics by Ronald Millar. Music by Ron Grainer. From an original idea by Fred G. Morrit. Based on *The Barretts of Wimpole Street* by Rudolph Besier.

Rockasocka. Book and lyrics by John Gardiner. Music by Andrew Parr.

Rose Marie. Book and lyrics by Otto Harbach and Oscar Hammerstein. Music by Rudolf Friml and Herbert Stothhart.

Rosie and the Bad, Bad Apples. Book and lyrics by Valerie Hall. Music by Paul Whittington.

Rumpelstiltskin Racket. Book, music and lyrics by Kjartan Poskitt.

Runaways. Elizabeth Swados.

Ruthless! The Musical. Book and lyrics by Joel Paley. Music by Marvin Laird.

Salad Days. Book and lyrics by Dorothy Reynolds and Julian Slade. Music by Julian Slade.

Saucy Jack and the Space Vixens. Book by Charlotte Mann. Lyrics by Charlotte Mann and Michael Fiddler. Music by Jonathan Croose and Robin Forrest

Leslie Bricusse's **Scrooge**. 55 minute adaptation for smaller societies and schools. Book, music and lyrics by Leslie Bricusse.

Scrooge – the Musical. Book, music and lyrics by Leslie Bricusse. *Restrictions apply.*

The Secret Garden. Book and lyrics by Marsha Norman. Music by Lucy Simon. Based on the novel by Frances Hodgson Burnett.

The Secret Life of Walter Mitty. Book by Joe Manchester. Lyrics by Earl Shuman. Music by Leon Carr. Based on the story by James Thurber.

Seesaw. Music by Cy Coleman. Lyrics by Dorothy Fields. Book by Michael Bennett. Based on the play *Two for the Seesaw* by William Gibson.

The Selfish Giant. Based on the short story by Oscar Wilde. Music, lyrics and adaptation by David Perkins. Additional lyrics by Caroline Dooley

70, Girls, 70. Book by David Thompson and Norman L. Martin. Music by John Kander. Lyrics by Fred Ebb. Based on the play *Breath of Spring* by Peter Coke, adapted by Joe Masteroff

sex, drugs & rick 'n' noel. David Tristram

Shake, Ripple & Roll. Book and lyrics by Jenifer Toksvig. Music by David Perkins.

Side Show. Book and lyrics by Bill Russell. Music by Henry Krieger.

Skool & Crossbones. Book and lyrics by Jenifer Toksvig. Music by David Perkins.

Sleeping Beauty. Book and lyrics by Simon Brett. Music by Sarah Travis.

A Slice of Saturday Night. Book, music and lyrics by The Heather Brothers.

Smoke on the Mountain Homecoming. Connie Ray, conceived by Alan Bailey, with musical arrangements by Mike Craver.

Some Canterbury Tales. Freely adapted from Chaucer by Ken Pickering. Music by Derek Hyde.

Something's Afoot. Book, music and lyrics by James McDonald, David Vos and Robert Gerlach. Additional music by Ed Linderman.

Songbook. Music by Monty Norman. Lyrics by Julian More. Book by Monty Norman and Julian More.

Spend Spend Spend. Book and lyrics by Steve Brown and Justin Greene. Music by Steve Brown. Based on the book by Viv Nicholson and Stephen Smith

Steel Pier. Book by David Thompson. Music and lyrics by John Kander and Fred Ebb. Conceived by Scott Ellis, Susan Stroman and David Thompson.

Stepping Out – the Musical. Book by Richard Harris. Lyrics by Mary Stewart-David. Music by Denis King. Based on the original play by Richard Harris.

Strider. Adapted from Leo Tolstoy's story.

Suburban Strains. Book and lyrics by Alan Ayckbourn. Music by Paul Todd.

Summer in the Park. Book by Ellen Dryden, lyrics by Don Taylor, music by Charles Young.

Summer Song. Book by Eric Maschwitz and Hy Craft. Lyrics by Eric Maschwitz. Music by Bernard Grun, from themes of Anton Dvorák.

The Tale of Little Red Riding Hood. An untraditional pantomime. Book and lyrics by Simon Brett. Music by Sarah Travis.

A Tale of Two Cities. Adapted from Charles Dickens' novel by Dave Ross, Michael Mullane, Neil Parker and Vivienne Carter.

Tarantara! Tarantara! Book, music and lyrics by Ian Taylor, using songs by Gilbert and Sullivan.

Teller of Tales. A Musical Adventure from the life of Robert Louis Stevenson. Book and lyrics by Neil Wilkie. Music by Neil Wilkie and David Stoll.

1066 – And All That. Book and lyrics by Reginald Arkell, from the memorable history of the same name by W. C. Seller and R. J. Yeatman. Music by Alfred Reynolds.

They're Playing Our Song. Book by Neil Simon. Music by Marvin Hamlisch. Lyrics by Carol Bayer Sager.

Thick as a Brick. Book and lyrics by John Godber. Music by John Pattison.

♦ **Thrill Me**. The Leopold and Loeb Story. Book, music and lyrics by Stephen Dolginoff

Treasure Island. Adapted from Robert Louis Stevenson by Willis Hall. Music by Denis King.

Trelawny. Book by Aubrey Woods. Music and lyrics by Julian Slade. Adapted from Sir Arthur Pinero's *Trelawny of the 'Wells'* by Aubrey Woods, George Rowell and Julian Slade.

The Vagabond King. Book and lyrics by W. H. Post and Brian Hooker from Justin Huntly McCarthy's romance *If I Were King*. Music by Rudolph Friml.

Valmouth. Book music and lyrics by Sandy Wilson.

Waldo and Sons. Book and Lyrics by Andrew McGregor. Music by David Pickthall.

Walking Happy. Roger O. Hirson, Ketty Frings, Sammy Cahn and James Van Heusen. Based on the play *Hobson's Choice* by Harold Brighouse.

Waltz Without End. Eric Maschwitz and Bernard Grun. To music from the works of Frederick Chopin.

The Water Babies. A play by Willis Hall with songs by John Cooper. Based on the story by Charles Kingsley.

Water Gypsies. Book and lyrics by A. P. Herbert. Music by Vivian Ellis.

Wedding in Paris. Vera Caspary. Lyrics by Sonny Miller. Music by Hans May.

Whenever. Musical play for children. Alan Ayckbourn. Music by Denis King.

White Horse Inn. Adapted by Hans Muller and Erik Charell from a play by Blumenthal and Kadelburg. Original lyrics by Robert Gilbert. Music by Ralph Benatsky and Robert Stolz. English book and lyrics by Harry Graham. The whole adapted by Eric Maschwitz and Bernard Grun.

The Wind in the Willows. A musical based on Kenneth Grahame's novel. Book and lyrics by Willis Hall. Music by Denis King.

The Wiz. The new musical version of *The Wonderful Wizard of Oz* by L. Frank Baum. Book by William F. Brown. Music and lyrics by Charlie Smalls.

A Word from Our Sponsor. Words by Alan Ayckbourn. Music by John Pattison.

Worzel Gummidge. Keith Waterhouse and Willis Hall. Music by Denis King. Based on the book by Barbara Euphan Todd.

Zip Goes A Million. Book and lyrics by Eric Maschwitz. Music by George Posford. Based on an idea by Winchell Smith and Byron Ongley.

Zombie Prom. Book and lyrics by John Dempsey. Music by Dana P. Rowe. Based on a story by John Dempsey and Hugh Murphy.

E

E

SECTION F
Technical Books

CONTENTS

F

MUSICAL INTEREST

Four Bars of 'Agit'. Incidental Music for Victorian and Edwardian Melodrama. David Mayer and Matthew Scott. With a preface by Sir Peter Hall

This is a unique collection of original incidental music for Victorian and Edwardian melodrama. The majority of the works come from the folio of Alfred Edward Cooper, which was found by chance and purchased for the nation by the Theatre Museum, London. A fascinating introduction by David Mayer sets the scene for these fifty-nine original melos. Matthew Scott has faithfully reproduced the music, adding his own transposition, into a minor key, of several pieces. With notes on the use and meaning of the melos this book is not only a wonderful insight into Britain's theatrical heritage but also a work of great importance to all concerned with theatre and history – a working book for today stepping straight from the pages of history.
ISBN 978 0 573 09010 3

SPEECH TRAINING

Anthology of British Tongue Twisters. Ken Parkin

The first collection of the best traditional and new tongue twisters, divided into sections according to the oral exercise they are best suited to. Practical and instructive, but amusing too.
ISBN 978 0 573 09028 8

Ideal Voice and Speech Training. Ken Parkin

How often teachers of speech must long to discover some fresh exercises – here is a book of exercises which have been proved in the author's classes.
ISBN 978 0 573 09013 4

THEATRE

The Art of Coarse Acting. Michael Green

Revised and updated in 1994 to take account of changes in the amateur theatre world in the forty-eight years (heavens – that long!) since it was first published, Michael Green's work is consistently funny and required reading for all devotees of theatre, amateur and professional!
ISBN 978 0 573 19029 2

Title Index

Sections A-F

Title Index

A

C

D

E

F

G

H

K

L

M

O

P

T